GENERAL ANTHROPOLOGY

Edited by

FRANZ BOAS

With contributions by

Ruth Benedict	Robert H. Lowie
Franz Boas	James H. McGregor
Ruth Bunzel	N. C. Nelson
Julius E. Lips	Gladys A. Reichard

D. C. HEATH AND COMPANY

BOSTON   NEW YORK   CHICAGO   ATLANTA

DALLAS   SAN FRANCISCO   LONDON

Reprinted with the permission of D. C. Heath and Company

JOHNSON REPRINT CORPORATION
111 Fifth Avenue, New York, N. Y. 10003

JOHNSON REPRINT COMPANY LIMITED
Berkeley Square House, London, W. 1

Landmarks in Anthropology, a series of reprints in cultural anthropology

General Editor: Weston La Barre

First reprinting, 1965, Johnson Reprint Corporation

Printed in the United States of America

PREFACE

Anthropology covers such a wide scope of subjects that it is difficult for one person to be equally conversant with all its aspects. For this reason coöperation of a group of students, most of whom have worked in close contact for many years, seemed a justifiable solution of the task of preparing a general book on anthropology. Thus a greater number of viewpoints could be assembled, and the unavoidable divergence in the handling of diverse problems by a number of authors is, we hope, offset by the advantage of having the special points of view in which each author is interested brought out.

The necessity of limiting the book to a certain compass has compelled us to treat a number of problems rather briefly. Thus the relation of personality to culture, education, acculturation, the historical development of anthropological theory have been only lightly touched.

The editor wishes to express his thanks to his collaborators.

FRANZ BOAS

NEW YORK
May, 1938

iii

CONTENTS

CHAPTER   PAGES

INTRODUCTION, by Franz Boas   1–6
Subject matter: History of mankind, 1 — Methods: Archaeology,
1 — Methods: Comparative, 2 — Limitations of comparative
method, 3 — Problems of laws of historic development, 3 — Historic sequences, 3 — Dynamics of change, 4 — Problems of anthropology, 4 — Aspects of culture: Man and nature, 4 — Man and
man, 4 — Subjective aspects, 5 — Interrelations between the various aspects of social life, 5 — Descriptive anthropology, 5 — Anthropology, history, and sociology, 5 — Purpose of book, 6.

I. GEOLOGICAL AND BIOLOGICAL PREMISES   7–23

Geological Premises, by N. C. Nelson   7–16
Geological background, 7 — Divisions of the Cenozoic era, 9 — Subdivisions of the Pleistocene epoch, 9 — Glacial moraines, 11 —
Pluvial and interpluvial evidence, 12 — Valley terraces and marine
shore terraces, 12 — Absolute chronology of the Holocene epoch, 15.

Biological Premises, by Franz Boas   16–23
Description of species, 16 — Heredity, 16 — Selection, 19 — Environment, 20 — Origin of species, 20 — Footnotes, 22.

II. HUMAN ORIGINS AND EARLY MAN, by James H. McGregor . . .   24–94
Primates, 25 — Australopithecus africanus (the Taungs ape), 28
— Man and apes, 31 — Origin of the human branch, 38 — Man, 42
— Types of man, 43 — Pithecanthropus erectus (Ape-man of Java),
44 — Homo modjokertensis, 50 — Sinanthropus pekinensis (Peking
man), 51 — Eoanthropus dawsoni (Piltdown man), 56 — Homo
heidelbergensis, (Heidelberg man), 60 — Homo neanderthalensis
(Neanderthal man), 61 — Homo sapiens, 74 — The "Grimaldi
race," 79 — Cro-Magnon man, 81 — Rhodesian man, 87 — Footnotes, 91 — General references, 94.

III. RACE, by Franz Boas   95–123
Races and local types, 95 — Variability of local types, 95 — Methods of observations, 95 — Types, 99 — Phenotypes and genotypes,
100 — Generalized types, 101 — Parallel development, 102 — Selection, 103 — Environmental changes, 103 — Population and
race, 104 — Local races, 105 — Mixture, 106 — Isolation, 107 —
Domestication, 108 — Internal secretions, 110 — Races of man, 111
— Theories of the origin of modern races, 116 — Racial physiology
and psychology, 117 — Eugenics, 121 — Footnotes, 122 — General references, 123.

IV. LANGUAGE, by Franz Boas   124–145
General characteristics of language, 124 — Communication between
animals, 124 — Categories of classification, 126 — Phonetics, 127

v

CHAPTER   PAGES
    — Selection of material used for expression, 128 — Sound symbol-
ism, 132 — Grammar, 132 — Grammatical processes, 133 — History of languages, 134 — Linguistic families, 135 — Mixed languages, 136 — Independent origin of similar grammatical processes,
138 — Distribution of languages, 139 — Culture and speech, 141
— Footnotes, 144 — General references, 145

V. PREHISTORIC ARCHAEOLOGY, by N. C. Nelson 146–237
    Definition, 146 — Problems of prehistoric archaeology, 148 —
Methods, 148 — Achieved results, 149 — Technological evolution
of material culture traits, 150 — Stone-flaking process, 152 —
Stone-chipping process, 157 — Stone-pecking and grinding proc-
esses, 160 — Stone-chiseling, sawing, and drilling processes, 162 —
Bone and wood-working industries, 164 — Metal industries, 167
— The Eolithic phase, 170 — The Paleolithic industries, 172 —
Development of archaeology in Africa, 196 — Southern Asia, 199
— Central Asia, 200 — Northern Asia, 200 — Indonesia, 201 —
Australia and Tasmania, 202 — Melanesia, 203 — Micronesia, 204
— Polynesia, 204 — Oceanian-American connections, 208 — Amer-
ica, 212 — General world considerations, 216 — General conclu-
sions, 230 — Footnotes, 235 — General references, 237.

VI. INVENTION, by Franz Boas 238–281
    Discovery and invention, 238 — Fire and cooking, 239 — Mechan-
ical principles, 241 — Mechanical principles used in implements, 243
— Compound implements, 250 — Search for materials, 251 —
Stone, 252 — Wood, 253 — Food, 253 — Intoxicants and narcotics, 255 — Medicine and poison, 255 — Preparation of skins, 255
— Bark cloth, 256 — Basketry and mat weaving, 256 — Spinning,
258 — Weaving, 258 — Sewing, 258 — Pottery, 259 — Metal work,
260 — Application of inventions, 261 — Devices for obtaining food,
261 — Protection against attack, 263 — Shelter, 263 — Clothing,
265 — Ornaments, 266 — Transportation, 267 — Games and tricks,
269 — Medicine, 270 — Writing, 271 — Science, 274 — Footnotes,
278 — General references, 281.

VII. SUBSISTENCE, by Robert H. Lowie 282–326
    General categories, 282 — Appraisal of the hunting stage, 285 —
Cultivation, 290 — Domesticated animals, 302 — Pastoral nomad-
ism, 312 — Economic determinism of culture, 318 — Footnotes, 322
— General references, 326.

VIII. THE ECONOMIC ORGANIZATION OF PRIMITIVE PEOPLES, by Ruth
Bunzel 327–408
    Introduction, 327 — Value, 331 — Property, 340 — Types of eco-
nomic structure, 351 — The Zuñi, 351 — The Kwakiutl, 357 —
The Trobriand Islands, 361 — Economic mechanisms in primitive
cultures, 367 — The division of labor, 369 — Individualism and
collectivism in production, 374 — The distribution of wealth, 377
— Kinship claims in the distribution of wealth, 381 — Dowry, 382
— The bride price, 383 — Affinal exchange, 387 — Gifts and hos-

CHAPTER   PAGES
pitality, 390 — Intertribal economics, 396 — War, 400 — Footnotes, 404 — General references, 408.

IX. SOCIAL LIFE, by Gladys A. Reichard 409–486
Family organization on different economic levels, 411 — The sib,
414 — Totemism, 426 — Marriage, 430 — Exogamy and endogamy, 431 — Forms of marriage, 431 — Extramarital relations, 435
— Restrictions and preferences, 437 — Betrothal, engagement,
wedding, 440 — Divorce, 449 — Kinship terms, 450 — Prestige,
458 — Woman in primitive society, 465 — Education, 470 — Ethics and etiquette, 478 — Footnotes, 483 — General references, 486.

X. GOVERNMENT, by Julius E. Lips 487–534
Food-gatherers and hunters, 491 — Arctic hunters and related
tribes, 498 — Harvesters and related tribes, 502 — Indians of the
Plains, 512 — Simpler farming societies, 515 — Herdsmen and related societies, 519 — Polynesia, 523 — Conclusion, 525 — Footnotes, 527 — General references, 534.

XI. ART, by Ruth Bunzel 535–588
Antiquity and universality of art, 535 — Esthetic emotion, 536 —
The decorative arts, 539 — Problems of form, 540 — General
formal principles, 558 — Style, 564 — Symbolism, 576 — Footnotes, 586 — General references, 588.

XII. LITERATURE, MUSIC, AND DANCE, by Franz Boas 589–608
Literature, 589 — Music, 602 — Dance, 605 — Footnotes, 607.

XIII. MYTHOLOGY AND FOLKLORE, by Franz Boas 609–626
Myth and folk tale, 609 — Mythological concepts, 609 — Origin
of tales, 610 — Dissemination of tales, 612 — Origin of elements of
tales, 613 — Character of mythological concepts, 614 — Myths,
616 — Effect of individual thought upon mythology, 618 — Esoteric and exoteric mythology, 620 — Relation of mythology to
other aspects of culture, 622 — Footnotes, 624 — General references, 626.

XIV. RELIGION, by Ruth Benedict 627–665
The concept of the supernatural, 628 — Mana—supernatural power
as an attribute of objects, 634 — Animism—supernatural power as
will and intention, 635 — Techniques of religion, 637 — Behavior
toward the personalized universe, 639 — Forms of religious behavior, 642 — Prayer, 642 — Divination, 643 — Sacrifice, 644 —
Taboo, 644 — Fetishes and amulets, 645 — Tutelary spirits, 646
— Summary, 647 — Varieties of primitive religions, 647 — Siberia,
648 — The Pueblo Indians of the Southwest, 650 — The Plains
Indians, 652 — The Dobuans of Melanesia, 654 — Recurring
aspects of the religious complex, 656 — Ceremonialism, 656 —
Vision and ecstasy, 658 — Cosmology and belief, 660 — Ethical
sanctions, 663 — Footnotes, 664 — General references, 665.

XV. METHODS OF RESEARCH, by Franz Boas 666–686

FIGURES

FIGURES   PAGE

1. Diagrammatic correlation of Mediterranean and Baltic marine terraces
   with Alpine glacial phases   15
2. A tentative phyletic tree of the Primates   27
3. Skull of *Australopithecus africanus* (the Taungs ape)   30
4. Left lower molar teeth of anthropoid apes and man to show the fifth
   cusp, characteristic of the Dryopithecus pattern   33
5. Median sections of anthropoid ape and human skulls to show extent of
   frontal and sphenoidal sinuses   34
6. The *os centrale* of the carpus   35
7. Skull of *Pithecanthropus erectus*   45
8. Comparative views of sectioned lower jaws showing the inner surface
   of the right half   57
9. Reconstruction of the skeleton of a Neanderthal man   73
10. Points of measurements of the skull   97
11. Cross sections of faces   99
12. Distribution of frequencies of form in fraternities, and distribution of
    family lines   101
13. *Os Incae*   108
14. Elementary flake production   153
15. Improved flaking of Acheulian-Levalloisian times   156
16. Precise flaking of Upper Paleolithic and Neolithic times   157
17. Pressure chipping of Solutrean and Neolithic times   158
18. Pecking and grinding processes   161
19. Chiseling and grinding processes   162
20. Sawing process   163
21. Drilling processes   164
22. Eoliths of exceptionally artificial appearance derived (one excepted)
    from the Pliocene gravels of the Kent Plateau, England   176
23. Typical Pre-Chellean core and flake implements derived from valley
    terrace formations of Pleistocene date   176
24. Typical Chellean core implements derived from valley terrace deposits   176
25. Typical Acheulian core implements   178
26. Typical Levalloisian implements   178
27. Typical Mousterian implements   178
28. Typical Aurignacian implements, ornaments   180
29. Typical Solutrean implements, ornaments   182
30. Typical Magdalenian implements, ornaments   183
31. Typical Azilian-Tardenoisian-Maglemosian implements   184
32. Typical Early Neolithic implements   186
33. Typical Middle and Late Neolithic implements   188
34. Typical Neolithic (Robenhausian) implements   190
35. Typical bronze implements   192

FIGURES   PAGE

36. Typical implements of the later Iron Age   194
37. Map showing known geographic range of culture stages   220
38. Diagram representing section of the American continent from north
    to south   224
39. Diagram of a section of the continental world showing the estimated
    space and time distribution of the successive culture levels   228
40. The fire drill   240
41. Throwing clubs and knives   242
42. Australian boomerangs   243
43. Eskimo throwing board   244
44. Noose trap of the Kwakiutl Indians   245
45. Friction drums   247
46. Musical instrument, New Ireland, and Mexican two-tongued drum .   248
47. Bushman gora player and end of gora   248
48. String instruments   249
49. Types of weaving   256
50. Twilled matting   256
51. Cat's cradles of Eskimo   257
52. Knots used by Eskimo   257
53. Coiled basketry   258
54. Cross section of smelting furnace   260
55. Wolf trap   261
56. Fish basket   262
57. Plan and sections of Eskimo tent   263
58. Menominee hut   264
59. Eskimo snow hut and section   265
60. Suspension bridge of rattan, Celebes   268
61. Dog travois   269
62. Ojibwa picture writing   272
63. Dakota symbols of names   273
64. Pictographic writing of Ibo   273
65. Mexican picture writing   273
66. Nautical map, Marshall Islands   275
67. Maya numerals   276
68. Symbols of numbers, Aztec   276
69. Quipu   277
70. Diagram showing method of squaring sides of a box   278
71. Rawhide box, Sauk and Fox Indians   537
72. Coiled clay water jar, Prehistoric Pueblo   541
73. Wooden mask, Urua, Congo   548
74. Carved house post, Haida   548
75. Canoe prows, New Zealand and Dutch New Guinea   549
76. Prehistoric clay bowl, Arkansas   550
77. Terra cotta head, Yoruba, Africa   550
78. Modeled clay vessels, New Mexico and Costa Rica   551
79. Primitive basketry   555
80. Poncho, Titicaca, Peru   556

FIGURES   PAGE

81. Blanket of mountain goat wool, Tlingit, Alaska 559
82. Zuñi medicine altar 559
83. Fringe from legging, Thompson Indians 561
84. Coiled basketry tray, Hopi Indians 562
85. Designs from ancient pottery bowls, Mimbres Valley, New Mexico . . 563
86. Wooden shield, Dyak, Dutch East Indies 563
87. Ancient Pueblo bowl, Hopi 564
88. Diagram of Hopi water jar 564
89. Painted house front representing Thunderbird catching a whale, Kwakiutl Indians 571
90. Carved spoon handles representing beaver, Tlingit Indians 572
91. Painted wooden box, Tlingit Indians 573
92. Haida drawing illustrating a myth 574
93. Tlingit mask representing dying warrior 574
94. Ancient Bushman drawings 580
95. Female Figurine, Baoulé, Ivory Coast and Fetish Representing Antelope, French Sudan 581
96. Feather sticks, Zuñi 582
97. Votive placque, Huichol Indians, Mexico 583

PLATES

I. Skulls of seven Paleolithic types of man 53
II. Neanderthal and Cro-Magnon man: A comparison 75
III. Winged being pollinating sacred tree 292
IV. Casa de las Monjas, Chichen Itzá, Maya, and Maya relief carving . . 544
V. Head of a maize goddess, Copan, Honduras 545
VI. African Negro Mask, Dan Ivory Coast 547
VII. Clay effigy vessel, Chicama, Peru 553
VIII. African pile cloths, and carved wooden bowl 557
IX. Pueblo Indian pottery 565
X. Masks, Sepik River, New Guinea 579

INTRODUCTION

FRANZ BOAS

Subject matter: History of mankind. The science of anthropology deals with the history of human society. It differs from history in the narrower sense of the term in that its inquiries are not confined to the periods for which written records are available and to peoples who had developed the art of writing. Anthropological researches extend over the whole of humanity regardless of time and space. Historical inquiry reaches out hesitatingly beyond the domain of written records. Archaeological and later remains, and survivals of early times that persist in modern culture, are utilized to extend the span of time and to fill in details for which written records are not available. In these inquiries the fields of anthropology and history are in close contact.

Since anthropology deals with mankind as a whole, the problem of the earliest appearance of man and his rise from lower forms, the differentiation of human races, and the development of languages and of cultural forms are included in its field of researches. Every manifestation of human life must be utilized to clear up the march of historical events.

In anthropological research relating to early times and primitive people the individual appears rarely, if ever. For prehistoric times no record of individual activity exists, and the tradition of illiterate peoples gives no clue of considerable value or reliability throwing light upon the influence of individuals upon historical events. In the general history of humanity the individual disappears in the social group to which he belongs. Among illiterate peoples the dynamic processes that shape history must be studied mainly by observation of the living generations.

Methods: Archaeology. It may well be asked whether a history of mankind can be reconstructed when no written records of events are available. Archaeological remains may be placed in chronological order by a study of the sequence of deposits in which they are found. Under favorable conditions, as for instance in Scandinavia, the regularity of deposits permits even a fairly accurate chronological de-

1

termination of the age of deposits. In other cases also an approximate absolute chronology is made possible by means of geological or other evidence.

Sometimes remains may be dated through affiliation with objects of known age that belong to neighboring cultures for which written records are available. Thus many of the remains of past cultures of Europe have been dated with a fair degree of certainty. The written records of Egypt and western Asia throw light upon the history of contemporaneous European peoples who lacked the art of writing.

Archaeology, however, can do no more than give us a very partial record of the life of man. The earlier the time of deposit and the more unfavorable the climate for the preservation of objects, the more fragmentary will be the remains, for only the most resistant material will outlast the ravages of time. Even under the most favorable conditions only the remains of the material culture of man will be preserved. Nothing pertaining to the intangible aspects of life can be rescued with the help of the spade. Thus we may learn about skeletal types, about implements and utensils used, about the steps in their manufacture; but no information is forthcoming to tell us about languages, customs, and beliefs. These are evanescent, and there would be no way of recovering them if they did not leave traces in the lives of later generations.

Methods: Comparative. The science of linguistics shows most clearly how and to what extent conditions found at the present time may be utilized for reconstructing the past. The written history of some European languages carries us back to periods that lie centuries before our era. Sanskrit is known for even earlier periods. Linguistic science, by comparing the present forms of speech and their known development, has enabled us to reconstruct the history of words and of grammatical forms and to demonstrate that most of the languages of Europe and many of those of western Asia are derived from a common fundamental source which in course of time has given rise by differentiation to the modern languages. The ancient language cannot be reconstructed, but the probable forms of many roots and in part the manner of their grammatical treatment can be discovered. Comparison of related forms throws light upon the history of their differentiation. Experience has shown that studies of this kind, particularly in languages for which no historic records exist, must be carried on with great caution, because accidental similarities occurring in the speech forms of remote parts of the world may easily give a deceptive impression of relationship. For this reason geographical contiguity is not unimportant in the interpretation of isolated similarities in vocabulary or grammar.

Limitations of comparative method. The study of cultural forms may avail itself of similar methods. The geographical distribution of the same or decidedly similar cultural traits may be utilized for a reconstruction of cultural dissemination and development. When only slight and incidental cultural similarities occur, caution is necessary in assuming historical connections.

It is one of the important methodological problems of anthropology to investigate how far geographical distribution of cultural phenomena may be used for historical reconstruction. The mere fact of historical connection may be interpreted in diverse ways, for ordinarily there is no evidence of chronological sequence. Dissemination may have occurred in one of at least two opposite directions, so that it may be impossible to determine the source of cultural elements. Neither is it possible to be sure whether a particular phase of culture is not rather the local development of a widely spread ancient trait that has flourished than the source from which the more generalized trait sprang.

Similar problems confront us, although not to the same extent, in the study of bodily form. When the same bodily type occurs among the inhabitants of neighboring countries there is little doubt as to their common origin. When slight similarities are found in regions far apart it is conceivable that this may be due to common origin or to parallel biological development.

The study of the geographical distribution of similarities, if used with due caution, is a means of clearing up part of the history of mankind. The materials secured by these methods reveal a fragmentary picture at least of its course.

Problems of laws of historic development. When these data are assembled the question arises whether they present an orderly picture, or whether history proceeds haphazardly; in other words, whether an orthogenetic development of human forms may be discovered and whether a regular sequence of stages of historical development may be recognized. If this were true, definite laws governing historical sequences could be formulated.

Historic sequences. These problems may be attacked from two points of view. We may compare the observed sequences and see whether in all parts of the world they fall into regular order or whether each area has its own peculiar character that is not comparable with the sequences observed in other districts.

Dynamics of change. We may also study the changes that are happening under our eyes in various countries and observe how they are brought about. If homologous sources of change are found, they may be called laws of social change and we may expect that they manifest themselves in every country and among every people. Biological, linguistic, and cultural change may be studied from this angle. For these inquiries we have to understand the interrelations between individual and society: the life of the individual as controlled by his social experience, and the modifications that society undergoes through the actions of individuals. We must also inquire whether society as a whole undergoes autonomous changes, biological, linguistic, and cultural, in which the individual plays a passive rôle. We might call this subject the dynamics of cultural change.

Problems of anthropology. These considerations enable us to define three great problems of anthropology:

1. The reconstruction of human history.
2. The determination of types of historical phenomena and their sequences.
3. The dynamics of change.

These problems have to be investigated in the domains of biological and of social phenomena. The latter include language, the study of which, on account of its technical requirements, is best separated from other cultural manifestations.

Aspects of culture: Man and nature. Culture itself is many-sided. It includes the multitude of relations between man and nature; the procuring and preservation of food; the securing of shelter; the ways in which objects of nature are used as implements and utensils; and all the various ways in which man utilizes or controls, or is controlled by, his natural environment: animals, plants, the inorganic world, the seasons, and wind and weather.

Man and man. A second large group of cultural phenomena relate to the interrelation between members of a single society and between those belonging to different societies. The bonds of family, of tribe, and of a variety of social groups are included in it, as well as the gradation of rank and influence; the relations of sexes and of old and young; and in more complex societies the whole political and religious organization. Here belong also the relations of social groups in war and peace.

Subjective aspects. A third group consists of the subjective reactions of man to all the manifestations of life contained in the first two groups. These are of intellectual and emotional nature and may be expressed in thought and feeling as well as in action. They include all rational attitudes and those valuations which we include under the terms of ethics, esthetics, and religion.

Interrelations between the various aspects of social life. In a systematic presentation of the data of anthropology we are compelled to treat these subjects separately. Nevertheless the biological and cultural life of man is a whole, and we cannot do justice to all the important problems of human history if we treat social life as though it were the sum of all these separate elements. It is necessary to understand life and culture as a whole.

Descriptive anthropology. A descriptive anthropology would represent the lives of all the peoples of the world and of all times. Certain types may be selected, and a number of peoples will appear as varieties of such types. According to the purpose of the presentation, the order may be geographical, if primarily intended to elucidate the order of cultural phenomena in space and time; or it may be according to types, if the object is the study of laws of sequence or the investigation of dynamic relations.

Anthropology, history, and sociology. While the results of the former arrangement connect anthropology with history, those of the latter connect it with sociology. If regular cultural sequences could be found, these would represent an orderly historical cycle. If laws of sequence and of social dynamics could be found, these would be sociological laws. It is one of the important tasks of anthropology to determine how far such regular sequences and sociological laws exist.

When this task has been achieved the principal problem remains, that of understanding a culture as a whole. Neither history nor sociological laws are of considerable help in its solution. History may tell us the sources from which bodily form, customs, and beliefs have been derived, but it does not convey any information regarding the way in which a people will behave owing to the transmitted characteristics. Sociology may teach us the morphology and general dynamics of society; it will give us only a partial insight into the complex interaction of forces, so that it is not possible to predict the behavior resulting from the historical events that made the people what they are. This problem is essentially a psychological one and beset with all the difficulties inherent in the investigation of complex mental phenomena of the lives of individuals.

Purpose of book. The purpose of the present book is to present those data that are necessary for an intelligent handling of the problems here outlined.

CHAPTER I

GEOLOGICAL AND BIOLOGICAL PREMISES

GEOLOGICAL PREMISES

N. C. NELSON

Geological background. Human remains have been found in strata of great antiquity. To understand their significance it is necessary to explain the general results of the study of the origin and nature of their chronology.

Paleontologists and geologists have been equally active unraveling the later history of the earth as recorded respectively by the stratified rock formations and by the gradually changing character of the fossilized organic remains inclosed in them. The thickness of the deposit is said to be more than fifty miles. Earth movements of various kinds have buckled and often disarranged the proper order of the successive formations. In many regions the strata have been so tilted that they stand in vertical order or even completely tipped over, although first deposited as horizontal layers. The total time required for their formation has lately been calculated by physicists to lie somewhere between a billion and a billion and a half years. Such round-numbered figures are not of course to be taken literally; still their general reliability is vouched for by a variety of objective evidence, as for example the rate at which new formations are built up today and the relative radium contents of the ancient rocks in question. This geological column serves therefore as a convenient time scale; and by a study of the thickness of its successive formations, of the nature of the rock materials which compose them, and of the plant and animal fossils inclosed in them, a fairly orderly and intelligible story has been unfolded concerning the shifting positions of land and sea and concerning the changes of climate, as revealed by the responsive changes in the form of organisms. In this time-and-life scheme early man and the precursors of man take their place; for that reason it is imperative for archaeology to take some account of an otherwise essentially extraneous body of knowledge.

The ideally rearranged formations composing the geological column have been subdivided on the basis of important geological changes. The principal divisions have been called the *Primary, Secondary, Tertiary,* and *Quaternary rock systems* or *periods,* though some would omit the last-named as unwarranted.

Another, partly corresponding, subdivision of the column has been made on the basis of the changing characteristics of the fossilized life forms inclosed. The progressively shortening stretches of time so delimited are termed *eras.* Four and sometimes five such eras are recognized. While their names have not been definitely agreed upon, the following are in common use:

1. *Eozoic* (dawn life) — characterized by the simplest forms of organisms.
2. *Paleozoic* (ancient life) — characterized by molluscs, early fishes, and amphibians.
3. *Mesozoic* (middle life) — characterized by numerous swimming, walking, and flying reptiles, as well as the earliest mammals and birds.
4. *Cenozoic* (recent life) — characterized by a gradually evolving succession of birds and mammals, including the Primate order of which man himself is a recognized member.
5. *Psychozoic* (thinking life) — characterized especially by the evolution of the various races of man and of their cultural achievements.

European archaeologists at once fitted their discoveries into this geo-zoölogical scheme of chronology in the following manner:

PERIOD OR EPOCH	CLIMATE	FAUNA	CULTURE
1. Tertiary (Cenozoic)	Warm	Rise of present mammal families and orders	Eolithic industries?
2. Quaternary	Cold and warm alternating	Rise of present mammal genera	Paleolithic industries
3. Holocene, Recent or Present	Temperate, as at present	Present species	Neolithic industries Bronze industries Iron industries

As has been stated, some systematists prefer to omit the Quaternary period as such; they also omit the term "Psychozoic" as smacking of human vanity; and they unite the two nearly equivalent time periods with the preceding Cenozoic under the designations *First* and *Second Cenozoic (Cainozoic)*. The latter scheme has certain advantages for our purposes and will be employed.

Divisions of the Cenozoic era. This Cenozoic or Recent Life era — the only one with which archaeologists are concerned — is further subdivided into *epochs*, based primarily on the classification of the molluscan shells ranging through the Tertiary formations. The names applied to the six subdivisions[1] are as follows:

1. *Eocene* (dawn of the new — referring to surviving faunal species)
2. *Oligocene* (few of the new)
3. *Miocene* (minority of the new)
4. *Pliocene* (majority of the new)
5. *Pleistocene* (most of the new)
6. *Holocene* (all of the new — viz., our present-day fauna)

The expressions *Pleistocene, Quaternary,* and *Ice Age* are by most experts regarded as practically equivalent, at least so far as time duration is concerned, and in that sense therefore are used without distinction.[2]

This insertion of subsidiary steps in the great time sequence makes it possible to fix more definitely the relative chronological positions of the various archaeological discoveries, as is imperative not only for the exact determination of the antiquity of man but also for the determination of the precise time order of his evolving culture.

Thus far in archaeological research the important discoveries have been confined largely to the last two geological epochs — that is, to the Pleistocene and the Holocene.

The Pleistocene epoch has of late been further subdivided by means of certain newly recognized physiographic features left behind by the widespread glacial ice phenomena which have characterized it at repeated intervals.

Subdivisions of the Pleistocene epoch. The evidences of the Ice Age, being of relatively recent date, are mainly superficial and easily observed. Since 1802, opinions have been hazarded about the origin of the erratically strewn boulders — often of great size — found in such otherwise stoneless areas as the Baltic lowlands and the prairies of Minnesota, as well as in the open valleys of Switzerland and Scotland, and in Central Park, New York City. Likewise, the smoothly rounded and often striated rock exposures visible in Central Park, and as low as the 6000-foot altitude on the slopes of Mt. Shasta in California, were a puzzle until about 1832, when Louis Agassiz and others observed that the present Alpine glaciers were producing just such results. Since then it has been ascertained that permanent snow and ice mantles like those now covering completely the interior of Antarctica and Greenland, as well as the higher mountain tops in temperate and tropical latitudes, were once much more extensive than they are now. In northern latitudes all of Europe was covered as far south as the fiftieth parallel, or to a line roughly marked by the situations of London, Prague, and Kharkov; while in North America the snow cover ranged nearly to the fortieth parallel but is more definitely marked by the locations of New York City, the Ohio and Missouri rivers, and the head of Puget Sound. There appear to have been islands or uncovered spots in the snow and ice mantle here and there, as for example in southwestern Wisconsin, in western Newfoundland, and in the Yukon valley of Alaska, where a rich Pleistocene fauna has recently been uncovered precisely suitable for the sustenance of man. Glaciation was also practically absent from northern Asia — that is, from the Ural mountains eastward — probably owing to lack of precipitation. On the high mountains of this region as well as on those throughout the rest of the world, even in the torrid zone, the line above which permanent snow lay was much lower than it is at present. It seems therefore plausible that the condition then prevailing was in the main of astronomical origin. The average lowering of the snow line is estimated at about 3500 feet, though Mt. Tunari in South America registers a drop of over 8000 feet. It is believed that this condition could have been brought about through a lowering of the world's average temperature by merely five degrees centigrade and a sufficient amount of precipitation.

The snow cover reached depths amounting in places to several thousand feet, so that by mere pressure it became solidified into glacial ice which, in the same way as the glaciers of Greenland and Antarctica, advanced in all directions from the principal high centers, such as the Scandinavian, British, and Alpine uplifts. So great indeed was the amount of the earth's water envelope locked up in these snow accumulations that the ocean level is estimated to have been lowered by from 400 to 600 feet. So far as the relative height of sea and land is concerned, this was apparently partly counterbalanced by a contemporary subsidence of some of the glaciated lands, due possibly to the weight of their ice burden. The lowered sea level may have laid bare much of the submerged continental shelf, bordering, for example, both Europe and America, to about the 100-fathom line and thus have connected Europe with Africa, and Alaska with Siberia, giving opportunities for redistribution of plant and animal life. This would help to account for the present wide dissemination of many Arctic species.

In general, the habitable portions of the northern latitudes were reduced in size by the advancing glaciers, which inflicted marked destruction on the relatively fixed plant life and forced the mobile fauna to migrate. Man necessarily had to adjust himself to the changing conditions, and many investigators believe that it was this fact which was mainly responsible for the origin and development of culture. That such a disturbance took place is amply proved by the presence of fossilized plant and animal remains found in the deposits carried along by the glaciers and further distributed by the streams which, like the Rhine, the Rhone, the Ohio, the Missouri, and the Columbia, were nursed by the melting ice fronts. The wind also took part in moving the finer particles from barren exposures near the glaciers and depositing the dust elsewhere on hill and valley alike in the form of unstratified loess (a process of transfer observable during recent years in the United States) which also incloses fossil remains, both animal and human.

Glacial moraines. The lowering of the snow line happened not once but several times. Penck and Brückner, the foremost glacialists in Europe, have found evidence in the Alpine valleys of four major advances, each marked by a terminal moraine (debris dropped along the glacial fronts); and these they have named in chronological order after four valleys in which the respective deposits are well marked. The names are: Günz, Mindel, Riss, and Würm. Three minor advances or stops connected with the last grand retreat have in similar manner been called Bühl, Gschnitz, and Daun. In French territory only three advances seem to be discernible, the Günz phase being regarded as lacking. In England the number — three or four — is as yet uncertain, the earlier glacial deposits perhaps having been removed or disturbed by the action of later ice sheets. In Scotland, however, the geologist Geikie has distinguished no less than six advances, of which the later ones may correspond to the minor post-maximum cold spells registered in the Alps; but on the other hand only one advance, with minor oscillations, is claimed for Russia. In North America (although the evidence for Greenland is disputed) the geologists Chamberlin and Salisbury have similarly recognized five or six advances, and these have been named in proper sequence:

Jerseyan, Kansan, Illinoian, Iowan, Early Wisconsin, and Late Wisconsin, the various designations giving a hint as to where each particular terminal moraine is readily discernible. But whatever the precise number of advances, they were necessarily separated by equally important retreats, some of which were marked by warmer climates than that of the present day. This fact is revealed in many places by the occurrence in the jumbled morainal debris of old land surfaces marked by indications of peat bogs and forest growth, as well as by osteological remains. Switzerland, England, and Alaska [3] are especially noted for such evidence.

We see, therefore, that the Pleistocene epoch, in the northern hemisphere at least, is broken up into no less than seven subdivisions: namely, four major glacial and three major interglacial phases. The Present, Recent, or Holocene epoch — also called the Postglacial — makes the eighth interval; and lately botanical evidence [4] has been produced which suggests that the present interval has already passed its maximum of warmth and that another glacial phase may be slowly approaching, in which case the Holocene epoch would have to be stepped down in rank to take its place as a mere interglacial episode. We shall follow the common practice of referring to the alternating cold and warm episodes by their numerical designations as First Glacial, First Interglacial, Second Glacial, and so on to the Present or Postglacial phase.

Pluvial and interpluvial evidence. Recent studies by climatologists and others have made it fairly certain that, as the successive ice sheets advanced southward over Europe, the cyclonic storm belt also moved south in corresponding measure, with the result that North Africa, including Egypt and the Sahara, received a much greater rainfall than at present and was consequently more habitable. This succession of pluvial and interpluvial phases is traceable, by archaeological and other evidence, as far north as the Gobi desert and North China for the Asiatic continent,[5] and for the southern hemisphere as far south as Rhodesia in South Africa.[6] This suggests that while glaciation took away habitable areas in the north it added or improved equally great areas farther south, including the whole series of vast deserts ranging from Morocco to Mongolia. It is worthy of remark that it was within this desert zone that all the higher civilizations sprang up, and not in the regions bordering the great glaciers.

Valley terraces and marine shore terraces. A striking series of gravel terraces — usually four — appears to be bound up in some as yet unexplained way with the glacial fluctuations. Such terraces parallel the sides of many river valleys — for example, the Thames, the Rhine and its tributaries, the Danube, the Somme, the Loire, the Garonne, and the Rhone in Europe; the Nile and the Isser in North Africa; and the Connecticut [7] in North America — and demonstrate that the valleys in question during certain stages in their history have been partly filled up with water-borne detritus, which during other intervening stages was mostly swept out to sea, either by an increased water flow or by a steepening of their gradients. This, as indicated, has happened apparently four times, the proof being the four levels or remnants left in the shape of terraces on one or both of the valley sides above the present flood plain.

In certain cases, like the Rhone valley, the upper ends of these lateral terraces merge into the terminal glacial moraines, indicating that the original deposits of which the terraces are remnants were derived from the glacial moraine debris. In fact the small Günz, Mindel, Riss, and Würm valleys show just such four lateral terraces, which interdigitate with the four principal terminal moraines. However, there are four similar terraces in certain other valleys, like the Somme and the Isser (Algeria), which are not directly connected with water flow and debris dispersal from the glacial fronts. It follows that the characteristic four valley terraces are not entirely dependent upon glaciation but have other contributory causes. This is made still more evident by recent investigations. L. deLamothe, C. Deperet, and others have revealed that a series of four or more terraces or old beaches are observable at many points around the Mediterranean shore. These have been named after places where they are especially prominent: Sicilian, Milazzian, Tyrrhenian, and Monasterian — unfortunately not in alphabetical order like the Alpine glacial moraines. The same terraces can be traced also along the Atlantic coast as far as Scotland and perhaps to Scandinavia. These four marine terraces merge into the four river valley terraces wherever the latter actually reach the sea and are at heights approximating respectively 100, 60, 30, and 15 meters above the present sea level. The inevitable conclusion is that whatever may be the origin of the four valley terraces at their upper ends, near the glaciers, the lower ends, in common with the marine beaches, are the results of land subsidence, during which the rivers were unable to carry their burden of detritus out to sea. Further to complicate the problem, the old sea beaches are strewn with molluscan and other fossils belonging in the main to fairly warm seas, suggesting interglacial rather than glacial times.

As a reasonable way out of this maze Professor Sollas has advanced the explanation of "composite origin" of the valley terraces, crediting their upbuilding chiefly to subsidence during preglacial and interglacial times, instead of, as formerly, to deposition during glacial times.[8] This means that prior to the first Pleistocene glaciation much of Europe and North Africa subsided to about 100 meters below the present level, where the eustatic balance was maintained long enough for a shore bluff to be excavated and for the drowned valleys to be filled up with detritus to the same height. That accomplished, a land rise set in which reached a height as yet undetermined (perhaps sufficient to expose the continental shelf) but which may have had something to do with the apparent lowering of the snow line and the coming of the glaciers. At any rate, during the First Glacial or elevated phase the valley detritus, it is supposed, was largely swept out and the first or upper terrace produced. This process of rise and fall was repeated at least four times on a successively smaller and smaller scale and thus the four South European marine and valley terraces were formed. In northern Europe — Scotland, Denmark, Norway, Sweden, and Finland — there are two additional post-Würmian terraces, known in the Baltic area as Yoldia and Littorina, which probably correspond to the last two minor Alpine glacial oscillations — namely, Gschnitz and Daun — the prior Bühl movement not being registered in the north because at that early stage of the grand Würm retreat there were here no exposed beaches. At the present time, therefore, we may be supposed to be experiencing a subsidence, of which there is actually some evidence, ranging in Europe from central Denmark at least as far south as Brittany and taking in eastern England, for here archaeological remains of the late Paleolithic and Neolithic horizons are found inclosed in fresh-water peat deposits now at considerable depths below sea level. A similar though perhaps not related phenomenon is indicated also in North America by partly submerged shellmounds on the coast of New Jersey, Florida, and San Francisco Bay.

Elsewhere, however, as for example in northern Denmark, in Norway and Sweden, and also in the northern Hudson Bay country, there are equally positive proofs of recent steady elevations, with periodic arrests marked by beaches, which are of importance for dating the archaeological remains found upon them. Perhaps this rise of northern land masses correlates with the southward retreat of the forest mentioned before and corroborates the suggested advance of yet another presumably mild glacial episode.

Were we to attempt a summarizing correlation of all these Pleistocene and Holocene events, that is, the formation of the glaciers and their attendant moraines — the valley terraces and the ocean shore beaches — in the form of a diagram, it would be somewhat as follows:

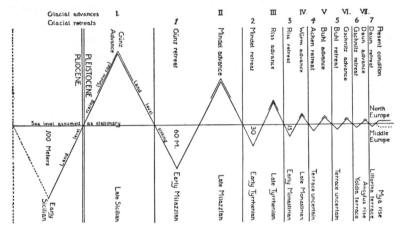

Fig. 1. Diagrammatic correlation of Mediterranean and Baltic marine terraces with Alpine glacial phases. Modified after Sollas, p. 38.

Absolute chronology of the Holocene epoch. Thus far the related sequences of events embraced by the Pleistocene and Holocene epochs supply the basis for a merely relative chronology. Several serious attempts have been made, however, to convert it into terms of solar years. These estimates vary all the way from 300,000 years (Obermaier) to a full round million years (Chamberlin and Salisbury); but it should be added that the balance of opinion in recent years strongly favors the larger figure. Only for the Holocene or Postglacial epoch has any approach to definiteness been attained. Baron G. de Geer, of Sweden, and his pupils, R. Lidén and E. Antevs, by counting the seasonal layers of glacial silt laid down in natural depressions in the wake of the receding glaciers in Sweden and in New England, have obtained astonishingly accurate figures and dates. They have determined, for example, that the last glacier, the Würm, began to retreat from southern Sweden about 15.500 years ago and that it reached its present position on the Scandinavian uplift near the Arctic Circle in about 5000 years.[9] The time it took for this glacial front to recede from its southernmost terminal moraine in Germany, across the Baltic to southern Sweden, is not yet worked out, but it is estimated at about another 5000 years; and the total time elapsed since the Würm climax has by various methods been independently figured in both Europe and America at approximately 25,000[*] years.[10] In the Connecticut valley and in Canada, farther north, the investigation is as yet unfinished and it is known only that the last glacier retreated in places at the rate of about a mile in twenty-two years and for a period covering several thousand years. This segment of time, unfortunately, hangs in the air, as it were, because neither the beginning nor the end series of clay bands has been tied into our own calendar. Sooner or later this will be done, and we may also expect a correlation between these clay bands and the seasonal rings of embedded trees, living and dead, to be effected, so that we shall have an accurate chronometer by means of which our later human culture periods may be dated. Already in our own country Douglass has, by means of the California redwoods (reaching 3000 years in age) and other conifers of the Southwest, tied in and accurately dated many of our principal Pueblo ruins,[11] and there seems to be no limit to the possibility of counting backward into geological times these seasonal pulsations thus faithfully recorded both in sediments and in trees, living and fossil.

BIOLOGICAL PREMISES

Franz Boas

Description of species. The characteristics of the group of individuals composing a species are determined by three causes: heredity, selection, and influence of environment. Heredity is active only in family lines. Its action depends upon the way in which characteristics are transmitted from parents to children. It is assumed that in a stable species no new mutations develop. Selection modifies the species as a whole by the increase or decrease in the occurrence of certain individual types. Environment influences the group as a whole, or its influence may depend upon the way in which various types composing the species react upon it.

Heredity. The fundamental law of heredity may be expressed in

* See also page 74.

the following way: when conditions remain equal and a pair of parents have a very large number of offspring, then the numerical frequencies of definite bodily forms of the offspring are determined by the genetic characteristics of father and mother. The numerical frequencies may follow a great variety of laws, according to the traits studied and the genetic characteristics of the parents, but they are fixed for every trait by the genetic characteristics of the parents. It is assumed in this that no spontaneous hereditary mutations occur.

When individuals possess hereditary traits which are so sharply contrasted that they may be considered as alternative, the frequency of their occurrence in the offspring follows often simple numerical rules. These were first discovered by Gregor Mendel, and therefore these laws are called Mendelian laws.

It is not necessary to enter here into details, but a brief presentation is unavoidable. When the one parent has a trait called A, the other a trait called a, the descendants of the first generation will be mixed and be characterized by the combination Aa. And if Aa is mated with Aa, the characteristics A and a will appear in four combinations AA, Aa, aA, aa. In other words, there will be three types exhibiting the trait in question: the type A, the type a, and the type Aa. These numbers will be such that in a large group of individuals one fourth will be of the first and second type each, one half of the last-named type. It happens sometimes that the particular trait of the type Aa cannot be distinguished by its outer appearance from A. Then the ratios in a large number of individuals will be such that three fourths have the trait A, and one fourth the trait a. In this case we call A the dominant type. If any one of the individuals of trait A is mated with another one of the same apparent kind, some descendants will be genetically A, others Aa. Among their descendants the type a may recur when one Aa happens to be mated with another Aa. On the other hand, a and a can give only individuals with the trait a. We call a, therefore, recessive because in matings of a with a the descendants always revert to the type a.

It will be understood that all these remarks refer only to single traits, not to the whole organism. The genetic traits may also be more complex. Thus one may be AB, the other ab. Then the descendants in the first generation will be $ABab$. When these are mated among themselves a new series of types will develop.

The frequency of the occurrence of various combinations is given to the left of the table of combinations on page 18. If AB is dominant,

Frequency of Occurrence

			AB	Ab	aB	ab
ABAB	1					
ABAb	2	9	AB	ABAB	AbAB	aBAB	abAB
ABaB	2					
ABab	4		Ab	ABAb	AbAb	aBAb	abAb
AbAb	1					
aBaB	1	6	aB	ABaB	AbaB	aBaB	abaB
abaB	2					
Abab	2		ab	ABab	Abab	aBab	abab
abab	1	1				

the first four groups will show the traits AB. There are nine of these. Six will be mixed, and one will be recessive.

It is possible to explain almost any numerical relation by multiplying the unit elements assumed in the parents. Furthermore, if it is assumed that dominance is incomplete or variable, practically every numerical arrangement found in the series of offspring may be accounted for. It is also likely that the vitality of the various resultant types is not the same, that they may be entirely or partly sterile, or even not capable of developing or maturing. The genetic composition and the body forms of a population may be unstable on account of the complex effects of these causes.

Empirically it is found that the characteristics of a species that remains in the same environment remain fairly stable. This would mean that a state of equilibrium between the various genetic elements has been established.

The way in which stability of a population is secured may be illustrated by the example of simple Mendelian inheritance.

When there are two traits, A and a, from which the population is derived we have, as shown before, in the first generation only Aa; in the second, one part A, one a, and two Aa; or $\frac{1}{4}A$, $\frac{2}{4}Aa$, $\frac{1}{4}a$.

If intermarriage is by chance, we find:

$$\frac{1}{4}A \times \frac{1}{4}A = \frac{1}{16}A$$
$$\frac{1}{4}A \times \frac{1}{4}a = \frac{1}{16}Aa$$
$$\frac{1}{4}A \times \frac{2}{4}Aa = \frac{1}{16}A + \frac{1}{16}Aa$$
$$\frac{2}{4}Aa \times \frac{1}{4}A = \frac{1}{16}A + \frac{1}{16}Aa$$
$$\frac{2}{4}Aa \times \frac{2}{4}Aa = \frac{1}{16}A + \frac{2}{16}Aa + \frac{1}{16}a$$
$$\frac{2}{4}Aa \times \frac{1}{4}a = \frac{1}{16}Aa + \frac{1}{16}a$$
$$\frac{1}{4}a \times \frac{1}{4}A = \frac{1}{16}Aa$$
$$\frac{1}{4}a \times \frac{2}{4}Aa = \frac{1}{16}Aa + \frac{1}{16}a$$
$$\frac{1}{4}a \times \frac{1}{4}a = \frac{1}{16}a$$
$$\overline{\frac{4}{16}A + \frac{8}{16}Aa + \frac{4}{16}a}$$

This is the same grouping as before. If there is no disturbing element the distribution of individual forms composing the species will remain stable. The same is true of other Mendelian ratios.

If the forms A and a occur with different frequencies — for instance A very rarely and a very frequently — and Mendelian splitting prevails, the relative frequencies of A and a will remain the same, provided there is no selective mating. The ratio of different forms remains the same.

The species as a whole is composed of a large number of hereditary lines each set off from the other by slightly divergent characteristics. Such a line is called a *genotype,* while the species which is composed of many genotypes is called a *phenotype.* If all the individuals composing a genotype were identical in form, they could be readily assigned by a study of their form each to its own line. As a matter of fact the individuals composing a line differ among themselves and are often so similar to individuals of other lines that it is impossible, even by the most minute examination, to determine the genetic line to which each belongs. In most cases, study of the family lines of the individual is required for a determination of the genetic line to which it belongs.

In all bisexual species a constant intermarrying of family lines occurs.

It follows from all this that in a generalized description only the major, fundamental characteristics of a species can be defined, while the differentiation of genetic lines within the species requires genealogical studies.

Selection. When mating in a stable population is entirely at random and no other disturbing factors make their appearance, each generation will be, individually and in composition, identical with the preceding and following ones. If for some reason the families constituting the species are isolated by geographical conditions or other causes, random mating is no longer possible; and if the individuals composing each community belong to distinct genetic lines, local varieties will develop. Whatever the causes of selective mating may be, they present conditions that may lead to the rise of varieties and to shifts in the composition of the species which may separate in a number of recognizable varieties provided the genetic differences of the segregated genetic lines are great enough.

There may be other disturbing causes due to different birth rate or mortality of certain types, or to the inclination of certain forms, males and females, to band together and to mate preferentially. If, for instance, the genetically tall lines of the species should be more fertile and have a lower mortality than the genetically short ones, the result would be a gradual increase in the general size of individuals of the species. Changes in environment due to migration or to other causes may become an important factor in eliminating or at least decreasing the frequency of certain genetic lines at the expense of others.

The effect of the kind of selection here discussed will not produce new forms, but will bring about differentiation of varieties within the range of variation of the original species.

Environment. The species are not absolutely stable, but undergo changes under the influence of environment. So far as observations show, such changes are not hereditary. They indicate merely that the bodily form of an individual must be taken as an expression of its hereditary characteristics in a definite environment. An absolute form uninfluenced by environment does not exist.

The amount of influence of environment is considerable among lower forms, but is less pronounced in the higher animals. Plants taken from low places to high altitudes change their habitus. Their stems are shortened. Crustacea living in salt or brackish water change their types according to the salinity of the medium in which they live. The pupae of butterflies adjust their color to the background on which they are placed. Rats change the length of their tails according to the temperature in which they are raised. Lions born in captivity differ in details of bodily form from wild lions.

Origin of species. All these data indicate that varieties may occur that remain within the range of the genetic lines composing a species and within the range of its adjustability to environment. They do not throw light upon progressive differentiation that would lead to the formation of new species.

Both paleontological evidence and the results of the study of the morphology of plants and animals prove that such changes have occurred. Two problems present themselves: How did these changes come about, and what means have we at our disposal to determine the forms from which modern species have been derived? The former problem is a general biological one and beyond the scope of the present book. The second is of fundamental importance for the understanding of the descent of the races of man.

Two distinct aspects of change must be distinguished. The one relates to the gradual modification of species in the course of geological time. From a common source, forms develop that differ in varying ways and lead to a series of forms that may be represented by a genealogical tree. The other refers to parallel changes that occur in an equal manner in species and genera entirely distinct in descent, without genetic relationship.

The gradual changes of some types of animals, like those of the horses and elephants, from extinct species have been traced by the study of fossilized remains found in consecutive geological strata. Although the changes that occur in course of time are not by any means continuous, they are close enough together to allow us to infer that the bodily forms of these animals were gradually modified and, as time went on, gave rise to new forms. The periods during which these modifications took place were very long, and we may not conclude from the apparent permanence of living types, the history of which we can follow for a few thousand years, that this indicates an actual permanency of form. We must, therefore, assume also that precursors of man different from modern man occur in geological strata preceding those found at the present time, and the study of their remains enables us to follow the gradual emergence of man from earlier forms.

A second method of approach is based on the study of morphological similarities. A comparison of the structure of animals of different species and genera shows that they may be graded according to their similarities and dissimilarities. The chemical behavior of the blood can be studied for the same purpose. Furthermore, the most characteristic traits of each species and variety become more and more pronounced in the course of the development of the individual, so that early stages may be assumed to be more generalized forms. These we may be allowed to consider analogous to lower forms of corresponding age, from which they developed in different directions. Since the paleontological record is always incomplete, partly on account of the lack of specimens and partly on account of the absence of all soft parts, the inferences from morphological comparison are a most valuable and indispensable aid in the reconstruction of the history of species. It is unavoidable that the conclusions drawn from morphological studies, being more indirect, are more uncertain than those obtained from the study of actual paleontological specimens, the chronological sequence of which is more or less accurately known; nevertheless the conclusions cannot be omitted. The interpretation of the differences between paleontological and modern forms itself requires a knowledge of the significance of morphology, so that the evaluation of the differences between paleontological and modern forms depends also on morphological judgment. This is the reason for much of the uncertainty in the interpretation of the significance of differences between closely related forms.

A second important consideration is based upon certain homologies — that is, parallelisms that occur in forms which are not distinctly genetically related, but are distant branches of a main trunk.

Parallelism occurs frequently among plants and animals. Plants which live in high altitudes or in Arctic climates are characterized, regardless of their systematic position, by shortness of stems and the formation of leaf rosettes. The Cactaceae of the American desert and the Euphorbiaceae of the African desert have a similar habitus, characterized by the suppression of leaves and deeply embedded stomata that retard evaporation. Animals of the Arctic and of high altitudes, such as the polar bear, the hare, and the ptarmigan, have white fur and feathers. W. M. Wheeler has treated fully the remarkable convergence in structure of the ant lion and worm lion,[12] and A. Willey has given a comprehensive treatment of the observations proving convergent evolution.[13]

A particular phase of convergence is observed in the bodily form of domesticated animals. Loss of pigment is of frequent occurrence. Horses, dogs, rabbits, and swine with blond hair and blue eyes occur. Wild forms that have such loss of pigment are very rare, although complete albinism occurs. The great variety of coat color in domesticated forms is not found in the same way among wild forms. Variations in size are common in domesticated races. The tiny Pekinese dog and the St. Bernard, the pony and the heavy dray horse, are examples. Variations in the form of the ear develop, particularly the hang ear of the dog and of the rabbit.

FOOTNOTES

1. The translations are taken from Macalister, R. A. S., *A Text-book of European Archaeology* (Cambridge, 1921), vol. 1, p. 25.
2. Boule, M., in *Fossil Men* (Edinburgh, 1923), takes a different view. See pp. 36, 49, etc.
3. *Science*, vol. 71, Supplement (Jan. 3, 1930), p. xii.
4. *Science*, vol. 74, Supplement (Sept. 4, 1931), p. xii; also Jochelson, W.,

Archaeological Investigations in Kamchatka, Carnegie Institution of Washington Publications, No. 388 (1928), p. 35.

5. Berkey, C. P., and Nelson, N. C., *Geology and Prehistoric Archaeology of the Gobi Desert*, American Museum Novitates, No. 222 (1926).

6. Leakey, L. S. B., *The Relation between Past Pluvial and Glacial Periods*, 98th Report of the British Association for the Advancement of Science (Bristol, 1930), pp. 372–375.

7. Osborn, H. F., *Men of the Old Stone Age* (1924), p. 120, fig. 57.

8. Sollas, W. J., *Ancient Hunters* (1924), p. 36; see also Osborn, H. F., and Reeds, C. A., "Influence of the Glacial Age on the Evolution of Man," *Bulletin of the Geological Society of America*, vol. 40 (1929), fig. 3, for a diagram of correlation of glaciations and marine terraces, p. 596.

9. Sollas, *op. cit.*, pp. 648–656; Peake, H., and Fleure, H. J., *The Corridors of Time* (1927), vol. 2, pp. 1–12.

10. Penck, A., and Brückner, E., *Die Alpen im Eiszeitalter* (Leipzig, 1909); summaries of the same in MacCurdy, G. G., *Human Origins* (1924), vol. 1, p. 50; or Peake and Fleure, *op. cit.*, vol. 2, pp. 11 and 135. See also *Science*, vol. 71, Supplement (Jan. 3, 1930), p. xii.

11. Douglass, A. E., "The Secret of the Southwest Solved by Talkative Tree Rings," *National Geographic Magazine*, vol. 56 (1929), pp. 737–770.

12. Wheeler, W. M., *Demons of the Dust* (1930).

13. Willey, A., *Convergence in Evolution* (London, 1911).

CHAPTER II

HUMAN ORIGINS AND EARLY MAN

JAMES H. MCGREGOR

One of the great intellectual achievements of the nineteenth century was the discovery of "man's place in nature," to use a phrase which became famous as the title of the small volume containing T. H. Huxley's essays on "The Man-like Apes" and "Man's Relation to the Lower Animals." [1] During the seventy-odd years which have passed since these masterly essays appeared, practically all enlightened people have come to accept the idea of man's origin by descent from lower animals, even though they may be quite ignorant of the evidence for it or the stages in the slow progression from simple beginnings to mankind's present estate.

This chapter is intended primarily to give a brief account of the physical characters of the more important ancient and extinct types of man, especially those that are distinctly more primitive than the modern races. Secondarily, though space will not permit a consideration of the evidence for the evolution of man from early vertebrates or even from the lowest mammals, an attempt will be made to compare the most primitive known types of man with their nearest subhuman kin, the great apes, and to indicate the probable relationship between the human and simian branches.

The layman sometimes gains the impression that organic evolution leads only in the general direction of man, which is far from the truth. The fossil record of the horse family, or of the elephants, is much more completely known, and these would have pursued their way if the order called *Primates*, the branch to which man belongs, had never sprouted among the other early ordinal shoots of the mammalian stock at the beginning of Tertiary time, or if, having flourished for a while, it had withered and died as many other branches did. Limiting the discussion to the Primates, one sometimes hears the apes referred to as "nature's unsuccessful attempts to make a man," but this is mere rhetoric. As well might man be called nature's failure in trying to evolve an ape. Still it is but natural for us to consider evolution from our own human point of view, and from this standpoint the emergence of the mind of man is the most stupendous product of nature, the crowning achievement of creative evolution. Yet we must consider it not as something supernatural, a miracle, or even as a single sudden mutation, but as a gradual growth. There are many grades of intelligence even among men of today, and in the individual history of every one of us the mind develops as truly as the body. These facts considered in relation to the mentality of our remote cousins, the anthropoid apes, surely point to the conclusion that our prehuman and barely human ancestors of Tertiary time must have been respectively subhuman and incipiently human in their mentality.

Primates. The group of animals which especially concerns us here, the Primates,[2] comprises the lemurs, monkeys, apes, and man. This name as given by Linnaeus in the mid-eighteenth century denoted "first" (in the sense of highest in rank), and doubtless many persons assume the primates *ipso facto* to be the most highly specialized and the latest to be evolved of all the mammals; but as a matter of fact the lowest primates, the lemurs, appear to be somewhat allied to the East Indian tree shrews, a group of small primitive mammals usually classified among the insectivores, an extremely primitive and generalized order. The higher primates, especially the great apes and man, are of course greatly advanced in the development of their brains, but in their anatomy otherwise they form a relatively generalized group. Nor were primates especially late in the time of their appearance. Fossil lemurs are known from the Eocene, and one or two small forms which appear to be early anthropoid apes from the Lower Oligocene of Egypt; numerous large apes resembling the chimpanzee, orangutan, etc., are known as Miocene and Pliocene fossils, especially in India; and recent evidence (cultural, not skeletal) tends to show that man himself of a primitive sort may have emerged before the end of the Tertiary.

Though there are different opinions as to just when the human family split off from the apes, there is rather general agreement, among those familiar with the evidence, that man and modern ape are both descendants of some common progenitor somewhere in Tertiary time, and this after all is the essential point.

The data for determination of interrelationships of primate groups are drawn from comparative anatomy, embryology, paleontology, biochemistry, physiology, and psychology; and the evidence from all these sources is mutually corroborative in the highest degree.

The order Primates comprises two suborders: the *Lemuroidea* or lemurs and the *Anthropoidea*, which comprise all tailed monkeys of both the Old and the New World, together with the tailless great apes and man. With few exceptions the primates are arboreal in habit. The Lemuroidea include the true lemurs, recent types of which are found chiefly in Madagascar, with allied forms in Africa and the East Indies, and the very aberrant *Tarsius*, a remarkable little East Indian primate of very puzzling affinities, which in many ways is intermediate between lemurs and monkeys. This creature is sometimes, and perhaps properly, placed, together with certain fossil relatives, in an intermediate suborder, *Tarsioidea*. Fossil lemuroids and tarsioids found in Eocene deposits in North America and Europe are the oldest known primates, and descendants of these appear to have migrated to Asia and Africa in early Tertiary time. It is quite possible, however, that North American and European fossil lemuroids may both be derived from still earlier unknown Asiatic forms, related to the tree shrews which, appearing in the Paleocene, still inhabit the East Indies. The lemurs with their foxlike muzzles do not appear very monkeylike; their intermediate character is expressed in the German name *Halb-affen* (half monkeys); but nevertheless these lemurs and especially the tarsioids appear to stand very close to the ancestral line of the second suborder, the Anthropoidea.

This suborder readily falls into two great divisions: first, the American monkeys or *Platyrrhines* (with the nostrils widely separated); and second, the *Catarrhines*, which are characterized by a narrow septum between the nostrils, and which comprise all the Old World monkeys, baboons, apes, and also man. These two branches are very definitely characterized and differ in many structural features which render it improbable that either has descended from the other, and make it practically certain that the two groups evolved independently, Platyrrhines in Tropical America and Catarrhines in the Old World, from two already separate lemuroid or tarsioid stocks. This would mean that the resemblances between Old and New World monkeys largely represent parallel evolutions, though the two ancestral stocks probably had a remote common progenitor in some Eocene lemuroid, such as *Notharctus* described by W. K. Gregory. The Catarrhines, or Old World Anthropoidea, comprise four families: (1) the *Cercopithecidae*, or Cynomorph monkeys (including all Old

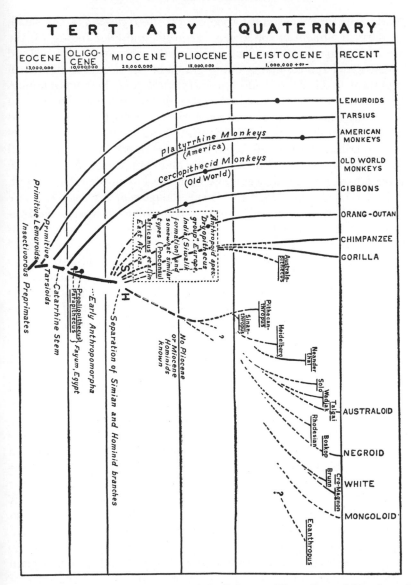

Fig. 2. A tentative phyletic tree of the Primates. The estimated durations of the geological epochs are from Charles Schuchert (1931). The interrelationships of the various Pleistocene human types are extremely dubious.

World tailed monkeys and baboons); (2) the *Hylobatidae*, the small, long-armed gibbons of the Malay Peninsula and East Indies; (3) the *Simiidae* (also called *Pongidae*), including the orangutan of Borneo and Sumatra and the chimpanzee and gorilla of Africa and a number of important fossil forms; and (4) the *Hominidae*, or the human family. The gibbons are frequently included with the large manlike apes in the family Simiidae, but their separation as a distinct family seems to be thoroughly justified. The South African fossil ape *Australopithecus* described on page 29 is even more manlike in certain cranial and dental characters than the gorilla and chimpanzee. A very small lower jaw of Lower Oligocene age from the Fayum desert in Egypt, which has been named *Propliopithecus*, though representing a creature no larger than a very small monkey, has molar teeth with the five-cusped pattern characteristic of anthropoid apes, and hence has a special interest as affording evidence that forms close to the stem of the great apes and man lived at a time so remote; for this jaw, dating back some forty million years, according to the geologic calculations based on radioactivity, is actually older than any remains thus far known of tailed monkeys, either American or Old World. *Parapithecus*, another primate represented by a still smaller jaw from the same geological formation, may also be a protoanthropoid. Miocene deposits of Europe, and especially of the Siwalik Hills of India, have yielded teeth and jaws of several types of manlike apes somewhat resembling the chimpanzee and orangutan, and fossil anthropoid teeth and jaws apparently of Miocene age were reported in Kenya, East Africa, in 1932. Several genera of apes of Miocene and Pliocene age, found chiefly in India, are called collectively the "*Dryopithecus* group" from the name of the best known genus. The peculiar plan of their teeth, characterized by five-cusped lower molars, the "Dryopithecus pattern," has been the subject of detailed comparative studies by Dr. W. K. Gregory and Dr. Milo Hellman, who find it to be the basic pattern of these teeth in all anthropoid apes and also in man, where it is well developed in the earlier and more primitive types but often reduced in civilized groups, especially in Europeans, to a simpler four-cusped "plus pattern." It should be made plain here that "Anthropoidea" as the name of the second suborder of Primates, including all monkeys, apes, and man, is not to be confused with the term "anthropoid" as specifically restricted to the manlike apes or Simiidae.

Australopithecus africanus (*the Taungs ape*). Among fossil anthropoid apes the one which has the greatest interest from its likeness to man is represented by a juvenile skull found at Taungs in Bechuanaland, Africa, in 1924. The discovery consists of the entire facial region and the base of a skull, together with a natural limestone cast of the endocranial cavity. It was found in a filled-in cave in a travertine limestone deposit the geological age of which is uncertain but is now believed to be Lower or Middle Pleistocene.

The Taungs skull was carefully cleaned and studied by Professor Raymond A. Dart of Witwatersrand University, Johannesburg, who gave it the name *Australopithecus africanus* (Southern ape of Africa).[3] The skull is that of a young animal at a dental age corresponding to that of a human child of about six years, as the first permanent molars are just becoming functional. The entire milk dentition is preserved. The skull has some resemblance to that of a young chimpanzee, the main differences being that the anterior teeth are very much smaller, the chin is better developed, and the forehead is fuller, more nearly vertical, and lacking entirely the supraorbital ridge (see Fig. 3) which is slightly developed even in infant chimpanzees. The brain, as may be seen from the natural endocranial cast, is considerably larger than that of a chimpanzee of corresponding dental development, and is distinctly more humanlike in form than that of any other anthropoid ape. The teeth also are far more manlike than those of any other known ape, living or fossil; but in contrast with the very small milk incisors and canines, the first permanent molars are considerably larger than in the chimpanzee. Professor Dart has been so strongly impressed by the manlike features of this fossil that, notwithstanding his giving it the name "Australopithecus," he regards it as related to the ancestral stock of man rather than to the great apes. Had the skull been that of an adult instead of a child, the manlike features would doubtless have been far less obtrusive, as the jaws would have projected quite as much as or more than they do in chimpanzees to accommodate the enlarged permanent teeth. In a modern anthropoid ape of the dental age of this fossil, the brain has attained very nearly its adult size, from which we may infer that the adult of this type would have a, brain no larger, or little larger, than that of a gorilla; so that, with large jaws and relatively small cranium, it would appear much more apelike than the young animal. Professor Dart believes that the creature walked upright, but there is nothing in the skull to warrant this or to indicate that its balance on the spinal column was essentially different from that of a young chimpanzee. In all discussions of Australopithecus it is important to keep in mind that the skull is that of a very young individual and that no other part of the skeleton is known. It exhibits a remarkable mixture of simian and human features and is beyond question the most manlike of known anthropoid apes, but this special manlikeness may well be an example of parallelism. Sir Arthur Keith [4] considers it as definitely an anthropoid ape, but he states that "of all the fossil apes yet discovered, Australopithecus comes nearer to our expectation of what our anthropoid ancestors should

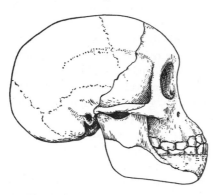

be like than any which has come to light so far." Though apparently too late geologically to qualify as an ancestor of man, the Taungs fossil appears to represent an especially advanced member of the simian branch which became extinct during the Pleistocene period.

Dr. Robert Broom [5] of the Transvaal Museum at Pretoria has announced the discovery of what appears to be the long-hoped-for adult Australopithecus. The specimen is a skull found in the summer of 1936 at Sterkfontein near Krugersdorp, Transvaal, somewhat more than

Fig. 3. Skull of *Australopithecus africanus* (the Taungs ape). Juvenile specimen, milk dentition with first permanent molars. Posterior cranial region and part of lower jaw restored. (One third natural size.)

200 miles northeast of Taungs. Like the Taungs specimen, the new skull was embedded in limestone which had filled in a former shallow cave, and the fossil was shattered by the blast which exposed it. Among the parts recovered is a nearly complete natural cast of the brain cavity which indicates an endocranial capacity of about 600 cubic centimeters, equal to that of a large gorilla (the greatest endocranial capacity recorded for the gorilla is 655 cubic centimeters) and much greater than the maximal capacity of the chimpanzee. Frontal sinuses are large. The maxillary bones and several upper teeth are preserved; the molars are distinctly larger than those of the chimpanzee or of man, but the empty socket of an upper canine shows that this tooth was relatively small, as are the milk canines in the Taungs skull. The fossil is still partly embedded in matrix,

but enough is exposed to enable Dr. Broom to make a number of important measurements, and he has attempted a provisional reconstruction drawing in lateral view which resembles a female gorilla but with somewhat weaker jaw development. On the whole, this drawing realizes rather closely the adult conditions inferred from the juvenile Australopithecus skull, and Dr. Broom assigns the new fossil provisionally to that genus, though he believes that it represents a distinct species which he names *transvaalensis*. Dr. Broom places the Sterkfontein formation provisionally as Upper Pleistocene, thus somewhat later than the Taungs discovery. If this is correct, both are much later than the emergence of man. This part of Africa is over 1000 miles south of the present great rain-forest area, and there is no conclusive evidence that it was ever forested. The fact that both the Taungs and Sterkfontein skulls were found in filled-in limestone caves suggests that Australopithecus may have been a ground-living genus possibly frequenting rocky regions like some species of recent baboons. The discovery of the rest of the skeleton, especially the pelvis and feet, is greatly to be hoped for.*

Man and apes. One who has not made a special study of the subject can have no conception of the all-pervading and detailed structural similarity of man to the three great anthropoid apes, especially the gorilla and chimpanzee, even though these likenesses are disguised by very conspicuous adaptive differences. If we compare the chimpanzee with its protruding jaws, its long arms and hands and grasping feet adapted to arboreal life, and man with his expanded brain, reduced jaws, and long legs and feet specialized for erect, bipedal habit, the differences at first sight seem to be enormous; but careful analysis shows that the likenesses are far more impressive and far more fundamental. As Charles Darwin in the *Descent of Man* [6] states: "There can . . . hardly be a doubt that man is an offshoot from the Old World Simian stem; and that under a genealogical point of view he

---

* In 1938, in the light of additional discoveries, Dr. Broom proposed a new generic name, *Plesianthropus*, for this form, and also found near the same location another type of large fossil ape which he named *Paranthropus robustus*. In both forms, although the brain is no larger than in some modern apes, the incisor and canine teeth are much more manlike in size and form than in any other known anthropoid ape, living or fossil. Indeed the small canines seem so inadequate for offense and defense that Dr. Broom considers it likely that these creatures walked erect and used sticks and stones as weapons. This surmise is further supported by the discovery of some incomplete arm and leg bones which are strikingly human in structure and very unlike those of the living great apes.

must be placed with the Catarrhine division." And further, "If the anthropomorphous apes be admitted to form a natural subgroup . . . we may infer that some ancient member of the anthropomorphous subgroup gave birth to man." And Haeckel remarks in *The Last Link* [7]: "In fact it is very difficult to show why man should not be classed with the large apes in the same zoölogical family. We all know a man from an ape; but it is quite another thing to find the differences which are absolute and not of degree only." Over fifty years ago (1883) Robert Hartmann [8] in Germany proposed uniting the two families Simiidae and Hominidae in one group which he called the *Primariae*, but this proposal, while entirely logical, has not been adopted. H. H. Wilder [9] in *The Pedigree of the Human Race* (1927) drops the Simiidae and unites the great apes with man in the human family, Hominidae, but zoölogical usage still generally recognizes the two families, though the most profound difference between them is a psychic one rather than physical.

Many features which at first glance would be cited as conspicuous differences are shown by careful analytical study to be, on the contrary, essential similarities; for example, the huge air sacs in the throat of the great apes, especially the orangutan, would surely seem to have no counterpart in man; yet they have unquestionable homologues in the small laryngeal ventricles or sinuses of Morgagni, which are outpocketings from the sides of the human larynx. On the other hand, many Old World monkeys have air sacs in the throat which superficially resemble those of the apes, but which are morphologically quite different in their essential relation to the larynx, and hence cannot be regarded as homologous, so that, as regards these throat sacs, the great apes are actually closer to man than to monkey. Almost everyone would say that a "hairy ape" was more like a monkey than like man in the matter of coat, and yet careful counts by Professor A. H. Schultz,[10] of the number of hairs per square centimeter of skin on back and chest, show conclusively that, compared with monkeys, the apes are relatively hairless, approximating the human condition. "Man," says Schultz, "is the least hairy primate, but in this respect there exist much smaller differences between man and some anthropoid apes than between the latter and the majority of the lower monkeys." These comparisons of laryngeal sacs and hair are only two of many which might be cited, but they are sufficient to indicate that the proper evaluation of resemblances and differences requires considerable training in anatomy and related sciences.

At this point we may enumerate a few of the features common to man and the great apes which differentiate these collectively from the Catarrhine tailed monkeys of the Old World. Space will permit only a partial list. One feature is the absence of an external tail, which is present only in the early embryo. The number of trunk (presacral) vertebrae is also less than in monkeys; that is, the body is relatively shorter. The pelvis is much wider, the chest broader than deep, reversing the condition in monkeys, and the sternum short and flattened. The teeth have primarily the "Dryopithecus pattern" with five cusps in the lower molars (Fig. 4). The chimpanzee and gorilla (but not the gibbon and rarely the orangutan) are manlike

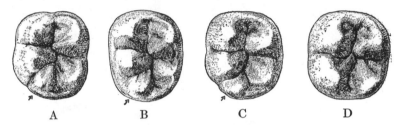

Fig. 4. Left lower molar teeth of anthropoid apes and man to show the fifth cusp, characteristic of the Dryopithecus pattern. All drawn same size. *A*. Dryopithecus. *B*. Gorilla. *C*. Human molar with fifth cusp. *D*. Human molar showing plus pattern lacking fifth cusp. (Fifth cusp indicated by arrow.)

in possessing the frontal sinus (Fig. 5) and in having no free central bone in the wrist, this bone becoming fused with another wrist bone as in man (Fig. 6). The great apes and man also lack the cheek pouches present in most Old World monkeys, and they are the only primates which possess a vermiform appendix. The ischial callosities or horny seat-pads which are so conspicuous in Old World tailed monkeys are lacking, except in the gibbons, though slight traces are occasionally present in the chimpanzee. The tailed monkeys are rather generalized in limb proportions; arm and leg are of nearly equal length, the walk is quadrupedal, and the posture is pronograde; that is, the back is horizontal.

In the anthropoid apes the arms have become greatly elongated, an adaptation to the habit of hanging to branches and progressing in part by "hand walking" with suspension from the branches, and swinging hand leaps somewhat like those of a trapeze performer. Sir Arthur Keith has aptly described this suspended posture as "downright" in contrast to the upright, bipedal posture of man, and has termed the arm walking habit "brachiation." The most perfect brachiators are the gibbons, next the orangutan, then to a lesser extent the chimpanzee, and least of all the gorilla. The arboreal habit of the anthropoid apes is really quite different from that of monkeys, and is accompanied by many adaptive changes in the mechanical relations of the muscles and viscera. The secondary

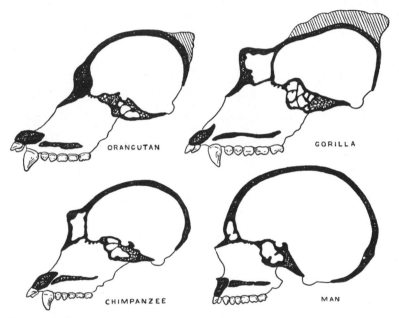

Fig. 5. Median sections of anthropoid ape and human skulls to show extent of frontal and sphenoidal sinuses. Ape skulls redrawn from H. Weinert.

elongation of the fingers of the great apes, especially marked in the orangutan, is plainly an adaptation to brachiation, while the thumb has remained small or has even undergone reduction in size. When on the ground the great apes are quadrupedal, but owing to the disproportionate length of the arms and the fact that the hands rest on the knuckles the shoulders are higher than the pelvis so that the posture is between pronograde and orthograde. In the gibbons progression on the ground is erect and bipedal, the long arms being used as balancers, but the knee joints are considerably flexed, so that the gait differs markedly from the erect walk of man. Though the feet of the apes appear to be essentially monkeylike, having opposable great toes, careful studies have shown that they are much closer to the human foot anatomically than is the foot of any monkey. The anthropoid foot most resembling the human is that of the mountain gorilla, *Gorilla gorilla beringei*, of the eastern Belgian Congo. The least manlike hands and feet are those of the orangutan, which are extremely specialized in adaptation to arboreal life.

Recent studies show that the uterus and also the placenta of anthropoid apes are structurally almost identical with the human. The placenta is single, as in man, not double as in Old World monkeys. In the chimpanzee the female physiological sexual rhythm is almost exactly like that in the human species except that the cycle is about five weeks instead of four. The period of gestation in the chimpanzee, according to records of thirteen presumably full-term pregnancies in the Yale Laboratories of Primate Biology, shows an average of 236 days or about eight months, one month less than the human.[11] The female chimpanzee is capable of reproduc-

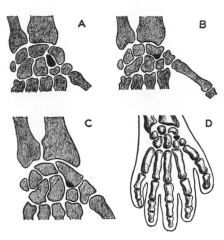

Fig. 6. The *os centrale* of the carpus. The *os centrale* (indicated in black) is a separate bone in the wrist in tailed monkeys, in gibbons, and in the orangutan. In the chimpanzee, gorilla, and man it is evident only in embryonic life, later being resorbed or more probably becoming fused with the navicular bone. *A* represents carpus in the orang, *B* in chimpanzee (and gorilla), *C* in man (slightly modified from H. Weinert), *D* in hand of a ten weeks human foetus (from Graefenberg).

tion at the age of seven or eight years, though full growth is not attained until two or three years later. The potential life span probably approximates that of man. R. M. Yerkes and A. W. Yerkes [12] mention a captive female chimpanzee said by Calmette and Wilbert to be sixty years old. Blood tests of relationship, both the earlier precipitin tests of Nuttall and the more recent agglutination methods of Landsteiner, also indicate much closer kinship of the great apes, especially the chimpanzee, to man than to any of the tailed monkeys. Nuttall, indeed, found the blood of the chimpanzee indistinguishable from that of man, while the more delicate method of Landsteiner reveals a slight difference; but both methods show a marked difference from the blood of even the Old World monkeys.

The biochemical likeness of the anthropoid apes to man is also indicated in their susceptibility to human diseases. "It seems that all microbic maladies of the human race can be transmitted to chimpanzees, and that many of them are transmissible to the lower apes. This is true for syphilis, typhoid fever, cholera, bacillic and amoebic dysenteries, exanthematous and recurrent typhus, yellow fever, pestilence, acute poliomyelitis, measles, scarlet fever, small-pox, trachoma, pneumonia, grippe. It is equally true for maladies produced by protozoa or by parasites: trypanosomiasis, leishmaniosis, bilharziosis." [13] A young gorilla in the Bristol (England) zoölogical garden had whooping cough during a local epidemic of that disease.

Though anthropoid apes and man are so closely allied in the essentials of their anatomical and physiological make-up, there are conspicuous adaptive differences chiefly correlated in the former with tree living, more or less brachiating habit, and quadrupedal gait; in the latter with perfectly erect posture, and bipedal progression on the ground with complete emancipation of the arms and hands from locomotion. Marked examples of such adaptation are seen in the limbs, pelvis, curves of the vertebral column, and the balance of the head on the neck. In the head itself, of course, man is marked by an enormous increase in the size of the brain and reduction in size of the jaws and teeth. The large cranium is balanced on the top of the vertical backbone, instead of thrust forward as in the ape. The human dental reduction is especially striking in the canines, as these teeth in the apes, especially in the males, are of considerable size; but despite the conspicuous differences the human teeth have the same basic pattern.

The brain of man, as the "organ of mind," might, of all bodily structures, be supposed to present the most fundamental divergence from the ape; but except that it is some three times as large, with more than ten times as many nerve cells in the cortex (which implies an enormously more complicated system of intercellular connections), it is essentially an enlarged and more complicated model of the anthropoid brain. The structural difference is solely one of degree. The general convolutional pattern is the same, and there is no definite anatomical structure in either one which is lacking in the other. Experimental work on cerebral localization in the chimpanzee and gorilla (by Sherrington, et al.) shows that the motor areas are essentially alike, the chief difference being the far greater expansion of the association areas in man; and recent studies by Tilney demonstrate that the microscopic structure within the brain stem of these apes is practically identical in pattern with the human, much closer to man than to any monkey.

Of course the mind of the most primitive normal man is incomparably superior to that of the most intelligent ape, which at best has only a brute mentality. But the careful experimental studies of Köhler, Yerkes, and others have shown that the great anthropoids, and especially the chimpanzee, which has been the most fully investigated, are far superior in intelligence to the tailed monkeys and all other animals, and qualitatively more like man in their mental operations. Instead of relying on mere aimless, fumbling methods, the apes in these experiments show real insight in problematical situations, and solve them in a purposive manner, often voluntarily using sticks, boxes, and other objects as instruments. In memory, as shown by delayed response experiments, they are greatly superior to other animals. W. Köhler [14] says, "The chimpanzee manifests intelligent behavior of the general kind familiar in human beings," and that "they also behave in a way which counts as specifically human." Notwithstanding this qualitative manlikeness in the mental operations of anthropoids, the range of their minds in a quantitative sense is brute rather than human. They lack utterly the capacity for speech, which is perhaps the chief criterion of human mentality, and this deficiency seems absolutely to preclude the attainment of any culture or social inheritance.

Speech, the essentially human faculty, is an extremely complicated mental phenomenon, involving not merely the functioning of the neuromotor apparatus for uttering words — that is, vocal symbols for things and actions; the auditory recognition of the spoken word as a specific symbol; the interpretation of visual impressions such as gestures, signs, and pictorial or graphic symbols — but also an elaborate associational mechanism rendering possible the syntactic combination of auditory symbols which constitutes language. There is no single "speech center" in the human brain, but a number of motor, auditory, and associational regions all interacting to produce speech.

Students have sometimes asked why the manlike apes never learn to talk, when parrots, obviously far less intelligent, do so readily.

The answer is that parrots do not really *talk*: they imitate sounds of various kinds, inanimate and animate, including the human voice, and certain words and sentences may come to be repeated associatively or in appropriate circumstances, thus giving an impression of understanding of their meaning; but the parrot has no comprehension of the real significance of words, nor is there any true syntactic sense when it repeats a phrase. As Professor L. A. White has aptly expressed it, animals (and this includes both parrots and apes) use sounds as emotional *signals*, but not as *symbols*. Most birds and mammals utter these vocal signals which are spontaneous or instinctive, such as the barking, howling, whining, and growling of a dog. Crying and laughter in man do not have to be learned; they are like the vocalizations of animals. The chimpanzee, according to R. M. Yerkes and B. W. Learned,[15] has a considerable gamut of these vocal signals, but they express emotions and are not symbols or names for definite things or actions — not true words. The failure of the chimpanzee to talk is not due to structural inadequacy of the larynx and oral region so much as to cerebral deficiency, lack of development of the elaborate brain mechanism necessary for speech. It does not *occur to* the animal to use words as symbols. A closely parallel condition is seen in certain low grades of human imbeciles who, though susceptible of some degree of training, remain incapable of speech. Somewhat similar is the condition of a normal baby of eight or nine months; or better for comparison, a somewhat older baby in whom, though considerable intelligence is manifest, the speech mechanism is somewhat retarded in development. In the ape it *never* develops. Attempts to teach apes to speak are commendable, but the outlook for success does not appear very hopeful.

Origin of the human branch. Notwithstanding the close relationship of the human family to the anthropoid apes, no one who has any knowledge of the primates believes that man is a descendant of any living type of ape. The gorilla and chimpanzee, our living next-of-kin, represent only remote cousins, not ancestral species. The great questions are: Where and when did the hominid branch separate from the anthropoid ape stock, and what were the latest common ancestors of man and the great apes? We might also postulate a third question: What were the earliest members of the human branch, the "protohominids," like? Unfortunately it is not yet possible to give a perfectly definite answer, satisfactory to all inquirers, to any of these questions.

First, as to the *time* of hominid origin. As we have seen, the earliest anthropoids (the qualifying phrase "thus far discovered" is always implied when we speak of any fossil form as the "earliest") are of early Oligocene age (the little Parapithecus and Propliopithecus of Egypt); then a number of genera and species of great apes (the Dryopithecus group) are found in Upper Miocene and Pliocene formations in Europe and especially in India. Very recently (1932 and later) somewhat similar fossil anthropoids have been reported in Kenya, Africa. One of the Indian forms, *Sivapithecus*, is believed by Pilgrim to be a possible ancestor of man, but this seems extremely unlikely since, as in all the others, its dentition is definitely specialized in the direction of the modern great apes. In 1934 G. E. Lewis described a fragmentary jaw of a new Indian Pliocene genus and species, *Ramapithecus*, which appears to be more manlike than any of the others of this group in the small size of the canine teeth. The weight of opinion may be said to favor the separation of the protohuman branch in Miocene time. The Oligocene Propliopithecus, so far as can be judged from a lower jaw, may be as well qualified to be an ancestor of man as of the modern apes, but if other parts of the skeleton were known it might be disqualified as an ancestor of either branch.

As to the *place* of origin of the Hominidae it is almost certainly either Asia or Africa. Africa has the most manlike of living apes, the earliest fossil apes, and the most manlike simian fossil Australopithecus, but the last named is too late geologically to be a direct ancestor of man, and probably represents a sort of super-ape. Asia, on the other hand, has yielded more species of fossil apes and also the two earliest and far the most primitive known types of the human family. On the whole, the evidence for Asia as the "cradle of humanity" seems somewhat more impressive.

There cannot be the slightest doubt of man's more or less remote arboreal ancestry, but his latest *subhuman* tree-living forebears of (probably) Miocene time were almost certainly less specialized than the modern great apes. We may be pretty certain that the extreme length of the arms in proportion to the legs in the modern apes is a specialization for brachiating habit, just as the long legs of the human branch are specially adapted to walking and running in the erect bipedal posture. In the common ancestor the arm and leg were probably more nearly of equal length, as is the case in the tailed monkeys. The erect bipedal gait is probably more difficult for a modern chimpanzee or gorilla than it was for the late common ancestors of Miocene time owing in part to the great weight of the long arms and the consequent shifting of the center of gravity higher up in the body in the present-day apes. As to the incipient proto-humans, we are not to conceive of the creatures as coming down suddenly out of the trees and becoming purely terrestrial in habit. They probably retained for a long time a habit very similar to that of the gorilla, dividing their time between the trees and the ground. As their arms were shorter and less heavy the center of gravity was lower, nearer the region of the pelvis, so that upright gait would be easier than in the gorilla or the chimpanzee. Such a creature might find it comparatively easy to progress either on all fours or as a biped. The legs were probably relatively shorter than in any known type of man, and the feet no doubt retained the divergent grasping great toe for a long time.

It is not necessary to postulate a gradual disappearance of the forests as forcing our protohuman ancestors to adopt terrestrial life, since the gorilla, primarily semiarboreal, is largely terrestrial though living in dense forests. The early protohuman, at first equally at home in the branches of trees or on the ground, may have found the terrestrial habit increasingly to his advantage. For one thing, he was probably more omnivorous than the apes of the present day, living less exclusively on leaves and fruits, but finding part of his food in roots and small ground animals, lizards, insects, etc., as do the baboons, which are large, ground-living monkeys. Professor O. Abel [16] suggests that the transition from arboreal to ground life may have involved an intermediate climbing phase in rocky and mountainous environment somewhat like that of the baboons in certain regions of Africa today. The African Pleistocene ape Australopithecus may have had a similar habit. The protohuman probably became grad-ually more and more perfectly adapted to bipedal habit in correlation with the increasing use of the hands in manipulating food and other objects, and eventually with the use of sticks and stones as tools and weapons.

As G. Elliot Smith [17] has pointed out (1927), the development of eye and brain also proceeded step by step with the increasing use of the hands. As to the great question when and how the fac-ulty of speech evolved, marking the real dawn of humanity, we can only surmise. Language was doubtless acquired very gradually. In the foot the great toe lost its opposability by slow degrees and the grasping foot became reduced to a mere walking organ, but the exact method of the evolution of the human type of foot presents many problems. The grasping foot of the ape, with its thumblike great toe, forms such a conspicuously different member from the human foot that most writers before T. H. Huxley followed the old classification of *Quadrumana* (four-handed) and *Bimana* (two-handed) for the two groups. And yet comparative anatomy shows that the human foot has the same bones and still retains in reduced form those muscles which in the ape's foot function for adduction and abduction of the great toe. In fact the likenesses are more essential by far than the differences, and the human foot bears in its anatomy and in its embryonic development convincing evidence of descent from the grasping apelike type and of arboreal ancestry. The whole question of the evolution of man's posture has been ably discussed by Sir Arthur Keith, W. K. Gregory, Adolph H. Schultz, and Dudley J. Morton.

Having contrasted the simian and human lines of descent, we may consider very briefly the common ancestral stem whence these two divergent branches sprouted, probably back in early or middle Miocene time and perhaps somewhere in Asia.

A creature near the extremity of this ancestral stem, one of the latest common progenitors of anthropoid ape and man, cannot be pictured as a "missing link" in the sense of a creature halfway between the modern chimpanzee and *Homo sapiens*, but rather as a primitive generalized Catarrhine type of fairly large size, though probably not so large as a chimpanzee, with a hairy coat, apelike jaws and teeth, but with canines less specialized than in most anthropoid apes, the molars with the Dryopithecus pattern, since even the still earlier Oligocene types (Parapithecus and Propliopithecus) had it. The arms were shorter than in modern apes, the legs shorter than in man, so that the limbs were nearly equal, as in monkeys. The hands were of moderate proportions, without the disharmony in relative size of thumb and fingers present in recent great apes, and the feet were of grasping type with opposable great toe. The tail was probably already lost (as in all apes and a few monkeys). The animal was undoubtedly arboreal and probably somewhat monkey-like in habit, not yet greatly specialized for brachiation, and it was also quite at home on the ground, where it was quadrupedal and pronograde in posture, but with the habit of sitting erect like monkeys and apes in general. In brain development and mentality it was probably somewhat inferior to the modern anthropoid apes, but not greatly so. The creature here pictured is not protohuman but subhuman and also sub(modern)anthropoid, but it must be admitted that it is more apelike than manlike. Man, with his big brain and uniquely modified foot, marks a far wider departure from the ancient primate pattern than does the modern ape.

Has man descended from an ape? The answer hinges upon our definition of an ape, and unfortunately the words "ape" and "monkey" are variously and loosely applied, and often used interchangeably. (A comparison of the definitions of these words in a number of dictionaries will confirm this statement.) But as to man's descent from monkey or ape, prejudice and sentiment blind many persons to the facts. One well-known zoölogist in a popular book, after denying categorically the descent of man from any sort of monkey, says, "All the present primates, including monkeys, apes, and man, have been derived from *a generalized ancestral primate stock not at all like* [italics mine] any of the present-day specialized end products." This statement, while not strictly untrue, is evasive and misleading. Why not admit that this "generalized ancestral primate," if we could see it in the flesh, would be identifiable by anyone as a "kind of monkey or ape"? However, there was no single ancestor, but a long series of "ancestral primates" in man's genealogical tree, and the early or middle Miocene type we have attempted to picture, the immediate progenitor of both anthropoid apes and of man, may appropriately be called a "primitive generalized ape" — unless one objects to the name "ape" on sentimental grounds. This creature is hypothetical, but the fossil realization of it may some day be found. It is regrettable that no protohuman stages between this hypothetical precursor and *Pithecanthropus*, the most primitive known hominid, have yet been discovered. At the present time there is not a single subhuman fossil primate known which can be definitely identified as a direct ancestor of man.

Man. Thus far we have endeavored to indicate the main steps in the evolutionary line up to the dawn of humanity. The rest of the chapter will be devoted to an account of the physical features of the earlier and more primitive types within the human family, those which lived before the Holocene or Recent epoch.

Some ancient writers, notably Lucretius, realized that civilization was not the original condition of man, but something which he had gradually acquired, working up from savagery, and in the seventeenth and eighteenth centuries rough stone weapons found in various places in Europe were recognized by French and English writers as the work of "ancient barbarians," but there was no suspicion of the extent of their antiquity. Indeed, well into the nineteenth century the dawn of humanity was rather generally assumed, even by scientific men, to have been only some 6000 years ago. Bones of extinct animals — elephant, rhinoceros, cave bear, and various others — from caves in Germany, Belgium, and England had long been known, but they were regarded as merely antediluvian relics, their extinction accounted for by Noah's flood. In 1825, a young English priest, the Reverend J. MacEnery, found embedded in the stalagmite floor of Kent's Cavern, near Torquay on the coast of Devon, stone and bone implements associated with bones of some of these extinct animals, proving that man had been contemporaneous with them. Similar discoveries in Belgium and France were made shortly after those of MacEnery, whose notes on his researches were not published until 1859, long after his death (1841). Other caves later yielded not only stone implements but human bones mingled with those of extinct animals. The year 1856 is especially notable in human prehistory as marking the discovery of the Neanderthal skeleton in Germany and thus yielding the first definite proof of ancient man of a distinctly different physical type from modern man. (A skull of the same race had been found eight years earlier at Gibraltar, but its importance was not suspected until long after the Neanderthal discovery.) The first discoveries of prehistoric art were also made about the middle of the nineteenth century, so that knowledge of the extinct human races may be said to date from about that period.

Practically all of the examples of early man which we shall consider lived during the Pleistocene epoch. (The transition to a cold climate has been described before.*) It is the Glacial epoch or Great Ice Age. Since the men of this entire epoch are largely known from the flaked or chipped stone implements which they made and used, it is known as the *Paleolithic* or Old Stone Age in distinction from the *Neolithic* or age of more advanced culture, which intervened between the Paleolithic and Recent periods.

Types of man. We shall present only the more noteworthy features of the principal types of ancient man. Attention will be given chiefly to the structural conditions and the evidences of physical evolution. A reader not already somewhat familiar with human paleontology

* See page 8.

may be surprised to find that so many of the discoveries considered important consist of but meager fragments such as a jaw or a few pieces of a skull, often of somewhat uncertain geological age and sometimes with neither contemporary animal remains nor artifacts to aid in locating them in the scheme of human prehistory; and yet such relics yield a vast sum of definite information regarding extinct types. We shall begin with those members of the human family which seem "lowest" — that is, the earliest and least removed from sub-human ancestors in structure and presumably in mentality — and follow what appear to be general lines of ascent toward the higher types and especially toward that diversified group of races, fossil and recent, generally included in *Homo sapiens*.

Knowledge of extinct man has grown rapidly during the present century; conclusions regarding new discoveries are at best provisional as new finds are constantly shedding light on earlier ones and necessitating reinterpretation of evidence. Without doubt some of the opinions generally held today regarding certain early types will require revision in the light of future discoveries.

Pithecanthropus erectus (Ape-man of Java). *Pithecanthropus erectus*, the "ape-man of Java," was the first fossil form to be seriously considered as a "missing link" in the sense of an intermediate form between ape and man, and it is still the least human of all known types of mankind. As long ago as 1868 Ernst Haeckel, the great German apostle of Darwinism, constructed a hypothetical phyletic tree in which he derived man from the apes and postulated as an annectent form a creature physically halfway between the two but lacking the faculty of speech. On this fantasy he bestowed the name *Pithecanthropus alalus*, the "speechless ape-man." [18]

In 1889 Dr. Eugene Dubois of Holland, a young graduate in science and medicine, declined a position in anatomy in the University of Amsterdam to go instead to the Dutch East Indies as a military surgeon on a geological survey promoted by the Netherlands government. Dr. Dubois was keenly interested in the evolution of man and declared in advance his intention to find the "missing link." When, in 1894, he announced the success of this quest, surprise must have been tinged with incredulity, but his claims soon were shown to have a substantial basis. His announcement was in the form of an illustrated description of the fossil bones of the creature on which he bestowed Haeckel's old name *Pithecanthropus*; but in reference to the thigh bone, which indicated upright, bipedal gait, he proposed

the specific name *erectus*[19] (Pl. I, *A*). The remains, consisting of the top
of a skull, a left thigh bone, and two upper molar teeth, were found
in 1891 and 1892 in the bed of the Solo River, near the village of
Trinil in central Java, where they had been deposited in a layer
of volcanic lapilli overlying a stratum of conglomerate of marine
origin. Remains of numerous other mammals were found in the same
stratum, among them boar, hippopotamus, rhinoceros, deer, elephants of the extinct genus *Stegodon*, and some bones of tailed monkeys, but no trace of anthropoid apes. Dubois at first believed all

these animals to be of
species now extinct, and
he was inclined to place
the bone-bearing stra-
tum as late Pliocene.
In recent years, the
question of geological
age has been carefully
considered by a number
of European and Amer-
ican geologists, and the
consensus of opinion
today dates the Pithe-
canthropus layer as
Pleistocene. There is,
indeed, considerable ev-
idence indicating that

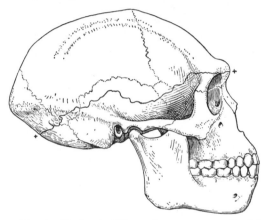

Fig. 7. Skull of *Pithecanthropus erectus*. Facial
and basicranial regions (below irregular transverse
line indicated by +) restored.

these beds may be rather well advanced in the Pleistocene, perhaps
even near the middle of that period. From a study of the associated
fossils, especially the plants, Professor Berry of Johns Hopkins University states that Pithecanthropus must have "fallen well within the
Pleistocene period . . . we are thus led to the conclusion that Pithecanthropus lived in the tropical evergreen jungle of Java during the
first or second periods of glaciation in Europe and North America."
There is abundant geological evidence that Java was in that period
a part of the Asian mainland, forming, together with Sumatra and
Borneo, a great extension of what is now the Malay Peninsula. The
question of the geologic age of the remains is important, for unless
Pithecanthropus lived fairly early in the Pleistocene it cannot be
regarded as an actual ancestor of Homo, since at least two types of
early man, those of Heidelberg and Piltdown (the validity of the

Piltdown *Eoanthropus* is somewhat questionable), inhabited Europe not later than mid-Pleistocene or even earlier, and there is considerable archaeological evidence of man sufficiently advanced to fabricate stone implements even in the late Pliocene epoch. There is also a probability that *Sinanthropus*, recently discovered in China, may have been earlier than Pithecanthropus.

The brain case of Pithecanthropus (Fig. 7) is much larger than that of any ape; in fact its size falls barely within the lower limit of humanity, but the low cranial vault and retreating, narrow forehead give the skull an apelike form. The very heavy ridge over the brow is especially suggestive of the great African apes (though an even heavier supraorbital ridge is to be seen in Rhodesian man), and this ridge contains enormous frontal sinuses. The height of the cranium is much less than in any normal skull of Homo, but that of the Peking Sinanthropus is almost as low. The area for attachment of the temporal muscles indicates that the jaws could not have been of very great size, nothing like those of the gorilla or orangutan. The general resemblance in form of this cranium to that of the gibbons — the small, agile, tree-living apes of the Malay region — has often been noted; but the early theory that Pithecanthropus was a giant gibbon is fantastic and can no longer be seriously defended. The maximum exterior length of the skull is 18.4 centimeters, its maximum breadth 13.1 centimeters, which gives the markedly dolichocephalic (external) index of 71.2. Owing to the enormous expansion of the frontal sinuses the skull is very much longer than the brain cavity. Thus the endocranial index is 80, which is barely brachycephalic, very different from the external index. Dr. Dubois formerly estimated the probable intracranial capacity as 855 cubic centimeters, but he later admitted that this was considerably too small. A careful reconstruction of the entire intracranial form was made by the writer by the method of restoring the missing portions of an endocranial cast by comparisons with similar casts from skulls of anthropoid apes and various primitive types of man. The model thus completed gives an endocranial capacity of about 940 cubic centimeters, which must conform pretty closely to the actual dimensions. This equals the minimal capacity of normal human skulls of today (occasional female Veddas and Australians). The endocranial form and size are fully as important as the external configuration of the skull in their bearing on the status of Pithecanthropus in relation to apes and man. The largest endocranial measurement of the gorilla thus far recorded is 655 cubic centimeters; thus Pithecanthropus exceeds it by about fifty per cent, and it is fully twice the size of the adult chimpanzee brain case. But the form of the brain is also significant, and careful comparisons have shown that in this regard the likeness to man and difference from the apes is very striking from every aspect. One manlike feature is the well-marked sylvian notch separating the frontal and temporal lobes. Rather extensive deductions regarding the mental capacity of Pithecanthropus have been made independently on the basis of the cranial cast by Professors G. Elliot Smith and Frederic Tilney. These investigators agree that the great frontal and parietal association areas in Pithecanthropus show great advance beyond anything seen in the brains of the higher apes, and in view of the apparent humanlike development of the so-called motor and auditory speech areas they agree that Pithecanthropus probably had at least a rudimentary language and that he must have possessed the beginnings of the social inheritance or culture which this capacity implies. This subject is rather fully discussed by Dr. F. Tilney.[20] It is only fair to add that some neuroanatomists are rather hesitant to admit the reliability of deductions, based on endocranial casts, as to the development of the various motor, sensory, and association areas of the brain, because such casts represent not the actual brain surface but merely an impression of the inside surface of the skull, which, however, conforms rather closely to the brain.

The two molar teeth, a left upper second and a right upper third, are very large with widely divergent roots. They are not quite like any human molars, but Dr. Dubois's belief that they belong with the cranium has been widely accepted. The third molar was only slightly worn and its crown was wrinkled in a manner resembling the molars of the orang, but this ape was not known to be represented in the fossil fauna of Trinil. Recently, however, many fossil orang teeth have been found by G. H. R. von Koenigswald, who reports that "Since we have discovered orang in the Trinil zone much more variable than the living orang we can prove that these molars belong to that ape." Having seen the newly discovered orang teeth, I am in full agreement with Dr. von Koenigswald's opinion that the two supposed Pithecanthropus molars are those of a Pleistocene orang. A third tooth, a left anterior lower premolar, was found later in the same locality and sent to Dr. Dubois after his departure from Trinil. The mineralization of this tooth, its color, etc., are exactly the same as those of the two molars. Its remarkable feature is its small size. It is entirely human, in no sense apelike. Moreover, it is certain that the possessor of this tooth did not have greatly enlarged canine teeth such as the apes have. In these animals there is an occlusion between the upper canine and the lower anterior premolar which is also somewhat enlarged. The tooth in question shows no surface for such contact with an upper canine. This fact proves that it belonged to a human type of dentition, and if the premolar is that of Pithecanthropus, it adds another manlike character to that creature.

Even before the discovery of the bones already mentioned, Dr. Dubois had found a small fragment of a lower jaw at Kedung Brubus, a place some twenty-four miles from Trinil, but in the same geological formation as that in which the Pithecanthropus remains occurred. This fragment, belonging to the chin region, he regarded for a long time as merely a part of an aberrant early human jaw, but later critical study led him to the conclusion that it belonged to another specimen of Pithecanthropus. Enough of the jaw is preserved to show that it had no chin prominence as in most modern races, though the front surface of the chin was almost vertical, quite different from the chin in the great apes. Fortunately it contains a part of the right lower canine, and this tooth is small, as in man. A part of the right lower premolar, which is also in place, is small and very similar to the one from Trinil, and together with the small lower canine it proves that the upper canine could not have been enlarged, thus (if it really belongs to Pithecanthropus) confirming the evidence from the Trinil premolar that Pithecanthropus was essentially human in dentition. It should be emphasized that this jaw fragment is distinctly different from any known human type in the form of the area of attachment for the digastric muscle, but it differs still more from the corresponding region in any of the great apes. It clearly belongs within the human family, and there seems to be a strong probability that it may represent a second specimen of Pithecanthropus, as Professor Dubois believes.[21]

The femur, or thigh bone, had it been found alone, would certainly have been assigned to the genus *Homo*. It was perfectly evident from its linea aspera that it indicated upright, bipedal posture; hence the specific name *erectus*. Dr. Dubois is still of the opinion that this bone presents some unique features, but most authorities hold that these are occasionally present in human thigh bones. The bone indicates a stature of about 5 feet 6 or 7 inches, near the average for modern man. A large pathological exostosis on the inner surface of this bone is purely accidental and has no bearing on its relationships. The femur was found in exactly the same level as the skull but some fifty feet distant from it, a fact which has been used as an argument (a rather weak one) against the probability that both belonged to the same individual. Of course the chief importance of the femur is the absolutely conclusive evidence which it yields that its possessor walked upright, and, as above stated, it was on this bone that Dr. Dubois founded the specific name *erectus*.*

At the present day, in the light of later discoveries of early Pleistocene man, no one believes that Pithecanthropus is a "missing link" in quite the same sense that Dr. Dubois at first considered it, but still in a way it is a "link" in that it is more apelike as regards the skull and brain than any other human fossil. And even though it may not be the earliest member of the human family, it is certainly the lowest in brain development and, by inference, in mentality and cultural capacity. No artifacts were found associated with Pithecanthropus, and there is no direct evidence as to culture. In 1935 a few stone implements were found at Trinil, but in the opinion of von Koenigswald they are much too advanced for a type as primitive as Pithecanthropus.[21a] Pithecanthropus may not be directly ancestral to any other human type, but it may mark instead the end of its particular branch of the family. Even in this case it would be vastly important as representing at least a collateral ancestor — "a great-uncle rather than a grandfather." The recent discovery of the Peking man, a slightly higher and closely related form, and of the Javan Wadjak man, and the finding in Java, in 1931 and later, of eleven skulls of a very primitive type, Ngandong or Solo man (possibly a direct descendant), tend to enhance the importance of Pithecanthropus in relation to human phylogeny. As the lowest member of the Hominidae thus far known, one which has barely crossed the threshold of humanity, Pithecanthropus erectus well merits the designation "ape-man" (Pl. I, *A*).

* In September, 1937, Dr. G. H. R. von Koenigswald discovered in central Java a second adult cranium of Pithecanthropus. It is more nearly complete than the Trinil skull, which it closely resembles in form, though considerably smaller, having an estimated endocranial capacity of only 750 cubic centimeters. In the same region a fragment of a lower jaw was found, containing four teeth of definitely human form but of enormous size. A brief account of the discovery together with photographs was published in the *Illustrated London News* of December 11, 1937, while the present chapter was in press. (See note, page 94.)

Homo modjokertensis. A recent discovery, quite possibly of major importance, reported by Dr. G. H. R. von Koenigswald, was the excavation in February, 1936, of a cranium of a hominid infant in the Djetis zone (Pleistocene) of eastern Java.[21b] The location is near Modjokerto, west of Surabaya. Dr. von Koenigswald regards the Djetis zone as definitely of lower Pleistocene age, and thus older than the Trinil zone which yielded Pithecanthropus. If this is correct the new skull may represent the oldest human skeletal remains thus far found, but the lower Pleistocene age of the Djetis zone is questioned by some authorities, who regard it as middle Pleistocene, though older than the Trinil beds.

The fossil consists of a fairly complete cranium including the upper border of the left orbit and both tympanic bones, together with the auditory meatus and the glenoid fossa for jaw articulation; but unfortunately the facial bones are missing. The absence of the teeth renders it impossible to determine accurately the age of the child, but the fontanelles are already closed, a condition attained in modern infants at about the age of two years. This closure is remarkable as the cranium is much smaller than that of a modern child even one year old. The total length is 138 millimeters, greatest width 110 millimeters, but the calotte height (the height above the plane of greatest length) is extremely low, only 62 millimeters — incidentally, the same as in Pithecanthropus. The forehead is sloping and lacks the fullness seen in a modern infant, and the posterior parietal region is remarkably depressed. The cranial capacity, as estimated by Professor Dubois from a cast, is only about 650 cubic centimeters, which is slightly more than two thirds the capacity of a modern baby one year of age. As the modern human brain at one year has attained nearly two thirds its adult size, this indicates an extremely small brain in the adult of the present type, a fact which, considered together with the depressed form of the skull, suggests, as noted by von Koenigswald, that it belongs to the Pithecanthropus group, though possibly not to the species found at Trinil. (Hence the discussion of it at this point.) An infant Pithecanthropus of course would not have the brow ridge, large frontal sinus, and occipital torus of the adult. Profile photographs showing the Modjokerto cranium together with skulls of modern Papuan and Chinese infants exhibit impressive differences, though naturally these are less striking than the differences between the crania of the adult Pithecanthropus and modern man. I have had the privilege of examining a *cast* of the Modjokerto skull, and am in full agreement with Dr. von Koenigswald in the opinion that its affinities are with the Pithecanthropus group. On the other hand Dr. Dubois believes it to be the skull of an infant of Solo man, a Javan type of upper Pleistocene age.

Sinanthropus pekinensis (*Peking man*). Certain paleontologists, notably Professor H. F. Osborn, have long maintained that the birthplace of mankind is to be sought in Asia. Among the numerous geological and paleontological data which give support to this view may be cited the following facts: Numerous genera of anthropoid apes of the Dryopithecus group flourished in India in Miocene and Pliocene time, and some of these animals, chronologically and biologically, were not widely removed from the point of divergence of the simian and human branches. Pithecanthropus, barely human, lived in Java in the middle Pleistocene. Just at the dawn of the present century a fossilized human tooth was found in China, and during recent years stone implements of Paleolithic type have come to light in China and Mongolia. Such facts, taken collectively, obviously indicate that Asia should prove to be a promising hunting ground for traces of early man and his subhuman forebears. In 1926 two human teeth were found at Choukoutien, thirty-seven miles southwest of Peking (Peiping) in cave deposits believed to be of early Pleistocene age. In 1927 another tooth, a fossilized lower molar, was found. It was plainly from a young person, as it was practically perfect and unworn. On the basis of this single tooth the Canadian anatomist, the late Davidson Black, professor of anatomy in the Peking Union Medical College, had the temerity to establish a new genus and species of hominid, which he named *Sinanthropus pekinensis* (Chinese man of Peking). Happily his seeming rashness won early and dramatic vindication in a series of discoveries which have offered to science a new type of ancient hominid of major importance, slightly if any more advanced in humanity than Pithecanthropus, and very well documented as to geological age. Abundant evidence from associated animal fossils was believed to show the cave deposits containing the remains to belong to early Pleistocene (Basal Lower Quaternary), but recent correlation studies of the Pleistocene of China, India, and Java (by Teilhard de Chardin, de Terra, von Koenigswald, and others) indicate that the Choukoutien cave deposits are of middle Pleistocene age corresponding to the Trinil beds of Java. As the beginning of the Pleistocene is variously estimated as from 500,000 to 1,500,000 years ago, a fair surmise as to the age of Peking man might be 500,000 years and possibly considerably greater. The Choukoutien fossils are found in filled-in clefts and fissures at the base of low limestone hills. In Pleistocene times these clefts were open caves and were frequented by both men and beasts, but in the course of succeeding ages they became gradually filled with deposits of red clay, limestone, and bones, which by secondary calcareous infiltration became cemented together.

Following the discovery of the type tooth in 1927, further excavation of the cave deposits was actively pursued by the Cenozoic Research Laboratory of the Geological Survey of China with the collaboration of the Peking Union Medical College under the able direction of Professor Black. A number of loose teeth and two lower jaws — only fragments but highly important in the anatomical information they afford — were found in 1928. In one of these, that of a child, the chin region is very receding and suggestive of that of the apes in form as well as in the marks of attachment of muscles; rather more apelike than the Heidelberg jaw, but less so than the jaw from Piltdown (both to be discussed later).

The most famous Sinanthropus discovery, and one of the most significant discoveries ever made in the field of prehistoric anthropology, was a nearly complete brain case found on December 2, 1929 (Pl. I, B), by Mr. W. C. Pei, a young Chinese paleontologist.[22] This skull is called No. 1, since a second skull, consisting of a large part of the brain case with a portion of the nasal bones, was secured in June, 1930. The dimensions of skull No. 1 are very slightly greater than those of Pithecanthropus. The form is somewhat similar — a very low vault, narrow retreating forehead, and supraorbital torus or ridge above the eyes — but the fullness of the forehead is more pronounced, this region closely resembling the Neanderthal type. A striking feature is the narrowness of the upper parietal region as compared with the lower temporal width. Some appreciation of the character of this cranium may be gained by contrasting the early opinions of two competent anthropologists, expressed on the basis of published measurements and photographs, before casts were available. H. Weinert[23] remarks (translation), "The skull find of December, 1929, proves so plainly to be Pithecanthropus that now — for the first time since Dubois's discovery — the Trinil calotte no longer stands alone"; while on the contrary A. Hrdlička[24] says, "The skull is clearly Neanderthaloid. It appears to represent no distinct

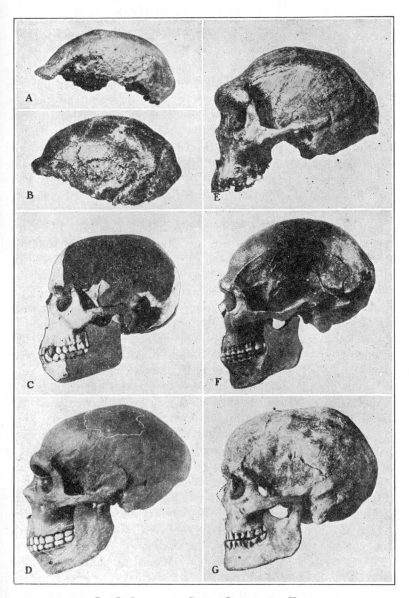

PL. I. SKULLS OF SEVEN IMPORTANT TYPES

All photographed to same scale, oriented (where possible) on the Frankfort horizontal.

A. Pithecanthropus erectus, Java; *B. Sinanthropus pekinensis*, China; *C. Eoanthropus dawsoni*, Sussex, England; *D. Homo neanderthalensis* (Chapelle-aux-Saints), Corrèze, France; *E. Homo rhodesiensis*, Northern Rhodesia, Africa; *F. Homo sapiens* (Brünn ace), Předmost, Czechoslovakia; *G. Homo sapiens* (Cro-Magnon race), French-Italian Mediterranean coast.

genus, species, or even a pronounced variety." Dr. Hrdlička states that this diagnosis is "necessarily provisional," and both anthropologists have modified their opinions since complete descriptions and casts and the second skull have become available, but the diversity of their early opinions affords a vivid idea of the status of Sinanthropus as intermediate between these two paleoanthropic types. Davidson Black early stated that the Peking man "might well be regarded as pre-Neanderthaloid in type," and the reported finding of relics of Mousterian culture in China points to the possible existence of later Neanderthaloids in that region, and justifies hope that the suggested evolution may in time be confirmed by skeletal discoveries.

On removal of skull No. 1 from the matrix, Professor Black discovered that the cranial wall was excessively thick, so that the brain cavity was smaller than had been supposed. At first he believed the skull to be that of a female, but the development of the supraorbital and occipital tori later convinced him that it was a male. The open sutures which permitted the separation of the bones show it to be that of an adolescent. A cast of the endocranial cavity, made by Dr. Black, has a surprisingly small volume, somewhat over 900 cubic centimeters, about the same as the Trinil Pithecanthropus. Skull No. 2 is less complete than No. 1, somewhat larger, with a higher vault and thinner walls, and undoubtedly the cranial capacity is considerably greater. It is distinctly less like Pithecanthropus and somewhat more like the Neanderthal type. Several fragmentary lower jaws practically without chin and with teeth resembling those of Neanderthal men were discovered, but except for an incomplete clavicle almost no remains of the rest of the skeleton had been found up to the time of Professor Black's lamented death in 1934.

Professor Franz Weidenreich of Frankfurt succeeded Professor Davidson Black in the Cenozoic Laboratory and the Peking Union Medical College and has actively continued the investigations at Choukoutien. He has reported the finding of fragmentary jaws, numerous teeth, and, in November, 1936, three additional skulls, two of them apparently adult males with cranial capacities estimated at 1200 and 1100 cubic centimeters, and one an adult female with a capacity of 1050, all very much larger than the first skull described by Black. As the Steinheim (female Neanderthal) skull, according to Weinert,* has an endocranial capacity under 1100 cubic centimeters,

* See page 66.

we see that some Sinanthropus brains may have been as small as that of Pithecanthropus while others exceed the minimal size in Neanderthals and recent men. In form all the Sinanthropus skulls are essentially similar, with the low crown narrowing above the ear region, and with a heavy supraorbital torus. In the three new skulls various portions of the facial bones are preserved, including the nasal bones, which are broad and rather flat in form, a cheek bone, and parts of the maxillary. The cheek bone is quite prominent and does not slope obliquely backward as in the European Neanderthal man. He believes that the teeth exhibit a definite sex difference in size, those of the males being larger, as is markedly the case in the great apes and true to a slight extent in modern man.[24a] The teeth in general exceed in size those of recent and also of Neanderthal man. The molars usually have greatly wrinkled crowns, and the upper incisors show a peculiar "shovel-shaped" form of the lingual surface, a condition characteristic of Neanderthal man and also, strange to say, of the Mongoloid division of recent man, as is well known from careful studies by Dr. A. Hrdlička.[25] Professor Weidenreich also notes the presence in Sinanthropus of peculiar hyperosteoses on the inner face of the lower jaw, somewhat below the alveolar border, a condition observed in recent Chinese and Eskimo jaws, and he concludes that "therefore Sinanthropus must be in closer relationship to this race than to the European Neanderthal on one side and to the Whites or Negroes on the other," and adds that it "indicates direct genetic relations between Sinanthropus and the Mongolian group of recent mankind."[26] I am unable to agree with Professor Weidenreich in this opinion. The fact that Sinanthropus lived in China carries no possible implication that it was specifically proto-Mongoloid. A type so ancient as to antedate, perhaps by hundreds of millennia, the emergence of Homo sapiens cannot, even if directly ancestral, have a special relationship to any one racial subdivision of "Wise man."

There is no positive evidence that Peking man was a remote direct ancestor of Homo sapiens, but I quote with approval Professor Black's cautious statement that "its dental characters certainly would seem to indicate that Sinanthropus could not have been far removed from the type of hominid from which evolved both the extinct Neanderthal and the modern Homo sapiens."[27] This is by no means an assertion that Peking man *was* our ancestor, but he may have been. This early opinion of Dr. Black's was based on dental characters, but it is strongly supported by most of the known morphological features.

As to the cultural status of Peking man, continued researches at Choukoutien have shown that he used fire and made very crude implements of chipped stone, especially of chert, and also that he utilized the jaws and pieces of the antlers of deer as tools. The fact that the human remains comprise practically no bones other than skulls is very remarkable and difficult to explain. It is certain that heads alone were not carried into the cave by animals. Professor Weidenreich believes the probable explanation to be that the severed heads of men, women, and children were the spoils of cannibalistic head-hunters of the same race. There is no evidence of any other local contemporary hominid type, though the Choukoutien caves have yielded implements made by later Paleolithic men.

All in all, the great antiquity and extreme primitiveness of the Choukoutien fossil men, the relative abundance of the remains, their geological documentation, their likeness to Pithecanthropus and to Neanderthal man, and the promise of further finds render the discovery one of the most important in the history of anthropology.

Eoanthropus dawsoni (Piltdown man). The Piltdown man was discovered in Sussex, England, in 1911-12 (Pl. I, *C*). It has been the subject of much discussion and even dissension among anatomists and has attained wide popular notoriety. To state only the more salient facts, there were found in a shallow bed of alluvial gravel at Piltdown several fragments of a human cranium which differed scarcely at all from modern man except that the bones were excessively thick. The cranial fragments, had they been found alone, would almost certainly have been identified simply as an early example of Homo sapiens; but within a few feet of some of them was also found most of the right half of a remarkable lower jaw containing two molar teeth. This jaw so closely resembled that of a chimpanzee, a creature not previously found fossilized in England, that it is safe to say that if only the jaw had been found it would have been generally regarded as that of a fossil ape, possibly a species of Dryopithecus (Fig. 8, *C*). However, the close juxtaposition of the cranial fragments and jaw, their similar mineralization, and the absence of known fossil apes in England led Dr. A. S. Woodward of the British Museum of Natural History to the conclusion that the remains all belonged to the same creature, which he forthwith named *Eoanthropus dawsoni*, or the "Dawn man." [28] The specific name was given in honor of Mr. Charles Dawson, the discoverer of the remains. The association of cranium and jaw has been widely questioned. Mr. Gerrit S. Miller,[29] of the United States National Museum, in 1915 placed the jaw as that of a fossil chimpanzee which he called *Pan vetus*, restricting the name "Eoanthropus" to the cranium. The lower molar teeth, however, though very primitive and possessing the fifth cusp characteristic of anthropoid apes and primitive human types, have considerably higher crowns than the teeth of the chimpanzee. Somewhat later a canine tooth and also the nasal bones apparently from the same skull were found. In 1915, at a distance of some two miles from Piltdown, two other fragments from the frontal and parietal regions of a closely similar cranium were found, together with a single lower molar tooth practically identical with those of the Piltdown jaw. This second discovery obviously strengthens the case for the validity of Eoanthropus. The original cranial remains from Piltdown comprise the left temporal bone, the left parietal with a considerable portion of the frontal, a large piece of the right parietal, the posterior part of the occipital and the nasal bones, sufficient indeed to permit the restoration of the missing parts of the cranium with a high degree of probability. When the missing portions of the lower jaw are similarly restored and articulated with the cranium, the facial region can also be reconstructed with a fair approximation to the actual conditions (Pl. I, *C*), *if the assumption that cranium and*

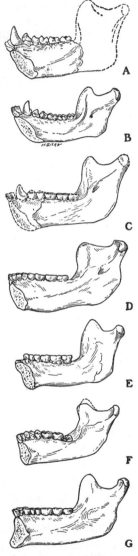

Fig. 8. Comparative views of sectioned lower jaws showing the inner surface of the right half. From *Our Face from Fish to Man*, by W. K. Gregory. Putnam (1929).

A. Dryopithecus. *B*. Chimpanzee. *C*. Piltdown man. *D*. Heidelberg man. *E*. Ehringsdorf type (Neanderthal man). *F*. Neanderthal man. *G*. Cro-Magnon man.

jaw belong together is correct. The skull, as restored, is of mesocephalic form and markedly prognathous. A small part of the supraorbital border which is preserved proves conclusively that the forehead was fairly vertical and that it lacked entirely the heavy brow ridge which distinguishes the Neanderthal and all other paleoanthropic types from Homo sapiens. The mastoid processes are well developed. The posterior border of the foramen magnum is preserved, and there are clear indications that the head was balanced on the neck in a fully upright position as in modern man. Owing to the great thickness of the cranial vault, the brain volume is considerably smaller than would be supposed. An endocranial cast made from the restored skull by the present writer measures 1240 cubic centimeters, but some estimates by others are considerably smaller. The sex of the skull is doubtful; if it is a female, as has been asserted, the male intracranial capacity would be somewhat larger. The lower jaw, as already stated, is unquestionably apelike. Not only is there no chin prominence but the apelike horizontal floor in the chin region — the "simian shelf" as Sir Arthur Keith has named it — is quite conspicuous. In neither Heidelberg man nor Sinanthropus, in both of which the chin is retreating, is this region really so apelike as in the Piltdown jaw. A careful restoration of the symphysial part of the jaw indicates that the anterior teeth must have been large and somewhat apelike. The canine tooth found in 1915 is large, resembling that of a female chimpanzee; from this it may be deduced that the anterior lower premolars must have been of larger size than in other human races. This canine tooth is rather generally considered to be a right lower, but some persons, including the present writer, regard it as more probably a left upper. Though the structure of the anterior teeth is deduced solely from the single canine and from the form of the chin region, it appears practically certain that the dentition was more apelike than in any known human skull. In view of the apelikeness of the jaws and teeth, it is surprising to find the glenoid fossa (the jaw socket) rather deep and formed as in Homo sapiens. When restored with sufficient width to fit the cranium the lower jaw has a most anomalous appearance.

Unfortunately the geologic age of Eoanthropus is uncertain, but the Piltdown gravels in which it was found are now generally accepted as an early Pleistocene deposit. A number of eoliths were found and one well-preserved Paleolithic worked flint, possibly of Mousterian age; also a large bone implement. Among associated animal bones and teeth were remains of both Pleistocene and Plio-cene mammals. These include a tooth of the fossil elephant Stego-don, teeth of rhinoceros, hippopotamus, beaver, and various other forms. Professor H. F. Osborn considers the tooth of a Pliocene Stegodon as definite proof that Piltdown man is a late Tertiary form, and thus the oldest known human fossil; but the consensus of opinion regards the Pliocene animal remains as having been washed out of the original beds and mingled in the river gravels with much less ancient bones of the Pleistocene period. On the whole, the Piltdown skull is one of the most perplexing of human fossils. A jaw so apelike in form of chin region and with apelike features in the teeth seems to be a decided misfit with a cranium so completely human. The composite creature seems to have no close relation to any other ancient or modern human type. It is widely divergent from all the paleoanthropic forms with heavy supraorbital ridges, depressed cranial vaults, and small mastoids — the Pithe-canthropus, Sinanthropus, and Neanderthal types. Professor Elliot Smith makes much of a resemblance to Sinanthropus in the thick-ness of the cranial bones and in the narrowness of the upper (parie-tal) part of the skull as compared with the lower temporal region, but these likenesses, in view of more essential dissimilarities, may well be considered as representing mere fortuitous parallelism. Some remarkably divergent views have been expressed regarding this fossil. H. F. Friederichs [30] has published a study of Eoanthropus in which he concludes that the cranium belongs to an individual of Homo sapiens of essentially modern type (as many others have in-sisted) — and *probably not older than Neolithic!* — while he holds the jaw and the canine tooth to be those of a hitherto unknown great ape of Tertiary age, to which he gives the name *Boreopithecus dawsoni.* H. Weinert, in 1933,[31] after a thorough study of the Pilt-down material, arrived at a very different conclusion: namely, that the jaw and cranium are undoubtedly from the same individual, and that the jaw, if properly reconstructed, is far less apelike than hitherto believed and indeed *strikingly human!* He even denies the great antiquity of the type, holding that it cannot be older than Neanderthal man, and suggests that the name *Homo piltdownensis* might be appropriate, though he has no objection to allowing the designation "Eoanthropus" to stand "until we really know what it is and where it belongs." Weinert believes that while the type may be important as an early example of *Homo sapiens fossilis,* it cannot be regarded as a true "Dawn man" in human phylogeny. The diverse opinions here cited indicate what a puzzle Piltdown man is.

On the European continent and in America there have been from the first numerous sceptics as to the validity of Eoanthropus (perhaps fewer now than formerly), but the English anthropologists and anatomists (inspired perhaps by a patriotic sentiment that British fossils are best) very generally accept Eoanthropus with loyal complaisance as the veritable "Dawn man."

As regards the validity of Eoanthropus the circumstances of the discovery, especially the two discoveries, taken together, must be considered very strongly "pro," while the anatomical incongruities seem generally "contra." As new finds of low-browed paleoanthropic types continue to turn up, all of them conforming more or less perfectly to a consistent scheme, the comparison seems to enhance the isolation of Eoanthropus and to render it more and more anomalous. Does this mean (recalling a famous remark) that one is loath to see "a beautiful theory killed by an ugly fact" — namely, Eoanthropus?

Homo heidelbergensis (Heidelberg man). A highly important relic of early man, dating back to the Second Interglacial Period or possibly the First, a human fossil probably at least 150,000 years old and quite possibly twice that, is the so-called Heidelberg jaw. This jaw was discovered in 1907 in a sand quarry at Mauer, near Heidelberg, Germany (it is often called the Mauer jaw), and is the sole relic of its type (Fig. 8, *D*). It represents one of the earliest unquestioned human bones yet found. This jaw was embedded in ancient river sand at a depth of over 79 feet below the present surface in a stratum which has yielded many bones of Pleistocene mammals of a warm interglacial period, the most notable of which are the straight-tusked elephant, the Etruscan rhinoceros, and the lion. Above the jaw had been deposited many strata of river sand, gravel, clay, and loess. The jaw is very heavy and large; it lacks any suggestion of a chin prominence, and therefore suggests the jaw of an ape, but the teeth and dental arch are definitely human and not larger than in some primitive modern types. One striking feature is the great width of the ramus (the lateral ascending portion of the jaw) and the extreme shallowness of the mandibular notch at its top. Many anatomists have noted that this jaw, while heavier and in some ways more apelike, has certain features in common with the later Neanderthal race, and it seems highly probable that *Homo heidelbergensis,* as it was named by Professor Schoetensack, is to be regarded as a pre-Neanderthaloid type representing an ancestor of Neanderthal man. Bonarelli, in 1907, proposed for it the generic name *Paleanthropus*. The apelikeness of this fossil has often been exaggerated. It is not true, as has sometimes been stated, that this jaw, if it had been found without the teeth, would have been placed as that of an ape. There are certain ape likenesses but they do not obscure its essential humanity. Nor is the assertion which is sometimes made that this is the heaviest known human jaw strictly true, since, though very large, it is no larger or heavier than some others. The humanity of the Heidelberg man is beyond question. The teeth, though they retain certain features regarded as primitive, are entirely human and the canines are no more enlarged or apelike than in other human types. The third molars, or wisdom teeth, are slightly smaller than the second molars. From the lower jaw it is possible to reconstruct the upper dental arch and the maxillary and zygomatic regions with a close approximation to the truth. The upper dental arch thus reconstructed by the writer is rather large and U-shaped, but no larger than the Neanderthal arch which it resembles. There is, however, one point in which the reconstruction differs from the Neanderthal type: that is in the form of the cheek region. Upon reconstruction of the zygomatic region with due regard to jaw muscles and their attachments, and the movements of the jaw, it is seen that the cheek bones could not have sloped obliquely backward as in Neanderthal man, but must have stood out squarely, giving Heidelberg man a somewhat wider and flatter face. This at least was true of the original possessor of this single known jaw. There appear to be good reasons, both geological and anatomical, for regarding Heidelberg man as a possible pre-Neanderthal or rather proto-Neanderthal type. Nothing is positively known as to his cultural status, as no artifacts have been found associated with the jaw or in the same horizon. The opinion has been expressed that the Heidelberg type may have been in the Chellean culture stage, but this is only a surmise. As he lived in the genial climate of an interglacial period, he was probably not forced to take shelter in caves to any great extent. There is a possibility that further discoveries may show the Peking and Heidelberg types not to have been very dissimilar.

Homo neanderthalensis (*Neanderthal man*). Among the ancient human types sufficiently divergent from modern man to be excluded from *Homo sapiens*, the first to attain such recognition, and the only one known from fairly abundant anatomical and archaeological data, is the type known as Neanderthal man. The discovery which led to the recognition of the specific type and which also gave it its name was made in 1856 when some workmen digging in a limestone cave in the Neanderthal, a narrow ravine near Düsseldorf, Germany, unearthed portions of a skeleton, including the top of the skull, several arm and leg bones, and fragments of a shoulder girdle and pelvis. The cranium was remarkable for the low vault and enormous arched supraorbital ridges which extended across the entire width of the forehead, giving it an "apelike" form as noted by various anatomists who examined it. The arm and leg bones also showed a number of unusual features. In 1864 the remains, by reason of the possession of many distinctive features, were made the type of a new species, *Homo neanderthalensis*, by Dr. William King, a professor of anatomy in Ireland, but for many years the weight of opinion followed T. H. Huxley in regarding Neanderthal man as merely an ancient, aberrant, and exceptionally "apelike" example of Homo sapiens. By some anatomists the great antiquity of the remains was questioned. The famous German pathologist, Rudolf Virchow, asserted that it was merely a pathologically malformed skull, while others considered it to be that of an idiot. It was not until many years later, after other discoveries of the same type had been made, that the new species attained general recognition, for unfortunately no bones of contemporaneous animals and no implements were found in the Neanderthal cave to give proof of its antiquity, though a similar cave near-by yielded bones of cave bear and rhinoceros. In the light of later exploration the Neanderthal discovery ranks as one of the greatest events in prehistoric anthropology. Since this original discovery abundant skeletal remains of Neanderthal people have been found in many parts of Europe. Germany, Belgium, France, the Channel Islands, Spain, Italy, Jugoslavia, the Crimea, and Palestine have yielded their bones and also thousands of stone implements of the Mousterian phase of flint industry definitely associated with this species. Associated bones of many contemporary animals, notably the woolly mammoth, woolly rhinoceros, reindeer, wild horse, and cave bear have been found with the human skeletal remains. Neanderthal man had acquired the art of making fire, and in a few instances at least there are indications of burial of the dead. The race inhabited Europe for a very long period, certainly from the Third Interglacial until well past the climax of the Fourth Glacial Period. Some of the earlier remains, such as those found in the region of Weimar and Steinheim in Germany and the skulls from Rome (mentioned below) dating from the Third Interglacial, may be as old as 75,000 or even 100,000 years, others perhaps no more ancient than 25,000 years, so that the time interval between very early and very late Neanderthal men is actually far longer than the interval between the latter and the present day!

As a matter of fact, the Neanderthal skeleton found in 1856 was not the earliest discovery of its species. Eight years earlier, in 1848, a human skull was unearthed in an excavation known as Forbes's quarry at the northern base of the Rock of Gibraltar, but for many years its importance remained unsuspected, though in 1864 certain likenesses to the Neanderthal skull were pointed out by an English geologist, George Busk. It was not until 1906 that this fossil was carefully studied and measured by Professor Sollas of Oxford, who showed it to be unquestionably a female Neanderthal skull of mature age. Though lacking the lower jaw, it is especially important since the facial region is intact. It is markedly smaller than the male skulls of this race, the endocranial cast, as carefully restored, showing a cranial capacity of only 1280 cubic centimeters. As recently as 1926 a second Neanderthal skull, that of a child about five years of age, was found at Gibraltar by the English archaeologist, Miss Dorothy Garrod. It was found in a filled-in rock shelter only a few hundred yards from the site of the first discovery. Knowledge of Neanderthal man was greatly advanced by the discovery in 1886 of two partial skeletons in the Spy cavern near Namur, Belgium. In addition to fairly well preserved crania, the jaws and many of the limb bones of both individuals were preserved. The crania, though somewhat broken, are much more complete than those from the Neanderthal cave, and one of them is almost its counterpart in the form of the calvaria. The geologic age of the Spy skeletons was amply documented by association with remains of woolly rhinoceros, mammoth, and other contemporary animals, and with flint implements of Mousterian type.

The most complete skeleton of Neanderthal man thus far found (except the discoveries in Palestine in 1932, not fully described at time of writing) is that named from the cave of La Chapelle-aux-Saints, in the Corrèze, France. The remains were found in 1908 in a shallow pit in the original floor of the cave, and apparently this was a case of deliberate burial. Among the debris which had accumulated in the cavern were bones of the cave hyena, woolly rhinoceros, reindeer, and other forms now extinct in Europe, as well as many flint implements of Mousterian culture phase. A masterly monograph on the Chapelle-aux-Saints skeleton by Professor Marcellin Boule [32] of Paris has become a classic; based as it is on detailed comparative studies, it has added more to our knowledge of the European Neanderthal type than any other single work. In addition to the skull and long bones, parts of the shoulder girdle, the pelvis, the vertebral column, and portions of the hands and feet were preserved among these remains. The form of the cranium is remarkably similar in size and form to that of the original Neanderthal and to one of the Spy specimens (Pl. I, D).

The same year, 1908, witnessed the discovery of another Neanderthal skeleton at Le Moustier in the Dordogne, very close to the locality which, just forty years earlier, had yielded the type specimens of the Cro-Magnon race. This skeleton, that of a boy about fifteen years of age and of very low stature, is especially important as showing adolescent skeletal conditions of this type. The teeth are all preserved, and as they are but slightly worn they give a valuable picture of Neanderthal dentition. Notwithstanding the youth of the individual, the supraorbital ridge is already clearly indicated, as are most of the other specific skull characters.

About the same time this part of France yielded several other skeletons. At La Ferrassie in 1909 and 1910 two were disinterred under a rock shelter which had previously yielded a large number of worked flints of the early Old Stone Age. One skeleton was that of an adult man, the other that of a woman. The male skull, considerably shattered, was skillfully put together by Professor Boule. While unmistakably of Neanderthal type, the lower jaw has considerably more indication of a chin than most examples of this species. In the female skeleton the hands and feet are well preserved and have supplied valuable data regarding these parts, though they have never received the minute study which they merit. It will be noted that the three discoveries just mentioned were all made within a comparatively limited area in southwest central France. A short distance to the westward, at La Quina in the Charente, other important Neanderthal discoveries have been made by Dr. Henri Martin. In 1911 he brought to light a fairly well preserved skull, apparently an adult female, and in 1916 a skull of a child, nearly complete except that the lower jaw is lacking. This skull, though that of a child of not more than eight years, already shows pronounced Neanderthal features. The forehead lacks the fullness of the skull of a modern child of the same age and exhibits marked indications of the brow ridge. The first permanent molars are erupted and already show clear indications of wear, though the permanent incisors are just erupting.

A group of skeletal discoveries made at various times in the vicinity of Weimar in Germany are especially important as proving that men of Neanderthal type inhabited this part of Europe as early as the Third Interglacial Period, the warm interval following the Riss and preceding the Würm glaciation. The Ilm River valley in this region exhibits a series of distinctly stratified deposits, some twenty meters in thickness, composed chiefly of calcareous tufa or travertine, and containing fossils which demonstrate climatic successions over a long period. In certain of the older layers which yielded bones of the straight-tusked elephant (*Elephas antiquus*) and Merck's rhinoceros (*R. merckii*), remains of hearths with charcoal and worked flints have long been known. Many of these artifacts are of Mousterian workmanship, but others appear to be of Acheulian or even of the still earlier Chellean type. In 1892 a lower molar tooth was found at Taubach, near Weimar, which was described by Nehring as a Neanderthal tooth. In 1914 and 1916 two lower jaws were found at Ehringsdorf in the same vicinity, the first that of an elderly individual, the second a child's jaw, both clearly of the Neanderthal species (Fig. 8, *E*), and in 1925 the cranial portion of a young adult skull of this type was unearthed also at Ehringsdorf.

Though all these remains antedate the last glaciation and are thus far more ancient than most of the other known Neanderthal remains, the cranium is no more "primitive" in form than in later members of the race. On the contrary, it seems to be a rather advanced example of its species. The chief interest of these fossils of the Weimar-Ehringsdorf region is not in anything they add to our knowledge of the structure of Neanderthal man but to their being the first to afford definite proof that this type inhabited Europe so early, as attested by geological data, associated artifacts, and animal bones. In July, 1933, another skull belonging to the Riss-Würm interglacial period, and the most nearly complete Neanderthal skull thus far found in Germany, was unearthed at Steinheim, some forty miles east of Stuttgart and 160 miles south of the Weimar-Ehringsdorf region. The Steinheim skull was described by Dr. F.'Berck-hemer of the Stuttgart Museum [33] and has lately been the subject of a detailed comparative study by Professor H. Weinert.[34] It is the skull of a female of early adult age. One striking feature is the very low endocranial capacity, which is estimated by Weinert as under 1100 cubic centimeters, far smaller than any other adult Neanderthal skull known and even smaller than two of the Sinanthropus skulls found in 1936.

Another Neanderthal discovery of the Riss-Würm interglacial period was that of a nearly complete adult skull in 1929 just outside the city of Rome. This skull, an account of which has been published by Professor Sergio Sergi,[35] was found in a layer of alluvial gravel containing, like the travertine at Weimar, remains of the straight-tusked elephant, Merck's rhinoceros, *Hippopotamus major*, and other mammals of the warm interglacial period. It is nearly complete, except that it lacks the lower jaw, and is somewhat similar in form to the Gibraltar skull which belongs to a much later period. Though Mousterian implements have been found in many localities in Italy, this skull is notable as being the first skeletal discovery of the Neanderthal race in that peninsula. In July, 1935, a second Neanderthal skull was found at the same site.

At Krapina in Croatia (Jugoslavia) in 1899 and later, fragments of a dozen or more Neanderthal skeletons, including several children, were discovered in a rock shelter. These were described by Professor K. Gorjanovic-Kramberger of the University of Zagreb (Agram).[36] Some of the skulls and long bones had apparently been crushed intentionally, and some of the fragments were charred, facts which have been regarded as suggestive of cannibalism.

The known range of Neanderthal man has been greatly extended eastward by recent discoveries in Palestine.[37] The first of these was the so-called "Galilee skull," found in 1925 during excavations in a cave near the Sea of Galilee. The specimen, consisting chiefly of the frontal bone and right cheek bone, is identifiable at a glance as of Neanderthal type. A few years later, remains of at least ten other individuals were discovered near Athlit, Palestine, in a group of three caves at the western foot of Mount Carmel, close to the Mediterranean coast and some thirty-five miles west of the site of the Galilee skull. This rich material was excavated by the British School of Archaeology in Jerusalem working jointly with the American School of Prehistoric Research. An exhaustive report on the

Mount Carmel discovery by Sir Arthur Keith and Mr. T. D. McCown is nearing completion at the time of present writing. At the International Symposium on Early Man held at the Philadelphia Academy of Sciences in March, 1937, these authors presented a brief paper from which the present notes are largely taken.[37a] In 1931 Mr. Mc-Cown found in the floor of a rock shelter called Mugharet es-Skhūl (Cave of the Kids) the skeleton of a three-year-old child, and in 1932 he removed eight other skeletons of individuals of both sexes, all representing intentional burials.

A neighboring cave, called et-Tabūn (The Oven), yielded a nearly complete skeleton of a woman. Similar animal remains and stone tools in the two caves indicate that the human remains in both were contemporaneous, and there is convincing evidence from the associated animals that these people lived in the latter part of the Riss-Würm interglacial period, thus being contemporaries of the early Weimar Neanderthals and antedating those of France and Spain. Acheulian and Levalloiso-Mousterian stone implements were found associated with the bones. At first it was believed that all the skeletons were essentially similar to the European Neanderthals, but further study brought out the surprising fact that while the Tabūn woman is like the western Neanderthal type in most characteristics, the skeletons from the Skhūl cave present a remarkable mosaic of Neanderthal and "modern" features. The skulls have the Neanderthaloid supraorbital torus and show considerable prognathism, but the vault is higher and the occiput is not "bun-shaped." Of two jaws found in the Tabūn cave at nearly the same level, one is practically chinless while the other has a fairly developed chin as have several of those from the Skhūl cave. The teeth lack the "taurodont" condition present in many European Neanderthals. Several skulls from the Skhūl cave have cheek bones like modern man, and in general the skeletons from this cave show a predominance of neoanthropic features. Their closest resemblance seems to be to the tall Cro-Magnon type of France. Estimates of stature, based on length of limb bones, give, in one male, the surprising height of 5 feet 10½ inches, in others 5 feet 8 inches. The Tabūn cave woman is short, barely 5 feet, and the women of the Skhūl cave are nearly as small.

Among the more significant anatomical features may be mentioned the fact that the feet, even in the Tabūn woman, are essentially modern in structure, "there was no greater mobility of the great toe; it was human in every respect," and posture and gait were evidently as in modern man. The spinal column is short in relation to height as in the European Neanderthals. The combination of definite neoanthropic with paleoanthropic features in human types which antedate the Neanderthals of western Europe is most remarkable. It raises perplexing questions regarding the definition of *Homo neanderthalensis*, the relationship of the two types, and the origin of the neoanthropic type.

In 1924, only a few months before the Galilee skull was found, a Neanderthal skeleton, apparently representing an intentional burial, was unearthed in the floor of a cave near Simferopol in the Crimean Peninsula, on the Black Sea. This locality is almost as far eastward as the Galilee region, but some 800 miles farther northward. Previous to these discoveries, the Krapina station, mentioned above, marked the easternmost limit of actual skeletal remains of the Neanderthal type, though the finding of stone implements apparently representing Mousterian culture has been reported from Mongolia and the Shensi Province of China. As the Peking man, Sinanthropus, though far more "primitive" than Neanderthal man, seems from the evidence thus far available to have been a possible ancestor, it would not be surprising if skeletal remains of Neanderthaloid type should be found in Asia much further eastward than Palestine.*

Attempts have been made to divide the European Neanderthals into several "races." Of course there are differences, and it is not unlikely that there may have been local subspecies and varieties, for the range of variation within a species is often very considerable even among individuals from the same locality as in the Palestine skeletons. If the same criteria were used in classifying man which some zoölogists on purely taxonomic grounds use in establishing species of mammals, *Homo sapiens* would have to be split up into

* The opinion here expressed received prompt substantiation in the finding, in 1938, of unquestionable Neanderthal remains in a limestone cave in southern Uzbekistan, Central Asia. This discovery, made by Dr. A. P. Okladnikov, and described by him in an illustrated report in 1939, included a practically complete skull of a child about 8 years of age, together with a few other bones of the skeleton, artifacts of Mousterian type, and some animal bones. The human remains had been intentionally buried in the cave floor. This discovery is of especial importance in the fact that its location is nearly 1800 miles farther eastward than any previously known Neanderthal skeletal remains, and about midway between western Europe and the locality of Peking man. It seems not unlikely that Neanderthal man may have been a widespread Eurasian type rather than primarily European.

numerous species. In the same sense, *Homo neanderthalensis* may comprise several subspecies, but in the present state of knowledge such subdivision would be premature. It is possible that more complete knowledge of the Palestine discoveries may render it necessary. In 1897 the name *Homo primigenius* was proposed by L. Wilser for Neanderthal man, but as King's *neanderthalensis* has well-established priority, it must be retained. Certain recent writers, however, have assembled the various early types which have in common a low vaulted skull with heavy supraorbital ridges — namely, Pithecanthropus, Sinanthropus, and Homo neanderthalensis — as the "primigenius group" to distinguish them from the "super species" *sapiens*. Beyond question the Heidelberg man, though the cranial characters can only be inferred from the jaw, would also belong in such a primigenius group, but Piltdown man would have to be excluded.

We may now proceed to a consideration of the physical features of the Neanderthal type. (It should be clearly understood that this description is based upon the European material. Complete knowledge of certain recent discoveries, especially the Palestine skeletons and the Steinheim and Roman skulls, may show the species to be less homogeneous than has generally been believed.) Many parts of the skeleton are quite diagnostic even though individuals may show wide variation. For example, the long bones of arm and leg, the scapula, and certain bones of the ankle are distinctly different from the corresponding parts of any type of Homo sapiens. This is especially true of the skull, not merely as a whole but in regard to the individual bones and even the teeth. Further knowledge is very desirable in regard to some portions of the skeleton. No adequate description of the foot has thus far been published, though several practically complete feet, notably from the Ferrassie skeletons, have been preserved. The available data regarding the vertebral column leave much to be desired. (The recently discovered Palestine material will go far toward filling the gaps in our knowledge of these parts.) Notwithstanding these deficiencies, enough is known of the skeleton to warrant a fairly accurate description of the physique of this remarkable extinct species.

Neanderthal man was short of stature. Professor Boule estimates the height of the Chapelle-aux-Saints man as 1.55 meters (about 5 feet 2 inches). The men of Neanderthal and Spy were nearly of the same height, the male from La Ferrassie about 1.60 meters (5 feet

4 inches). The fifteen-year-old boy from Le Moustier was very short, less than 5 feet, and the female Ferrassie skeleton about 4 feet 9 inches. These "measurements" are mere estimates based chiefly on the length of the long bones, and are not very accurate as proportions show considerable variation. (The exceptional height of some of the Palestine skeletons has been noted before.) The long bones are particularly heavy, thick in the shaft, with large joints and well-marked muscle attachments. The ribs are somewhat triangular in section, thicker and less flattened than in Homo sapiens, and indicate a large chest. The skull features are so characteristic that anyone after carefully examining one or two Neanderthal skulls could readily identify the type. The cranium is variable in size, the intracranial capacity varying from about 1280 cubic centimeters in the Gibraltar woman (less than 1100 in the Steinheim skull according to Weinert, 1936) to over 1600 in the Chapelle-aux-Saints man. The cranial form is dolichocephalic, the cephalic index (breadth-length) according to Boule varying between 70 and 76. The cranial height above the ear openings is relatively low (platycephalic), the forehead very retreating, and as seen in posterior view the cranium has the peculiarly depressed form called "bun-shaped" by some of the English anthropologists. (There are a few exceptions to this.) Unquestionably the most striking feature is the huge supraorbital torus, the cornicelike ridge over the eyes, which is especially well developed in adult males. The orbits themselves are very large and round, the interorbital width very great. The face, as compared with modern man, is extremely long; the nasal aperture is of enormous width. The nose, though of great width, was not flat but outstanding, much more prominent than the nose of any Negroid type, and it must be emphatically stated that there is nothing apelike about the nose in any way. In fact, the lower border of the nasal aperture is especially sharp and the nasal spine quite prominent, proving that the nose did not merge gradually into the upper lip in a snoutlike manner as one writer has asserted. The subnasal space is very long. The cheek bones slope obliquely backward in a most remarkable manner, so that there is no cheek prominence as in Homo sapiens. In correlation with this the canine fossa, a depression in the maxillary bone below the cheek, is lacking. These specific characters of the cheek region are very marked. This is in no sense an apelike feature, as apes have quite marked cheek prominences. (In the Steinheim skull and in some of the Palestine skulls the cheek region approxi-

mates that of Homo sapiens.) Looking at the skull in side view, it is seen that the mastoid processes are very small, a feature possibly correlated with the somewhat imperfect balance of the head on the neck. The squama of the temporal bone is low and the zygomatic arch very massive. There is a marked occipital torus, and the attachment of the neck muscles extends high up on the occiput. The foramen magnum is very far back, but this feature appears unduly accentuated by the forward extension of the jaw region. The palate is very long, broad, and U-shaped, not paraboloid as in Homo sapiens. The lower jaw presents several characteristic features. The condyles are of great size and articulate with remarkably shallow glenoid fossae so that the jaw articulation may be said to be more apelike than in other human types. There is no more than the slightest mental eminence or chin prominence — in some cases none at all — and the anterior surface of the jaw is sloping, or at best barely perpendicular. The exception in some of the Palestine jaws which have a slight chin has been noted before. The spine for the attachment of the genio-hyoid muscles is only slightly developed or even wanting, while the areas for insertion of the digastric muscles are very large. The mylo-hyoid ridge is absent or but slightly developed. There is ample space for the tongue, but the tongue muscles and some other muscles used in articulation seem to have been inferior, judging from the marks of their attachment, though this is not proof that Neanderthal man lacked the faculty of speech. The dental arches and the teeth are large in all their dimensions, the lower molars, at least the first and second, frequently show the fifth cusp characteristic of anthropoid apes and primitive human types (the Dryopithecus pattern of W. K. Gregory), and the third molars are frequently, though not always, as large as the others. The anterior teeth are especially large, but the canines do not project markedly above the other teeth and are completely human with no suggestion of apelikeness. The molars frequently show a remarkable condition to which the name "taurodont" (= ox-toothed) has been applied by Sir Arthur Keith. In taurodonty the pulp cavity is enlarged and extends downward from the crown into the roots, which are confluent to a great extent, in some cases almost to their tips, so that the entire tooth has a somewhat columnar form. This feature, though common, is not found in all Neanderthal molars and must not be regarded as a primitive feature but as showing specialization or degeneration. Another specialized dental feature is the frequent wrinkling of the enamel on the molar crowns. The bite of the anterior teeth is even, or nearly so, upper and lower incisors meeting. The teeth are in all cases free from caries, but they frequently show an extreme degree of wear, and in some cases, notably the Chapelle-aux-Saints skull, most of the teeth have been lost through suppurative disease of the alveolar process. The limb bones are strikingly robust and the forearm and shin are short in comparison respectively with the arm and thigh. This shortness is extreme in the case of the female skeleton of La Ferrassie where the radius-humerus ratio is only 70.4 and the tibia-femur ratio 74.4. In males of modern races these range from 75.4 to 96.4 for the radius-humerus ratio; from 77.3 to 86.6 for the tibia-femur ratio. These limb proportions are in no sense apelike — in fact, quite the contrary — but in certain structural details the limb bones approximate the simian condition. For example, the radius is curved to a degree suggesting the condition in the gorilla. The femur is very massive and curved forward, and has a huge head. The short, heavy tibia has the articular surface at its upper end sloping backward and downward, indicating a slight flexure of the knee joint, but a similar condition in certain modern men is a result of the squatting habit. The fibula is extremely stout, and has an unusually extensive articulation with the astragalus.

Knowledge of hand and foot structure in primitive mankind is especially important since these parts, especially the foot, show such divergent adaptations in anthropoids and man. On the basis of a single slightly deformed thumb bone (of the Chapelle-aux-Saints skeleton) it has been asserted that the Neanderthal thumb was imperfectly opposable, but the nearly complete hand of the woman of La Ferrassie disproves this, as the thumb is apparently as well developed as in modern man. It might belong to an individual of the present day. The foot also of this skeleton, in which the bones are preserved in place, is completely human, and the great toe is emphatically not opposable and was probably little if any more widely divergent or more movable than in some primitive modern men who never have worn shoes. The Neanderthal foot does, however, possess some distinctive features in the ankle bones. Of these the most striking is in the astragalus, as known from some half-dozen examples. It has a somewhat infantile form, and the "neck" of the bone is very short. The calcaneum, or heel bone, also has certain peculiarities in its articular relations and its torsion.

On the whole the foot, though thoroughly human, retains, according to Boule, a number of apelike features, which means that it had not evolved so far beyond its prehuman ancestors as has Homo sapiens. In general the anatomy of the Neanderthal foot is somewhat like that of a modern infant, and there appears to be a very high degree of mobility of the ankle. Various studies have been published of the mechanics of the Neanderthal foot, and usually it has been described as more reminiscent of simian conditions than is the foot of modern man. A thorough investigation of the well-preserved foot from La Ferrassie and of the Palestine material is greatly to be desired. The clavicle, known from several skeletons, is strongly curved but surprisingly delicate, though it might have been expected to be massive, and the scapula is remarkable in possessing a subspinous crest near the shoulder joint. The pelvis is large in both height and width. The ilia in two or three known examples are less concave than in Homo sapiens, the ischial tuberosities very large.

The vertebral column is especially important in the evidence it yields as to posture, but unfortunately this part of the Neanderthal skeleton is very imperfectly

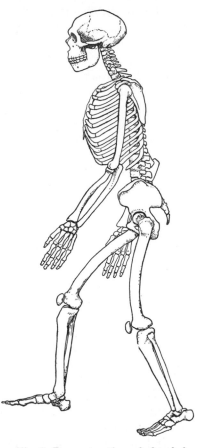

Fig. 9. Reconstruction of the skeleton of a Neanderthal man. Redrawn from H. Weinert, *Menschen der Vorzeit*, Ferdinand Enke (Stuttgart, 1930).

known, and quite unjustified generalizations have been made as to the apelike spinal column and semi-erect attitude of Neanderthal man. In the Chapelle-aux-Saints skeleton twelve of the twenty-four presacral vertebrae are more or less preserved, but in most of these the centra are not sufficiently complete to warrant the unqualified statement commonly made that there is scarcely any lumbar curvature. The last three neck vertebrae of this specimen are nearly complete, and in these the neural spines project almost straight out, somewhat resembling those of the chimpanzee. From this it has been assumed by some writers that the neck of Neanderthal man was enormously thick and even gorillalike, but a carefully constructed mesial section of the skull and neck vertebrae, plotting in all the soft structures, does not warrant the extreme "bull neck" that is shown in some of the attempts at restoration. Three cervical vertebrae from the Krapina remains, preserved in contact, do not differ in their neural spines from corresponding modern bones. Nearly all the descriptions and restorations of Neanderthal man represent him as standing and walking in an imperfectly erect position (Fig. 9). It is doubtful whether there is really any warrant for this in anatomical mechanics. It is probably traceable largely to a mere feeling that Neanderthal man, being so ancient, must have been imperfectly human in his posture. The fact that the face projects so far in front of the neck vertebrae would give the impression that the whole head is protruded forward further than it really is.

Neanderthal man is markedly different from Homo sapiens, and it is quite true that in some features he differs slightly less from the apes than does any type of modern man, but he was not nearly so apelike as some popular writers would have us believe (Pl. II).

Homo sapiens. The climax of the last glacial advance in Europe and the beginning of the recession of the ice cap marked the extinction of Neanderthal man (at least as a pure type) and the termination of the Mousterian phase of stone workmanship, the final stage of Lower Paleolithic culture. The climate of Europe, though still cold, was becoming drier as the ice began to recede; and though many of the animals of the glacial period remained, some, such as the reindeer, became much more abundant, so that this age is often called the *Reindeer period.* The duration of time since the climax of the last (Würm) glaciation has been calculated at approximately 35,000 years.* Neanderthal man apparently survived for a few millennia after the ice began to recede, but at a period tentatively estimated at some 25,000 to 30,000 years ago, he seems to have disappeared and to have been superseded by men much more like ourselves and clearly falling within the limits of *Homo sapiens.*

* According to E. Antevs; see page 16 for estimate of 25,000 years.

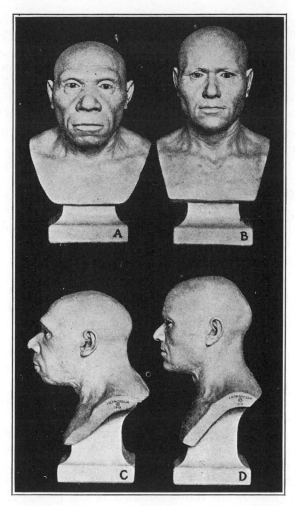

PL. II. NEANDERTHAL AND CRO-MAGNON: A COMPARISON

A and *C* represent front and profile views of the hairless phase of a head modeled by J. H. McGregor on the Chapelle-aux-Saints (Neanderthal) skull. *B* and *D* show a head similarly constructed on a male skull of the Cro-Magnon race (from Les Eyzies) for comparison. The contrast facilitates recognition of the characteristic Neanderthal features such as form and relative size of cranium and face, the heavy brow ridge, slope of forehead and chin, wide but prominent nose and retreating cheeks. Cro-Magnon features are essentially as in certain European types of the present day.

These people were culturally far superior to the primitive Mous-
terians. The industry identified with them, the Upper Paleolithic,
merges into the Neolithic phase some 10,000 years ago, so that it
had a duration of approximately 15,000 years. The cultural anthropology of the late Paleolithic men of Europe (Chapter V) is in a
far more satisfactory state than the knowledge of their racial origins
and relationships, for ethnically these people of the late Old Stone
Age present a number of perplexing problems. Their origin, their
possible relation to their Neanderthal predecessors, the interrelationships of the several physical types which they comprise, and
their kinship to their Neolithic successors and through these to the
modern European races are all questions regarding which positive
knowledge is well-nigh nil, though a great mass of conjecture, reflecting wide diversity of opinion on every phase of the subject, has
been published.

As the general question is one of the most important in the entire
field of prehistoric anthropology, involving as it does the origin of
our own species, it is most unfortunate that positive knowledge regarding it is thus far so limited. It is perhaps no exaggeration to
say that less is known about the immediate origin of Homo sapiens
than of Homo neanderthalensis. In the latter case we have a
progressive series of paleoanthropic types coming up from early
Pleistocene time, including the Trinil, Peking, and Heidelberg examples, which represent, at least as parallel or collateral ancestors,
a succession of stages in the evolution of Neanderthal man. On the
other hand the *sapiens* type or neoanthropic man appears in Europe
suddenly in the period of the glacial retreat. Where were his ancestors (and this means our ancestors) during the long ages of
paleoanthropic dominance? Certain ethnologists, especially of the
British school, have hailed the Piltdown Eoanthropus as the long-
sought progenitor, but the uncertainty of the geological incidence
of the remains and the paradoxical conjunction of apelike jaw and
human cranium, as mentioned before (p. 56), render it highly dubious in this rôle.

The prevalent opinion regarding the origin of Homo sapiens or
neoanthropic man in Europe is that men of this species were immigrants from Asia or North Africa who brought with them the
Aurignacian culture, and vanquished and eventually exterminated
the Neanderthals. The evidence for this is chiefly indirect. The
suddenness of the transition and the lack of definite intermediate

stages as regards both physical type and culture are commonly cited as evidence precluding the evolution of neoanthropic man from paleoanthropic, for there is no apparent time-interval between the Mousterian and Aurignacian periods. The cultural remains of both have been found at closely contiguous levels in the same rock shelters and caves, and there are evidences in some localities that the two were contemporaneous toward the end of the Mousterian epoch, as indeed they must have been if the Neanderthals were overcome by superior invaders. Even in such a case it seems probable that there would have been some interracial crossing notwithstanding the physical divergence of the two types. Regarding this point G. G. MacCurdy[38] says "there are not lacking both skeletal and cultural remains suggestive of intermediate stages, the results probably of intermixture." E. Fischer has also expressed the opinion that Neanderthal blood survived, and H. Weinert[39] asserts very positively that the Neanderthal form cannot be considered as "spurlos verschwunden." Skeletal evidence believed by a few ethnologists to indicate such intercrossing is observable in a number of Upper Paleolithic skulls, especially those of the so-called "Brünn race," named from a partial skeleton found in 1891 at Brünn, Moravia (in Czechoslovakia), and represented by numerous remains exhumed later at Předmost (Pl. I, F), also in Moravia (these people are sometimes referred to as the "Předmost race"); possibly also by a skull from Brüx, Bohemia, the Aurignacian Combe-Capelle man from the Dordogne, France, 1909, and several others. (One of the male skulls from Předmost is represented in Plate I, F.) The special interest of these types is in the dolichocranial form of the skull, the low vault, rather prominent superciliary ridges, and the slight prominence of the chin, since these are the features which have been regarded by some as intermediate between the Neanderthal and the true Cro-Magnon type and which doubtfully suggest a racial mixture of the two, though the characters of the latter distinctly predominate and the remains are properly classified as *Homo sapiens*. Two other discoveries assigned by some ethnologists to this questionably intermediate position are a fragmentary skull found in 1918 at Podkoumok in the Caucasus, and another more recently at Chwalynak on the Volga River. If these two skulls really have any relation to the Neanderthal stock, their far easterly location is a fact of considerable interest. But the Neanderthal-sapiens hybrid theory is by no means generally accepted, and all these remains are regarded by many anthropologists as merely primitive or aberrant examples of the Cro-Magnon type (mentioned below). The intermingling of two types in the Mount Carmel caves merits careful consideration in this connection.

An essentially different theory of the origin of Homo sapiens in Europe has recently been revived and very ably defended by Dr. A. Hrdlička.[40] Space is lacking to present his interesting argument, but his conclusion is that Neanderthal blood persisted in late Paleolithic time, not because of intermingling with any invading race of neoanthropic man, but as a result of direct *evolution* of Neanderthal man into Homo sapiens. Dr. Hrdlička admits that "this proposition is not yet capable of fully conclusive demonstration. There is not yet enough material definitely to decide it. But the thoroughly sifted indications appear to the writer to favor this assumption. . . . Meanwhile there appears to be less justification for the conception of a Neanderthal *species* than there is for that of a Neanderthal *phase* of man." As opposed to the immigration of neoanthropic man into Europe, Hrdlička says "there has been discovered no previous home of the Homo sapiens outside of that of Neanderthal man, nor any remains whatsoever of his ancestors." In reply to this it may be pointed out that the Solo and Wadjak skulls from Java and the Talgai skull from Australia (mentioned below) are Pleistocene examples of Homo sapiens which may well be as ancient as the European Aurignacian period, and the same may be said of the Boskop and Rhodesian remains from Africa, though there is no reason to consider any of these as actual ancestors of the invaders of Europe. In the present lack of positive knowledge I feel that, while the problem cannot be regarded as settled by any means, the balance of evidence, such as it is, favors the theory of invasion of Europe and replacement of the Neanderthals by Homo sapiens, possibly with some interspecific mixture of victors and vanquished. But Dr. Hrdlička's discussion of the question is strongly recommended for reading.

Besides the questionable "Brünn race" above mentioned, three other more or less distinct *sapiens* types are found in deposits belonging to the late Paleolithic period of Europe. An early one of these is the so-called "Grimaldi race," known from only two skeletons of early Aurignacian age notable for their supposed Negroid features; another, the "typical" Cro-Magnon people, the best known and apparently the dominant one during the greater part of the late

Old Stone Age; and a third type, of Magdalenian age, sometimes designated as the "Chancelade race," the chief interest of which is its remarkable resemblance to the modern Eskimo, a member of the Mongoloid branch of humanity. It would be a most astonishing fact, if the Negroid, White, and Yellow divisions of *Homo sapiens* were all represented in the late Pleistocene population of western Europe. But we shall see that anthropologists are by no means unanimous in accepting these somewhat diverse types as representatives of three distinct races. The three types will now be briefly described.

The "Grimaldi race." On the Mediterranean coast, in the region of Monaco, are nine grottoes (now partly destroyed) known as the Grimaldi caves, several of which have yielded important remains of Pleistocene man. In one of these, called the Grotte des Enfants, in which among other human remains one of the "typical" tall Cro-Magnon skeletons had previously been found, there were unearthed in 1901 two complete skeletons of a strikingly different character, which had been interred at a lower level, and which belong to an earlier period in the Aurignacian. They are the remains of a woman of mature, though not advanced, age, and a boy of approximately fourteen years. They are of medium height, the woman some 5 feet 3 inches, the boy (not fully grown) slightly over 5 feet. Their ages, close similarity in physical features, and the fact that they were buried together suggest that they were mother and son. The special importance of these skeletons is the surprising fact, stressed by Professor R. Verneau [41] who described them, that they possess a number of characteristics generally regarded as Negroid. Thus the crania are markedly dolichocephalic, the chins rather slightly developed, and the teeth very large. There is pronounced alveolar prognathism, the nasal bones are somewhat flattened, and the nasal aperture, in width and form of the lower border, suggests the Negro type. Other Negroid features are observable in the relatively long legs and in the great length of forearm and shin in comparison to arm and thigh. An especial physical resemblance to the South African Bushman type, noted by Boule and other writers, has been thought to derive cultural confirmation from certain similarities to Bushman art in the realistic, incised rock drawings of animals made by late Paleolithic Europeans. Numerous statuettes of soapstone and ivory dating from this period represent steatopygous female figures which strongly recall the physical peculiarities of Bushman women and thus lend additional support to the idea of racial kinship.

The Negroid character of the "Grimaldi race" has been until recently quite generally accepted, but its occurrence in Europe has been a puzzle and has led to much conjecture regarding its origin and migrations. Verneau believes that notwithstanding their Negroid features these people may have been ancestral to the later Cro-Magnon hunters of the Reindeer period, and various skeletal remains of Neolithic Europeans have been cited by him and others which exhibit somewhat Negroid features of skull and limb bones. Even the "typical" Cro-Magnon people, though certainly not Negroes, have somewhat Negroid proportions of arm and leg. Recently the special Negroid character of the "Grimaldi race" has been questioned and rejected by Sir G. Elliot Smith [42] and by Sir Arthur Keith.[43] These anatomists have independently arrived at the conclusion that the Grimaldi people had no special relation to any Negro group, but merely represent early and rather primitive examples of the Cro-Magnon stock. Recent comparative anthropometric studies by G. M. Morant disclose no basis for separating the Grimaldi type from the general Upper Paleolithic series. Elliot Smith also points out that many of the so-called Negroid features are even more strongly Australoid. In his opinion the remains in question are "undoubtedly related to the people of the Upper Paleolithic, commonly known as the Cro-Magnon race (and in particular to the intermediate type represented by the Combe-Capelle and Předmost skeletons)." These last-named, as remarked above, also present certain likenesses to the Australoid type in skull features. This does not imply any special kinship with the modern Australians, but there is a possibility that some primitive neoanthropic type in southern Asia may have given rise in Pleistocene time to a stock which migrated southward toward Australia and at the same time to another which worked westward, gradually invading Europe and Africa. Such terms as "Negroid" and "Australoid" are often used very loosely and may mean no more than that the example in question "looks like" or suggests the type referred to, when careful study and measurement may prove the fancied likeness to be quite illusory. Even fairly close resemblance may signify no more than fortuitous parallelism. Misinterpretation of such cases is an ever-present hazard in physical anthropology. On the whole, the status of the "Grimaldi race" as a people having special Negroid affinities and quite distinct from the Cro-Magnon group must be considered as extremely doubtful.

Cro-Magnon man. The best known type of late Paleolithic man in Europe, and apparently the dominant people of this period, is that known as Cro-Magnon man. This name was applied by Quatrefages and Hamy to five skeletons found buried in the Cro-Magnon rock shelter at Les Eyzies in the Dordogne, France, in 1868. Others of similar type have since been found along the Mediterranean border in the region of Monaco and Mentone and at various locations in western Europe. As described by Verneau, it constitutes a well-defined race. The men are tall, in some cases over six feet, and of powerful frame. The cranium is high, capacious, and dolichocephalic in form, but the face is short and broad, presenting rather unusual proportions. The forehead is vertical, the cheeks wide, the chin prominent, the jaws of othognathous type, and the nose narrow (Pl. I, *G*). Forearm and shin are long in comparison to upper arm and thigh, recalling the proportions in tall Negroid types, but this feature has been observed in other tall races. Other characteristics noted are a front-to-back flattening of the femur, while the tibia is transversely flattened with a sharp anterior edge, a condition known as platycnemia. These features are not, however, limited to this race. These tall Cro-Magnon men constitute a fine physical type, and it has been rather generally assumed that they were the people chiefly responsible for the skillfully worked flint and bone implements and the realistic cave paintings and sculptures of animals, characteristic of the Upper Paleolithic culture. The women, judging from the few known skeletons, seem to be considerably shorter than the men. It is popularly supposed that the Cro-Magnon men were all of great stature, but this is not necessarily the case. Where several very tall individuals are found buried together they may have been a related family group and not at all racially typical as regards stature. Some ethnologists have used the name "Cro-Magnon" in a more broadly inclusive sense to comprise also a number of other physical types which exhibit scarcely any of the diagnostic features of this race as defined by Verneau. Thus, the Brünn types above mentioned are sometimes included as early and primitive members of the Cro-Magnon race. Among the most noteworthy of the "aberrant" examples may be mentioned the Chancelade man, found near Périgueux in France in 1888, the skeletons of a man and woman discovered in 1914 at Obercassel near Bonn in Germany, and a few others. These are all of short stature, none of them greatly exceeding five feet in height, but rather massively built with large skulls.

In the Chancelade skeleton there are numerous resemblances to the Eskimo type, especially in the skull, which is practically identical with that of the Greenland Eskimo. The likeness is so marked, indeed, that several well-known anthropologists (Sollas, Saller, *et al.*) are strongly of the opinion that the Eskimo represent modern survivors of this type who followed the northward retreat of the ice. As the Eskimo represent a branch of the Mongoloid division, this theory if true carries highly significant implications as to the mixed population of western Europe in Upper Paleolithic time. Similar resemblances to the Eskimo are exhibited by the Obercassel skeletons, though in less marked degree. Sir Arthur Keith [44] on the other hand denies the Eskimo relationship, and, considering these likenesses as mere chance parallelism, regards the Chancelade and Obercassel skeletons, despite their low stature and cranial peculiarities, as merely aberrant examples of the Cro-Magnon race, thus placing them as early members of the White rather than the Mongoloid division. M. Boule,[45] who holds a somewhat similar opinion regarding Chancelade man, sums up his discussion of the Cro-Magnon people thus: "In short, from the osteological point of view, the true Cro-Magnons may be considered as a median type, around which there already gravitate variations, due probably to the influence of varying geographical environments, and perhaps also to racial intermixture. But as a whole they really form one stock, a fine race which, as de Quatrefages has said, played an important part over a considerable area and throughout a considerable period of time."

There is strong reason to believe that the Cro-Magnon people did not "die out," but that they gradually intermingled with other stocks, so that their descendants survive today in various parts of France and the Iberian peninsula, and elsewhere in western Europe. Examples of these so-called "modern Cro-Magnons" are photographically portrayed in several works on ethnology. Resemblance to the ancient type in measurements of face and·cranium combined with geographic location is the chief reason for so designating them. The evidence is not entirely convincing, though there would seem to be a strong presumption in favor of such survival. Many years ago Quatrefages and Hamy, and later Verneau, maintained that the Guanchos of the Canary Islands, who are generally believed to have been largely exterminated in the fifteenth century, represented late survivors of the Cro-Magnon stock, and similar assertions have been made regarding the Kabyles of Algeria. On the other hand,

Professor E. A. Hooton[46] of Harvard, who has investigated the question with care, is very doubtful of the derivation of the Canary Islanders from the Cro-Magnon stem and even admits that he is "so unregenerate as to be sceptical of the reality of the Cro-Magnon 'race,' if the term 'race' be used in its proper anthropological connotation."

Interesting conclusions regarding the fate of the ancient Guanchos of the Canary Islands and their relation to the Cro-Magnon race are found in recent studies by E. Fischer[47] (1930), who, with the coöperation of Dr. D. J. Wölfel, applied statistical anthropometric methods in the study of the present-day populations of the various islands of the Canary group and compared their findings with data obtained by Verneau and other investigators of the ancient Cro-Magnons, the Guanchos, and various populations of western Europe. The results are quite at variance with Hooton's conclusions. Analysis of the combined data considered with reference to Mendelian laws of heredity indicates, in Fischer's opinion, that among the mixture of many component races there is clear evidence of the survival of the Cro-Magnon stock as a definite type. One especially surprising result of Fischer's analysis is his assertion that the Cro-Magnons at the time of their migration to the Canary Islands were apparently a blond race; but the important result, if his conclusions are correct, is the evidence of the reality of a definite Cro-Magnon race and of its survival to the present.

A detailed investigation of the human types of the late Old Stone Age has been made recently by G. M. Morant,[48] who finds, as a result of comparative anthropometric studies based upon twenty-seven skulls of Paleolithic Europeans representing all the so-called races of that period, that "the Upper Paleolithic series is rather less variable than some modern European series which are considered racially homogeneous." Regarding those types which have been supposed to occupy an intermediate position between Neanderthaloid and Homo sapiens, Morant finds that craniometry lends no support to this "link" idea. He concludes that "the Upper Paleolithic type is modern in almost all respects. . . . It resembles most closely the modern dolichocephalic races of western Europe and there can be little doubt that the latter population is directly descended from the earlier."

Though the preponderance of present-day opinion appears to admit the essential unity of the late Paleolithic Europeans and to regard them as progenitors of the modern inhabitants of western Europe, their origin, as we have observed, is still an unsolved problem. We dare hope that its solution may be aided by future discoveries in Asia or Africa, both of which have yielded skeletal as well as cultural relics of Pleistocene man, some of which are certainly more ancient than the Aurignacian period in Europe. Some of these discoveries may be briefly reviewed.

To take Asia first — it will be recalled that the two most primitive known members of the human family, the Javan Pithecanthropus and the Chinese Sinanthropus, are both Asian types (Java having been originally an extension of the Malay Peninsula). Java is also the site of two other discoveries of Pleistocene man, more advanced types which may have important bearing on the origin and migration of the Australian race. The first of these discoveries consists of two skulls found near the surface of an ancient alluvial deposit by Dr. Eugene Dubois. These skulls, which from their locality Dr. Dubois [49] called Wadjak man, *Homo wadjakensis*, were found in 1889, two years before his discovery of Pithecanthropus; but he did not publish a full description until 1921. The skulls, which are incomplete, are of dolichocephalic form, and the essential features are those of the Australoid race, with marked supraorbital ridges, low orbits, and large palate. The skulls in general are massive, especially the jaws. There is some prognathism, and the chin is but slightly developed. On anatomical grounds Dr. Dubois seems to be justified in regarding the Wadjak remains as proto-Australoid, which is important as corroborating other evidence (from living types in southern India and Ceylon) that the proto-Australian stock migrated from southern Asia. G. Pinkley [49a] (1936) holds that the teeth are too small and too specialized to permit Wadjak man to qualify as an ancestor of the modern Australian.

In April, 1932, a report appeared of still another discovery of Pleistocene man in Java. This was by W. F. F. Oppenoorth [50] of the Geological Survey of Java, who described and figured a nearly complete human brain case, and two fragments of other crania, one an adult, fairly complete, the other a frontal bone of a child. These were found in 1931 near Ngandong, a village near the Solo River and only six miles from Trinil, the site of the famous Pithecanthropus discovery of forty years earlier, but the fossiliferous beds of Ngandong are evidently of upper Pleistocene age, not quite as old as the

Pithecanthropus layer. Oppenoorth considers them as probably comparable to the Riss-Würm interglacial period of Europe. The original discovery at Ngandong was followed by others, so that by 1936 eleven skulls of this type, known as Solo man, had been found. The crania are remarkably similar in form, and in all of them parts of the basal region are missing, suggesting, as in the case of Peking man, that they had been opened for the removal of the brains. No facial bones, jaws, or teeth have yet been found, and two imperfect tibiae are the only bones known in addition to the skulls. The calvaria is of fair size, with a heavy supraorbital torus and very low retreating forehead, but it is larger and much more obviously human than the cranium of Pithecanthropus. The occipital torus is enormously developed, indicating very heavy neck muscles. The mastoid region is of the *sapiens* type. Oppenoorth correctly observes that the skull does not belong to the Neanderthal type, but he notes very close likenesses to the Rhodesian skull (described below) and he states that "the back of the Ngandong skull also bears resemblance to that of the Australian race, so perhaps we may see in it a much more primitive prototype of that race than was the Wadjak man of Dubois." Photographs show the skulls to be more "primitive" — that is, less like a modern man — than the Wadjak skulls. In view of its distinctive features Oppenoorth made Ngandong or Solo man the type of a new species, *Homo (Javanthropus) soloensis*. (He later dropped the sub-generic name *Javanthropus*.) A number of tools, fashioned of bone and deer antler, and some stone balls of andesite have been found associated with the skulls.

This new discovery is highly significant, for it actualizes a quite plausible intermediate form or "link," hitherto missing, between Pithecanthropus and the Wadjak man, the whole series in the same region; and incidentally it enhances the importance of Pithecanthropus (which some anthropologists have regarded as merely the fag end of a degenerate side branch) as a possible progenitor of Homo (Pl. I, *A*), though of course there is no proof of these suggested relationships. Weidenreich, von Koenigswald, and some other anthropologists regard Solo man as a Javan type of the Neanderthal species, but perhaps a larger group, including myself, agree with Oppenoorth in the view that the two represent quite distinct types. There are a number of resemblances, but careful comparison shows these to be parallelisms which obscure more essential differences. Oppenoorth expresses the opinion that "we have in *Homo soloensis* the

oldest at present known representative of *Homo sapiens fossilis*.`
Dr. Dubois holds the view that Solo and Peking types are identical.`
Homo sapiens, not improbably relative or offspring of a Javar
stock, arrived in Australia before the end of the Pleistocene perioc
as evidenced by two discoveries which may be briefly mentioned
One of these was a "proto-Australoid" skull discovered at Talga
on the Darling Downs in Queensland in 1884 and first described ir
detail by Dr. S. A. Smith in 1918.[51] This fossil, known as the Talga
skull, is that of a boy fifteen or sixteen years of age. The skull, whick
was badly crushed, is distinctly of Australoid type but surpasses
the modern Australian in size of palate and of teeth, especially of
canines. The geological incidence of this skull appears to be late
Pleistocene, a fact of importance in its implication that the ancestors of the modern Australian type had thus early migrated to
that part of the world.

More recent discoveries which apparently belong to a somewhat
similar proto-Australoid type have been made in Victoria, Australia,
a short distance south of the Murray River, where an adult male
skull was found in 1925, and later parts of several skeletons. The
bones were found near the surface embedded in ancient silt deposits,
and there is a possibility that they represent intentional burials. It
is most unfortunate that no artifacts or bones of animals have beer
found in association with the human remains, and the only proof of
great antiquity is the inherent evidence of heavy mineralization of
the bones and their morphological character. A full account of these
discoveries has not yet been published, but is said to be in preparation by Sir Colin MacKenzie at the time of present writing. The
data here given are taken from Sir Arthur Keith's *New Discoveries
Relating to the Antiquity of Man*. The first skull found, referred to as
the Cohuna skull from the place of discovery, is that of an adult
man clearly of Australoid race; but, as in the Talgai youth, those
features which are considered primitive are much more accentuated
than in recent Australians. It is in the enormous palate that the
specimen is most remarkable. In area of the palate and size of the
canine teeth as well as in prognathism, the Cohuna skull surpasses
all other known human examples, though the brain case is not very
different from the modern Australian. "Taking it all in all," says

---

* *Early Man* (1937), edited by George Grant MacCurdy, contains three
separate illustrated articles treating of Solo man and related subjects by W. F. F.
Oppenoorth, G. H. R. von Koenigswald, and E. Dubois.

Sir Arthur Keith,[52] "the Cohuna skull — with the exception of the
Java and Peking specimens and perhaps the Piltdown — represents
the most primitive human form known to us." (This statement was
published before the Ngandong or Solo man was found; otherwise,
doubtless this also would have been placed among the "exceptions.")
Rhodesian man. A remarkable and in many ways extremely prob-
ematical example of ancient humanity is that known as Rhodesian
man, found during mining operations at Broken Hill, Northern
Rhodesia, in 1921. The remains were found at the extreme end of a
long cave under a hill from which for some years many bones of
animals had been taken so heavily encrusted and impregnated with
lead and zinc salts that it had been the habit to throw them into the
smelters with the metallic ores of which the hill was largely composed.
The human remains consist of a nearly complete skull, lacking the
lower jaw, with a sacrum, fragments of a pelvis, and a few leg bones.
Together with them were found a few crude stone implements. The
bones were not fossilized in the usual sense of the word, as they still
contained some organic matter, but they were heavily encrusted with
zinc salts. When cleaned the skull was found to be uncrushed and
perfectly preserved with the exception of a portion of the right side,
which had been lost. At first glance it seems to be more apish than
any other known human skull. It has a superficial resemblance to a
male Neanderthal skull and has been regarded by a number of
anthropologists as an African variety of that species, but critical
examination shows that it lacks many of the specific Neanderthal
characteristics, and it may, with equally good or better reason, be regarded as a very aberrant example of Homo sapiens. Sir Arthur Smith
Woodward named it *Homo rhodesiensis* (Pl. I, *E*). The cranial vault
is greatly depressed, and the supraorbital torus even more pronounced
than in any Neanderthal skull, though different in form. The face,
in all its measurements, is enormous. The subnasal space is greater
than in any other human skull, and the palate is of enormous size.
This skull is almost unique among ancient types in showing marked
caries of the teeth. The occipital torus and the attachments for neck
muscles in general are greatly overdeveloped, and the occipital region
is quite unlike that of the Neanderthals. The mastoid processes also
are different from that type and fairly well developed. The leg bones,
which are not certainly known to belong to the same individual or
even the same type, indicate tall stature, and the knee joint entirely
lacks the indication of permanent slight flexure seen in the Neander-

thals. A very perfect endocranial cast made by Mr. F. O. Barlow of the British Museum (Natural History Division) has a volume of 1300 cubic centimeters, surprisingly small for a skull with such a huge facial region. According to G. Elliot Smith,[53] this cast indicates that in brain development "the Rhodesian man conforms to a type definitely more primitive than that of the Neanderthal species" as regards the expansion of the prefrontal, parietal, and temporal association areas. But conclusions as to specific cortical areas based on endocranial casts must be at best somewhat conjectural. G. M. Morant[54] has made anthropometric comparisons of the Rhodesian skull with skulls of Neanderthals and the *sapiens* species, which indicate that each of the three is racially distinct from the other two, but he says: "It appears from a comparison of individual measurements that the Neanderthal type is rather less widely removed from modern man than the Rhodesian, but a generalized coefficient based on twenty-three measurements suggests the reverse order. The difference is at any rate small and the conclusion that Rhodesian and Neanderthal man are equally related to modern man is probably the most reasonable one." Craniometric studies such as those of Morant, though of great value, must necessarily disregard certain small structural features which may be diagnostic to the experienced eye, yet beyond the range of gross diameters, arcs, and indices. The Rhodesian skull, in comparison with a fairly well preserved Neanderthal specimen (such as that of La Chapelle-aux-Saints), illustrates this distinction very well. In many features — for example, the character of the sutures, region of ear, and mandibular fossa, form of squama, etc. — the Rhodesian resembles the *sapiens* skull more closely than it does the Neanderthal, notwithstanding the striking likeness to the latter in general form.

Whether Rhodesian man should be placed in the paleoanthropic or neoanthropic division is a question. Many anthropologists would ally it with the former, but others, including myself, are inclined to regard it as an aberrant example of the neoanthropic group. Its location has led to the assumption that it represents a proto-Negroid, but there is no adequate anatomical warrant for this view. H. Weinert considers it to be, if anything, closer to the European and Australian types. But of one thing we may be certain: the Rhodesian skull is not that of a Neanderthaloid.

Unfortunately the geological age of the remains is quite uncertain. They may be as old as Pleistocene, but there are many reasons in the condition of the skull and teeth and associated animal bones for suspecting them to belong to a more recent period. A very complete description and discussion of the type is given by Dr. Hrdlička,[55] who states very aptly that "the Rhodesian skull is a tantalizing specimen to the student, who is wholly at a loss as to just where it belongs taxonomically or chronologically. It is a comet of man's prehistory." But its isolation is considerably diminished by the discovery of the strikingly similar Javan Solo man.

Africa has recently yielded several other skeletal remains of Pleistocene age which clearly are to be placed within the neoanthropic *sapiens* group. Several from South Africa are of Negroid type, and apparently represent a proto-Bushman stock, a matter of importance as indicating the antiquity of that race. Others, from East Africa, are believed by various ethnologists to be allied to the true Negro, the Hamitic people, and the Aurignacian Cro-Magnon men of Europe.

The Boskop man, the first of the African Pleistocene discoveries, was found in the Transvaal in 1913.[56] The remains include a skull and some limb bones, all of them fragmentary. Enough of the skull is preserved to show that it is a type of Homo sapiens with dolichocephalic cranium, vertical forehead, orthognathous face, and a very large brain, as the endocranial capacity is estimated at 1630 cubic centimeters, though the leg bones indicate only moderate stature. Dr. R. Broom considered the Boskop man a new species for which he proposed the name *Homo capensis*. A second incomplete skull and other bones of similar type were found in 1921, buried in a rock shelter at T'zitzikama on the South African coast, some 500 miles from Boskop, and more recently a third at Fish Hoek, fifteen miles from Cape Town. The importance of these remains lies in their remarkable likeness in cranial form to the modern Bushman, whose skull has very striking racial characteristics and marked differences from the true Negro. The Boskop proto-Bushmen were much taller than, and greatly superior in brain volume to, their modern descendants, indicating that the latter have undergone physical degeneration.

Various other skeletal remains of greater or less antiquity have been reported from South Africa, and also from East Africa; among the latter is the Oldoway skeleton found by Dr. Hans Reck in 1913, in German East Africa (now Tanganyika). The antiquity of this skeleton has been the subject of much controversy. A few human paleontologists follow Reck in placing it as Lower Pleistocene, and one even hails it as the oldest known example of Homo sapiens, while others maintain that it is modern. It is not primitive in any way, and apparently represents an intentional burial. The German anthropologists Mollison and Gieseler find in this skull evidence of racial kinship to the modern Masai, an East African group. Keith [57] would group with it, racially, some skeletal remains recently found by Mr. L. S. B. Leakey in Kenya, and also a skull unearthed in 1929 in the Springbok Flats in the Transvaal, a locality some 1600 miles to the southward of the other discoveries. In Keith's opinion all these remains, though not belonging to a true Negro type, represent a Negroid stock allied to the people of northeastern Africa, such as the tall, slender Somali, while H. Weinert [58] regards the Oldoway, Springbok, and even the Boskop man as African Cro-Magnons, and believes that this type migrated from Europe, finally reaching East Africa through Egypt, and later penetrating to South Africa. In his opinion these Cro-Magnons preceded the Negroes in East Africa. In view of the present incomplete knowledge and conflict of opinions regarding the ethnological aspects of these recent finds, it would be unwise to prolong discussion here.

On the whole, although we know nothing whatever regarding the ancestral derivation of the proto-Negroid stock, it seems fairly evident that there were several Negroid types before the end of the Pleistocene epoch, and that the Negroid branch of *Homo sapiens* developed its distinctive characteristics in Africa. There is no sound reason for regarding the Negroid branch as less ancient than the White or Yellow. While there is no warrant for assuming that Africa rather than Asia is the birthplace of humanity, we may recall that it is the home of the two most manlike of living great apes, and the still more manlike fossil ape Australopithecus. Possibly the rocks of the Dark Continent may in time give forth the bones of still higher apes or lower man.

The discussion of early man in the Western World does not fall within the scope of the present chapter (see page 113). All the ancient human remains thus far discovered in America, some of them possibly as old as late Pleistocene, judging from geological evidence and the testimony of associated animal bones, are ancient examples of the American Indian type, representing an early branch of the Mongoloid division of *Homo sapiens* which emigrated from Asia. If man arrived in America before the end of the Pleistocene, the Mongoloid, like the

White, Negroid, and Australoid divisions, must already have been distinct in Pleistocene time. However, no skeletal remains identifiable as specifically proto-Mongoloid have thus far been found (see page 55), though in time they probably will be discovered somewhere in Asia. E. Antevs,[59] in a discussion of the advent of man in America states his conclusions as follows:

According to the best of our belief the findings may be summed up thus: The first man to arrive in North America was of modern type and probably at the Neolithic stage of culture. He came from northeastern Asia to Alaska and probably spread along the eastern foot of the Rocky Mountains where an ice-free corridor had formed some 20,000 to 15,000 years ago. He seems to have reached the Southwest at the age of transition between the pluvial and the post-pluvial epochs, or roughly 12,000 years ago.

The fact that no fossil remains of anthropoid apes or any sort of Catarrhine primates have ever been found in America, although negative evidence, renders the evolution of man from prehuman ancestors in the Western World extremely unlikely.

FOOTNOTES

1. Huxley, T. H., *Man's Place in Nature* (London, 1863).
2. In the first edition of the *Systema Naturæ* (1735) Linnaeus grouped these animals, together with the sloths, as "Anthropomorpha" (= man form). In the edition of 1758 "Anthropomorpha" was replaced by "Primates."
3. Dart, R. A., "*Australopithecus africanus:* The Man-Ape of South Africa," *Nature*, vol. 115 (London, Feb. 7, 1925), pp. 195–198.
4. Keith, A., *New Discoveries Relating to the Antiquity of Man* (1931), p. 116.
5. Broom, R., "A New Fossil Anthropoid from Sterkfontein near Krugersdorp, South Africa," *Nature*, vol. 138 (Sept. 19, 1936), pp. 486–488; and "The Dentition of Australopithecus," *ibid*. (Oct. 24, 1936), p. 719.
6. Darwin, C., *Descent of Man* (London, 1871), vol. 1, pp. 196–197.
7. Haeckel, E., *The Last Link* (London, 1898), p. 12.
8. Hartmann, R., *Anthropoid Apes* (English translation, 1887).
9. Wilder, H. H., *The Pedigree of the Human Race* (1927).
10. Schultz, A. H., "Man as a Primate," *Scientific Monthly*, vol. 33 (Nov. 1931), pp. 385–412.
11. Elder, J. H., and Yerkes, R. M., "Chimpanzee Births in Captivity," *Proceedings of the Royal Society, London*, Series B, vol. 120 (July, 1936), pp. 409–421.
12. Yerkes, R. M., and Yerkes, A. W., *The Great Apes* (1929), p. 259.
13. *Ibid.*, p. 240. Statement is quoted from Dr. A. Calmette, late director of the Pasteur Institute of Paris, (1924).
14. Köhler, W., *The Mentality of Apes* (1925), pp. 275–276.

15. Yerkes, R. M., and Learned, B. W., *Chimpanzee Intelligence and Its Vocal Expressions* (1925).
16. Abel, O., *Die Stellung des Menschen im Rahmen der Wirbeltiere* (Jena, 1931), pp. 378–380.
17. Smith, G. Elliot, *The Evolution of Man* (2nd ed., London, 1927), chap. 3.
18. Haeckel, E., *The History of Creation* (English translation, 5th ed., 1913).
19. Dubois, E., *Pithecanthropus erectus, eine menschenaenliche Uebergangsform aus Java* (Batavia, 1894).
20. Tilney, F., *The Brain from Ape to Man* (1928).
21. Dubois, E., "On the Principal Characters of the Cranium and the Brain, the Mandible and the Teeth of Pithecanthropus erectus," *Proceedings, Koninklikje Akademie van Wetenschappen te Amsterdam*, vol. 27 (1923–24), pp. 1–14.
21a. von Koenigswald, G. H. R., "Early Palaeolithic Stone Implements in Java," *Bulletin Raffles Museum, Singapore*, Series B. no. 1 (1936).
21b. von Koenigswald, G. H. R., "Erste Mitteilung über einen fossilen Hominiden aus der Altpleistocän Ostjavas," *Proceedings, Koninklijke Akademie van Wetenschappen te Amsterdam*, vol. 39, no. 8 (1936).
22. Black, D., "On the Adolescent Skull of *Sinanthropus pekinensis* in Comparison with an Adult Skull of the Same Species," *Palaeontologica Sinica*, Series D, vol. 7, fasc. ii (Peiping [Peking], 1931).
23. Weinert, H., *Menschen der Vorzeit* (Stuttgart, 1930), p. 39.
24. Hrdlička, A., "The Skeletal Remains of Early Man," *Smithsonian Miscellaneous Collections*, vol. 83 (1930), p. 368.
24a. Weidenreich, F., "The New Discovery of Three Skulls of *Sinanthropus pekinensis*," *Nature*, vol. 139 (Feb. 13, 1937), pp. 269–272.
25. Hrdlička, A., "Shovel-shaped Teeth," *American Journal of Physical Anthropology*, vol. 3 (1920), pp. 429–465.
26. Weidenreich, F., "The Sinanthropus Population of Choukoutien (Locality 1) with a Preliminary Report on New Discoveries," *Bulletin of the Geological Society of China*, vol. 16, no. 4 (1935), p. 438.
27. Black, D., "Preliminary Notice of the Discovery of an Adult Sinanthropus Skull at Chou Kou Tien," *Bulletin of the Geological Society of China*, vol. 8, no. 3 (1929, pub. in 1930), p. 211.
28. Woodward, A. S., with Dawson, C., "On the Discovery of a Palaeolithic Human Skull and Mandible, etc., at Piltdown, Fleching, Sussex," *Quarterly Journal of the Geological Society, London*, vol. 69 (1913), pp. 117–124.
29. Miller, G. S., Jr., "The Jaw of Piltdown Man," *Smithsonian Miscellaneous Collections*, vol. 65, no. 12 (1915), pp. 1–30, 5 pls.
30. Friederichs, H. F., "Schaedel und Unterkiefer von Piltdown ("Eoanthropus dawsoni Woodward") in neuer Untersuchung," *Zeitschrift für Anatomie und Entwicklungsgeschichte*, vol. 98 (1932), pp. 199–262.
31. Weinert, H., *Das Problem des Eoanthropus von Piltdown* (Stuttgart, 1933).
32. Boule, M., *L'Homme fossile de la Chapelle-aux-Saints* (Paris, 1913).
33. Berckhemer, F., "Der Steinheimer Urmensch und die Tierwelt seines Lebensgebietes," *Aus der Heimat*, Naturwissenschaftliche Monatsschrift, vol. 47 (April, 1934), pp. 101–115.

34. Weinert, H., "Der Urmenschenschaedel von Steinheim," *Zeitschrift für Morphologie und Anthropologie*, Bd. 35, Heft 3 (1936), pp. 463–518.
35. Sergi, S., "La Scoperta di un Cranio del Tipo Neanderthal presso Roma," *Revista di Antropologia*, vol. 28 (1929), p. 3.
36. Gorjanovic-Kramberger, K., "Der palaeolithische Mensch und seine Zeitgenossen aus dem Diluvium von Krapina in Kroatien," *Mitteilungen Anthropologische Gesellschaft Wien*, vol. 31 (1901), pp. 189–216, 4 pls.
37. MacCurdy, G. G., "Prehistoric Man in Palestine," *Proceedings of the American Philosophical Society*, vol. 76, no. 4 (1936), pp. 523–541, 16 pls.
37a. Keith, A., and McCown, T. D., "Mount Carmel Man," in *Early Man*, edited by George Grant MacCurdy (1937).
38. MacCurdy, G. G., *Human Origins* (1924), vol. 1, p. 158.
39. Weinert, H., *Menschen der Vorzeit*, p. 83.
40. Hrdlička, "The Skeletal Remains of Early Man," *Smithsonian Miscellaneous Collections*, vol. 83 (1930), pp. 347–349.
41. Verneau, R., "Les Grottes de Grimaldi (Baoussé-Roussé)," *Anthropologie*, Tome II, fasc. i (Monaco, 1906).
42. Smith, G. Elliot, *op. cit.*, pp. 138–139.
43. Keith, A., *op. cit.*, p. 385.
44. *Ibid.*, p. 391.
45. Boule, M., *Fossil Men* (English translation, London, 1923), p. 288.
46. Hooton, E. A., *Up from the Ape* (1931), p. 371.
47. Fischer, Eugen, "Sind die alten Kanarier ausgestorben?" *Zeitschrift für Ethnologie*, vol. 62 (1930), pp. 258–281.
48. Morant, G. M., "Studies of Palaeolithic Man," *Annals of Eugenics*, vol. 4 (1930), pp. 109–204, 12 pls.
49. Dubois, E., "The Proto-Australian Fossil Man of Wadjak, Java," *Proceedings, Koninklikje Akademie van Wetenschappen te Amsterdam*, vol. 23, no. 7 (1920).
49a. Pinkley, G., "The Significance of Wadjak Man, a Fossil Homo Sapiens from Java," *Peking Natural History Bulletin*, vol. 10, Part III (1936), pp. 183–199.
50. Oppenoorth, W. F. F., "Homo (Javanthropus) soloensis," *Wetenschappelijke Mededeelingen, No. 20, van den Dienst van den Mijnbouw in Ned.-Indië* (Batavia, 1932), pp. 51–63.
51. Smith, S. A., "The Fossil Human Skull Found at Talgai, Queensland," *Philosophical Transactions of the Royal Society, London*, Series B, vol. 208 (1918), pp. 351–387, 7 pls.
52. Keith, A., *op. cit.*, pp. 304–311.
53. Smith, G. Elliot, *op. cit.*, p. 127.
54. Morant, G. M., *Annals of Eugenics*, vol. 3 (1928), p. 358, 6 pls.
55. Hrdlička, A., "The Skeletal Remains of Early Man," *op. cit.*, p. 130.
56. Keith, A., *The Antiquity of Man* (1925), vol. 1, pp. 365–371.
57. Keith, A., *New Discoveries Relating to the Antiquity of Man*, chap. 10.
58. Weinert, H., *Ursprung der Menschheit* (Stuttgart, 1932), pp. 290–291.
59. Antevs, E., *Geographical Review*, vol. 25 (1935), pp. 302–309.

GENERAL REFERENCES

The following list comprises a brief selection of works, mostly rather general books, which can be read with understanding and profit by persons without much technical acquaintance with the subject. A few outstanding monographs and papers on particular topics are included.

Abel, Othenio, *Die Stellung des Menschen im Rahmen der Wirbeltiere* (Jena, 1931).

Boule, Marcellin, *Les Hommes Fossiles* (2nd ed., Paris, 1923); *Fossil Men* (English translation of the same, London, 1923).

Gregory, W. K., "The Lineage of Man," in *Creation by Evolution*, edited by Frances Mason (1928); and *Man's Place among the Anthropoids* (Oxford, 1934).

Hooton, E. A., *Up from the Ape* (1931).

Hrdlička, A., "The Skeletal Remains of Early Man," *Smithsonian Miscellaneous Collections*, vol. 83 (1931).

Keith, A., *The Antiquity of Man* (2 vols., 1925) and *New Discoveries Relating to the Antiquity of Man* (1931).

MacCurdy, G. G., *Early Man* (1937) and *Human Origins* (2 vols., 1924).

Obermaier, H., *Fossil Man in Spain* (1924).

Osborn, H. F., *Men of the Old Stone Age* (3rd ed., 1919).

Schultz, Adolph H., "Man as a Primate," *Scientific Monthly*, vol. 33 (Nov., 1931), pp. 385–412 and "Characters common to Higher Primates and Characters specific for Man," *Quarterly Review of Biology*, vol. 11, no. 3, pp. 259–283, and no. 4, pp. 425–455 (1936).

Smith, G. Elliot, *The Evolution of Man* (2nd ed., London, 1927).

Warden, C. J., *The Origin of Human Behavior* (1932).

Weinert, H., *Menschen der Vorzeit* (Stuttgart, 1930) and *Ursprung der Menschheit* (Stuttgart, 1932).

Yerkes, R. M. and A. W., *The Great Apes: A Study of Anthropoid Life* (1929).

SUPPLEMENTARY NOTE. Since the first printing of this book the finding of a third skullcap of Pithecanthropus has been reported by Dr. G. H. R. von Koenigswald (*Nature*, Oct. 15, 1938). The new skull, that of a juvenile individual, though less complete than the other two, shows resemblances to Sinanthropus and tends to strengthen the evidence that the two genera are rather closely related. Dr. R. Broom (*Nature*, Aug. 27, 1938) reports the discovery of new fossil anthropoid material from the Transvaal. He believes the material to comprise remains of two forms, the one formerly described as *Australopithecus transvaalensis* he now calls *Plesianthropus*, while a second specimen (the Kromdrai skull), of which he has a partial endocranial cast, large portions of the face, palate and lower jaw, he names *Paranthropus robustus*. Both forms (if indeed they represent separate genera) are remarkable in having a brain no larger than that of a great ape but approximating the human brain in form, combined with teeth which resemble those of man rather more closely than those of any ape. The canine teeth are no larger than those of many men. Fragments of limb bones have also been reported (*Nature*, Nov. 19, 1938). Though only preliminary notes have been published to date (Dec. 15, 1938), it may be stated that the new South African apes, so far as can be judged from the skull and teeth, are in many ways intermediate between the other anthropoid apes and man. They are of course too late geologically to represent actual ancestors of man.

CHAPTER III

RACE

FRANZ BOAS

Races and local types. In descriptions of the anatomical characteristics of the principal races, only those traits are discussed which set off one large group from the other and which are common to all its members. The lesser differences between individuals and between neighboring local groups are naturally disregarded. Thus a somewhat schematic view of the bodily characteristics of the varieties of mankind is obtained unless the characteristics of the individuals composing a local group or a race are clearly understood. We have to consider the characteristics of a population before we can take up a description of races.

Variability of local types. A description of a population cannot be given in a summary way, but must consist of an enumeration and description of all its component forms. Their frequency distribution is the only way by which an exhaustive description can be given. When alternative forms are distinguished, such as blue eyes and those not blue, or blood of distinct chemical behavior, the frequency of occurrence of each type must be given. Since in most cases the differences between the observed forms, like stature or headforms, are of such character that differences between the individuals of a population who are alike in form are minute, verbal descriptions are no longer satisfactory; numerical values must take their place. For this reason the description of a population is largely based on anthropometric studies. The dimension of the body, grades of pigmentation, numerical values of chemical constituents, frequency and grade of development of characteristic anatomical traits, are substituted for vaguer descriptions. For these reasons the method to be used is analogous to the one employed in the study of any type of variable quantities. It is the statistical method.

Methods of observations. Detailed methods of the study of the human body have been elaborated. These are based in part on morphological observations but much more on quantitative determinations of various measures of linear extent, area, and volume of the body and its organs; on the frequency of occurrence of various forms; on attempts at quantitative studies of the chemical properties and physical functions of the organism.

By far the greatest attention has been paid to a determination of form by means of measurements, and more attention has been given to the bony structure than to any other part of the body. The reason for this is not that the bony structure is more important, but that nothing else remains of past generations, and a comparison between present and past can be based only on comparisons of skeletons. The comparative study of soft parts is receiving increasing attention in anatomical institutes but has not been elaborated to the same extent as the observation of the skeleton and of easily ascertainable measures on the living, many of which depend largely upon the dimensions of bony structures.

The size of the body is measured by stature (the height standing in erect posture), by weight, and sometimes by volume. The length of the limbs is measured on the skeleton by the length of the long bones; on the living, by the determination with the greatest possible accuracy of the corresponding lengths. The transversal measures of the body are determined at the shoulder girdle, in connection with the length of arms by the span between the tips of the second fingers of the horizontally extended arms, on various points of the chest, and on the hips. Anteroposterior measures are taken on chest and pelvis. Further information regarding size and form of the body, in conjunction with the linear measures, is given by the determination of the circumference at various levels.

A comprehensive system of measurements of the head, respectively of the skull, has been developed. The head measures most commonly used on the living are length of head, measured from the glabella (the point between the eyebrows) to the most distant point of the occiput; the greatest transversal diameter of the head; and the greatest width of the face measured between the zygomatic arches. These are preferred on the living, because they can be taken with the greatest accuracy since the points from which the measurements have to be taken are well defined and the soft parts covering these regions are rather thin. Height of nose and face are determined with much greater difficulty. Measurements on the skull may be taken with much greater accuracy, since the bone is unyielding and the points may be accurately determined.

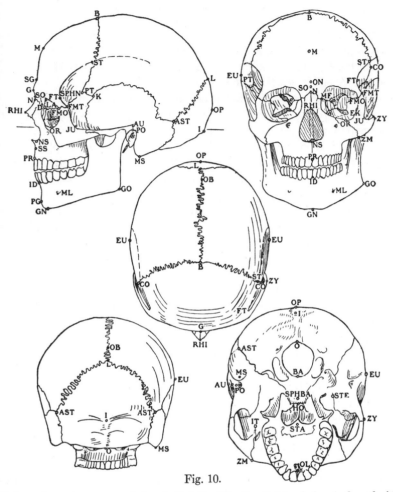

Fig. 10.

Points of measurements of the skull (after Martin, *Lehrbuch der Anthropologie*).

ast	Asterion	*id*	Infradentale	*op*	Opisthokranion
au	Auriculare	*it*	Infratemporale	*or*	Orbitale
b	Bregma	*ju*	Jugale	*pg*	Pogonion
ba	Basion	*k*	Krotaphion	*po*	Porion
co	Coronale	*l*	Lambda	*pr*	Prosthion
d	Dakryon	*la*	Lakrimale	*pt*	Pterion
ek	Ektokonchion	*m*	Metopion	*rhi*	Rhinion
eu	Euryon	*mf*	Maxillofrontale	*sg*	Supraglabellare
fmo	Frontomalare orbitale	*ml*	Mentale	*so*	Supraorbitale
fmt	Frontomalare temporale	*ms*	Mastoideale	*sphba*	Sphenobasion
ft	Frontotemporale	*n*	Nasion	*sphn*	Sphenion
g	Glabella	*ns*	Nasospinale	*ss*	Subspinale
gn	Gnathion	*o*	Opisthion	*st*	Stephanion
go	Gonion	*ob*	Obelion	*sta*	Staphylion
ho	Hormion	*ol*	Orale	*ste*	Stenion
i	Inion	*on*	Ophryon	*zm*	Zygomaxillare
				zy	Zygion

On account of the importance of obtaining accurate and comparable measurements, it has been found advantageous to define and name those points which are utilized. Figure 10 shows the points, and the legend gives their definition.

When comparing the conformation of two skulls it is obviously important to bring them into homologous positions, because the apparent slope of the forehead or the apparent degree of prognathism will depend upon the position chosen. Generally the attempt is made to place the skull as nearly as possible in its natural position when looking straight ahead, and two planes are principally used as nearly coinciding with this position: namely, the plane passing along the lowest points of the occipital condyles and the prosthion (alveolar point), or the one passing on each side of the head through the central point of the upper rim of the meatus auditorius and the lowest point of the lower rim of the orbit. By giving to these pairs of points a stable position, all other points are made the more variable the farther removed they are. In a purely morphological study the two objects studied should be made to approach each other as near as possible in all points.

The natural horizontal position is particularly important for determining the characteristic physiognomic angles of the face and forehead. The alveolar arch and the teeth appear more prominent, the forehead flatter, when the skull is tilted back more than it is in normal position; the reverse is true when it is tilted forward. On account of the uncertainty of the normal position, some of these angles are more safely determined by means of measurements of lines drawn between fixed points of the skull.

Observations on other points can also be made with much greater accuracy on the skeleton than on the living. Here also exact measurements of dimensions and angles have been made exhibiting differences between individuals and racial groups. Thus the relative lengths of the extremities show considerable differences both individually and in racial groups. Details of form and curvature of single bones have also been described by means of metrical methods.

The soft parts of the body may be studied with a fair degree of accuracy on plaster casts, partly because the material is unyielding, partly because lines may be studied that are not readily observed on the living. As an example the cross section of the faces of two Indian tribes may be given (Fig. 11).

Besides measurable dimensions and angles many significant forms occur which cannot be readily represented by numerical values. Irregularities in the development of bones, such as the persistence of the suture dividing the two frontal bones and the occurrence of a ridge along the middle of the palate, may be described according to their frequency and intensity, but are not readily measured. This is even more true of such complex configurations as the fingerprints which may be classified and occur with varying frequency in local groups.

Types. The anatomical characteristics of individuals may be described by many measurements. Some of these may be related, so that the one determines, at least in part, the other one. Thus among the members of the same population a wide face may be found together with a wide head; broad shoulders with broad hips; a long arm with a long leg. Others are very slightly related, if at all. Transversal measures are in general slightly related to longitudinal measures — that is, to those in a line from feet to head. The width of the foot is hardly related at all to the length of the head, and so on.

Fig. 11. Cross sections of faces.
—— Indians of coast of British Columbia
------ Indians of interior of British Columbia

If we describe individuals composing a population by a number of measurements that are not related, and count how many will have the most frequent measurements, it appears that only very few are what we might call typical specimens of the population. When we count the one half who have the normal length of head, and of these the one half who have the normal length of foot, meaning by this that we consider as "normal" those who belong to the middle half of the population, we see that only one fourth of the total number will have the normal form in regard to both characteristics. If new independent measures are added, the third one will be found combined with the first two with only one half of one fourth, or one eighth of the whole number. If ten such measures are considered, then only one individual among 1024 will have the normal measures in all these ten traits. Since a type has many characteristics, some of which are unrelated while others are more or less closely or loosely related, it follows that very few individuals will correspond to what we might call the norm of the population. The norm is an abstraction which is hardly ever found realized in any single individual.

There are, however, cases in which a population is so uniform in regard to special traits that these impress themselves as the prominent characteristics. Examples are the blondness in some parts of Sweden and the flat occiput in parts of Asia Minor.

Types are also subjectively construed in another manner. When the observer has become familiar with two populations and has formed his impression of their "types" and turns his attention to a third population in which both of these types may be recognized, he will be inclined to consider this new population as mixed, although there is nothing to prove that it may not be genetically a type quite analogous to those previously studied. The taxonomic classification thus obtained would not necessarily represent a genetic fact which would have to be investigated by the study of family lines (see also p. 19).

Phenotypes and genotypes. The whole population consists of families, and the bodily form of each individual depends not only upon the characteristics of the population as a whole, but primarily upon those of the family (genotype) to which he belongs. In a population of absolutely uniform descent all the constituent families would be alike. This would be expressed by the fact that the averages and variabilities of each family line, provided there were very many children, would be the same. These values can be computed. Experience shows that there is not a single population in which the family lines are identical. Their uniformity is the greater the more the community has for a long time been inbred, while a recent intermingling of different lines of descent results in considerable differences between family lines. Since the population as a whole is composed of many family lines, the characteristics of every one of these are not those of the whole population. The population as a whole, representing many family lines or genotypes, is called a phenotype. The brothers and sisters constituting one genotype would also differ the less among themselves, the more uniform the ancestry of the population. On the other hand, in an inbred population of mixed descent the family lines may be very much alike, while the brothers and sisters, designated as fraternities, may be very unlike among themselves.[1]

Graphically this may be represented in the following way: Families of approximately the middle type will be frequent, while those divergent from the middle family lines will be rare. In each family line there will be differences between the members of the fraternity; and on the whole, the amount of variability in each fra-

ternity will be about equal. This will result in a distribution as indicated in Figure 12, for clarity's sake in somewhat exaggerated form.
Generalized types. If it were possible to reconstruct generalized
types, we might obtain a better insight into the origin of the modern
local races. Pronounced local types develop with age and are clearest
in the adult male, somewhat less so in the female, and least of all in
infants. In prenatal stages the differences are still slighter. It is well
known that the study of embryology throws much light upon the
morphological significance of the parts of the body, for there are
decided similarities of structure between the early stages of the

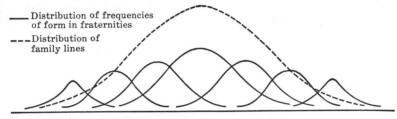

Fig. 12. Distribution of frequencies of form in fraternities, and distribution
of family lines.

organs in different species and even orders. In other words, the most
generalized forms may be recognized in the earliest stages of individual development. We may therefore conclude that the early
stages of development show the more generalized forms which in
later life become differentiated.

This may readily be observed in the development of the individual.
Very young children do not exhibit all the pronounced characteristics
of the race to which they belong. The Negro foetus may be distinguished from the White foetus in proportions of the body, but the
differences are less than those found among adults. The children of
European types with dark hair are often light blond as young children.
The form of the nose of children of most races does not exhibit the
pronounced differences found among adults, because the bridge of
the nose develops only during maturity.

Another approach to the problem is through an investigation of
those traits which are most constant in larger groups. It seems
plausible that traits which are common to large groups of mankind
must be very ancient, while those showing similar types of variation
in distinct groups have presumably developed independently and
at a later time.

Among the most constant forms that belong to large divisions of mankind are forms of hair, pigmentation, and form of nose, while most of the proportions of the body are more variable. This justifies the attempt to classify mankind on this basis and to distinguish as ancient ancestral forms the Negro, including Negroes of Africa and Melanesia, with dark skin and frizzly black hair; the Australian, with dark skin and wavy black hair; the Mongolian, including the American Indian, with straight hair, slighter pigmentation, and somewhat elevated bridge of nose; and the European, with varying form and color of hair, slight pigmentation, and narrow nose. There are other bodily traits that coincide more or less strictly with this classification, such as the form of the eye — wide open among Negroes and Europeans, with a heavy fold of the upper eyelid in the Mongolians; thickness of lips — greatest among Negroes and Australians, less so among Mongolians, least among the Whites.

In contrast to these the form of the head as seen from above shows wide variations in each race; elongated in one Negro group, rounded in another. Certainly this type cannot belong to the fundamental racial traits. It would seem that this is rather a parallel development which occurred independently in various racial types.

Parallel development. The genealogical grouping of races is made difficult by the possibility of occurrence of parallel traits in different groups of mankind. A difficulty of this kind is found in the interpretation of the bodily forms of the Ainu of northern Japan. They differ from their Mongoloid neighbors in certain traits that approach the bodily forms of the Europeans. Particularly the abundant hairiness of the body sets them off strongly from their neighbors, and it has been inferred that they must be descendants of a European group that migrated east to the Pacific Ocean. A similar case is that of the Tlingit and Haida of the coasts of Alaska and British Columbia. While most Indians are characterized by dark hair, deep pigmentation of the eye, and a moderate pigmentation of the skin, we find here individuals of very light skin color, red hair, and light brown eyes. This is not due to intermingling with Whites, for Shakes, the Tlingit chief who met the first European vessel that touched this coast, was characterized by these traits, a fact still remembered by his descendants. The "blond Eskimo" of Coronation Gulf present a similar variant. It seems therefore likely that the loss of pigmentation may be a trait which occurs sporadically among the Mongoloid type among groups that have no immediate genetic relation to Europeans. It follows from these remarks that we must be cautious in assuming a necessary genetic relationship between forms showing similarities that may be due to parallelism of development.

Selection. Whenever the mating between genetic types is entirely due to chance — in other words, whenever an individual of one type may mate with equal probability with any one of the other types, and when the population has been stable for a long time, the distribution of forms in the population will also be stable. In modern populations these conditions do not prevail. In New York, for instance, a person of European descent is much more likely to mate with another European, a Negro with another Negro, than is a European to mate with a Negro. To a lesser extent this is true of other groups. There is a decided social selection between the social groups. The probability that an Italian of the first generation will marry a Scandinavian of the first generation is not equal to the probability that an Italian will marry an Italian. Since the social groups such as Italians, Irish, Poles, Scandinavians, are not genetically identical, we have to take into consideration this inequality which results in changes of the genetic composition and which lasts until the selective mating disappears.

Similar conditions prevail in every population in which selective mating occurs, unless the genetic lines are equally distributed in all the classes in which selection occurs. Such equality does not exist in modern populations. Since in every population, even in small tribes, a number of distinct genetic lines occur, preferential cross cousin marriages, such as are found in many tribes, together with avoidance of parallel cousin marriages, must also be a disturbing element in the distribution of genetic traits.

It follows from all this that in most cases the distribution of genetic types, and hence that of physical types, in a population is not constant, but that gradual changes due to hereditary causes must be frequent. The character of these changes is due to the differences in physical form among the genetic types upon which the selective processes are at work. When there is no relation between social grouping and the genetic character of each group, no change due to selective mating will occur.

Environmental changes. Environmental conditions bring about slight modifications of human forms. Their influence is clear so far as the bulk of the body is concerned. The constant vigorous use of muscles of the arm results in forms different from those brought about by disuse. Ample nutrition and semi-starvation affect the form of the body. Diseases of early childhood may even result in modifications of the skeleton. It is necessary to determine how far the body responds to the differences of environment. In a single individual it would be difficult, if not impossible, to distinguish between environmental and hereditary causes. The bulk of the body, for instance, may be due to either cause. It may be influenced by favorable conditions of growth and adequate nutrition, or it may be largely determined by hereditary causes. At the present time a distinction between the two causes is in most cases impossible.

Population and race. Since populations consist of many distinct family lines, the question arises: What is a race? The genotypes are stable within a population. They form a continuous series, and while the extremes may be quite distinct, they are connected by many transitional forms. Apparently identical individuals are found in populations that live in contiguous territories. It is not possible to assign with any degree of certainty any individual, judged by his bodily form, to a particular population, excepting extreme forms and unusually marked local differences. Still, when areas far apart are compared, the two populations appear as decidedly distinct. A comparison of Europe and Africa illustrates this.

In general usage local forms — that is, populations — are described as local races, but it must be understood that this is merely a convenient way of describing the characteristics of a local form and that it does not prove that the local form is descended from an ancient fundamental variety of mankind. All we find at the present time are populations each containing markedly distinct family lines or genotypes which appear in ever-changing combinations.

In a strict sense a race must be defined as a group of common origin and of stable type. In this sense extreme forms like the Australians, Negroes, Mongolians, and Europeans may be described as races because each has certain characteristics which set them off from other groups, and which are strictly hereditary. Difficulties arise if forms are considered in which the racial characteristics are not pronounced. Since each population consists of many different genotypes, the problem arises whether it is possible to analyze the genotypes in such a way as to determine constituent fundamental races. In such an attempt we are all too ready to consider the extreme types as fundamental forms, without considering that these are established on the purely subjective impression of their striking

differences. It is not necessary to assume that the intermediate types
are always mixed types. They may well be the fundamental forms of
which the extremes are variants. The simple description of the population does not answer this question. In mixed races like the Mulattoes,
the parental types of which are known, the individuals and their
family lines may be grouped according to their greater or lesser
resemblance with the one or the other race. When they are so grouped,
the pure types, Whites and Negroes, stand at the ends of these
series.

When the original intermingling types are unknown, the analysis
of the descriptive features cannot lead to a similar result, because
according to the laws of Mendelian inheritance the individual traits
separate and recombine, and it is not possible to reconstruct with
any degree of certainty the "pure" ancestral types. All that can be
done is to distinguish arbitrarily certain morphological forms as
"pure" types, and then arrange all the others statistically in intermediate groups which will contain the more ancestors of the alleged
"pure" types the more their forms resemble one or the other "pure"
type.

The problem is quite the same as that of the study of varieties of
strongly varying animals or plants living in distinct localities. The
farther they are removed from one another the more they are likely
to differ. Sharp lines between the varieties cannot be drawn, and a
reconstruction of ancestral forms is not possible.

In some cases it can be shown that a population is actually mixed.
In a perfectly homogeneous group the size of an individual will
influence all his measurements. They will all increase with size,
although not necessarily at the same rate. If the population is
descended from two types having different measurements, these relations may be disturbed. Thus we find in northern France a population with rather long and narrow heads, and in central France one
with larger short and broad heads. The effect of their mixture in
Paris is that long heads are often narrow, short heads broad; in other
words, the normal correlation is disturbed and considerably lower
than in populations descended from a more uniform ancestry.
Nevertheless, the component elements could not be reconstructed,
unless they were actually found in some locality. The success of such
an analysis would require an exact knowledge of the manner in which
the traits in question are inherited.

Local races. We have seen that the characteristics of variable traits of local races can be accounted for in several ways. These may be due to a mixture of closely allied but by origin distinct forms; differentiation may be due to isolation, local selection, or to environmental influences.

Mixture. The history of mankind proves that mixture of different populations has been going on for thousands of years. The distribution of implements-dating back to the end of the glacial period suggests that, even at this early time, extended migrations occurred. They cannot be proved, because cultural traits may be disseminated by imitation without migration. In later times, when the elements of language or skeletal remains allow us to trace wanderings, the proof can be given. In Europe the Greeks invaded the Mediterranean at the end of the second millenium before our era. The people of Thrace migrated into Asia Minor, the Celts expanded their territory into Italy and wandered as far as Asia Minor; the Roman traders established colonies over a large part of Europe; the Germanic tribes migrated from the Black Sea into western and southern Europe, and into North Africa; the Arabs swept over North Africa and settled with North Africans in Spain; the Slavs superseded the Finnish people of Russia; the Bulgarians migrated from the Black Sea into the Balkan Peninsula; the Magyars into Hungary; Mongolian invasions of Europe followed. The European populations were almost constantly on the move until individual landholding developed and the people became attached to the soil. Remote parts, like Spain and England, were not spared the effects of such intermingling. The Jewish and Armenian diaspora were, notwithstanding their social isolation, undoubtedly accompanied by intermingling. The expulsion of people like that of the Moors and Jews from Spain could not obliterate the results of previous mixture. In Portugal plantations were worked by Negroes, but the Negro element has disappeared in the modern population. After the great Greek, Celtic, and Teutonic migrations, the Crusades and the numerous wars must have contributed to this process. In recent times the development of large cities has given a new stimulus to the process of intermingling of distinct local types. It has received its strongest impulse through the colonization of America, Australia, and South Africa.

Early conditions on other continents were not different. Although we have no historical data for Africa, America, and Polynesia, the linguistic and anatomical evidence is clear. The Bantu tribes of Africa spread over the greater part of the continent, and presumably supplanted an old pygmy or pygmoid population. In the Sudan there occurred invasions of people from the Mediterranean border of Africa; Abyssinia was peopled by Semitic invaders. In North America the sporadic distribution of Athapascan tribes from Alaska and the MacKenzie area along the Pacific coast to Arizona and New Mexico, the occurrence of Algonquian languages along the Western Plains and in the East, the relationship between the Cherokee of North Carolina and the Iroquois of New York, are proofs of extended migrations. In South America the distribution of the Caribs and Arawak shows displacements which extended over thousands of miles. In Asia historical, linguistic, and anthropological evidence gives clear proofs of migrations. The Malay crossed the Indian Ocean and settled in Madagascar. The Aryans in India, the Central Asiatic invasions southward and westward, the extension of the Turks westward into Europe and northward into Siberia, are a few examples. Owing to these conditions we may expect to find practically everywhere intermixture between various ancestral types which cannot be reconstructed by means of an analysis of the morphological traits of a population.

Isolation. It seems likely that, notwithstanding the mobility of the human race, there have been periods of isolation of small bands. In early times populations must have been sparse, and opportunities for isolation, partly for geographical and partly for social reasons, must have been frequent. Even in recent times there have been such areas of isolation, as for instance among the Eskimo tribe of Smith Sound in Greenland, in Australia, and on remote islands of the Pacific Ocean. Biological evidence shows that in cases of isolation with long-continued inbreeding well-defined types develop, no matter whether they are all descended from one ancestral type, or whether they are of mixed origin. Examples of such divergence of locally circumscribed variations are found in the Galapagos Islands, where lizards and birds of each island have well-marked characteristics that set them off from those of neighboring islands; or in some of the Polynesian islands where the snails of each valley have their own characteristics. We may discover such phenomena in man. Thus the Indians of some valleys of California differ in type from their neighbors, and in the Austrian Alps the inhabitants of the remote villages are markedly individualized.

It therefore seems admissible to assume that early isolation was a means of establishing distinctive types which persist in the more local races. This is illustrated also by the frequent occurrence of certain anomalies in small local groups. In the adult the parts of the occipital bone of man are fused, but sometimes the upper portion, the squama, which forms the occiput, is separated from the lower part (Fig. 13). This conformation is remarkably common among some Pueblo tribes of New Mexico. It must be considered a family trait which, on account of inbreeding, has become unusually prevalent in these communities. This is analogous to hereditary pathological forms which occur with unusual frequency in some family lines or communities. The smaller and the more strictly inbred the community, the more we are likely to find a pronounced local type.

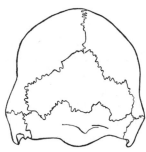

Fig. 13. *Os Incae.*

Differences of this kind can never be greater than the whole range of variations which occurred in the original population from which the isolated group became separated. It may therefore well be that the ancestral type contained a great number of variants that are now found with greater frequency in one locality which possesses local characteristics.

Domestication. For a clear understanding of the significance of racial differentiation we must not lose sight of the conditions in which man lives in all parts of the world. Man is the oldest domesticated form, self-domesticated by his inventions. The fundamental characteristics of the life of domesticated animals consist in the artificial control of food supply, in the modification of food consumed, and in artificial protection against enemies. The careful inbreeding of selected stable strains which characterizes modern methods of raising domesticated animals does not belong to early domestication and, except in a few cases, has not been an important element in the history of mankind. It can hardly be adduced as a factor in race formation.

The foundation for domestication was laid when man developed the use of tools for his protection, and particularly when he discovered the use of fire and began to modify his food by roasting and cooking and gave up the habits of a roaming animal that lived on the food that his hands and teeth could procure for him. Fire was used by man in middle Paleolithic times, about 35,000 or 50,000 years ago, long before animals became associated with him in his camp. The first to draw attention to the domestication of man were Johannes Ranke and Eduard Hahn.

It is therefore not surprising to see that man participates in those traits that differentiate domesticated animals from wild forms. Perhaps most striking are the changes in pigmentation and hair forms that are concomitants of the transition from wild life to domesticated life. There are hardly any wild forms known that have the peculiar pigmentation characteristic of blondness, often accompanied by loss of pigmentation of the iris which results in blueness of eye. The microscopical structure of the blue eye of the "Nordic" is, so far as pigmentation is concerned, identical with that of the blue-eyed rabbit. The blondness of hair is identical with that of the blond horses and pigs. On the other hand, blackness is also rare among wild mammals. The fur coats of the black panther and black bear are among the exceptions. Almost all domesticated forms — cattle, horses, dogs, cats — have black varieties. Furthermore, the form and amount of hair of domesticated forms is unusually variable. Most wild animals have straight hair, and except among the anthropoid apes all parts of the body are well covered. Some domesticated varieties, like angora cats and Pekinese dogs, have an excessive amount and unusual length of hair, while others, like Mexican dogs, are almost hairless. The form of the hair is also variable. The hair of wild animals is almost always straight. Forms like that of the hair of the poodle dog do not occur. A form analogous to the frizzly Negro hair is not found in nature. In domesticated fowl similar curvatures of the feathers may be observed.

The development of the long head hair of man is inconceivable in a wild species. It would make the arboreal life of the predecessor of man impossible and would be equally a hindrance in life in the open, unless man had learned to dress it. No mane of wild animals reaches the same excessive length.

Another trait of domesticated animals is great variation in size. The small Shetland pony may be contrasted against the heavy dray horse, the Pekinese dog against the great Dane. In man we find similar variations in size: on the one hand the pygmy Bushman, on the other hand the tall Scotchman or the Patagonian. It is true that the great variants in domesticated animals have been raised by careful breeding, but the fact remains that such variants do not develop among wild animals. In man, we may assume, isolation played a rôle similar to inbreeding of domesticated animals.

There are other characteristics of animals that are due to domestication, some of which are paralleled by traits in man, and some not. To the former group belongs the permanence of the female breast, to the latter the enlargement of the outer ear seen for instance in some races of dogs. Eugen Fischer[2] and B. Klatt[3] have studied in detail the analogies between the anatomy of domesticated animals and of man.

It is not possible to decide whether the great differences between races are rather the late effect of domestication, which seems to accelerate the process of formation of distinct varieties, or whether the origin of the modern races must be looked for in remote antiquity, previous to appreciable effects of domestication. Practically all the distinguishing features of races may be paralleled by modifications that occur in domestication. The elongation of the Negro face forward and the reduction of the European face find their parallels in breeds of dogs, horses, and pigs. Variations in the relative length of limbs as compared to length of the body, and concomitant variations in the form of shoulder girdle and pelvis are common.

Paleontological evidence, as described in the preceding chapter, does not yet give us a satisfactory clue by which we can determine the age of the existing principal races, much less the way in which they developed from a common root.

Internal secretions. Sir Arthur Keith bases his theory of racial origins first of all upon the action of the ductless glands. It has been found that harmonious growth depends upon the proper action of a number of glands. The pituitary gland, which is located at the base of the brain,[4] when overdeveloped gives rise to enlarged nose, chin, hands, and feet. The thyroid gland, which is located in front of the neck, controls growth. Its subnormal functioning causes poorly developed nose and hair and a flat face, and in extreme cases idiocy. The adrenal glands affect the color of the skin. The thymus seems to control rapidity of development. Its effect upon generation after generation is cumulative. The character of the individual is strongly influenced by the activity of these glands. Sir Arthur Keith assumes that racial differences may be due to differences in their chemical behavior. Less energetic activity of the thyroid gland may thus have influenced the somatic appearance of whole populations like the Mongols, Bushmen, and Hottentots. Deficiency of the adrenals, which control hairiness in addition to pigmentation, may be responsible for the meager growth of body hair of the Mongol and Negro as against its abundance in the European and the Australian. If this assumption is correct, the outer appearances of races might in part be influenced by the activity of the glands; but this would not give us any clue to the origin of races, since we should then be required to search for the origin of the differentiation of behavior of the glands.

The actual changes due to environment that have been observed may well be caused by slight modification in the chemical activity of the body. This seems the more likely, since some of the changes seem to become the stronger the longer the mother has been exposed to a new environment. In recent years Sir Arthur Keith has emphasized again the influence of isolation upon the rise of local types. He even sees in modern nationalism with its concomitant isolation a process by which new types originate.

Races of man. On account of the actual condition of modern populations a genetic classification of mankind presents peculiar difficulties. While it is possible to describe taxonomically both the fundamentally distinct varieties which may properly be called races and local populations, we have no means at present to account for their genesis. Minor local differences may be due to early isolation and inbreeding, to intermingling of types in varying ratios, and to selection. In his migrations man has reached almost every part of the habitable world and has been exposed to the greatest variety of external conditions. This also may have been an important cause of racial differentiation. The more fundamental differences between large groups, such as the Negroes and Chinese, must be looked for in earlier differentiation.

To a certain extent geographical distribution may give a clue to racial history. When we consider the land mass as a whole, remembering the early connection between the Old World and America in the region of Bering Sea, we recognize that a type with a moderate degree of pigmentation, straight hair, broad face, fairly large nose, rather small lips, and an eye form characterized by a heavy upper eyelid covering the inner corner of the eye inhabits a large part of Asia and America, while another type with dark pigmentation, frizzly or wavy hair, low nose, protruding face, thick lips, open eyes, and long limbs inhabits Africa, Australia, and the chain of islands stretching from New Guinea southeastward, and occurs sporadically in southern Asia. It might be said that the one group lives all around the Pacific Ocean, calling the whole of both Americas the east coast and a large part of Asia, including central Asia and Siberia, the west coast of the Pacific Ocean. The other group lives around the Indian Ocean, considering Africa as the west coast and southern Asia and Australia with the adjoining islands as the north and east coasts. Thus, at least two groups may be distinguished which, both geographically and morphologically, are fairly well defined.

Each of these groups contains many elements that seem to possess marked individuality, and their relations to the main groups are not by any means clear. The Europeans, Australians, and African pygmies offer the greatest difficulties.

In many respects the Australians seem to be a more generalized type and might therefore be considered as an older form that has developed in its own way. Since Australia has been separated from Asia for a long geological period, so that man and the dog are the only higher mammals existing there, it must be assumed that Australian man did not reach there until after he had learned to navigate the waters separating Asia from Australia. This accords with the observation made by Huxley that many of the South Asiatic types have Australoid characteristics. This refers for instance to the Vedda of Ceylon and other South Indian tribes. The Negroid Papua of New Guinea and many other isolated spots in southern Asia would have to be assumed, according to their geographical position, as a still later wave of migration.

The South African pygmies are lighter in color than the Negroes. Their skin color resembles that of tanned leather. The forms of hair, face, and nose are decidedly Negroid and they are most closely affiliated with the Negro type.

The European type is set off from all the others by the greatest degree of depigmentation. Nearest to him in this respect is the East Asiatic type, which in a number of localities exhibits the tendency to strong depigmentation. Some of the East Asiatic and American tribes are very light, and brown, wavy hair is found in a number of regions — for instance, in British Columbia. The nose tends to attain large size. In most cases it is rather low and heavy with wide alae, but in many regions its elevation over the face is very great — for instance, among the Indians of the Mississippi valley. While generally the hairiness of the body is very slight, the Ainu, who are otherwise of the same general appearance, have an abundance of body hair. Wide face and prominent cheek bones are

a fairly general characteristic of this type, although in some localities they are quite narrow. The development of the so-called "ob-
lique," eye, such as may be observed among the Chinese, is often
much weakened. The blue lumbar spot which is probably ever present in newborn infants of this race is sporadically observable among
the Europeans also. All in all, it may be said that the East Asiatic
type tends to produce here and there variations that approach European types, while variations in the direction of Negroid types are
exceedingly rare. Increase in pigmentation, lower noses, and protruding mouth parts are also found locally, but hardly to a greater
extent than they are found in varieties of the European type. I am
therefore inclined to associate the European type most closely with
the East Asiatic type.

Our picture of the principal races would thus be that of two
groups of doubtful affiliation inhabiting the shores of the Indian
Ocean, and of another large group inhabiting the shores of the
Pacific Ocean, including both Americas and a large part of Asia,
with the affiliated European type. It is obvious that this is an unduly generalized picture, because the numerous important local
varieties and their morphological characteristics have been disregarded.

Earlier classifications are based partly on morphological traits,
partly on geographical location. Thus Linné distinguished and
described the European, American, Asiatic, and African races;
Blumenbach the Caucasian (European), Mongolian, Ethiopian,
American, and Malayan.

These divisions are based on characteristics of color and hair, and
on descriptive features of the skull and face. In later classifications
the form of the nose, shape of the skull, form of hair, and color were
taken as the principal criteria by which races were distinguished.
According to the number of elements which were considered as important, three or four or a great many more races were distinguished.
Huxley establishes five races — Australoid, Negroid, Mongoloid,
xanthochroic, melanochroic. By a similar method Duckworth [5] established seven principal races, based mainly on the length-breadth
index of the skull, the degree of prognathism, and the cranial capacity. These are the Australian, African Negro, Andamanese, Eurasi-
atic, Polynesian, Greenlandish, and South African. Roland B.
Dixon [6] used a highly artificial classification, dividing the individuals
of each race, regardless of other characteristics, into fundamental

types according to threefold groupings: those with long, medium, round heads; with high, middle, low heads; with narrow, middle, and flat noses. Thus he obtained according to the possible combination of the extreme forms eight fundamental types, such as long- and high-headed, narrow-nosed; long- and flat-headed, narrow-nosed; long- and high-headed, flat-nosed; long- and low-headed, flat-nosed; etc. These he considered as fundamental and derived the middle forms from mixtures. There is no evidence that these mathematically derived forms have any biological significance. A. C. Haddon [7] uses as the basis of his classification hair, skin color, stature, length of head (length-breadth index), and forms of face, nose, and eyes. J. Deniker [8] established on similar principles six major groups and twenty-nine races.

The latest attempt at a classification of mankind is that made by E. von Eickstedt,[9] who distinguishes with Eugen Fischer the Europid, Negrid, and Mongolid races. He divides these as follows:

Races....................	Europid	Negrid	Mongolid
Number of subraces........	9	5	4
Collateral races..........	Polynesid	Melanesid	Indianid
Number of collateral subraces	0	3	8
Special forms.............	Veddid	Pygmid	Eskimid
Intermediate forms........	Ainuid	Australid	Khoisanid

The types of Europe have been described in particular detail. The divisions made by W. Z. Ripley [10] on the basis of previous work are still much used. He describes the blue-eyed, tall, long-headed Nordic; the darker, short-headed Alpine; and the short, long-headed Mediterranean. Later investigators have tried to establish finer divisions based largely on physiognomic traits.

It is but natural that a finer division of human types will give varying results according to the features which are considered as of prime importance in making a classification. A division of human types that is of value for determining the genetic relations must necessarily be based on significant hereditary traits not subject to environmental modification. For this reason stature can be used only in extreme cases, since we know that individuals growing up under changed conditions may differ considerably in stature from their parents. Thus, the average stature of European populations has increased almost everywhere during the last century. Still clearer is the result of comparisons between parents and their own children, or between brothers and sisters growing up in different surroundings. Thus, it has been shown that the sons of one generation of Harvard students excel the stature of their own parents by 3.4 centimeters. Similar observations have been made in regard to the cephalic index, which shows considerable change in a changed environment. Thus, the average cephalic index of immigrating East European Jews is 83.0, that of their children born in America 81.4, and that of their grandchildren 78.7. The width of face also is not stable in varying environments. In Europe a gradual narrowing of the face seems to occur. If, therefore, populations are classified as tall, or of medium stature, or short; as long-, medium-, or round-headed; as broad- or narrow-faced, arbitrary limits being set for the groupings of these measures, we have a classification of taxonomic, not of genetic, value. It is entirely inadmissible to assume such classes in any sense as fundamental racial groups. The assumption of a long-headed or round-headed race can only be made when it is possible to demonstrate that these features are stable.

It must be understood that these traits are hereditary in family lines. The genetic tendency of each individual is modified by environmental conditions. Unless the proof of stability can be given, these classes are no more than descriptions of certain populations without any implication as to the significance of the observed differences. The results of such classification will depend entirely upon the traits selected and upon the limits assumed for the arbitrary classification. If, for instance, the limits of headform are set at 75 and less for long-headed, 75–80 as medium form, 80 and more as round-headed, and if in another classification these limits are shifted, the results will be different. The same is true when the varying frequency of occurrence of each of these groups in each population is made the basis of classification.

The differences between the more fundamental racial types cannot be so interpreted that one of them would be higher than the other in the sense that the differences between one type and the higher apes would be greater than the analogous differences observed in others. On the contrary, every human type shows excessively human characteristics in certain directions. Thus the Eskimo have the largest brains and a slight amount of body hair; but proportions of limbs are not as excessively human as those of the Negroes, who also excel in development of the lips. The European has a marked narrowing of the face and elevation of the nose, most pronounced among the Armenians. At the same time their body hair is much more fully developed than that of the East Asiatics or Negroes. A scale of races in regard to their similarity to animals cannot be formed.

Theories of the origin of modern races. It has been shown before how selection may bring about changes in the numerical frequency of types represented in a population. Without the assumption of additional causes it cannot produce new types. Darwin sought these in the cumulative effects of selection, which would establish new variants of better adaptation to the environment that would survive and crowd out the older forms. This general theory has been applied specifically to human races by assuming as essential cause the climatic changes during the Pleistocene and the migrations that were forced by them. Othenio Abel [11] points out the effect of the gradual desiccation and increasing elevation of central Asia upon the migration of fauna and flora westward into Europe and eastward into America. A great change occurred at the end of the Miocene. Europe before that time consisted of a number of islands. Now the continent was formed, and at the same time the gradual rise and the increasing scantiness of vegetation in central Asia brought about the first great migration of mammals westward and eastward. The characteristic fossil of this period is the three-toed horse, Hipparion. The process of desiccation and the general rise of land continued into the glacial period. In central Asia woods had disappeared, and the higher apes substituted for the life in trees that of rock climbers like the modern baboon. In these forms Abel sees the ancestor of man and believes that at this early time when man first entered Europe with one of the late migrations the racial differentiation was already established. He bases this opinion on the observation that the chimpanzee and other apes show considerable variations in color of skin.

Halfdan Bryn [12] assumes three fundamental racial groups none of which can be derived from any one of the others but all of which go back to a human (or subhuman) ancestor of Tertiary time. The earliest, he thinks, are a number of pygmy races, each developing its own type after isolation. From these developed the lower races. Finally the higher races developed in Asia from an ancient uniform type before the rise of the Himalayas and the other chains of mountains and plateaus which brought about isolation and divergent development in each area.

Another highly speculative system is that of T. G. Taylor,[13] who assumes that the most primitive races must be found in the marginal areas of the continuous land mass. Consequently he assumes the Tasmanians, Bushmen, Eskimo, and the people of the southern parts of South America as the earliest types which were driven back by more and more highly developed races spreading eastward from central Asia.

Other attempts to account for the origin of races have been made on the basis of morphological characteristics. Gustav Fritsch [14] distinguished three fundamental races and derived from these metamorph or mixed races. Similar ideas were developed by C. H. Stratz [15] and H. Klaatsch,[16] who considered the Australians as representatives of the earliest surviving stage of human development from which the Negroid, Mongoloid, and European races developed by differentiation. In 1910 he had changed his opinion and advocated a polygenetic origin of the races of man. He tried to prove that gorilla, Neanderthal man, and Negro, on the one hand; and orang, European, Malay, Australian, and Mongol, on the other, go back to two separate anthropoid branches. Still other Negro types are associated with the chimpanzee. These views can hardly be maintained.

Racial physiology and psychology. The anatomical characteristics of an adult individual may be described with an accuracy that depends solely upon the refinement of measurement. They remain almost the same for a number of years. This is true at least for the skeleton, although the size of muscles, the amount of fat, of water contained in the tissues, and consequently weight, may undergo considerable fluctuations. Examples of dependence of form upon function are, for instance, found in the hand. Those of the blacksmith, clerk, and violin virtuoso differ on account of the development of the groups of muscles and their lesser or greater independence in use. Still, under the same conditions and for a reasonable length of time the forms and dimensions of the body are fairly stable.

Not so with bodily functions. These are much more subject to fluctuations. Attempts to obtain basal values for any physiological function, like heart beat, blood pressure, metabolism, require the most painstaking observance of physiological conditions, and even when all precautions are taken they fluctuate more or less. There is no one value for one individual, but each individual has his own value which is variable and changes from moment to moment according to the conditions of life. For this reason the mode of life and the environmental conditions are infinitely more strongly reflected in physiological function than in anatomical form. An individual who leads an inactive life will change his physiological behavior when he is compelled to assume a life of continued strenuous exertion. It follows that people of the same descent who live in different environments and pursue types of occupation that are diverse in their influence upon the body will also differ in their physiological functions. Thus it happens that genetic differences are easily overlaid by environmental influences.

For this reason the results of racial studies of physiological functions are often contradictory, and the contrasts between occupational groups in the same population are often much greater than the contrasts between racial groups. It also happens that groups of distinct genetic descent but living under the same environmental conditions function alike. In a few cases the influence of environment may increase the differences in type — for instance, in the effect of sunburn, which emphasizes the difference in pigmentation between very light and more strongly pigmented types, the former becoming reddish, the latter turning dark. Similar differences occur in reaction to epidemics against which one group has acquired partial immunity while another one has never been exposed.

The influence of environment upon physiological function may be observed in the reaction of the body to high altitude. The rarefied air and the lesser amount of oxygen supply secured by each breath require a readjustment on account of the demands upon the respiratory system. The exhausting influence of hot and humid weather in summer as against the bracing clear winter air is well known. The same individuals exposed to different climatic environment exhibit material changes in their physiological behavior.

Social conditions have a similar effect. The physiological functions of an undernourished, overworked individual differ from those of a well-nourished person whose bodily strength is not overtaxed. The Bushman and the South Sea Islander represent such a contrast, and it is not possible to determine how far the differences between their physiological reactions may be due to their descent, how far to environmental causes. Even their bodily forms must be in part an expression of the influence of these conditions upon their bodies during the period of growth.

The variability of mental reactions of the individual is also strongly affected by environmental causes. Even simple psychophysical phe-

nomena depend upon the closeness of attention paid to the stimuli. Reaction time, acuteness of hearing and sight, and other sense
impressions are subject to modifications. Not even the maximum or
minimum values obtained with the greatest possible precautions
intended to secure uniform conditions under which the tests are
made remain the same at all times, and their variability is not the
same in all individuals. While some react with a fair degree of con-
stancy, others are quite variable. More complex mental reactions
are even less constant. Everyday observation proves the variability
of emotional tone. The influence of fatigue and rest upon mental
reactions is well known and has been the subject of many observations, particularly on school children. On account of the variability
of mental traits under varying conditions, it is difficult to determine
how far they are genetically or environmentally determined. There
is no doubt that for each individual there exists a certain biological,
genetically determined basis of mental behavior. If we had no other
evidence, the contrasts between the mental behavior of the extremes, between the idiot and the genius, would be sufficient proof;
but we have also every reason to believe that the differences between mentally stable and unstable, between artist and logical
thinker, if not organically determined, are at least so influenced.

The actual problem lies in the differentiation between the two
sources of mental behavior, the organic and the environmental.
Two methods are open for this inquiry. On the one hand the same
individual, or individuals organically identical, may be investigated
under different conditions; or individuals of distinct genetic descent
may be studied under the same environment. Observations on the
mental behavior of the same individual are not easily made, because
time must elapse before mental habits change. For this reason the
behavior of identical twins — that is, of twins originated from a
single ovum — has received particular attention. Cases in which
identical twins are brought up under different conditions since the
time of birth are very rare, and since we do not know the length of
the period required for the establishment of habits, a considerable
amount of doubt is involved in the results of the few available
cases. On the whole, identical twins seem to show a higher degree of
similarity of behavior than dizygotic twins.[17] The difficulties of interpretation of these observations have been set forth by Lancelot
Hogben.[18]

Environmental determination of mental behavior is clearer in the study of larger groups than in the study of individuals, because sharper contrasts in social and cultural background are found in groups of similar descent than among individuals of the same group. The cultural changes among North American Indians due to the intrusion of modern civilization have brought about fundamental changes in behavior even among Indians of pure descent.

Quantitative studies based on various kinds of tests also show that a population of the same descent changes its reactions according to changes in its environment. Thus Otto Klineberg [19] has shown that Negro children transferred from rural districts to cities improve in the formal intelligence tests given to them in such a manner that those who have lived in the city longest approach other city children in their performance, while those newly arrived are decidedly inferior. Similar observations have been made in regard to Italian immigrants in North America.

If a decided difference existed between types like those inhabiting Europe and living under the same social conditions it ought to show when a socially homogeneous group is classified according to anthropological form. No such proof is available. On the contrary, Karl Pearson's [20] investigation of Europeans in regard to a possible correlation between bodily form and mental characteristics has given negative results.

As in the state of bodily form we recognized the existence of many distinct genetic lines in each population and the occurrence of similar lines in related populations, so we find the same degree of variability in physiological and mental functioning and the same kind of overlapping, but added to these dependence upon environmental conditions, both geographical and social, that obscures the biological determinants of behavior.

If in closely related populations it is impossible to speak of racial heredity, this is still more the case in regard to physiological and mental functions.

No proof has been given that the distribution of genetic elements that may determine personality is identical in different races. It is probable that limited differences of this kind exist, provided the differences between races are sufficiently fundamental. The differences which occur within each race are, however, equally important. The study of cultural forms in relation to the distribution of bodily types makes it more than probable that the racial differences, particularly in closely related forms, are irrelevant when compared with the powerful influence of the cultural environment in which the group lives. The behavior of the whole group conforms to its cultural standards to which each individual reacts in his own way.

The frequently made assumption that bodily build and mental behavior are closely related is based on the observation of the characteristic distribution of types and cultures, both of which occur in locally circumscribed areas, so that each region is characterized by a somewhat unique type and culture. In modern society similar conditions prevail among social classes. This locally determined correlation is taken without further proof as evidence of a causal relation although the two phenomena are subject to entirely distinct influences, the one to purely biological, the other perhaps to a slight extent to biological, but much more to cultural conditions. The inference that the correlation between bodily form and culture is due to the dependence of the latter upon the former would require the proof that, without regard to cultural environment and to location, the same type must always produce the same mental characteristics.

Eugenics. Experience gained in raising breeds of domesticated animals has shown that it is possible to produce stable varieties that fulfill certain requirements, like the production of an ample milk supply in cows or speed in horses. Theoretically it would be possible to breed also societies of men of definite qualities. While this ideal is held only by a few extremists, the thought that the quality of a population can be improved by encouraging the mating and fertility of healthy individuals and the gradual elimination of the unfit holds wide sway. The efficacy of such means is limited. The theory presupposes that certain stigmata are always hereditary and spring up independently either not at all or with extreme rarity. It lies in the nature of the case that families in which a hereditary disease exists can be found; while the negative evidence, that among the relatives of a person so affected no others affected are discovered, is not convincing. The assumption that such diseases do not spring up independently would lead to the absurd assumption that there must have existed one pathological and one normal race which intermingled, the ratio of the two depending upon the frequency of occurrence of the disease. A considerable number of hereditary diseases are assumed to be recessive according to the simplest Mendelian rules. If these did not originate spontaneously over and over again, we should have to assume such a large number of intermarrying pathological types that no healthy type could have existed among our progenitors.

It can also be shown by a simple statistical consideration that the effect of excluding the hereditarily affected individuals from propagation would reduce their relative number so slowly that many generations would pass before any effect could be felt. If conditions of life are of a low standard we may safely assume that the number of those eliminated would be filled largely by those spontaneously developing new deficiencies. The problem involved is the determination of the causes that lead to the spontaneous development of hereditary diseases. Are these dependent upon more or less favorable social conditions, or what other factors may be at work in forming pathological mutations? True eugenic measures relating to hereditary diseases can be taken only when these questions have been answered.

The question is quite different in those cases in which studies of heredity prove beyond cavil that a certain percentage of the offspring of a couple must be imbeciles or affected by incurable diseases which make them a burden to themselves, to their families, and to the community. What is to be done in those cases is a question of social ethics, not of anthropological inquiry. Anthropology can determine the effect of their presence upon the constitution and certain aspects of the functioning of society. It can be shown that individual suffering may be eliminated; but the general distribution of pathological forms in the population will not be greatly modified. The prevailing cultural ideals will decide what is to be done.

FOOTNOTES

1. More exact data illustrating such characteristics in a population will be found in Boas, F., "On the Variety of Lines of Descent Represented in a Population," *American Anthropologist*, vol. 18 (1916), pp. 1–9, and "Die Variabilität von Volksgruppen," *Anthropologischer Anzeiger*, vol. 7 (1931), pp. 204–208.
2. Fischer, E., *Rasse und Rassenentstehung beim Menschen* (Berlin, 1927), pp. 57 ff.
3. Klatt, B., "Mendelismus, Domestikation und Kraniologie," *Archiv für Anthropologie*, N.F., vol. 18 (1921), pp. 225–250.
4. Keith, Sir Arthur, *Ethnos* (London, 1931), p. 58; and "The Evolution of Human Races," *Journal of the Royal Anthropological Institute of Great Britain and Ireland*, vol. 58 (1928), pp. 310 ff.
5. Duckworth, W. L. H., *Morphology and Anthropology* (Cambridge, 1904), pp. 457 ff.

6. Dixon, R. B., *The Racial History of Man* (1923).
7. Haddon, A. C., *The Races of Man* (1925).
8. Deniker, J., *The Races of Man* (1900), pp. 285–286.
9. von Eickstedt, E., *Rassenkunde und Rassengeschichte der Menschheit* (Stuttgart, 1934).
10. Ripley, W. Z., *The Races of Europe* (1899).
11. Abel, Othenio, *Die Stellung des Menschen im Rahmen der Wirbeltiere* (Jena, 1931), pp. 371 ff.
12. Bryn, Halfdan, "Die Entwicklung der Menschenrassen," *Anthropos,* vol. 20 (1925), pp. 1053 ff.; vol. 21 (1926), pp. 435 ff.
13. Taylor, T. G., *Environment and Race* (London, 1927).
14. Fritsch, Gustav, "Geographie und Anthropologie als Bundesgenossen," *Verhandlungen der Gesellschaft für Erdkunde zu Berlin,* vol. 8 (1881), pp. 234 ff.
15. Stratz, C. H., *Naturgeschichte des Menschen* (Stuttgart, 1904), and "Das Problem der Rasseneinteilung der Menschheit," *Archiv für Anthropologie.* vol. 29 (1903–04), pp. 189 ff.
16. Klaatsch, H., *Weltall und Menschheit,* vol. 2 (Berlin-Leipzig, 1902–03).
17. Newman, H. H., Freeman, F. N., and Holzinger, K. J., *Twins, a Study of Heredity and Environment* (1937).
18. Hogben, L., *Nature and Nurture* (1933).
19. Klineberg, O., *Race Differences* (1934), pp. 186 ff.
20. Pearson, K., "On the Relationship of Intelligence to Size and Shape of Head, and to Other Physical and Mental Characters," *Biometrika,* vol. 5 (1906), pp. 105–146.

GENERAL REFERENCES

Baur, E., Fischer, E., and Lenz, F., *Menschliche Erblehre* (Munich, 1936); English translation, *Human Heredity* (1931).
Boas, F., *The Mind of Primitive Man* (1938).
Deniker, J., *The Races of Man* (1900).
von Eickstedt, E., *Rassenkunde* (Stuttgart, 1933).
Gates, R. R., *Heredity in Man* (London, 1929).
Hankins, F. H., *The Racial Basis of Civilization* (1926).
Hrdlička, A., *Anthropometry* (1920).
Jennings, H. S., *The Biological Basis of Human Nature* (1930).
Martin, R., *Lehrbuch der Anthropologie* (Jena, 1928).
Willey, A. W., *Convergence in Evolution* (London, 1911).

CHAPTER IV

LANGUAGE

Franz Boas

General characteristics of language. Language, in the widest sense of the term, embraces the means by which the sensory, emotional, and volitional experiences of an individual are expressed and conveyed to others. Body movements, touch, and sound, conveying visual, tactile, and auditory impressions, may be used for this purpose.

Communication between animals. Animals [1] convey their emotions by means of cries, touch, and visible movements, and in so far as these are related to experiences exciting fear, anger, or pleasure they are significant. The cry of the leader of a herd serves as a warning of approaching danger. The display of the plumage of the male bird affects the female. The touch of the antennae of an ant conveys a message upon which its comrade reacts. Some animals have a considerable number of distinct cries with which they react to different emotional states or by which they call their fellows. The grimaces of the monkey indicate the nature of its mental excitement.

In so far as a specific bodily reaction is related to similar sense experiences, it will excite in other animals of the same group, but not necessarily of the same species, the memory of similar situations, of an emotional rather than of a specific descriptive character. The range of experiences is very wide. The animal cry may convey the memory of danger and flight, of food and satiation of hunger, but nothing more definite. No case has been observed in which an animal represents a specific experience by visual, tactile, or auditory signs.

Certain movements of the body or changes in posture of animals are also indicative of situations that may be understood by other individuals. The direction of the gaze toward an object that excites interest, the rigid position of the body in close attention, the movements when a scent is taken, the erection of the hair in excitement, the wagging of the tail of dogs when in a pleasant mood, are certainly understood by other individuals who react to similar stimuli in the same manner. Movements of one individual solicit definite reactions in others. Here belong particularly the behavior of the male that intends to attract the attention of the female, such as the exhibition of the feathers in birds, and those movements that may be well described as dance; also the movements of animals, particularly of young ones, who invite others to play.

Man uses movements and sound in the same manner, but in addition to vague expressions there are others by means of which specific experiences are indicated. Both animal and man turn their heads in the direction of an object exciting their attention, but in addition to this, man has the free use of his hands, which point and follow the movement of the object. Emotional attitudes are accompanied by innervations corresponding to actions. When the stimulus is strong enough these follow, but when weak they lead only to expressive movements, such as a call, shrinking away from some object, or a hostile repulsion.

With the clearer differentiation of situations, these movements have multiplied and led to a gesture language [2] which in its primitive form presumably consisted solely of intensified innervations but which has developed everywhere in such a manner that it accompanies articulate speech. We cannot tell whether gesture language preceded speech or developed with it. In its simpler forms it consists of movements which correspond to the weak innervation accompanying thought and speech. For the development of both gesture language and speech it was necessary that man should have acquired the ability to express specific experiences. To make this possible the number of significant symbols must have increased enormously. The situations that present themselves in the course of life are so varied that differentiation never proceeded to such a degree that each experience was expressed by means of a single acoustic or visual symbol, except in cases in which the same situation, distinct from all others, presented itself with great frequency. In fact such differentiation would be impossible on account of the uniqueness of every experience. In gestures as well as in spoken language large numbers of situations are expressed by the same formal expression. In other words, a grouping together of similar experiences persisted, and these have found their representation in symbols. Thus *dog, water, running, sleeping,* expressed either by gestures or by sound, include each large numbers of varied experiences, all understood under a single vague symbol. Other aspects of the same experiences may be expressed in similar ways. By means of the combination of these symbols, the whole situation is described from various angles and is thus communicated.

It may be presumed that the possibility of calling attention to specific situations acted as a stimulus to further developments of communication by both gestures and sound. In many cases speed of communication must have been desired. Gesture presents the advantage that by pictorial movements a whole situation may be described at once, and it is still used when spoken language is not understood, as in the intercourse between individuals speaking different languages, or in the natural sign language of deaf mutes. It has the disadvantage that it must be seen and is therefore useless in darkness and in many other situations. Articulate sound has its precedents in the sounds uttered by animals. Its symbolic significance is not so apparent as that of imitative gesture, but must have developed from the significant signal. Articulate sound has proved so much more flexible than gesture that the latter is used only exceptionally as a means of communication, but occurs commonly accompanying speech.

Gestures and cries like those of animals still survive. They are immediate reactions to situations replete with emotion, like cries of pain, pleasure, anger, or fear. These lack the specific connotation of speech, even if the symbols themselves are derived from specific words. Here belong interjections like *ouch!* on the one hand, and *heavens!* on the other.

Categories of classification. The number of words — that is, of groups of sound symbols — used in any one language for various aspects of experiences cannot be unlimited. Recognition of a new situation implies that part of it is experienced as sufficiently similar to a previous sense impression, so that it merges with it. Many of the different forms in which water appears are combined in the same category and expressed by the same word. If a specific experience is to be communicated these wide categories must be specified and so limited that they apply to the particular situation. This is done by supplementing them by other categories. When I say, "The dog is barking," I do not add a new idea to the concept *dog*, but I express my single sense perception by denoting distinct aspects of my experience by means of a number of words sufficiently exhaustive to convey to the hearer its contents.

In other words, in language the experience to be communicated is classified from a number of distinct aspects, each expressed by certain groups of phonetic units or words. This implies that these units must be coördinated according to some system in order to express the way in which they are related. "The man killed the bull" and "The bull killed the man" exemplify the importance of the way in which the elements are put into relation.

These considerations show that every language must have a vocabulary, determined by the universe of experience, and the categories applied in its classification; and a grammar by means of which these elements are brought into relation. Language without both vocabulary and grammar is impossible. What is true of articulate language is equally true of gesture language. The single experience must be viewed from various points of view, and gestures expressing each aspect must be coördinated. Actually every spoken language has its vocabulary and its grammar, and every gesture language its signs and a rudimentary grammar in so far as the order of signs is significant. "The large dog bit me" would be expressed by signs as "Dog large bit me," or according to emphasis, "Me dog large bit."

Phonetics. Articulate language is produced by action of the lungs, larynx, tongue, palate, lips, and the posterior nares. By these, sounds of short duration are produced, some retaining a constant character during their production, others changing in character. Each is clearly set off against its neighbor. Thus it becomes possible to recognize each sound as a unit. Stable sounds are the vowels of many languages, or consonants like *t* or *s*. Unstable sounds are gliding, diphthongized vowels and consonants like *ts* or those with a gliding vocalic resonance. On account of the movability of the vocal cords and the organs of the oral cavity, particularly of the tongue, the number of sounds that can be produced is unlimited, although according to their acoustic qualities they may be combined in readily recognized groups, such as our vowels, and sounds similar to *t, k, s*, etc. Voluntary movements of the organs of articulation can be produced much more easily than those of any other part of the body. Complex combinations of positions producing various sounds can be produced with great rapidity. In slow speech a single sound requires hardly more than 0.07 of a second. Virtuosos may attain similar rapidity of movement by the successive use of fingers. The use of such rapidity of movement for conveying ideas is made possible by the sensitiveness of the ear, which can discriminate between sense impressions of shortest duration. Visual or tactile impressions could not be conveyed with equal rapidity because the momentary impressions would become blurred. Only with the development of reading has a means of communication been found that exceeds in rapidity the spoken word.

Selection of material used for expression. Articulate sounds, while physiologically unlimited in number, can be recognized only when the number of those habitually produced in speech is limited. Single sounds or assemblies of sounds seldom repeated would not impress themselves upon the memory. Furthermore, the rapidity of utterance is tied up with the automatic repetition of the same movements. Thus it becomes intelligible that each language employs a limited number of sounds, forming a system of phonemes. An unlimited number would make the language unpronounceable and unintelligible.[3]

The same may be said of words. An infinite number of words, one for each sense experience, would make language impossible, because the same experience is never repeated in an identical way. It has been pointed out that classification is unavoidable. The same dog in different positions or activities, or every individual dog as it appears at different times, is not designated, each by a specific word; rather, all kinds of dogs in all conditions and activities may be classed under one term.

While a limitation of sounds and of words is a necessity for the formation of speech, there is no reason to suppose that the principles of selection of sounds and of classification of experience will be the same in all languages. As a matter of fact we find the most diverse principles used. Some languages use musical pitch as a means of discrimination. Length of vowels and consonants may differentiate the significance of sound complexes, or they may be irrelevant. Some languages do not use the lips for the production of sounds (as we do in our *p, b, m*); others, like English, avoid the use of the soft palate. Sounds may be produced by the air streaming out from the lungs, or by air compressed in the mouth, or by air sucked into the mouth and rushing in through the opening lips or over an opening between tongue and roof of mouth.

Equally varied are the classifications under which sense experience is grouped. It has been pointed out that the cries of animals do not signify a specific situation. It might therefore be supposed that in the beginnings of human speech an ever-increasing restriction of the significance of various articulate utterances occurred until finally each group of articulations attained a specific meaning. If this was the case, we might expect to find undifferentiated expressions in primitive languages. This is true to a certain extent, for in languages in which the etymological processes are still transparent, many terms are formed by combining several elements of general significance which limit one another. Such generalized elements may be considered as early forms of linguistic expression. Still, it would be far from justifiable to claim that these languages represent an early state of human speech. Their present form is a result of a long historical growth no less than is the present form of our own language.

A few examples of generalized terms may be given. The Sioux (Dakota) Indian has no special terms for *to break, to tear, to cut up, to bite to pieces*, but he derives all these from a general term meaning "to be severed." [4] The Haida Indian uses a few verb stems of very general significance which are specialized by addition of other elements. The categories by means of which specialization is accomplished differ considerably. The Sioux uses elements expressing instrumentality. He says for our *to break*, "to sever by pressure"; for *to tear*, "to sever by pulling"; for *to cut up*, "to sever by cutting." In all of these the term "to sever" is very general. The Haida uses in addition to instrumentality elements limiting the form of the object acted upon. Instead of saying "He tears it," meaning a string, he has to say "By pulling a stringy object he severs it," thus limiting the general term "to tear" in two ways. It is important to note that these limiting terms are obligatory.[5]

The meaning of nouns which are not derived from verbs is likely to be much more specific than that of verbs, although stems occur which might almost be called empty of all specific significance. These attain their meaning only by the addition of specializing elements. It is as though we were to qualify the term "thing" by new elements: "a thing that is a so and so." Proper names and names of important objects may well have been specific in very early times.

We have reason to believe that these generalized concepts are not late developments from earlier, more specific meanings — a process of common occurrence in the history of language — but that we are dealing here with a fundamental characteristic of early language.

Generalized terms are not by any means the rule. On the contrary, large numbers of ancient elements are found that have very specific meanings. This is true of objects that are of cultural importance in many ways and for many purposes. In the life of the Eskimo *snow* means something entirely different as falling snow, soft snow on the ground, drifting snow or snowdrift.[6] Fresh water ice, salt water ice, an iceberg, play quite different rôles in their life and all these are designated by distinctive terms. As the horse-breeder has many terms for the horse, according to age, sex, coat color, and gait, so has the Chukchee a wide array of designations for the reindeer.[7] In many cases in which the specific functions of the object in the life of the people are quite distinct, a general term is missing.

In words expressing states or actions nice distinctions are often made in regard to form or consistency of the objects referred to. *To throw* may be expressed differently according to the form of the object thrown, as long, round, or flat, solid or fluid. We differentiate in this manner the verbs expressing existence at a place: a tree *stands*, a river *runs*, a log *lies*. In Dakota the word corresponding to *to break* is differentiated according to the hardness, softness, presence of grain, and other qualities of the material broken.

Thus it appears that, while undifferentiated expressions exist, which may be on the line of development from animal cries, the languages of our period contain also elements of highly specific character the scope of which is determined by the traditional principles of classification and by the pressure of culture.

The fundamentally different principles of classification employed by different languages may be illustrated by two examples, the numerals [8] and terms of relationship.[9]

According to our language, units are arranged in groups of ten. We may call ten the higher unit of first order. Hundred would be the higher unit of second order. We are not quite consistent in our nomenclature, for the third higher unit ought to be one hundred times one hundred, our ten thousand. Many languages group by fives — that is, by the number of fingers and toes on each hand and foot — and call twenty "one man." Eighteen would therefore be "three on the other foot," and seventy-two would be "three men (3×20) and two on the one foot (12)." The difficulty of translation appears still more clearly in high numbers. The number 5729 is for us five higher units of third order (5000) plus seven higher units of second order (700) plus two higher units of first order (20) plus nine. In the five-twenty (quinary-vigesimal) system it would be 14 × 400 (four-on-the-one-foot higher units of second order) plus 6 × 20 (one-on-the-other-hand higher units of first order) plus 9 (four-on-the-other-hand), or [(2 × 5 + 4) × 400] + [(5 + 1) × 20] + (5 + 4), or 14 × 400 = 5600, 6 × 20 = 120, 5 + 4 = 9; total 5729. The grouping of units is quite different from our own, and the expression of any higher number in one system requires a regrouping according to new principles that can be made only by arithmetical analysis.

Perhaps still more striking are the systems based on other higher units — for instance, four, so that the count would be: one, two, three, higher unit of first order, which we render by the symbol 10. The higher unit of second order, which we render by the symbol 100, would be four times four, our sixteen. If we were to write the numerals of such a language according to our system they would run 1, 2, 3, 10, 11, 12, 13, 20, 21, 22, 23, 30, 31, 32, 33, 100 and so on; and our 3 × 3 = 9 would be 3 × 3 = 21. Our arithmetic is based on a decadic system, theirs on a quaternary system.

Analogous observations may be made in regard to terms of relationship. We classify our nearest relatives according to generation, sex, and line of descent (as direct or collateral). Consequently we have the terms *father, mother, uncle, aunt; brother, sister, cousin; son, daughter, nephew, niece.* The term *cousin* does not quite follow the general rule, since in it sex is disregarded. The principles used in other languages may be quite different. The paternal and maternal line may be distinguished, and relative age in the same generation may be expressed. When these are added to our system we have four terms for *uncle* and *aunt.* Two of these determine paternal or maternal line (like Latin *patruus* and *avunculus*); and two express whether uncle or aunt is older or younger than father or mother. Our reciprocal terms *brother* and *sister* for siblings (that is, children of the same parents) of equal sex will be subdivided into double terms, *elder* and *younger* brother or sister. Conversely, when no distinction is made between direct and collateral lines of descent the terms for father and father's brother, mother and mother's sister, brother or sister and cousin, son or daughter and nephew or niece, will coincide. An attempt to find the correct term for each relative according to strange systems brings out clearly the fundamental differences of classification and the difficulties encountered in translating one into the other.

Sound symbolism. A special class of words are those expressing a
sense experience by imitation of the sounds associated with it.
Names of birds like *cuckoo* or *chickadee* in English imitate the calls
of the birds.[10] It is natural that the sound picture should not be
accurate. It depends to a great extent upon the sounds employed
by the language as well as upon other sound associations. Thus the
Navajo imitate the cry of the whippoorwill by *wăwŭ, wiu'w, wŭwŭ
wiu'w;* that of the chickadee by *chi'shi chishi běbě.* The Chinook
Indians render the cry of the blue jay by *k'esk'es,* the Tsimshian by
gus gus. In other cases the sound picture is immediately intelligible
to us, as *hehe,* "to laugh," *hoho,* "to cough," *humm,* "to smell" of
Chinook, an American Indian language spoken at the mouth of the
Columbia River. In this language as well as in many Bantu dialects
the formation of new words by sound imitation is a very live
process.

The relation between sound and concept is sometimes of a more
remote nature. Most of us will feel that a high pitch and exaggerate
length, perhaps also the vowel *i* (English *ee*), indicate smallness,
while low pitch and length and the vowels *a, o, u* (English *oo*) indicate large size. It is not by any means certain that the same impressions are conveyed in all languages, but similar phenomena are
not rare. Large or small size, or intensity, may be expressed by
variations of sound. Thus Nez Percé, an Indian language spoken in
Idaho, changes *n* to *l* to indicate smallness; Dakota has many words
in which *s* changes to *sh,* or *z* to *j,* indicating greater intensity. In
Chukchee, variations in meaning are brought about by a change
from *l* to *ch.* Undoubtedly the particular kind of synesthesia between sound, sight, and touch has played its rôle in the growth of
language.[11]

Grammar. It has been pointed out that grammar determines the
relationship between the various words expressing different aspects
of an experience; but grammar performs another important function. It determines those aspects of each experience that *must* be
expressed. When we say, "The man killed the bull," we understand
that a definite single man in the past killed a definite single bull.
We cannot express this experience in such a way that we remain in
doubt whether a definite or indefinite person or bull, one or more
persons or bulls, the present or past time, are meant. We have to
choose between these aspects, and one or the other must be chosen.
These obligatory aspects are expressed by means of **grammatical**

devices. The aspects chosen in different groups of languages vary fundamentally. To give an example: while for us definiteness, number, and time are obligatory aspects, we find in another language location near the speaker or somewhere else, source of information — whether seen, heard, or inferred — as obligatory aspects. Instead of saying "The man killed the bull," I should have to say, "This man (or men) kill (indefinite tense) as seen by me that bull (or bulls)." In some languages the aspects that *must* be expressed are very numerous, in others very few. When I say in English, "The sheep ate grass," the otherwise obligatory aspect of number is obscured, although the situation or the context may make clear whether one or more sheep are meant. This shows that paucity of obligatory aspects does not by any means imply obscurity of speech. When necessary, clarity can be obtained by adding explanatory words. Thus the vague "The sheep ate grass" can easily be specified by saying "My herd of sheep ate the grass on my neighbor's meadow."

While these obligatory categories vary in different languages, the relational functions of grammar have certain principles in common all over the world. Here belong, for instance, the relation between subject and predicate, noun and attribute, verb and adverb, and the relation of the experience to the speaker (the self) and to others — that is, the relations expressed by the pronouns *I*, *you*, and *he*. The methods by means of which these and other relations are expressed vary very much, but they are necessary elements of every grammar.

Grammatical processes. While the vocabulary consists of many independent units, grammar employs a small number of devices for handling these units: by varying their position, combining them, adding elements that have no independent existence, or by modifying their structure. In the phrase, "The men killed the rattlesnake," the functions of *men* and *rattlesnake* as subject and object are indicated by position; the addition of *-ed* to *kill* expresses past time; the change of *man* to *men* indicates plurality; and the composition of *rattle* and *snake* specifies the kind of snake referred to.

A few languages employ only position to indicate grammatical relations. Others make an extended use of composition, in which process the component elements may undergo considerable modifications; or they use subordinate elements (affixes) at the end (suffixes) or at the beginning (prefixes) or even in the middle (infixes) of words. The inner changes are varied. We have not only vocalic changes like the one mentioned before, or as in *see* and *saw, write* and *wrote,* but also consonantic changes, as *teeth* and *to teethe*. In other languages many kinds of changes occur: changes in pitch, extensions and contractions, duplication or reduplication — that is, partial duplication which extends over longer or shorter parts of the word and affects beginning, middle, or end of the word.

Owing to the close contact between the elements of a phrase that expresses the various aspects of an experience, purely mechanical modifications of the single elements may occur, such as in English the change from *in-possible* to *impossible*. In many languages such changes are much more important. They may be contact phenomena, like the one just referred to, or extend their influence forward or backward over the word. To this group belongs the vocalic harmony of languages like Ural-Altaic, Chukchee, and Nez Percé, which require a series of related vowels in the whole word or, at least, in part of the word.

History of languages. Languages are not stable. The sounds, meanings, and grammatical forms are changing. In times of cultural upheaval, particularly when due to intimate contact between peoples of different speech, linguistic changes may be very rapid. In times of cultural stability the changes may be slow. The claim frequently made that unwritten languages change rapidly cannot be maintained. The isolated Eskimo dialects of Greenland and of the Mackenzie River, notwithstanding their long separation, do not differ much. The Nahua of Mexico of the sixteenth century has undergone almost solely those changes that are due to changes in cultural life while the sounds have remained stable. Most of the Bantu dialects, notwithstanding their wide dispersion, have not undergone very fundamental changes. On the other hand, languages like the Indo-European, or in America the Siouan or Salishan languages, must have changed at times with great rapidity.

The change of sounds is to a great extent due to mechanical processes. Some of these, dependent upon the mutual influences of sounds and characteristic of language as spoken at a given time, have been mentioned before. Besides these there are historical changes. In the course of decades and centuries sounds are modified in varied ways. The modern dropping of the *r* in English dialects in words like *hard* or *bird*, and the local Spanish change from terminal *s* to *h*, are examples.

Some of these changes occur in many languages independently, such as the change from *k* to *s* or *ch* (pronounced as in English) which occurs particularly before the vowels *e* and *i* (continental pronunciation) in Indo-European, in the African Bantu and in the American Dakota, Salish, and Nootka. By contrast to this movement forward or palatalization of *k*, a movement backward or gutteralization of vowels anticipating later gutteral consonants may be observed in Eskimo (according to Thalbitzer).[12]

Vowels as well as consonants undergo such changes.[13] It may be observed that words and grammatical forms tend to be worn down and that unaccented syllables are liable to suffer rapid decay. The soundshifts that develop in course of time are often so far-reaching that only an intimate knowledge makes it possible to recognize the ancient forms from which words in related languages have sprung.

Meanings are even more unstable than sounds. Every change in details of culture gives to old words a new significance, and in closely related languages the course of development may be quite distinct. English *knight* and German *Knecht* (entailed servant), English *knave* and German *Knabe* (boy), may serve as examples. In similar manner the meanings of words change in the historical development of every language by extension or restriction of meaning, by analogy and metaphor.

Grammatical forms are no more stable than sounds and meanings of words. The forms suffer phonetic decay; they are shifted by analogy to word classes to which they do not belong by origin; old forms are lost or new ones may sometimes be added.

Linguistic families. This gradual differentiation of speech enables us to trace the early affiliations of modern languages. If the actual historical development of the Romance languages were unknown, it would be at once apparent that all must have sprung from the same root. Vocabulary and grammatical forms are so much alike that the common origin of all the languages of this group could not be doubted. More thorough comparison and a knowledge of the gradual shifting of sounds, meanings, and grammatical forms have proved in an analogous way that most of the languages of Europe and some of those of western and southern Asia are related and must have had an early historical connection. While it is impossible to reconstruct the ancestral language from which they have sprung, many of the original word forms can be reconstructed with a high degree of probability. For this reason the study of languages is a most important means of reconstructing the early history of mankind so far as it is reflected in language. Obviously the conditions under which bodily types on the one hand and languages on the other change are quite distinct. For this reason we may not expect to discover a history of *races* by a study of the history of *languages*. In many cases the study of languages gives us information in regard to early events in the history of man, much more precise than the study of bodily form; for it is difficult to give exact criteria of bodily form applicable to all individuals constituting a population, while distinct languages are sharply set off from one another. The numerous stems and grammatical forms are independent units and the common occurrence of any considerable number of these in distinct languages is incontestable proof of historical relation. Thus the proof that a language of Madagascar is related to Malay is sufficient proof of its historical connection with southeastern Asia; the occurrence of Athapascan speech in Alaska and in the Rio Grande basin proves that there must have been historical relations between these two districts.

The problem of a genetic relationship between languages can be solved up to certain limits. When the similarities between languages are remote, difficulties present themselves that are not easily overcome.

Mixed languages. It is well known that languages are apt to borrow words from one another.[14] Modern English contains many foreign loan words: *canoe, tobacco, chocolate* are words belonging by origin to American Indian languages; *alcohol, algebra* are Arabic; *boomerang* is Australian; *taboo*, Polynesian. The kinds of words that are borrowed do not always belong to the same categories. European languages borrow principally nouns and verbs; seldom numerals, prepositions, and conjunctions. Modern Kwakiutl has borrowed a Nootka numeral (both languages spoken on Vancouver Island). Modern Nahua (Mexican) has taken over, besides nouns and verbs, Spanish conjunctions and prepositions. This is due to the breakdown of the old syntax of the language and adaptation to Spanish syntax.

Languages with clear etymology, and capable of forming new compounds with ease, are not apt to borrow words, because they readily form descriptive words. In Kwakiutl a steamer is called "moving on the water with fire on its back"; the telegraph, "talk along a line"; the radio, "talk through the air." Still, some words like *tea, coffee, priest* (*laplête* from Chinook jargon for *le prêtre*) have been adopted. Some loan words will probably be found in all languages when close cultural contact between neighbors of distinct speech occurs.

Often these loan words undergo changes according to the phonetic character of the language adopting them. Thus the language of the Tlingit of Alaska contains some loan words taken from their inland neighbors. Since Tlingit has no labials (*b, p, m*), every *m* changes to *w*. Tillamook, a language of Oregon, has borrowed words beginning with *p* from the neighboring Chinook, but since it has no *p* it changes the sound according to its own phonetic rules to *h*. Other changes are due to assimilation to known words, as North German popular *reinefieren* for the literary *renovieren*.

What is true of words is also true of sounds. It is perhaps not easy to show by convincing historical examples that close contact between two languages, or superposition of one language over another, has led to considerable changes of phonetic systems. In modern Nahua the sound *r* has been introduced although foreign to the ancient form of speech. It occurs not only in loan words that are not subject to inflectional modification but also as part of stems in verb forms, like *hablar*, which are treated as though they were ancient Nahua stems. In many native American languages the effect of English schooling upon pronunciation may be observed, particularly in so far as the harsh, glottalized sounds lose in strength. Often the melody of the phrase is also modified.

Furthermore the wide spread of phonetic phenomena which are characteristic of continuous areas in which languages of very distinctive structures are spoken can hardly be explained except as the result of mutual phonetic influences. As examples may be given the superabundance of velar sounds, produced by contact between the back of the tongue and the soft palate, in arctic and northwestern America and their absence in eastern America; the wide area over which harsh, glottalized sounds are extended, the occurrence of mixed vowels in the Southwest and in California; the combined (affricative) sounds *tl, dl* and the voiceless *l* in the West; the clicks of South African Bantu languages which must be due to Bushman influence. The last of these are most convincing because true clicks do not occur in any other part of the world. They are produced by a strong sucking motion. Weaker sounds produced by drawing in breath occur in other parts of Africa and locally in one of the languages of California.

If it is difficult to show historically the influence of the sound system of one language upon another, it is still more difficult to prove convincingly that extended morphological borrowing has taken place. Influences of the syntax of one language upon another are easily proved. The change of Nahua syntax under Spanish influence has been mentioned. Latin syntax has had its effect upon English. Borrowing of affixes that conform with existing categories is also common. Thus in European languages the Latin *ex-* has gained admission as *ex-king;* and *-ieren* is used in German not only to transfer foreign verbs into German (*regieren, blamieren*) but occasionally also with German words (*stolzieren, hofieren*). It is more interesting to note that Chinook, which has no nominal cases, has borrowed case (or locative) endings where it is in contact with Sahaptin, a language which uses case suffixes. In Kwakiutl, among part of the young generation who go to English schools, the category of the definite article has been introduced, being expressed by an ancient device. The category itself is quite alien to the older Kwakiutl speech.

The strongest reason for assuming the occurrence of far-reaching morphological borrowing is found in the peculiar distribution of analogous categories or processes in languages of distinctive morphological types. These occur often in continuous territory, while outside of it the same categories or processes are not found; what is still more important, each trait has its own characteristic distribution distinct from that of other traits.

As an example might be mentioned the distribution of the process of reduplication, which is absent in the extreme northern part of America and among the Iroquois, but common in a large area farther south.* More striking is the occurrence of consonantic changes to indicate the diminutive, which is characteristic of an area extending from northern California over Oregon, Washington, and Idaho; the use of sex gender in a number of quite distinct languages around Columbia River; the expression of the idea of instrumentality (action done with the hand, with a knife, etc.) on the Plateaus, in California, and on part of the Plains; the obligatory distinction of position by demonstrative pronominal elements on the coast of British Columbia; the similarity of verbal modes in Eskimo and Chukchee; the grammatical distinction between proper names and common nouns in Kwakiutl and in the neighboring Tsimshian.[15]

Independent origin of similar grammatical processes. It must also

---

* The Algonquians of Labrador are an exception, but it is doubtful whether the home of the Algonquian languages is in the north or farther south.

be remembered that a linguistic trait found in distinct languages is not always due to historical transmission but may develop independently. Sex gender occurs in Indo-European languages and on the Pacific coast of America; a dual in ancient European languages and in many isolated spots all over the world; instead of our plural *we*, we find the more logical distinction between "I and you" and "I and he" in disconnected languages. Numeral systems based on five are common; reduplication is often used for expressing plurality or repetition. In many of these cases historical connection is quite inconceivable. The phenomenon is analogous to parallel developments in groups of animals or plants that are genetically unrelated.

It follows from all this that for many distantly related languages the history of which is unknown, a categorical answer in regard to their genetic relationship cannot be given. In many cases historical relation must be assumed, but whether we are dealing with mixture of languages or with divergent branches of an ancient stock will remain doubtful.

Distribution of languages. At present we find a number of closely related languages occupying extended areas.[16] Examples are the Indo-European or Aryan in Europe and Asia; Turkish languages and Chinese in Asia; Malay and related languages from Madagascar in the west across the Indian and Pacific Oceans to Hawaii and Easter Island in the east; Bantu in a large part of Africa; Algonquian in eastern North America and extending westward to the Mississippi River and beyond; Carib and Arawak in a large part of eastern South America. In contrast to these widely distributed groups of languages we find others, apparently unrelated, which are restricted to small areas, so that in a narrowly limited district many languages are found. Examples of such areas are California and the North Pacific coast as far as Alaska, the region around the Gulf of Mexico, including Central America; the foothills of the South American Andes; northeastern Asia extending from Japan northward over Siberia; the western Sudan.

In many cases it is possible to show that groups of languages which occupy vast territories have only recently been spread so widely. Parts of Europe were inhabited by people of non-Aryan speech, and the Mediterranean area particularly was non-Aryan until a comparatively late period. There is good evidence to show that the Bantu spread over South Africa at a recent time. Turkish-speaking people established themselves in Asia Minor, southeastern

Europe, and Siberia in historic times; Arabic was carried into Egypt and along the coast of North Africa after the time of Mahomet. Chinese has gradually extended its domain over a large area. The Malay-Polynesian migrations belong to recent times. In historic and presumably also in prehistoric times languages have disappeared in large numbers, but we do not know of a single example of the origin of an entirely new language with new vocabulary, new grammatical forms, and new categories. It seems plausible that in very early times the number of languages for which a genetic relationship cannot be established must have been much greater than it is now, and the areas of great linguistic differentiation, like the Sudan or the Pacific coast of America, presumably represent conditions such as existed in early times all over the world.

The great differentiation here referred to must be understood to refer to languages for which the proof of a genetic relationship cannot be given. It does not touch upon the question of a single or multiple origin of groups of these languages. The occurrence of parallel developments in languages without historic relation makes it very improbable that *all* languages should have had a single origin.

When we compare this picture with the diversity of human types it will be noticed that the number of early languages must have been much larger than the number of clearly distinct anatomical types. Some of these have also disappeared, but on the whole we find uniform types spread over areas much larger than those covered by languages. It follows from this that in an early period distinct languages must have been spoken by people of the same type, so that there must have been racial types which possessed or produced more than one of the early languages which in their present form can be proved to be derived from the same source. An identity of race and language may not be supposed even for the isolated bands that lived before intimate contact and the accompanying diffusion of languages occurred. It is probably true that in the earliest times possessors or originators of a language all belonged to the same racial type, but it is equally true that the possessors or originators of a number of different languages must have belonged to the same racial type.

Thus it appears that language has behaved in the same way as all other cultural traits, for in early times, when mankind had spread all over the world, we find a great differentiation of culture according to locality. The history of culture has resulted in an increased leveling down of local differences in so far as certain cultures became dominant over larger areas and as mutual influences increased in number and intensity.

Culture and speech. Much has been said in regard to the relation between speech and culture. It is true that in many languages it would be difficult to express the generalized statements of philosophic science, because the categories imposed by the structure of the grammar are too specific. It is not true that primitive languages are unable to form generalized concepts. We have given before (page 130) illustrations of wide generalizations which are used, although not necessarily conceived with any degree of clarity. There may be no term for *tree*, but there may be one signifying "the long thing standing." There may be no general term for *seal*, but one for "things that come up to breathe." On the whole the degree of specialization will depend upon cultural interests. Categories that are culturally unessential will not be found; those culturally important will be detailed. For us, paternal or maternal descent is culturally comparatively irrelevant, whereas generation is important. This is reflected in our terminology of relationship. In cultures in which the distinction between paternal and maternal lines is socially important, there will normally be a distinct terminology for them. When generation is irrelevant, this also may be disregarded in the terminology of relationship. In regard to all these matters language is exceedingly plastic and follows the demands of culture. Proof of this is found not only in our own language, but also in the modifications that so-called primitive languages undergo when the people become familiar with modern civilization and begin to participate in it. The vocabulary develops in conformity with the expanding or changing activities.

It is not only the vocabulary that is so influenced. In primitive culture people speak only about actual experiences. They do not discuss what is virtue, good, evil, beauty; the demands of their daily life, like those of our uneducated classes, do not extend beyond the virtues shown on definite occasions by definite people, good or evil deeds of their fellow tribesmen, and the beauty of a man, a woman, or of an object. They do not talk about abstract ideas. The question is rather whether their language makes impossible the expression of abstract ideas. It is instructive to see that missionaries, who in their eagerness to convert natives have been compelled to learn their languages, have had to do violence to the idioms in order to convey to the natives their more or less abstract ideas, and that they have always found it possible to do so and to be understood. Devices to develop generalized ideas are probably always present and they are used as soon as the cultural needs compel the natives to form them.

It is not unimportant to recognize that in primitive languages, here and there, our adjectival ideas are expressed by nouns. A poor person may be conceived rather as a person who has poverty; a sick person as a person who has sickness; and it is not necessary that these qualities should be conceived as concrete objects.[17] Sickness is often so conceived, but poverty or size is not. We find also cases in which the structure of the sentence demands the frequent use of abstract nouns, as when the Kwakiutl Indian of Vancouver Island says to a girl, "Take care of your womanhood"; when the Eskimo speaks of smallness or largeness of an object; or when the Dakota Indian speaks of strength and goodness.

In this sense it is not justifiable to consider languages as hindering or favoring cultural development. We should rather say that language is a reflection of the state of culture and follows in its development the demands of culture. In another way, however, language exerts an influence upon culture. Words and phrases are symbols of cultural attitudes and have the same kind of emotional appeal that is characteristic of other symbols. The name of a rite, of a deity, an honorific title, a term giving a succinct expression to political or church organization, may have the power to raise the passions of a people without much reference to the changing contents of the term. To us the words *liberty* and *democracy* have such an appeal, although the concept of liberty or of democracy may undergo such changes that they are no longer recognizable. The power of such phrases and symbols to excite masses to action or to stabilize existing institutions must not be underestimated. The cry of the Crusaders, "God wills it"; the halo surrounding the terms *Emperor, King,* and *Queen;* the inspiration given by national anthems, by the empty phrases of orators, are forces that mould culture. It would, however, be an error to assume that this is a purely linguistic phenomenon. It is rather an instance of symbolism and should be considered in that connection.

While the details of linguistic structure are a field somewhat remote from other aspects of culture, their value for historical reconstruction is clear. We have seen how early migrations may be traced by linguistic evidence. Other cultural facts are reflected in language. Loan words may indicate particular types of cultural relations, as when a particular style of weaving or an implement is called by a foreign word. In European languages such etymological relations demonstrate events in cultural history. This is exemplified by the influence of Greek upon Latin, of Latin upon the modern European languages, and by the addition of a multitude of foreign words taken over by all European languages. More interesting are those linguistic reflections of cultural phenomena which express present or past conditions. We have referred before to the classification of terms of relationship. These represent aspects of behavior of members of a family to one another, though not necessarily those prevailing at the present time. They are indispensable for our understanding of social organization. Their definition gives us an insight into the present or past structure of the family. Lack of consistency in the system may indicate historical changes or present conflicts of attitudes. Similarly the clear definition of other terms may reveal cultural data. The terms generally translated as "soul" vary considerably in content, and an accurate definition of their scope is indispensable for the understanding of religious concepts. The same is true for the concept of the supernatural. The meaning of words like *manitoo, wakanda, mana,* and *taboo,* which are used in a generalized sense by investigators of religion, have their own peculiar connotations in each culture, and the attitudes of the individual tribes cannot be understood without a painstaking analysis of the ideas represented by the words used for expressing the varying aspects of the supernatural. A crude translation of native terms into approximately corresponding terms of English or of any other language and psychological interpretations built thereon are often the causes of serious misunderstandings.[18]

Linguistic usages, like metaphorical expressions or allusions in phrases, are also illuminating. When the natural functions of the body are expressed euphemistically by suggestive terms (like "to go out" instead of *to defecate;* "to be near" instead of *to cohabit*), light is thrown upon the attitude of the people to these functions. Likewise the euphemistic substitution of "to become weak" or "to go to the end," instead of *to die;* "to lie down" instead of *to be sick,* is suggestive of attitudes and beliefs.

Allusions, as long as alive, are indicative of subjects that are generally present in the minds of the people; if formalized they show that in the past at least the ideas referred to were important to the people, as when we refer to the devil and witches. For example, Indians of the Northwest have an expression "Is this war, father?" which is a quotation from a tale and means that the person who quotes it is in great distress. Or the Dakota will say, "Did you not know that he had a striped palate?" referring to the mythical trickster who is said to have a palate of that kind. The saying means that the person referred to was known as a cheat. These allusions are most frequent in proverbs such as occur in great profusion in Africa.

It is obvious that for the understanding of the form of native literature, if we may use this term for their unwritten poetry and tales, a thorough knowledge of the language is indispensable, for, without it the elements that appeal to the esthetic sense of the hearer cannot be appreciated.

FOOTNOTES

1. Alverdes, F., *Social Life in the Animal World* (1927).
2. Mallery, G., *Sign Language among North American Indians*, Annual Report of the Bureau of Ethnology, vol. 1 (1881), pp. 263 ff.; Tylor, E. B., *Researches into the Early History of Mankind* (London, 1878), pp. 14 ff.; Wundt, W., *Völkerpsychologie. Die Sprache* (Leipzig, 1900).
3. Bloomfield, L., *Language* (1933), pp. 74 ff.
4. Boas, F., *Handbook of American Indian Languages*, Bulletin of the Bureau of American Ethnology, no. 40, Part I (1911), p. 26.
5. Swanton, J. R., in Boas, F., *op. cit.*, pp. 205 ff.
6. Boas, F., *op. cit.*, p. 25.
7. Bogoras, W., *The Chukchee*, The Jesup North Pacific Expedition, vol. 7 (1904–09), p. 74.
8. Bloomfield, L., *op. cit.*, p. 279; Conant, L. L., *Primitive Number Systems*, Annual Report of the Smithsonian Institution, 1892 (1893), pp. 583 ff.
9. Bloomfield, L., *op. cit.*, p. 278.
10. *Ibid.*, p. 156.
11. Jespersen, O., *Language* (1925), pp. 396 ff.; Hilmer, H., *Schallnachahmung, Wortschöpfung und Bedeutungswandel* (Halle, 1914).
12. Thalbitzer, W., in Boas, F., *op. cit.*, Part I, p. 998.
13. Sturtevant, E. H., *Linguistic Change* (1917).
14. Bloomfield, L., *op. cit.*, pp. 444 ff.
15. Boas, F., *op. cit.*, Part I (1911); Part II (1922).
16. Meillet, A., and Cohen, M., *Les langues du monde* (Paris, 1924); Finck, F. N., *Die Sprachstämme des Erdkreises* (Leipzig, 1909).
17. Boas, F., *op. cit.*, Part I, p. 657.
18. An interesting attempt at a careful analysis of the actual meaning of words is the *Ethnological Dictionary of the Navaho Language* (The Franciscan Fathers, St. Michaels, Arizona, 1910).

GENERAL REFERENCES

Bloomfield, L., *Language* (1933).

Jespersen, O., *Language, its Nature, Development, and Origin* (1923).

Meillet, A., and Cohen, M., *Les langues du monde* (Paris, 1924).

Sapir, E., *Language* (1925).

Sturtevant, E. H., *Linguistic Change* (1917).

Vendryes, J., *Language* (1925).

CHAPTER V

PREHISTORIC ARCHAEOLOGY

N. C. NELSON

Definition. Archaeology may be defined as the science devoted to the study of the entire body of tangible relics pertaining to the origin, the antiquity, and the development of man and of his culture. The remains of man himself have to be studied by the biologist. Archaeology in a narrower sense is concerned with the study of the remains of human handicraft. In the study of the origin of man it is often necessary to go back to the conditions of prehuman times, since no definite period can be fixed when man evolved from more primitive forms. Furthermore, it is customary to take the beginnings of written history — loosely synonymous with the beginnings of writing — as a dividing line and to call the investigation of the cultural record antedating this unique invention *prehistoric archaeology* and the remaining late portion *historic archaeology*. This separation also is indefinite because the beginnings of writing date back in Egypt and Mesopotamia about five thousand years, while in other parts of the world, like New Guinea and the Amazon basin, the beginning has not yet been made. The study of some of the advanced cultures of people who either had not developed the art of writing or whose records have not been deciphered, like those of Central America and Peru, also form a rather special field of prehistoric inquiry. In general, prehistoric archaeology lacks the helps supplied by history and must be based solely on the interpretation of the material objects discovered. These vary somewhat from place to place but for convenience may be listed under three general headings, with the items arranged in the approximate order of their appearance in time, as follows:

I. Monumental or fixed antiquities, usually found on the surface of the ground.

    1. Refuse heaps, in caves by the seashore, near ruins, etc.

    2. Caches and storage pits for food, treasure, offerings, etc.

    3. Hearths, firepits, temporary camp sites

4. House and village sites, tent rings, ruins, pile dwellings, etc.
5. Trails, portages, and causeways connecting the settlements, etc.
6. Workshops, smelters, foundries, etc.
7. Graves and cemeteries
8. Garden and field plots
9. Excavations, such as pitfalls for game, reservoirs, irrigation systems, quarries, mines, burial chambers, subterranean dwellings, artificial dwellings cut into loess, pumice, and limestone
10. Earthworks, including dams, ball courts, inclosures for fields and for cattle, fortification walls, mounds, and pyramids
11. Megalithic and other stone structures in the form of menhirs or monoliths, cromlechs or stone circles, alignments, cairns, dolmens and trilithons, stone chambered mounds or barrows, cist graves, pyramids, shrines, temples, fortification walls, nurhags or forts, treasure chambers, inclosures for fields and for cattle, fish weirs, boulder effigies and gravestones
12. Petroglyphs and paintings on cave walls and exposed rock surfaces

II. Movable antiquities, ordinarily obtained only by excavation in either artificial refuse or natural earth deposits

1. Chipped stone work: tools, weapons, ornamental and ceremonial objects
2. Wood work: tools, weapons, boats and other means of transportation, ornamental and ceremonial objects
3. Bone work: tools, weapons, utensils, ornamental and ceremonial objects
4. Shell work: tools, weapons, utensils, ornamental and ceremonial objects
5. Skin, hair, and feather work: clothing, shelters, utensils, boats, and ornamental accessories
6. Wood fiber work: mats, baskets, boats, nets, clothing, hats, sandals, and ornamental accessories
7. Clay work: utilitarian, artistic, and ceremonial pottery, etc.
8. Ground stone work: tools, weapons, utensils, ornamental and ceremonial objects
9. Metal work: tools, weapons, utensils, ornamental and ceremonial objects

III. From these data may be obtained information on many aspects of cultural life, in particular in regard to the following implied prehistoric arts and sciences:

1. All basic handicrafts
2. Hunting and warfare
3. Fishing by many different methods

4. Travel and exploration by land and by sea
5. Barter and trade — indicated by the spread of raw materials and finished articles beyond their localities of origin
6. Medical skill and knowledge — indicated by surgical operations and appliances and by the surviving use of herbal and other extracts as well as by psychological or magical treatment
7. Artificial preservation of raw materials —indicated by drying, smoking, or curing of meats and vegetables, tanning of hides, etc.
8. Artificial food production — indicated by agriculture and animal husbandry
9. Artificial production of raw materials — indicated by quarrying, mining, smelting, etc.
10. Constructive ideas — indicated by architectural remains of houses and bridges, by boats, sledges, game traps, etc.
11. Esthetic ideas — indicated by pictorial and decorative art
12. Religious ideas — indicated by ceremonial burials, shrines, temples, etc.

Problems of prehistoric archaeology. The chief problems of prehistoric archaeology are the *recovery* of as much of this material as necessary and its *interpretation.* This must be based on the study of the material, form, and function of the objects found, and their occurrence in place and time. Not every archaeological object reveals its specific purpose; and if, besides, nothing like it remains in use among primitive peoples, the function may remain unknown.

The end and aim of prehistoric archaeology is to extend our knowledge of human history, to put us in possession of all the procurable facts relating to man's early physical and mental development. It assists the paleontologist in determining man's antiquity and his biological origin and evolution, as well as his geographic distribution. Similarly our science is called upon to demonstrate the time and place of origin of all the principal inventions and to trace their spread over the world. Once we are in possession of the essential facts on both these lines of inquiry, it becomes possible to visualize the trend of the past and in the light of that past to understand the present and possibly to predict and in a measure to control intelligently the future of human development.

Methods. The technique employed by any branch of science is naturally governed by the nature of the subject itself. In general terms the methods of archaeology are those of direct *observation* and *comparison.* More specifically, the question of time order being all-important in archaeology as in paleontology, the principle upon which great stress needs to be laid is that of stratigraphy. This means simply the careful recording of the relative depths of the relics being excavated in an undisturbed deposit of some thickness, whether of natural origin or man-made. When actual superposition is lacking, time sequence may often be worked out by means of the geologic situation, or by the accompanying floral and faunal remains. When all else fails, it is still possible to determine the relative ages, say, of a given group of habitation sites within the same culture area by the process of "seriation," using one or more of the typical but gradually changing artifact series. This has been successfully done with pottery, for example, in the Pueblo region of southwestern United States [1] and with flint axes by North European archaeologists.[2]

Achieved results. Systematic investigations have until recent decades been confined largely to Europe and North America and there are still a number of essentially unexplored areas on each continent. Most likely these neglected regions will yield little that is either entirely new or of special importance, and we may therefore with some assurance accept the known facts and their interpretations as furnishing an approximately correct outline of all the outstanding prehistoric accomplishments as far as these have been preserved for us in tangible form.

Briefly stated, the present achievements of prehistoric archaeology are as follows. Positive indications of human activities have been traced back through the Quaternary geological period and probably some distance beyond into Tertiary time. The artifacts recovered have been studied as to raw material, character of workmanship, and types of implements, as well as to stratigraphic occurrence, and have as a result been separated into a chronological succession of stages and substages. Thus we speak of the *Stone Age*, the *Bronze Age*, and the *Iron Age* as indicative of the basic raw materials employed from time to time. The Stone Age in turn is divided into early and late phases, termed *Paleolithic* and *Neolithic*, which mark primary differences in materials employed and consequent primary differences in methods of treatment, percussion flaking and pressure chipping being characteristic of the former, while the latter adds pecking, grinding, and polishing. The Paleolithic is further subdivided into early, middle, and late phases, each marking a fairly definite stage in the evolution of the flint-working technique. Finally, these several Paleolithic stages are again sub-divided on the basis of secondary characteristics of form and finish which as a rule are more or less localized variations — sometimes contemporary — and which are generally named after the localities in which they were first discovered. These refined subdivisions will not be treated here; but for the sake of completeness the currently accepted chronological classification, as applying to Europe, is pre-sented in full as follows:

I. Stone Age
  1. Eolithic period (?)
  2. Paleolithic period
    a. Pre-Chellean epoch ⎫
    b. Chellean epoch   ⎬ Early
    c. Acheulian epoch ⎭
    d. Levalloisian-Clactonian-Mesvinian epoch ⎫ Middle
    e. Mousterian epoch ⎭
    f. Aurignacian epoch ⎫
    g. Solutrean epoch   ⎪
    h. Magdalenian epoch ⎬ Late
    i. Azilian-Tardenoisian-Maglemosian epoch ⎭
  3. Neolithic period
    a. Campignian-Asturian-Shell Heap epoch
    b. Robenhausian or full Neolithic epoch

II. Bronze Age (preceded here and there by a copper stage), with local subdivisions

III. Iron Age, with local subdivisions

Technological evolution of material culture traits. The concrete as-pects of culture are largely the product of man's reactions to his material surroundings. The history of material culture is therefore essentially a history of inventions and discoveries, or an account of man's progressive ability to manipulate and utilize the raw materials and forces supplied by nature. Leaving out of account for the pres-ent such useful forms of energy as wind and water, and concentrating our attention on fire and on the more immediately important raw materials, these latter — aside from the great variety of animal, vegetable, and mineral products which man shares with the rest of the mammals for food — are classifiable under no more than seven or eight general headings. These are (1) stone, shell, pearl, coral, amber, colored earths or oxides, and to a limited extent mica, lignite, petroleum, bitumen, and asbestos; (2) wood, bark, wood fiber, plant seeds, and derived dyes or extracts; (3) bone, teeth, ivory, antler, horn, turtle and tortoise shell; (4) hides, hair, feathers, guts, sinew, and derived glues and fats; (5) various clays and kaolins subject to firing; (6) free metals, such as copper, gold, silver, and meteoric iron; (7) metals derived by the artificial reduction of ore; and (8) such other heat-converted products as glaze, faïence, and glass.

Prehistoric man utilized every one of these groups of resources, beginning with the simpler forms, partly ready for his hand in their raw state (as, for instance, sticks and stones) and ending with those which, like clays and ores, required the energy of fire to convert them into useful products. This being the case, the details of the unfolding history of material culture must necessarily be written largely in terms not of the raw materials themselves, but rather of the methods employed in working them and of the forms and functions of the contrivances produced. For ceramic and metallic products the material itself permits a sure clue as to their approximate places in the inventive process. For materials found in nature the methods of working them and the specialized shapes of genetically related implements are far more useful guides. As a rule swift and clumsy working processes with crude results come first, while slow and refined processes with specialized and more highly adapted results come late. It must be remembered that not all of the objects made in prehistoric times have been preserved, though in many cases their existence may be safely inferred, if not indirectly demonstrated. Thus perishable items of wood and skin more often than not are missing in archaeological deposits. Sometimes even bone objects have completely decayed. Nevertheless, the general character of the remaining stone implements may indicate that wood and bone were worked and used. In the same way pottery, which like stone is relatively indestructible, is often modeled or decorated to represent other contemporary features of culture; or the fire-hardened clay may contain accidental impressions of basketry, textiles, and even seeds of wild as well as cultivated plants. In short, artifacts are not discrete or isolated objects that may come from any time or place, but are rather parts of more or less necessary combinations or complexes, taking consequently definite places in the general scheme of cultural history.

The relics through which the archaeologist may work out his

tangible results are, in ascending order of importance: objects of stone and shell, ceramic objects, objects of bone, wood, and metal. Of these basic materials stone is one of the most ancient in service and, up to the introduction of metal, the one almost always present in archaeological sites. In spite of its apparent refractory nature, it is capable of being worked in a variety of ways, and its products therefore lend themselves readily to technological and typological studies that are as a rule capable of chronological interpretation. The same is true also of pottery, once it arrives on the scene. As a plastic medium clay lends itself to being modeled into any shape that circumstances require or fancy may suggest; and its additional possibilities for accessory ornamentation are similarly almost limitless. These attributes of plasticity or workability, inherent in clay and ordinary stone, therefore enable their resulting artificial products to serve as fairly authentic guides. They present genetically related series constituting gradually modified or specialized form groups such as are required, in the absence of stratigraphy, for determining the time order of most of the other associated fragmentary traits. Ceramic products are of comparatively recent origin and partly in consequence of this have achieved only limited geographic distribution. By contrast, the use of stone for implements is very ancient; and as the raw material is also present in some form or other almost everywhere, its products have hitherto naturally served as guide forms and as the chief source of archaeological classification and nomenclature. In order to clarify this terminology and also to supply a key to the origin and nature of stone implements, as well as to afford a partial insight into the normal progress of invention in general, we shall next review the available observations on the gradually improving methods and results of the stoneworking technique.

Stone-flaking process. Assuming that man at first appropriated any convenient stick or stone to aid him in digging roots or killing game, and that by degrees he learned to select special forms for special purposes, the time came when he somehow hit upon the art of improving or adapting the natural forms by artificial means, and finally produced suitable forms *de novo.* In the case of stone implements, by trial and error he discovered that any boulder of convenient size was suitable equally for hurling at game or for pounding and crushing; that sharp-edged flakes served best for cutting and scraping, as did sharp-pointed ones for stabbing and digging. When suitable flakes were not available he learned ultimately to produce them by the process of shattering a flint nodule, either by hurling it against another rock or by striking it with a small boulder serving as a hammer. From the resulting flakes and splinters he could then make his selections for different purposes. When the flint or other rock was sufficiently tough so as not to shatter completely, the chance blow delivered by the hammer might result in merely dislodging a single flake; and if this flake was not suitable, repeated blows would sooner or later yield what was wanted. At all events we have here for the first time three important inventions: namely, the *hammer*, the *core*,

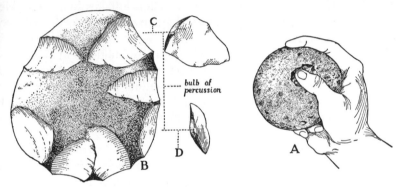

Fig. 14. Elementary flake production.
(About one half natural size)

A. Spherical hammerstone, used for flaking throughout the world.
B. Flint nodule with seven flakes removed.
C–D. Two flakes removed from nodule *B* by blows delivered near margin of rear face.

and the *flake*, which figure as basic to all the lithic industries for many thousands of years.

Thus far our description of procedure is largely theoretic or speculative and doubtless must always remain so. But whatever the precise initial steps, we possess from early Paleolithic times examples of the simpler, generally subspherical hammerstone, the rude core or nucleus with irregular flake-beds, and the equally rude flake to match, as shown in Figure 14.

This elementary flaking process was swift and the results were correspondingly rough and uncertain. The flake was clearly what was wanted, but there are no indications of studied effort at obtaining any particular form. All, we may suppose, was left to chance, and the resulting flakes were normally short, broad, and of every conceivable outline. The most desirable flakes were those provided with a long, straight cutting edge and those coming to a point at one end. When luck favored, the result sometimes combined these two features, as observed in moderately elongated, double-edged, and pointed examples (subtriangular), suitable at once as knives, scrapers, perforators, and perhaps as points for spears. No systematic marginal retouch or dressing is apparent, and such chips as have been removed seem to be due to strenuous usage rather than to deliberate fashioning or resharpening. In any case all the work was done by striking or percussion, and the chance flakes found suitable for use are the crude flake tools characteristic especially of the Pre-Chellean stage.

In course of time the initial flaking process underwent modification and improvement. In this particular case progress took place in two different directions, the first one leading toward a moderately refined style of percussion flaking and the second (possibly an outgrowth of the former) toward a highly specialized mode of flake production.

During the Chellean stage, or possibly somewhat earlier, the superficially flaked core (essentially a by-product) itself came to serve as an implement; in fact it became the first designedly dressed and fashioned implement on record, commonly known as the *coup-de-poing* or, as inaptly translated, the fist axe, cleaver, boucher. The original and preferable noncommittal term vaguely reveals our ignorance of its use, which was doubtless varied, judging by the many forms the invention received. Thus, while all are biconvex in cross section and therefore more or less sharp-edged, the outlines range from discoidal, through oval, amygdaloid, and triangular, to slender, elongated, daggerlike examples, pointed at one end, the opposite or butt end being either straight or convex, if worked at all (see Figs. 24, 25). The normal length ranges from about two to twelve inches. Geographically these more or less unwieldy blades are typical of Africa, southern Asia as far as India, and southern and southwestern Europe; and in a generalized form (blanks or unfinished implements, sometimes called tortoise cores) they occur also in the New World, especially in the eastern United States. Chronologically the type ranges, at least in Europe, from the Chellean or Pre-Chellean stage, up through the Acheulian, and into the Mousterian; while its analogue in America is rarely, if ever, found except in association with recent Neolithic inventories.* During this long interval the European coup-de-poing was subject to much refinement as regards both outline and cross section as well as general finish; and in Africa, for example, there are indications that the form may have given rise to large elongated biface and double-pointed blades (the Esbaikian industry) of Solutrean and Neolithic aspect, and possibly to other Neolithic implements, similarly derived from cores. At any rate, the art of delicate percussion flaking was almost certainly never completely lost. In western Europe, however, the coup-de-poing underwent degeneration during the late Acheulian and early Mousterian stages and was finally replaced by somewhat similarly shaped flake forms (the Levallois flake and the Mousterian point),'derived partly by actually splitting the coup-de-poing in two dorsoventrally. Elsewhere, or rather in the contemporarily inhabited Old World, the flake alone continued to serve as the chief basis for stone implements, and this did not begin to receive deliberate fashioning or specialization by systematic marginal retouch until about the time the coup-de-poing became extinct in Europe — that is, with the beginning of the Mousterian stage.

Turning now to the improvement of flake production, we meet with an extremely suggestive phenomenon. The coup-de-poing, which some have considered a sort of universal or combination implement, had in respect to form and finish reached a high state of excellence, but seemingly its serviceability was not deemed entirely satisfactory. And indeed, if it was actually used for every conceivable purpose such as stabbing, chopping, cutting, scraping, and perforating, it is easy to see that a chance flake, properly selected, might serve various special purposes far better. Besides, such flakes were more easily and quickly produced. At any rate, toward the end of the Acheulian subphase we find the flint-workers beginning to split the coup-de-poing in two, as it were; or rather, with a deft blow of the hammerstone, delivered on one face of the coup-de-poing near the butt end, they dislodged a flake from the opposite face of the old implement. If successful, they obtained an oblong

---

* The so-called *rostro-carinate* or eagle-beak core form, resembling a coup-de-poing split anteroposteriorly into right and left halves, and said to characterize especially the late Pliocene epoch and to be the forerunner of the true coup-de-poing, is here deliberately omitted as too problematic. But even if we must ultimately accept this pointed beak form as a designed implement, the general order of technological development as here presented will remain the same. The present chronology will merely be expanded.

subtriangular flake, concavo-convex in cross section. The convex face (that is, the outer or dorsal side) of this flake naturally carries a portion of the flake beds or scars of one face of the ancestral coup-de-poing while the concave face (the inner, ventral, or bulbar side) is plain, except at the broad butt end where, above the bulb of percussion (the point at which it was struck off), it exhibits a narrow margin of small flake beds belonging to the other face of the original coup-de-poing (see Fig. 15, *C*). This margin of preliminary retouch on the bulbar face of the new flake alone demonstrates that it was

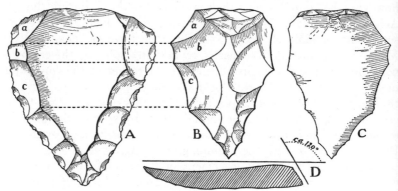

Fig. 15. Improved flaking of Acheulian-Levalloisian times.
(One half natural size)

A. Roughly prepared flint core with large flake-bed. Sometimes called turtleback core.
B. Flake of triangular outline removed from *A* — outer face.
C. Inner face of same flake showing bulb of percussion and part of striking platform.
D. Longitudinal section of same flake showing wide angle (*ca.* 120°) made by inner face and striking platform — a primitive characteristic.

derived from a previously prepared coup-de-poing and not struck from an ordinary chance-shaped tortoise core. However, once the method of thus obtaining a moderately long and pointed flake was hit upon, the expert artisan soon began to slur his preliminary preparations; that is, he did not go through the whole process of finishing his coup-de-poing, but merely made a rough imitation, sufficient for the purpose of obtaining the desired flake. This step is particularly well illustrated by many specimens from Egypt, an example of which is given in Figure 15.

While at first only a single flake was obtained as the result of this elaborate preparation, first of a finished coup-de-poing and then of a rough imitation, in due time (near the beginning of the Aurignacian stage) the flint knapper succeeded in removing several flakes from the same prepared form by the simple expedient of flattening its butt end, which gave him room to strike several blows at selected points near the margin of his roughly circular striking platform. The result was that the coup-de-poing was converted into a truly prepared core of roughly conical form, usually called the polyhedral core, an advanced example of which is shown in Figure 16, *B*.

This type of core remained the chief source of long slender prismatic flakes to the end of Neolithic times and is especially prominent

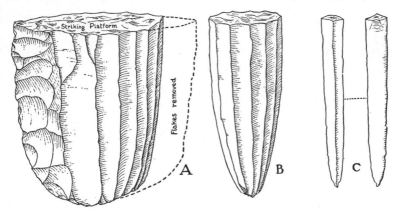

Fig. 16. Precise flaking of Upper Paleolithic and Neolithic times.
(One half natural size)

A. Prepared core with flaking begun. Note horizontal striking platform.
B. Conical core with flakes removed all around.
C. Flake removed from *A* and *B* cores, showing outer and inner faces. Note that angle made by inner flake face and striking platform is reduced to nearly 90°.

in various parts of Europe, Asia, and Mexico. The development of flakes shows that in the elementary working processes here described one phase grew out of the other.

Stone-chipping process. Having once mastered the production of long slender flakes, easily adapted to a variety of special purposes, the next great advance consisted in modifying these flakes to suit. As stated, some of the early crude flake implements exhibit irregularly chipped margins, due partly, no doubt, to hard usage on wood and bone and partly also to intentional shaping or resharpening after the manner of the coup-de-poing by delicate percussion flaking. However, during the Mousterian industrial stage, while the flakes were still comparatively broad and short, a new method of marginal chipping came into use, that of pressure chipping. This pressure method was much slower than the percussion method; but it was more easily controlled and therefore yielded correspondingly surer and better results. Precisely how or when this procedure came about is uncertain; but it is not clearly recognizable until Mousterian times, when it was used only or chiefly on thin flakes like the so-called Mousterian points, while the older percussion method continued to serve for dressing thick and stout flakes such as the Mousterian sidescraper or *racloir*. Presumably pressure chipping was

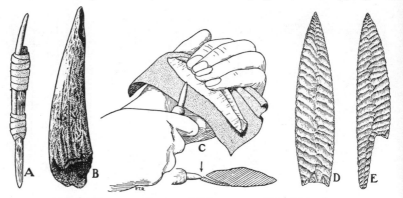

Fig. 17. Pressure chipping of Solutrean and Neolithic times.
(One half natural size)

A. Chipping tool of bone lashed to stick. North America. After W. H. Holmes.
B. Chipping tool of antler. Denmark.
C. Method of pressure chipping observed in California.
D. Spear point chipped by right-handed worker. Denmark.
E. Lance point chipped by left-handed worker. France.

effected then, as in historic times, with a blunt-pointed piece of bone or antler, or anything else sufficiently stout (Fig. 17, *A*, *B*).

In any case, this new process also began in a crude way and by the end of the Stone Age attained a high state of perfection in many parts of both the Old and New Worlds. Specifically this means that, as is demonstrated by the chipping beds on the surviving implements, the chips were at first very short marginal slivers (see Fig. 27, *2*, *6*) but later became long enough to reach the middle portion of the flake body and occasionally, as in Egyptian ceremonial knives, ran clear across the flake width. At first, also, the relatively flat bulbar face of the flake remained unretouched — that is, served merely as the chipping platform — while later on, in Solutrean and Neolithic times, both faces were chipped equally, the result being symmetrical blades of double-convex cross section (see Fig. 17, *D, E*). This flake industry, involving both percussion and pressure methods, ran a long peculiar course in Europe — from the Mousterian through Aurignacian, Solutrean, and Magdalenian to the Azilian-Tardenoisian — and, for reasons not very clear, ultimately degenerated. Except for the temporary and somewhat mysterious introduction of large Solutrean blades, in part at least derived from cores, most of the flint products were tools for use on wood and bone, materials which in the meantime gained favor for weapons. These tools were: the sidescraper (*racloir*), which was possibly used also as a chopper; the spokeshave — that is, a notched or strangulated scraper (*lame étranglé*); the saw (*scie*) or denticulated flake; the knife (*couteau*), a flake usually with a straight cutting edge and a convexly curved, blunt-chipped back, successive forms of which are often referred to as the *audi pointe* and the *chatelperron pointe;* the incising tool (*gravette pointe*) resembling the knife but more pointed and with a straighter back; the awl, drill, or perforator (*perçoir*); a few roughly stemmed points (*pointe de Font Robert*), possibly for arrows; the single-barbed point (*pointe à cran* of the Solutrean industry) suitable for the lance; rare Solutrean knives or spear points (*pointes de lances*) with either straight, concave, or stemmed base; the endscraper or planing tool (*grattoir*); the engraving or sculpturing tool (*burin*) of several varieties; and finally a number of tiny geometric forms which served at least in part as arrow points and as accessory barbs for bone harpoons — all of them derived from flakes. In addition there appeared during the Aurignacian phase a thick spall of triangular cross section and more or less oblong, with small flakes systematically removed from the ends and sides of the two dorsal faces — a form which might be regarded simply as a core but which may also, as generally supposed, have served as a stout endscraper. This is known as the *grattoir caréné* or keeled endscraper and occurs in variously modified or specialized shapes. (For illustrations of all these partly localized Upper Paleolithic forms see Figs. 28, 29, 30, 31.)

This brings us to the end of the strictly hunting era in western Europe. Flint by this time would appear to have become scarce, and in consequence the Paleolithic industries had degenerated. At any rate the next few thousand years witness what might be called a nearly complete industrial revolution. The tools thus far developed had served the hunter and all his handicrafts, but they were not adequate for such heavy work as clearing forests or building ships and houses. How the change came about is still a problem. It is explainable only by the introduction of outside influences or the immigration of new peoples with different arts and crafts.

Where these new people came from we can only guess. Presumably it was from the Near East and possibly also from North Africa. Whoever they were, they gradually revived old procedures and introduced new ones. As a beginning they overcame the lack of raw material for tools by mining deep in the ground for it, as was done especially in England, Holland, Belgium, and France. In this connection the first new tool appears: namely, a stout, oblong, sometimes slightly curved, picklike form (see Fig. 32, 4), which was probably used in gouging flint nodules out of the matrix containing them. This tool was made, as in the case of the old coup-de-poing, by the rough flaking process, and it was apparently this primitive form which in the course of time gave rise to other related forms like the chisel, the axe in several varieties, the adze, and the gouge. Meanwhile certain of the old flake implements survived, or perhaps were revived. Among these are especially the endscraper and in relatively ruder forms also the sidescraper (both plain and notched), the knife, and the perforator. The sidescraper soon gave rise to a temporary form of flake chisel or hatchet blade (the *tranchet* of Campignian times, illustrated in Fig. 32, *1*) and later the knife and perforator were developed into chipped-blade knives, daggers, spear points, arrow points, and drill points of highly varied forms in both the Old and New Worlds. In Egypt the saw or denticulated flake was inserted into a curved handle to serve as a sickle. A single new invention in chipped stone technique was the fishhook, which also appears occasionally on both sides of the Atlantic, while large spade and hoe blades are confined apparently to the United States.

Stone-pecking and grinding processes. With a marked increase in population even the artificially derived supply of flint, together with the use of obsidian, quartz, jasper, chalcedony, etc., proved insufficient. Before long we find the artisans at work on various other kinds of stone, such as chalk, limestone, marble, steatite, slate, sandstone, granite and other igneous rocks, as well as hematite, nephrite, and jade. A number of semiprecious stones, including turquoise or lapis lazuli, agate, carnelian, etc., were also in use.

These substances would neither flake nor chip readily, and consequently the workmen proceeded to shape them, as they had long done with wood and bone, by simply wearing them down, as it were. In the Old World the ancient flaking method continued in favor for the rough blocking out of the desired implement, which was then smoothed down by rubbing on a coarse sandstone surface and often finished by polishing on a stone of finer grain or with vegetable fiber. Sometimes, however, the preliminary reduction process was effected by hammering or pecking the surface with a hard boulder

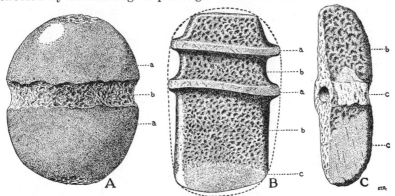

Fig. 18. Pecking and grinding processes.
(One half natural size)

A. Club head or hammer grooved by pecking with another stone.
B. Axe shaped by pecking and grinding. American.
C. Banner stone shaped by pecking and grinding. American.

Note. The *a* surfaces are natural, *b* surfaces are pecked, and *c* surfaces are ground or rubbed.

(often of quartz) after the manner of the modern stonecutter (see Fig. 18). This pecking or attrition process (with occasional substitution of grinding) was in particular favor all over America, especially for the preliminary shaping of grinding slabs and rubbing stones, metates and manos, mortars and pestles, celts or ungrooved axes, notched axes (Trinidad), T-shaped axes (northern South America), grooved axes, grooved hammers and club heads, mallets, sword-shaped clubs, spherical stones for bolas, arrow shaft polishers, and grooved sinkers. It was also employed in the fashioning of ornamental and ceremonial objects, such as earplugs, labrets, pendants, gorgets, discoidals, plummets or charm stones, bird stones and banner stones — all typical especially of North America; three-pointed stones, "collars," and animal effigy stools peculiar to the central West Indies; as well as elaborate cylindrical and U-shaped stools localized respectively in Costa Rica and Ecuador. Lastly, this pecking method was used in the preparation of building stones, both plain and ornamental; in the execution of petroglyphs of various types; and in the sculpturing of a great variety of representative art objects, including frog, snake, turtle, fish, bird, mammal, and human effigies, in sizes ranging from miniature to colossal. But the New World artisans also on occasion made use of the old flaking method. Once more it will be seen that while this preliminary flaking

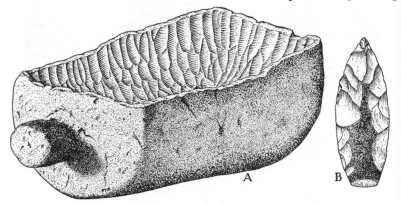

Fig. 19. Chiseling and grinding processes.
(One half natural size)
A. Vessel chiseled from steatite, ground on outside. American.
B. Chisel blade used for working steatite. American.

process was speedy it was liable to result in many failures, whereas the slow pecking process was fairly reliable and capable of yielding shapes not otherwise obtainable.

Stone-chiseling, sawing, and drilling processes. In the meantime other processes, formerly employed on wood and bone (occasionally even on stone during Magdalenian times), such as chiseling, sawing, and drilling, were also applied to these softer rocks, as well as to shell. A chisel not unlike the one used in flint-mining was employed, especially in North America, for quarrying, excavating, and shaping vessels, lamps, and other objects of soapstone or steatite (see Fig. 19). This industry was highly developed, for example, in southern California and to some extent among the Eskimo; and was also well advanced at least in Egypt and the Levant, where, however, serpentine, alabaster, and other talcose rocks, as well as marble, were in greater favor.

The sawing of jade and nephrite, which are relatively rare and very tough materials, was employed at least in the Near East, in China, in New Zealand, on the American North Pacific coast, and to a slight extent in Mexico. This method was used on ordinary stone in Tierra del Fuego in fairly early times. It was done by means of a string or with the edge of a thin stick of wood — sand being used as an abrasive — and sometimes actually with a thin sliver of sandstone (see Fig. 20).

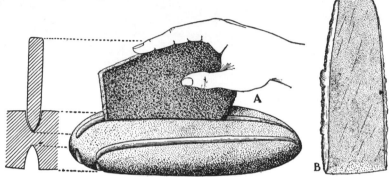

Fig. 20. Sawing process.
(One half natural size)

A. Sawing out an axe blade by means of a sliver of sandstone. Europe and America.
B. Axe blade of jadeite produced by sawing. North Pacific Coast.

Drilling in the harder rocks was similarly executed with the end of either a solid or a hollow wooden stick, again with the help of sand (see Fig. 21).

For softer varieties of rock and shell the ordinary flint drill points served admirably. As evidence of the success of these slow and simple perforation methods, Europe and the Near East furnish a unique series of socketed hammers, chopping axes, and war axes — that is, those provided with haft holes. Perforated sinkers and spherical and star-shaped club heads appear in both hemispheres. America alone supplies a great variety of drilled tobacco pipes and "medicine" tubes, as well as gorgets and other ceremonial and decorative objects, the most exquisite being a number of spool-shaped obsidian ear ornaments recently discovered in a tomb at Monte Alban in Oaxaca. Ordinary drilled beads, pendants, etc., are found nearly everywhere. With this we may claim to have accounted for all the outstanding traits typical of the successive lithic industries.

Bone and wood-working industries. For the sake of completeness we must also consider briefly the early stages of the other major prehistoric industries. Our task here differs somewhat from what has gone before. The stone-working processes, today all but lost arts, require full explanation; while the methods of dealing with other raw materials survive and are well known. In the development of

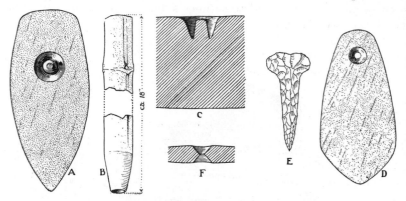

Fig. 21. Drilling processes.
(One half natural size)

A. Axe-hammer partly perforated with tubular drill. Europe.
B. Tubular drill of cane — hypothetical.
C. Section of tubular drill hole, showing core.
D. Pendant of slate drilled with pointed flint. American.
E. Drill of chipped flint. American, but typical also of Old World.
F. Section of typical pointed flint drill hole.

wood, bone, and metallic implements, therefore, the description may be couched largely in terms of form, function, and stratigraphic occurrence. Bone and allied materials were worked by chopping, cutting, sawing, scraping, and boring. In most cases there is no way of telling precisely when these different methods were first introduced. Referring to Europe, the first known and very crude bone implements were of the awl or dagger type and date from Mousterian deposits. Associated with them in time are also fragments of bone exhibiting cuts or nicks, suggesting that they were used as foundation rests on which to place the bottom end, say, of a wooden spear while it was being scraped into shape. The objects are therefore not strictly tools. With the arrival of the Cro-Magnon man and the Aurignacian industry, bone implements at once began to play a considerable rôle. Thus the bone awl appears in perfected forms; likewise cylindrical bone pins, perhaps for the coiffure; and in addition a modified point with either a slanting or a slit base, suitable for attachment to the wooden lance or spear, of which there is record already during Mousterian times. Bone needles appear for the first time, suggesting that garments were being made. Bone served also occasionally for artificially shaped and drilled beads. Antler was employed for wedges or chisel-shaped implements called "polishers" but probably used mainly for skin-dressing; and the same material was used also for perforated arrow-straighteners, commonly called *batons-de-commandement*. In addition, teeth (and shells) were perforated to serve as pendants, while ivory and other materials served for sculptured figurines of human and animal forms. The Solutrean deposits add ornamental wandlike implements of bone and ivory, also disks and pendants of ivory similarly decorated. During the Magdalenian phase bone and antler implements reached their acme of perfection and the period might properly be characterized as the Bone Age. The lance point, now usually made of antler, is converted into a detachable harpoon point, which undergoes a succession of improvements from a single to a double row of barbs. The spear-thrower, a new and isolated invention, is also made of antler. The perforated bone needle appears in considerable profusion. Of rarer occurrence are perforated bone disks that may have been either spindlewhorls or buttons, and also a spool-shaped toggle form that may have served the latter purpose. In Moravia two axes or adzes were found, each made of a bone blade set in a bone handle. Lastly, mention must be made of indirect proof from pictographs in eastern Spain of the bow and arrow, though doubtless these contrivances were made principally of wood. The majority of all these articles are covered with engraved geometric or realistic ornamentation, and the Magdalenian industry as a whole is accompanied by a great variety of sculptured and incised representations of contemporary life forms, both animal and vegetable.

Following the Magdalenian — that is, during the transition period represented by the Azilian stage and its contemporary Tardenoisian and Maglemosean phases — as well as during the succeeding Campignian stage and its allied Asturian phase in Spain and the early shellmound phase in the North, there is a marked decline in bone work, as in stone, at least in southwestern Europe. There are, to be sure, some indications that the art was transferred to the North, where, for example in Norway (also later on in the Eskimo region), something like a Bone Age flourished or lingered for a time. Probably it was never so nearly extinguished here as elsewhere in western Europe. However, with the introduction and gradual development of the true Neolithic culture European bone work, now mainly of a utilitarian character, revived somewhat and its products resemble not a little the more recent bone industry, for instance, of our own Iroquois region. The awl as a generic type of implement naturally survived and is to be found in a great variety of forms all over the habitable globe. The barbed harpoon survived and appears in many parts of the world, especially in the northern circumpolar regions, but is present also, for example, in New Zealand and Tierra del Fuego. The same is true for the needle, the hairpin or fastener, the arrow-straightener, the chisel, and allied spatulate forms, as well as of bone beads, etc. In the way of new inventions may be mentioned for Europe a crude L-shaped flint-mining pick, improvised from a pronged deer antler; punches of antler prongs; some curious transversely socketed antler axes and adzes of questionable function; antler haftings for axes, chisels, awls, etc. — especially from Switzerland; pressure chippers of bone and antler; bodkins, knives, and daggers of bone; cutting tools of beaver and boar tusks; combs for the hair or for compressing the woof strands in loom weaving; gorge "hooks" (straight, double-pointed) and ordinary curved fishhooks. All these forms, except the boar-tusk knife, are duplicated in America; and here in addition are found plain as well as denticulated endscrapers and long double-edged cannon bone sidescrapers — both used for skin-dressing; elaborate spatulas of bone (especially in the Southwest) presumably used in ceramic work; spear and arrow points of bone and antler; clubs of whalebone; gambling dice and game sticks of bone; notched tally sticks and weighing or scale beams of the same material; ladles, spoons, and shovel blades of horn; rattles as well as dishes of turtle carapace; and tubes of bird bone used for drinking and by the medicine man for sucking pain or disease from the patient's body. Of a more strictly esthetic nature there are also, in America at least, circular and oblong bone-plate pendants, occasional perforated shark-teeth pendants, bracelets of thin bent strips of bone, and lastly whistles, flutes, and flageolets, as well as innumerable beads of varying lengths of tubular bird bones. In certain of the Pacific islands (Gilbert, etc.) shark teeth, in the absence of other material, were extensively used for giving a cutting edge to both tools and weapons. We must conclude the inventory by merely stating that the Eskimo culture, still remarkably rich in bone implements, adds the bow drill, snow goggles, needle cases, and other minor items.

Wood as a workable substance allied to bone can be considered only in general terms. As stated, a large point-end fragment of a spear, found in England, is supposed to date from early Mousterian times. The bow and arrow as illustrated by Spanish pictographs date from the late Paleolithic, while the earlier presence of bone or antler points for lances and harpoons and the existence of the spear-thrower indicate a somewhat earlier age. From Neolithic deposits, especially in dry caves, come a large number of additional wooden objects, including for Europe such items as the handles for different implements, clubs, mallets, a unique V-shaped toggle or cinch device (Egypt, Southwest, and Peru), split log coffins, dugout canoes, boat paddles, fishhooks, the boomerang, the throwing stick (Denmark), knives and daggers. Other implements relating to ceramic and textile industries may be inferred and actually occur in more or less fragmentary condition. Nearly all of these forms, except perhaps log coffins and daggers, have been found also in America. In addition the New World exhibits such items as tongs for handling hot cooking stones; planting and digging sticks; and a spade or shovellike implement. Then, too, here are brushes and paddles for shaping and decorating pottery; spinning, netting, and weaving devices; dishes, headrests, stools, boxes or chests of different forms; traces of plank boats; frames for skin and bark boats; sleds; snowshoes; dwellings embodying several different principles of construction; house ladders of two types, namely, the notched log and the ordinary runged form. Lastly we have goggles, gaming sticks, rattles, notched musical sticks, drums, and a variety of ceremonial paraphernalia such as poles, wands, prayer sticks, panpipes, masks, and symbolic implements. A few of these American traits, it must be admitted, border on the present-day horizon; but their prehistoric origin can scarcely be questioned. Specifically the same might be said of such presumably ancient and widespread inventions as the blowgun, the pump drill, and many other contrivances belonging to the wood-working inventory. In conclusion it must be remarked that while the later or Neolithic bone and wood products are mainly of utilitarian character, neither embellishment nor purely artistic items are entirely wanting, especially in America.

Metal industries. There remains to consider very briefly the final step, the reproduction in metal of many of the inventions previously achieved and the addition also of new ones. This transition, since the classical archaeologists have dug deep enough in Egypt and the Levant, is no longer a strictly prehistoric event, except in a limited or local sense. The most that can be safely claimed is that prehistoric man in widely separated parts of the world independently came upon such peculiarly malleable substances as copper (earliest occurrence usually credited to the island of Cyprus) and gold and that he worked them for a time much after the manner of stone by simple hammering. The application of heat to assist in forging may also be of some antiquity, but actual melting of the native metals and the reduction of metallic ores would appear to be approximately contemporary with the beginnings of megalithic structures and the invention of writing or other simple forms of record-keeping, in the Old World ca. 3000 B.C. and in the New World sometime after the beginning of the present era. Preliminary experimentation with native copper doubtless accounts for the fact that in most places the melting and casting, first of copper and later of copper mixed with tin — that is, bronze — preceded iron work, which latter no one ventures to place much before 1500 B.C. and then only for the eastern Mediterranean lands. Succeeding this earliest Asiatic beginning, the first distinctly European iron industry, called the Hallstatt culture after the type station in upper Austria, is regarded as dating from about 1000 B.C., while the last "prehistoric" phase, named after the type site at La Tène in Switzerland, dates from close to 500 B.C. and thus overlaps with Roman historical times.

The implemental products derived from these metallic industries were naturally at first limited largely to substitutes for the earlier elemental tools and weapons, though decorative objects are not entirely wanting. Confining our interest mainly to the so-called prehistoric regions of the Old World, copper and bronze tools include awls, needles, anvils, hammers, a varied series of axes ranging from flat imitations of stone forms to longitudinally socketed specimens; similarly socketed picks, hoes, adzes, and chisels; saws, sickles, tweezers, choppers, razors, and knives of many different forms. The weapons are limited to daggers, swords and rapiers, halberds, spear and arrow points, harpoons (rare in the Old World), shields, helmets, and armor for man and horse. The ornamental objects comprise hairpins with elaborate heads, rings, bracelets, torques or neck rings, crescentic gorgets or lunulae, necklaces with beads and pend-

PREHISTORIC ARCHAEOLOGY   169

ants, fibulae or ornamental safety pins, brooches, chain belts, buckles, buttons, plaques, mirrors, decorative urns or vases, horse gear, harness trappings and other minor accessories, for instance for the sword and spear. Of a distinctly ceremonial nature there are bells, trumpets, and sun disks, both separate and elaborately mounted. Finally there are also a number of miscellaneous items such as ingots, rivets, fishhooks, cups, cauldrons, and money rings. Were we to include the bronze traits of the early historic centers like Egypt, Mesopotamia, Greece, and Rome, we should have to augment the list by such items as wheeled chariots, lamps, flesh-hooks, forks, spoons, ladles, toilet articles, surgical instruments, and other inventions too numerous to record.

Many of these modern-looking contrivances were wrought into highly pleasing shapes and were often elaborately ornamented by either geometric or realistic patterns, generally incised but sometimes in low relief. The dot and the spiral figured especially in northern Europe, while in southern Siberia human and animal representations were in particular favor. And over and above all these useful articles there was a considerable variety of purely artistic figurines, cast in both realistic and conventionalized form, giving expression not only to natural facts of daily observation but also to mythological con-cepts and traditional ideas.

The preceding inventory pertains to the Old World; but, as would be expected, many of the simpler New World contrivances are almost identical. The practical requirements or the purposes for which implements were made being the same, a general resemblance in form could scarcely be avoided. Even the longitudinal and trans-verse socket methods of hafting chisels, axes, and other implements were hit upon, for example, in Wisconsin and Peru; but they never came into general or widespread use. Closer inspection reveals striking variations of details even in such generic type groups as knives, spear and arrow points, harpoons, tweezers, hairpins or fasteners, axe forms and vessel forms; and this difference becomes especially marked in gold and silver work, both of decorative and symbolic nature. Here, it seems, America is richer than the Old World, and its products, whether realistic or conventionalized, are often strangely grotesque and clearly of an entirely different tradi-tion both in conception and execution. Some practical appliances like sickles, saws, swords, trumpets, and horse gear are missing in America; on the other hand, there are present here at least a few unique forms, such as earplugs, nose rings, grooved axes, sword-shaped clubs, star-shaped club heads, and bolas, as well as several forms and styles of repoussé work, which were not duplicated in metallic forms in the Old World. Incidentally, the American goldsmith's work at its best, while admittedly of a much later date, is fully equal to the finest product of classical antiquity.

When finally we come to iron implements, we take leave of the New World for good and at the same time begin to recognize a great variety of forms still in use at the present day. Hammers, axes, and adzes are perforated transversely for insertion of the haft and only the chisel remains longitudinally socketed, though it is also sometimes tanged as today. The sickle is lengthened out to a scythe; the hoe or digging stick is converted into a plow; the fish spear or harpoon is transformed into a trident. Many new forms are developed, such as tongs, pincers, shears, scissors, thimbles, drawing knives, pruning knives, augers, braces and bits, files, rasps, planes, mounted saws, compasses, squares, plumb bobs, trowels, boat hooks, pitchforks, rakes, plowshares, wagon trappings, andirons, locks with keys, etc. Even nails and horseshoes are present at a fairly early date. Evidently all but the most recent manual occupations were originated and equipped with specialized tools. In short, as far as mechanical appliances are concerned we have entered the modern world.

With the view to objectifying what has been summarized in the preceding pages, the following series of typical illustrations, grouped by chronological stages, have been placed in juxtaposition for purposes of ready comparison. The selection has been confined (with rare exceptions) to Europe for the reason that there alone the sequence has been all but completely determined. As far as possible, original specimens from the collections of the American Museum of Natural History have been used. In addition to the legends describing the given illustrations, lists have been supplied of all other known inventions, both those illustrated from earlier stages and the new ones not illustrated, the aim being to furnish a complete inventory for each culture stage. (See pages 176–194.)

The Eolithic phase. At the lower extremity of the culture column a succession of the so-called eoliths — that is, supposedly utilized natural flint flakes, etc., with more or less of accidental rather than purposive marginal chipping — has been introduced. These problematic forms range throughout all the Tertiary epochs up into early Pleistocene and are therefore, chronologically at least, a problem for the geologists. Archaeologically or culturally the "industry" was named by G. de Mortillet in 1883 and the inventory is believed by Professor A. Rutot of Belgium to comprise five generic forms of implements: namely, the hammer, the chopper, the knife, the scraper, and the perforator; though sometimes the anvil and the throwing stone are also included. The earliest discovery bearing on the subject was made in 1863 by M. Desnoyer in Pliocene gravels at Saint Prest, Eure-et-Loir, France. Since then other collections have been made at more than eighty locations, distributed as follows: Denmark 1, Germany 7, Holland 1, England 17, Belgium 20, France 16, Spain 1, Portugal 2, Italy 1, Greece 1, North Africa 2, South Africa 4, Egypt 1, India 3, and alleged finds also in Australia, South America, and possibly Mongolia. The most productive sites have been Puy Courny and Puy de Boudieu in Cantal, France, and the Kent plateau in England, representative respectively of Miocene and Pliocene geological times. The latest contribution to the study has come from East Anglia where, in the Red Crag and earlier formations of Pliocene date, Reid Moir since 1910 has found eoliths of Kentian type in part associated with other and apparently true implements which he has called both Pre-Paleolithic and Pre-Chellean.[3]

Rutot as the outstanding champion of eoliths records the following more or less indistinguishable phases:

II. Early Quaternary

    7. Reutelian — from Reutel, near Ypres, Flanders, Belgium

I. Tertiary

    6. Saint Prestian — Upper Pliocene (?) — Eure-et-Loir, France

    5. Kentian — Middle Pliocene — Kent, England

    4. Cantalian — Upper Miocene — Cantal, France

    3. Thenayan — Upper Oligocene — Loir-et-Cher, France

    2. Fagnian — Middle Oligocene — Boncelles, Liége, Belgium

    1. Thanetian — Lower Eocene — Belle-Assize, Oise, France

Formerly three additional horizons, called Mafflian, Mesvinian, and Strepyan, topped the column, but these have recently been accepted by Rutot as equivalents of the Lower Paleolithic facies. Aside from these three late stages the remaining horizons of eoliths present very little difference so far as form and possible function are concerned. Their reality as implements or even as mere artifacts is a problem on which expert opinion is about evenly divided, but on the whole the sponsors have been mostly geologists and not archaeologists. The Thanetian phase is definitely known to be of natural origin, but it does not therefore follow that those of Pliocene and even Miocene date may not ultimately have to be accepted as of human origin.[4]

The Paleolithic industries. The subdivision of the Paleolithic Age has proved difficult and is a task still in progress. This industrial stage is recognized as contemporary with Pleistocene time. It has been broken up, first by means of its associated succession of glacial and interglacial phenomena and later by its marine shore terraces. As we should expect, the paleontologists, both European and American, have also in their own way sought to subdivide the period, using extinct faunal remains as a guide.

While in the beginning the sequence of forms was considered as generally valid, more extended researches in many parts of Europe have proved that local variations existed at early times. An attempt to localize the very earliest centers of distinct cultural types has been made by O. Menghin, who distinguishes for early Paleolithic time a culture based on the use of bone which he assumes to have originated in northern Asia and to have spread from there over part of Europe; another based on the use of the cleaver (coup-de-poing) which spread from India westward over the Mediterranean area by way of Africa; and a third one characterized by flint blades which originated in eastern Asia and spread in a wide sweep over central Asia and the Mediterranean.[5]

Since the beginning of systematic research it has been customary to name each type from the locality where it was first identified. This has resulted in a considerable confusion of terms. The origin of our present nomenclature is the natural outcome of the fact that France and the Scandinavian countries took the lead in prehistoric archaeology. So long as the investigations were confined to western Europe the provided terminology served fairly well. Today, however, when it is becoming apparent that the course of development of the flint-working technique did not everywhere repeat the western European order step by step, there is no help for it but to abandon the general use of at least one of the two classes of terms now in use. Such designations as Lower, Middle, and Upper Paleolithic are readily understandable and as far as they go are adaptable for world-wide purposes. On the other hand, such expressions as Chellean, Clactonian, Acheulian, Micoquian, Levalloisian, Mousterian, Aurignacian, Solutrean, Magdalenian, Azilian, Tardenoisian, Maglemosean, Campignian, Asturian, Cromerian, Foxhallian, Capsian, Esbaikian, and a score of similar terms, all apply to separate localities and sometimes to individual sites and as mere words are meaningless. They simply designate French, Danish, English, Spanish, and African specializations and as such will always be serviceable; what is wanted for world purposes is a classification system, in terms either of *time* or of *industrial technique*, which readily conveys its meaning. Various incomplete efforts have already been made in this direction. We have, for example, such expressions as *flaked core industries, flake industries, pressure-chipping industries, microlithic industries,* and *polished stone industries,* all of which tell more or less their own story. Recently Oswald Menghin [6] of Vienna has made a deliberate effort to meet the new demand. His system drops the term "Paleolithic" and takes the following form:

I. Protolithic Stage
 1. Lower or Early phase (Eolithic and Pre-Chellean)
 2. Middle phase (Chellean and Acheulian)
 3. Upper or Late phase (Mousterian)

II. Miolithic Stage
 1. Lower or Early phase (Aurignacian)
 2. Middle phase (Solutrean, Magdalenian)
 3. Upper or Late phase (Azilian-Tardenoisian-Maglemosean-Capsian)

III. Neolithic Stage
 1. Early or Proto-Neolithic phase (Campignian, Asturian, etc.)
 2. Full or Mixo-Neolithic phase (Final Neolithic with agriculture, etc.)

The essential facts as expressed in current nomenclature have been summarized in the table on pages 174–175. It will be understood that such a correlation scheme, while convenient and useful, is not to be taken too literally. Schematization unavoidably makes the problems dealt with seem simpler than they really are. The facts themselves — the rise and fall of continents, the succession of advancing and retreating glaciers, the presence during the interval of changing types of men and animals, as well as the gradual specialization of culture — are indisputable; but the chronological juxtaposition of some of these facts is a subject about which there is no absolute agreement. In some respects it is tentative and subject to future rectification.

COMPARATIVE CHRONOLOGY WITH CORRELATIONS OF CLIMATIC AND CULTURAL CHANGES

(Partly modified after Penck, De Geer, Sollas, Daly, Sandford and Arkell, Breuil, and others)

Alpine and Scandinavian glacial oscillations with corresponding changes of sea level and climate (Compare Fig. 1)	Approximate dates, partly estimated	Principal Culture Stages as determined for the most thoroughly studied areas			
		Northwestern Continental Europe	West Central Europe	Egypt and the Near East	Human Types
Present conditions or Mya Period in Baltic area	A.D. 1000	Historic Times			
	A.D. 500	Viking Age	Historic Times		
	0	Roman Period of Iron Age			
	500 B.C.	Iron Age introduced	Iron Age introduced	Iron Age begins	
	1000 B.C.	Bronze Age introduced			
Final land rise in Baltic area or Late Tapes Period	1500 B.C.	Traces of copper	Bronze Age introduced	Bronze Age begins	
	2000 B.C.	Late Neolithic with thick-poll axe	Copper Age introduced	Alloys in use	
	2500 B.C.			History begins	
	3000 B.C.	Middle Neolithic with thin-poll axe	Late Neolithic		
	3500 B.C.				
	4000 B.C.	Early Neolithic: Shellmound or Campignian industry	Middle Neolithic or Robenhausian industry	Use of iron begins	Modern Man
Daun and Ragunda retreats. Land sink with Littorina Sea (Early Tapes Period) preceded by Late Ancylus Lake	4500 B.C.				
	5000 B.C.		Early Neolithic or Campignian and Asturian industries	Use of copper begins	
	5500 B.C.	Norse industry with petroglyphs		Amratian industry	
	6000 B.C.	Maglemose industry		Badarian industry	
	6500 B.C.		Azilian, Tardenoisian, and Capsian industries		
Daun and Ragunda pauses with Ancylus Lake	7500 B.C.	Lyngby industry	Late Magdalenian	Tasian industry	
Gschnitz and Fini-glacial retreats with Yoldia Sea	8500 B.C.		Early Magdalenian and Capsian industries		
Gschnitz and Fini-glacial pauses with Baltic ice lake			Solutrean industry. Late Aurignacian industry	Probable beginning of Neolithic culture in Nile valley floor silts	Cro-Magnon Man
Buhl and Gothi-glacial retreats with Baltic ice lake	13,500 B.C. (De Geer)				

COMPARATIVE CHRONOLOGY WITH CORRELATIONS OF CLIMATIC AND CULTURAL CHANGES—Continued

Buhl and Gothi-glacial pauses with Baltic ice lake	13,500 B.C. (De Geer) 18,500 B.C. (Sollas)		Early Aurignacian and Capsian industries	Sebilian industry of Nile valley terrace silts	Grimaldi Man
Würm or Achen and Dani-glacia retreats with Frankfort and Pomeranian pauses. Flandrian terrace				Late Mousterian of the 10-ft. Nile terrace	
Würm and Brandenburg or Dani-glacial advances	Ca. 50,000 yr. (Penck and Daly)		Final Mousterian of the caves, etc.		
			Mousterian of the caves, etc.		Neanderthal Man
Riss and Polonian retreats with Monastirian terrace	Ca. 75,000 yr. (Penck and Daly)		Contemporary Acheulian, Early Mousterian (Mico-quian, Levalloisian, and Clactonian) industries from 1st Somme terrace, etc.	Early Mousterian of the 30-ft. Nile terrace	
Riss and Polonian advances	Ca. 125,000 yr. (Penck and Daly)		Derived implements		
Mindel and Saxonian retreats with Tyrrhenian terrace			Contemporary Chellean and Clactonian industries from 2d Somme terrace, Clacton-on-Sea, Mesvin, etc.	Acheulian industry of the 50-ft. Nile terrace	Heidelberg Man
Mindel and Saxonian advances	Ca. 450,000 yr. (Penck and Daly)		Derived implements		
Gunz and Scanian retreats with Milazzian terrace			Proto-Chellean industry from below the Cromer forest beds and 3d Somme terrace	Chellean and Early Chellean industries of the 100-ft. Nile terrace	Peking Man Piltdown Man
Gunz and Scanian advances	Ca. 600,000 yr. (Daly)		Pre-Chellean or Ipswichian flake industry of East Anglian crag formations	?	
PLEISTOCENE	Ca. 1 million yr.		Pre-Chellean or Ipswichian flake industry of subcrag formations	?	Pithecan-thropus
PLIOCENE Pre-Gunz time with Sicilian terrace		Eolithic stage?	Eolithic stage?	Eolithic stage?	

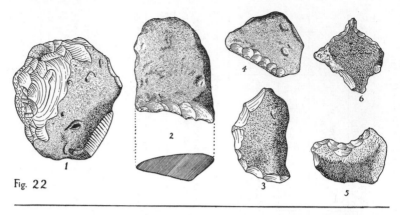

Fig. 22

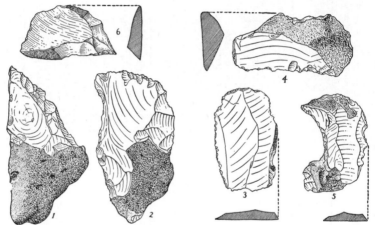

Fig. 23

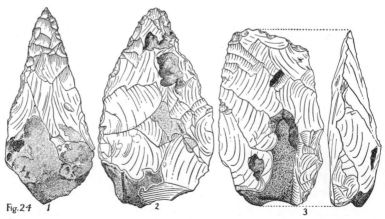

Fig. 24

Fig. 22. Eoliths of exceptionally artificial appearance derived (one excepted)
from the Pliocene gravels of the Kent Plateau, England.

(One third natural size)

1. Hammerstone type or battered flint nodule. Belgium. After G. Engerrand.
2. Chopper type or tabular flint nodule chipped at lower end. England.
3. Sidescraper type or tabular flint nodule chipped on convex edge. England.
4. Knife type or tabular flint nodule chipped on straight edge. England. After
    H. F. Osborn.
5. Sidescraper type or tabular flint nodule chipped on concave edge. England.
6. Perforator type or tabular flint nodule chipped to a point. England. Courtesy
    of H. F. Osborn.

Note. Anvil stones and slingstones are also alleged to occur.

Fig. 23. Typical Pre-Chellean core and flake implements derived from
valley terrace formations of Pleistocene date.

(One third natural size)

1. Pointed core implement with crusted butt for handhold. France.
2. Chopperlike implement with crusted butt for handhold. France.
3. Knife, adapted from simple flake, slightly chipped. France.
4. Sidescraper with thick back and partly chipped straight edge. France.
5. Sidescraper with chipped concave edge. France.
6. Pointed flake implement slightly chipped at point. France.

Note. The existence of the hammerstone as improvised or adapted from natural
boulders is implied, though it is rarely found before the Mousterian cave deposits
are reached.

Fig. 24. Typical Chellean core implements derived from valley terrace deposits.

(One third natural size)

1. Pointed coup-de-poing (dagger?) with crusted butt. France.
2. Oval coup-de-poing with crusted butt for handhold. France.
3. Chopperlike coup-de-poing. Note sinuous edge. France.

Note. For additional implements of the flake type see crude forms of knives,
scrapers, and perforators illustrated above in Figure 23, *3-6*.

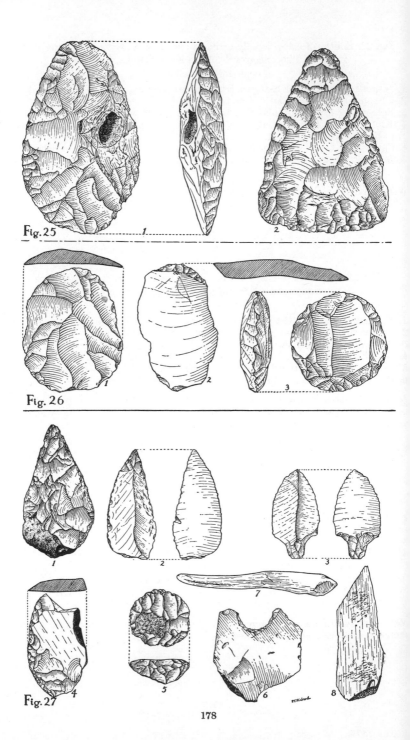

Fig. 25

Fig. 26

Fig. 27

Fig. 25. Typical Acheulian core implements.
(One third natural size)

1. **Coup**-de-poing or cleaver, oval outline, flaked on both faces all around, edge moderately thin and straight. France.
2. Coup-de-poing of subtriangular outline — possibly a weapon. France.

Note. Rude flake knives and scrapers similar to those of Figure 23 are also present; likewise discoidal core forms of the type illustrated below in Figure 26, *3.* See also note to Figure 26.

Fig. 26. Typical Levalloisian implements.
(One third natural size)

1. Scraper of flake derived from prepared coup-de-poing or turtleback core (as in Fig. 15), convex face, striking platform visible at bottom. Cross section above. France and Egypt.
2. Knife of flake derived from prepared coup-de-poing core, concave or bulbar face with part of striking platform. France and Egypt.
3. Scraper or core of discoidal outline, showing large flake-beds and subsequent marginal chipping. France and Egypt.

Note. Recent refinements based on studies of a large series of crudely worked flints found in situ at Clacton-on-Sea, England, have resulted in the recognition of a Clactonian industrial phase. This new phase, characterized mainly by flake tools, is contemporary with the Chellean, Acheulian, and Levalloisian stages above illustrated; it resembles the Levalloisian and Mesvinian technique of the continent, and the three related industries are consequently regarded as joint forerunners of the true Mousterian stage illustrated below. The Clactonian and its allied contemporary phases should therefore correspond in time and general characteristics to Obermaier's Early or Primitive Mousterian of central and eastern Europe.

The Clactonian inventory, incidentally, includes a portion of a wooden spear (see Sollas, *Ancient Hunters,* p. 193).

Fig. 27. Typical Mousterian implements.
(One third natural size)

1. Coup-de-poing or small pointed core implement. France.
2. Pointed flake with marginal pressure retouch on convex face. France.
3. Pointed flake with chipped stem for hafting to spear(?). North Africa.
4. Sidescraper of thick spall, crescentic edge, chipped on convex face only. France.
5. Sidescraper or slingstone(?), small, discoidal. France, Egypt, etc.
6. Notched sidescraper with marginal chipping — rare. France. After G. and A. de Mortillet.
7. Bone implement(?) with blunt spatulate point. Switzerland. After O. Menghin.
8. Anvil or rest of bone fragment showing tool marks. France.

Note. For hammerstone, generally of subspherical shape, see Figure 14, *A.* Mineral colors appear for the first time, likewise the use of fire and the practice of ceremonial interment. Rare finds of pitted stones, choppers, endscrapers, burins, and perforators are on record.

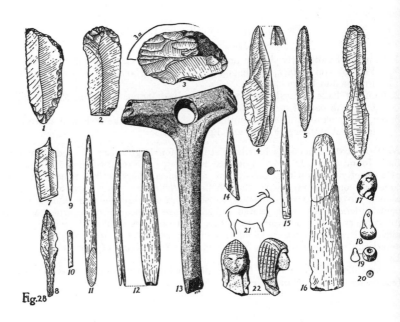

Fig.28

Fig. 28. Typical Aurignacian implements, ornaments, etc.

(One third natural size)

. Knife of flake, straight edge, curved bluntly chipped back. Audi type. France.
2. Endscraper of flake, bit end rounded by chipping. France.
3. Endscraper of core (keelscraper) viewed from above; profile indicated. France.
4. Burin or engraving tool with transverse chisellike bit — the simplest of several allied forms. France.
5. Incising tool or pointed knife of flake, with straight bluntly chipped back. Gravette type. France.
6. Notched sidescraper or drawknife. France. After H. Breuil.
7. Perforator prepared from flake by chipping near point. France. After D. Peyrony.
8. Stemmed point prepared from flake by chipping. Font-Robert type. France.
9. Double-pointed bone implement, possibly used in place of fishhook. France. After D. Peyrony.
0. Needle of bone, fragmentary. France. After L. Didon.
1. Dart point of bone with slant base for hafting. France. After D. Peyrony.
2. Dart point of bone with slit base for hafting. France.
3. Lance shaft straightener of antler, sometimes called baton-de-commandement. France.
4. Awl or perforator made from bone splinter. France.
5. Hairpin(?) of bone, circular cross section. France.
6. Spatulate implement of antler, perhaps for working skins. France.
7. Pendant or bead of univalve shell, perforated. France.
8. Pendant or bead of reindeer(?) tooth, incised ornamentation. France.
9. Bead of bone, basket-shaped. France.
0. Bead of stone, disk-shaped. France.
1. Profile of ibex(?) engraved on cave wall — early style. France. After J. Dechelette.
2. Head of female figurine carved in ivory. France. After E. Piette.

Note. Additional surviving forms previously illustrated or mentioned: Hammerstones, anvil stones, sidescrapers, burins — various forms, paint stones (hematite), ochre and carbon colors, pitted stones.

Note. Additional new items not previously illustrated or mentioned: Rubbing stones, vessel or lamp of stone, curved biconical bone points (see Fig. 29, *12*); pendant of ivory, egg-shaped, perforated; biconical bar-button or toggle, constricted middle, incised ornamentation; bracelets or rings of ivory; necklace, triple strand, made up of canine teeth, fish vertebrae and univalve shells; paint containers of tubular bones; cave-wall monochrome paintings and sculptures. A few geometric microliths, typical of the later Tardenoisian stages, are also present.

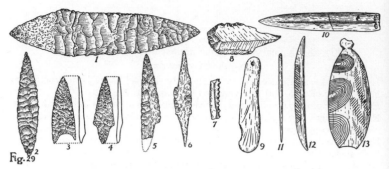

Fig. 29. Typical Solutrean implements, ornaments, etc.

(One third natural size)

1. Knife or spear point (laurel leaf type), pressure chipped all over on both faces. France.
2. Spear point or knife (willow leaf type), chipped both faces, pointed base. France. After J. Dechelette.
3. Arrow point(?) chipped on upper face only, concave base. Spain. After H. Obermaier.
4. Arrow point(?) chipped on upper face only, stemmed. Spain. After H. Obermaier.
5. Lance point or knife, chipped on upper surface only, stemmed, with single barb or shoulder. France.
6. Perforator, double pointed, of flake chipped on upper face only. France.
7. Saw or denticulated flake. France. After H. Martin.
8. Combination endscraper and burin. France.
9. Pendant of perforated pebble. France. After D. Peyrony.
10. Awl or pointed implement of antler, longitudinal groove. France.
11. Needle of bone. France. After D. Peyrony.
12. Harpoon point(?) of antler, curved, double pointed, flattened for lashing. Spain. After O. Menghin.
13. Pendant of ivory, incised ornamentation. Moravia. After O. Menghin.

Note. Additional surviving traits previously illustrated or mentioned: Hammer stones, sidescrapers, keelscrapers (rare), stemmed flake points, incising tools, ochre and oxide colors, spatulate antler tools, lance points of bone with slant base, lance shaft straightener of antler, pendants of perforated teeth, bracelets or rings of ivory, sculpture in bone and stone of human and animal subjects.

Note. Additional new items not previously illustrated or mentioned: Lance point of bone with single barb or shoulder, similar to Item 5 above.

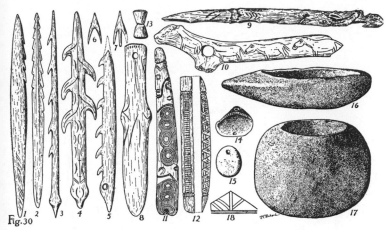

Fig.30

Fig. 30. Typical Magdalenian implements, ornaments, etc.

(One third natural size)

1. Dart point of bone, small barbs one side. France. After H. Breuil.
2. Dart point of bone, small barbs both sides. France. After H. Breuil.
3. Harpoon point of antler, lateral knobs on stem, barbed one side. France. After H. Breuil.
4. Harpoon point of antler, lateral knobs on stem, barbed both sides, incised ornamentation. France. After H. Breuil.
5. Harpoon point of antler, perforated stem, barbed one side. France. After H. Breuil.
6. Arrow point(?) of bone, forked base — called fishhook. France. After H. Breuil.
7. Arrow point(?) of bone with stem and barbs — called fishhook. France. After H. Breuil.
8. Dagger of bone, perforated and ornamented. France. After H. Breuil.
9. Spear-thrower of antler with carved image of mountain goat. France. After J. Dechelette.
10. Arrow shaft straightener or baton of antler with horse engravings. France. After Lartet and Christy.
11. Wand or baton of ivory with curved line ornamentation. France. After H. Breuil.
12. Spatulate implement of bone with straight line ornamentation. France. After G. Backman.
13. Bar-button or toggle of bone. France. After G. and A. de Mortillet.
14. Bead or pendant of bivalve shell, perforated. France. After G. and A. de Mortillet.
15. Pendant of small pebble, perforated. France.
16. Lamp of stone. France. (From cast.)
17. Mortar of stone. France.
18. Game trap or house frame(?) painted on cave wall. France. After G. and A. de Mortillet.

Note. Additional surviving forms previously illustrated or mentioned: Hammerstones, whetstones, endscrapers, keelscrapers, burins, incising tools, stemmed flake points, perforators, saws, shell beads, bone awls, needles, lance points with slant and slit bases, straight double-pointed "fishhooks," spatulate antler implements, ornamented bone pendants, pendants of teeth, bar button or handle with transverse groove, microlithic flake tools.

Note. Additional new items not previously illustrated or mentioned: Club head or weight for digging stick of perforated boulder, vessel adapted from human skull, whistle(?) of phalangeal bone, perforated disk button, perforated pendant of ivory, polychrome cave-wall paintings.

183

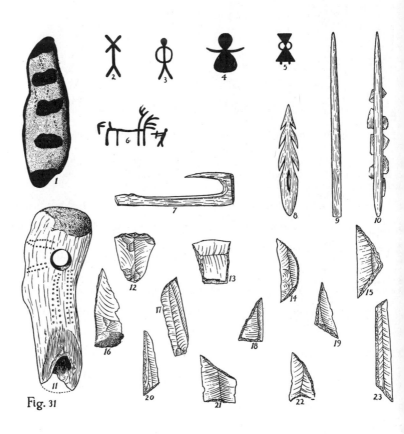

Fig. 31

Fig. 31. Typical Azilian-Tardenoisian-Maglemosian implements, etc.

(Nos. 1, 7–11 one third natural size; 12–23 two thirds; 2–6 reduction unknown)

1. Painted pebble. Azilian. France.
2–5. Conventionalized human figures painted on cave wall. Spain. After H. Obermaier.
6. Hunting scene showing bow and arrow, painted on cave wall. Spain. After H. Breuil.
7. Fishhook of bone. Maglemosian. Denmark. After K. F. Johansen, etc.
8. Harpoon point of deer antler, perforated, double barbed. Azilian. France. After G. and A. de Mortillet.
9. Dart point of bone, double slant base. Maglemosian. Denmark.
10. Dart point of bone with flint flake barbs. Maglemosian. Denmark.
11. Adze of antler, perforated, punctate ornamentation. Denmark. After K. F. Johansen.
12. Endscraper of flint, subtriangular. Tardenoisian. Germany.
13. Arrow point of flint, cross-cutting type, hafted by lower edge. Tardenoisian. Germany.
4–15. Arrow points, semilunar and triangular, hafted by right chipped edges. Tardenoisian. Germany.
16. Incising tool or knife with bluntly chipped back. Tardenoisian. Germany.
17. Incising tool or knife with slantingly chipped point. Tardenoisian. Germany.
8–22. Geometric flints with two chipped margins. Tardenoisian. Germany.
23. Incising tool, double pointed, three chipped margins. Maglemosian. Denmark. After K. F. Johansen.

Note. Additional surviving forms previously illustrated or mentioned: Hammerstones (oval), anvil stones (pitted), rubbing stones, grooved polishing stones, polishing pebbles, pendants of perforated pebbles, keelscrapers, discoidal scrapers, sidescrapers, notched scrapers, burins, saws, perforators, stemmed flake points, pointed antler implements (pressure chippers?), wedges or spatulate antler implements, barbed harpoon points of bone and antler, awls of bone, needle or bodkin of bone (rare), pendants of perforated teeth, crude geometric and realistic engravings on bone.

Note. Additional new items not previously illustrated or mentioned: Picks or crude pointed core implements, chisels or chisel-pointed core implements, chisels made from pebbles by rubbing, axe or chopper of flint spall (see Fig. 32, 1), rare; axe or chopper of flint hafted in antler, adze of flint hafted in antler, adze of antler hafted in antler, chisel or spatulate tool of hollow bone, chisel or chopper adapted from swine tooth, knives adapted from beaver and swine teeth, bifurcated bone implement resembling Figure 30, 6, lump of rosin, probably used as glue; lump of pyrites, probably for striking fire.

Fig. 32

Fig. 32. Typical Early Neolithic implements, etc., of Danish shell heap,
French Campignian, and Spanish Asturian facies.
(About one third natural size; No. 20 about one ninth)

1. Axe (tranchet) adapted from sharp-edged spall. Denmark and France.
2. Chisel adapted from sharp-edged spall. Denmark.
3. Pick flaked from quartzite boulder. Asturian. Spain.
4. Pick flaked from spall or core, triangular cross section. Denmark, France, etc.
5. Axe flaked from core, lenticular cross section, simple bit. Denmark.
6. Endscraper, chipped concave bit. Denmark.
7. Endscraper of short spall, chipped convex bit. Denmark, etc.
8. Arrow point of cross-cutting type, lateral margins chipped. Denmark, etc.
9. Rubbing stone, discoidal and faceted. France.
10. Mealing stone, slightly dished. France.
11. Axe of antler, perforated for hafting. Denmark, etc.
12. Awl of split deer bone. Denmark, but world-wide.
13. Awl or dagger of deer bone with natural butt. Denmark, etc. After W. Dreyer.
14. Awl of bird bone. Denmark. After C. Neergaard.
15. Boomerang(?) of wood. Denmark. After T. Thomsen and A. Jessen.
16. Fishhook of bone, barbed. Denmark. After W. Dreyer.
17. Pendant or bead of bone, basket-shaped. Denmark. After C. Neergaard.
18. Comb of bone, perforated. Denmark. After W. Dreyer.
19. Pendant of tabular bone. Denmark. After W. Dreyer.
20. Pottery vessel, indented rim, pointed bottom. Denmark. After T. Thomsen and A. Jessen.

Note. Additional surviving forms previously illustrated or mentioned: Hammerstones, sidescrapers (convex and concave bits), endscrapers of long flakes (convex bit), perforators or drills, adze, pressure chipper of antler, axe hafted in bone sleeve, knife of boar's tooth.

Note. Additional new items not previously illustrated or mentioned: Endscrapers with right or left slanting bit, arrow points of crude triangular form, bone pins with heads, axe hafted in wooden sleeve, antler axe with wooden handle, bow(?) of wood, side guards of wood for fish spear, bracelet or ring of bone.

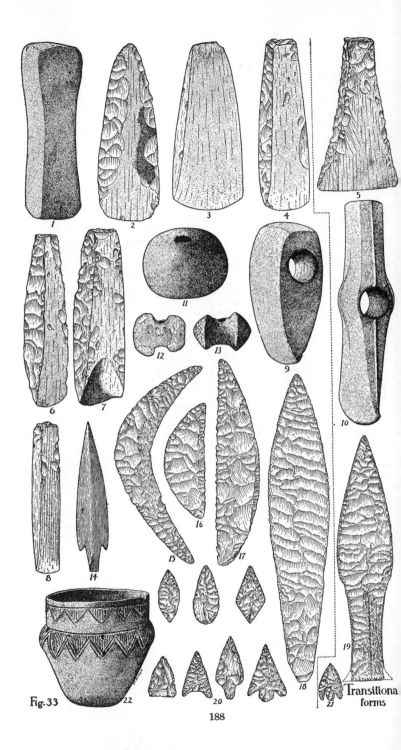

Fig. 33

Transitional forms

Fig. 33. Typical Middle and Late Neolithic implements, etc. Mostly from the Baltic area and derived from village sites, dolmen and chambered mound burials.

(About one third natural size)

1. Grindstone, for use in shaping flint axes, etc. Sweden.
2. Axe of flint, earliest form, pointed butt, thin edges, partly ground. Sweden.
3. Axe of flint, second form, thin butt, flat edges, ground. Denmark.
4. Axe of flint, third form, rectangular butt, flat edges, partly ground. Denmark.
5. Axe of flint, fourth and final form, rectangular butt, flat edges, flaring bit, partly ground. Probably of Bronze Age date. Denmark.
6. Adze of flint, partly ground. Denmark.
7. Gouge of flint, partly ground. Preceded by form similar to axe No. 2. Denmark.
8. Chisel of flint, ground. Preceded by ruder unground form. Denmark.
9. Axe-hammer of stone, perforated, ground and polished. Denmark.
10. War axe of stone, faceted, perforated and ground — one of several forms. Probably of Bronze Age date. Denmark.
11. Club head of stone, subspherical, perforated. Denmark.
12. Bead or pendant of amber, double-axe shape. Denmark.
13. Bead or pendant of amber, possibly a button, hourglass shape. Denmark.
14. Spear point of slate, ground. Of circumpolar distribution. Sweden. After O. Montelius.
15. Sickle blade of flint, stemmed and notched for hafting. Denmark.
16. Knife or saw of flint, semilunar, slightly serrated. Denmark.
17. Saw of flint, denticulated edge, arched back. Denmark.
18. Spear point or primitive dagger of flint, ripple chipped. Denmark.
19. Dagger of flint, fishtail handle with ornamental chipping. Probably of Bronze Age date. Denmark.
20. Arrow points of flint — seven basic forms. Denmark and British Isles.
21. Arrow point of flint, basal notches. Probably of Bronze Age date. Denmark and British Isles.
22. Pottery vessel, stamped ornamentation filled with chalk. Denmark.

Note. Additional surviving forms previously illustrated or mentioned: Stone: hammerstones, rubbing stones, mealing stones, pebble pendants strung as necklaces. Flint: spear points (see Fig. 17, *D*), arrow points of trapezoidal type, notched sidescrapers, endscrapers (long and short), drill points, picks. Bone and antler: awls, needles (rare), dart points with small barbs, harpoon points, with and without basal perforation, chisels or spatulas, pressure chippers (see Fig. 17, *B*), fishhooks, pendants of tabular bone, pendants of perforated teeth.

Note. Additional new items not previously illustrated or mentioned: Stone: pitted stones (ceremonial?), grooved sinkers, whetstones of slate, club heads (perforated disks), club heads (oval with groove), chisels with round flat top, perforated ceremonial axes, stemmed axes, grooved axes (American type), lamps or vessels (British Isles), petroglyphic inscriptions. In addition North America furnishes a variety of ceremonial objects such as pipes, banner stones, bird stones, gorgets, etc. Flint: pressure chippers, flake knives with stem or handle, food knives with parallel-sided blade and handle, fully chipped; spear points with straight, convex, pointed, and stemmed bases; stemmed arrow points with long triangular-sectioned file-shaped body; spoon-shaped or stemmed endscrapers, gouge with pointed butt and thin edges, gouge-chisel, axe of thin-butted type (see Fig. 33, *3*) hafted in wooden handle, sickle of flint flake hafted in wooden handle. Bone and antler: L-shaped picks of pronged deer antler, used for mining flint (England and Belgium), hairpins with disk heads and perforation, ornaments of boar tusks, game pieces. Many other specialized implements and ornaments are found in the Eskimo culture. Amber: beads, pendants, and studs of various shapes. Wood: spoons, skis. Textiles: fishnets, cords, etc. Burnt clay: spoons with holes like collander, bottlenecked vessels.

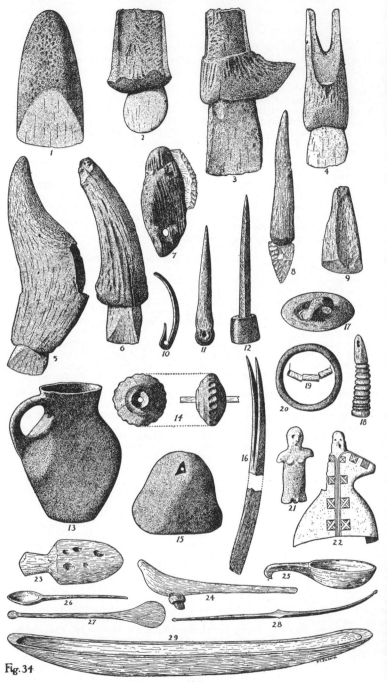

Fig. 34

204

Fig. 34. Typical Neolithic (Robenhausian) implements, etc., from the Alpine area and derived mainly from Swiss lake pile dwellings.

(Nos. 1–22 about one third natural size; the rest much reduced)

1. Axe of stone, pointed butt, pecked body, ground bit. Switzerland.
2. Axe of stone, set in simple antler sleeve. Earliest form of mounting. Switzerland.
3. Axe of jadeite, set in shouldered antler sleeve with spur. Second form. Switzerland.
4. Axe (or adze) of stone, set in bifurcated antler sleeve. Third form. Switzerland.
5. Axe of stone, set in antler with transverse perforation. Last form. Switzerland.
6. Chisel of jadeite, set in antler handhold. Early form. Switzerland.
7. Knife of flint, set in wooden handhold, perforated. Switzerland.
8. Knife of flint, set in antler handle. Switzerland.
9. Chisel or spatula of bone. Switzerland.
10. Fishhook made from boar's tooth. Switzerland.
11. Awl of split mammal bone. Switzerland.
12. Awl of bone, set in bone handle. Switzerland.
13. Pottery vessel in form of pitcher. Switzerland.
14. Spindlewhorl of burnt clay.
15. Loom weight of burnt clay. Switzerland.
16. Comb or bifurcated rib, for pressing down woof. Switzerland.
17. Button of bone, extra large. Switzerland.
18. Pendant of antler, transversely grooved. Switzerland.
19. Beads of stone, cylindrical. Switzerland.
20. Bracelet of lignite. France. After R. Montandon.
21. Human figurine of burnt clay. France. After J. Dechelette.
22. Ornamented idol of burnt clay. Austria. After A. Schenk.
23. Mallet of wood. Switzerland. After F. Keller.
24. Axe showing details of hafting. Switzerland. After F. Keller.
25. Dipper of wood. Switzerland. After F. Keller.
26. Ladle of wood. Switzerland. After F. Keller.
27. Club of wood. Switzerland. After F. Keller.
28. Bow of yew wood. Switzerland. After G. and A. de Mortillet.
29. Boat or canoe of wood. Switzerland. After F. Keller.

Note. Additional surviving forms previously illustrated or mentioned: Stone: hammerstones; perforated club heads, axe-hammers, and war axes; rubbing stones, mealing stones, whetstones, paint stones, pendants of perforated pebbles, bracelets or discoidal rings. Flint: geometric microliths, sidescrapers, endscrapers, saws, perforators or drills, knives, daggers, spear points with convex and stemmed bases, arrow points of all ordinary basic forms. Bone and antler: daggers or awls of olecranon bone, knives, gorge hooks, fishhooks, needles or bodkins, pins with plain and ornamented heads, spatulate tools, harpoons with barbs and perforations, combs, pendants of perforated teeth and bone plates. Pottery: vessels of various forms, plain and decorated with stamped or incised geometric designs.

Note. Additional new items not previously illustrated or mentioned: Stone: grooved hammers or net sinkers, grooved axes, pestles, plummets or pendants of limestone, discoidal rings, bracelets of schist, diminutive incised stone tablets representing idols, man-size idols sculptured in low relief, petroglyphic inscriptions. Flint: dagger blades hafted in wood, discoidal club heads with perforation, cutters or chisels set in bone or antler handles. Shell: pendants of tabular pieces, bracelets, coral objects. Bone, antler, etc.: hammers and hoes of antler with perforation for hafting, daggers, knives and chisels or burins of boars' teeth, skates of bone, arrow points of bone and antler with and without barbs, flute of bird bone with three vents, buttons of bone disks with two perforations. Wood: daggers, knives, chisels or wedges, dishes, churn dashers, suspension hooks, looms, ladders, wattlework houses, log houses, flails, ox yokes. Textiles: basketry, string, rope, fishnets, cloth of various weaves, embroidery. Pottery: vessels with birchbark inlay, needle holders, pot rings. Copper: beads, axes. Agriculture and animal husbandry: wheat, barley, millet, flax, poppy, grape; dog, sheep, goat, pig, ox.

Fig. 35

Fig. 35. Typical bronze implements, etc., of Bronze Age, derived mostly from the Baltic and Alpine centers but characteristic of all western Europe.

(Nos. 1–31, about one third natural size; the rest much reduced)

1. Axe blade, thin, flat, flaring bit (compare Fig. 33, *5*). Denmark.
2. Axe blade with lateral flanges. France.
3. Axe blade with stop and flanges. Hungary.
4. Axe blade with loop and wide flanges.
5. Axe blade with socket, loop, and ornamentation. Hungary.

Note. The above series presents the evolution of the Bronze Age.

6. Chisel with socket for insertion of handle. Switzerland.
7. Hammer with socket for hafting. Switzerland.
8. Awl hafted in antler. Switzerland.
9. Needle. Switzerland.
10. Tweezers, ornamented. Denmark.
11. Razor with perforated handle. Switzerland.
12. Razor with looped handle (boat-shaped). Denmark.
13. Saw, fragmentary. Denmark.
14. Knife with stem for hafting, ornamented. Switzerland.
15. Spear point with perforated socket for hafting. Denmark.
16. Dagger blade with rivets and rivet holes (hafting indicated). Denmark.
17. Sword, double-edged, with riveted hilt. Germany.
18. Arrow point, socketed and barbed. Hungary.
19. Arrow point, stemmed and shouldered. Switzerland.
20. Arrow point, straight base, perforated for hafting. Switzerland. After F. Keller.
21. Fishhooks, single and double. Switzerland.
22. Bit for horse bridle, linked. Switzerland.
23. Wheel for votive chariot or possibly a pendant. Switzerland.
24. Hairpins (6) with different types of head, plain and ornamented. Switzerland.
25. Fibula, or simple form of safety pin. Switzerland.
26. Pendant, or part of a pendant. Switzerland.
27. Bar-shaped button. Denmark.
28. Chain attached to pin. Switzerland. After F. Keller.
29. Bracelet, open, hollow, ornamented. Switzerland.
30. Sword hilt button with spiral ornamentation, typical motive. Denmark.
31. Sickle blade. Hungary.
32. Female figure, dressed in short-sleeved jacket and skirt tied with tasseled belt. Necklace, spiral armrings, belt buckle, and dagger indicated. Denmark. After S. Muller.
33. Warrior with bow, arrow, and sword — petroglyph. Sweden. After G. Ekholm.
34. Warrior with axe and shield — petroglyph. Sweden. After O. Montelius.
35. Warrior on horseback with spear and shield — petroglyph. Sweden. After S. Muller.
36. Plowing with oxen — petroglyph. Sweden. After G. Ekholm.
37. Horse-drawn chariot — petroglyph. Sweden. After O. Montelius.
38. Double-prowed vessel with warriors — petroglyph. Sweden. After O. Montelius.
39. Warrior blowing trumpet — petroglyph. Sweden. After W. Dreyer.

Note. By this time the surviving inventions previously mentioned, as well as the new forms not here illustrated, are so numerous that to name them becomes impractical. The approximate numbers are as follows: surviving old forms, 27; new inventions and practices, about 90.

Fig. 36. Typical implements, etc., chiefly of the later Iron Age, derived mostly from graves and habitation sites of the Baltic and Alpine areas.

(Nos. 1–7, 9–11, 17, 18, 20, 21, about one sixth natural size; Nos. 8, 12–15, 19, 22–38, about one third natural size; No. 16, two thirds natural size)

1. Anvil of iron. Denmark.
2. Hammer of iron, perforated for hafting in modern style. Denmark.
3. Axe of iron, socketed for hafting in Bronze Age style. Denmark.
4. Axe of iron, perforated for hafting in modern style. Denmark.
5. Tongs of iron. Denmark.
6. Auger of iron, spoon-shaped bit. Hungary and Denmark. After J. Dechelette.
7. Combination saw and knife, stemmed and hafted. Switzerland.
8. Spokeshave of iron with stems for hafting. Austria. After J. Dechelette.
9. Plowshare of iron, flanged for fastening on beam. Austria. After J. Dechelette.
10. Scythe blade of iron. Switzerland.
11. Shears of iron with bent spring handhold. Switzerland.
12. Horseshoe of iron, with heels and six nailholes — probably late. Denmark.
13. Harpoon point of iron, socketed and barbed. Hungary.
14. Spear point of iron, socketed. Denmark.
15. Arrow point of iron, lozenge-shaped, stemmed. Hungary.
16. Arrow point of bronze, trifoliate, socketed, perforated. Hungary.
17. Dagger with iron blade and bronze hilt. Switzerland.
18. Sword of iron, double-edged, stemmed for hilt, Switzerland.
19. Razor or knife of iron, twisted handle with ring. Hungary.
20. Fish spear of iron, three prongs with single barbs. Switzerland. After R. Munro.
21. Boathook of iron, with spike and socket. Switzerland. After R. Munro.
22. Cup of wood, apparently turned on lathe. Denmark.
23. Cup of bronze with riveted loop handle. Switzerland.
24. Dice of bone. (Tally marks should have been dots with two concentric circles.) Sweden. After O. Montelius.
25–28. Polychrome mosaic beads of glass. Denmark and Sweden.
29. Pendant of amber. Denmark.
30. Safety pin or fibula of bronze. Denmark.
31. Safety pin or fibula of iron. Switzerland.
32. Hairpin or garment fastener of bronze, flat head. Denmark.
33. Brooch of bronze in form of animal head, ornamented. Sweden.
34. Buckle of bronze with serpent head extremities. Sweden.
35. Belt hook and ring of iron. Switzerland.
36. Bracelet of bronze, bent bar with 15 knobs. Hungary.
37. Finger ring of gold, with ornamentation and stone setting. Sweden. After O. Montelius.
38. Strike-a-light stone with lateral groove for reception of metal band by which it was fastened to the belt. Denmark.

Note. Additional surviving culture traits, 55; additional new culture traits, about 155.

The chief sources of error are: the conflicting opinions as to the exact number of glaciations in various regions affected, the lack of unanimity concerning the synchronization, for example, of the Alpine, Scottish, Scandinavian, and North American glacial movements, the irregularity of the faunal changes in different localities incidental to glacial advances and retreats, and above all the difficulty of assigning absolute dates to the succession of events — except in the case of the Holocene epoch. Nevertheless, in spite of all these uncertainties, the general results are doubtless as nearly correct as are the so-called known events of documented historical writings. Finally, it must be emphasized that our schematized treatment applies primarily to France and secondarily at most only to western Europe. To what extent the results here observed hold true for the rest of the world is still to be determined.[7]

Development of archaeology in Africa. During the last fifty years several large surface collections of early Paleolithic types of stone implements have been gathered in Egypt, especially on the high desert plateau west of Luxor. Smaller surface finds of the same general character have also been made in Somaliland, in the Nubian and Lybian deserts, in Tunis, Algiers, and Morocco, as well as in scattered sections of the Sahara as far south as Timbuktu. Similar roughly flaked coup-de-poing forms, derived partly from the surface and partly from river gravels and cave deposits, have been recovered in small numbers in a few places in the Congo basin and in large quantities in many scattered sections of Rhodesia and South Africa. The majority of these implements, running into tens of thousands, are of Lower and Middle Paleolithic aspects (Chellean, Acheulian, Mousterian); but in so far as they are merely surface gatherings, their ages in terms of European chronology have not until lately been even approximately determinable. All that could be done was to separate them into type groups which in turn, in the case of the Egyptian specimens, could be arranged chronologically by means of the varying degrees of exhibited weathering or patination. Since 1926, however, K. S. Sanford and W. J. Arkell, of the University of Chicago, have identified the Nile valley lateral gravels as of Pleistocene age and have in addition removed numerous Chellean-Acheulian coups-de-poing from the older upper terraces and Mousterian forms from the later lower terraces (the Neolithic remains are in the latest valley floor silts), so that now it becomes possible to synchronize the Egyptian and western European Paleolithic stages and perhaps to say which is the older. Similarly, since 1926, L. S. B. Leakey has discovered in Kenya Colony numerous implements of Chellean, Acheulian, and Mousterian types embedded in geologic deposits belonging to the Pleistocene pluvial and interpluvial series, which, it is thought, can be definitely correlated with European glacial epochs.

Artifacts of Upper Paleolithic affinities are less·uniformly distributed in Africa, or else are more difficult to recognize because they do not everywhere conform to European standards. They are abundant, however, all along the Mediterranean coast and have been extensively excavated in the rock shelters and inland shell heaps (*escargotières*) of Tunis and Algiers. Here they characterize the so-called Capsian culture stage, which is a locally peculiar flake industry, in part contemporary with and very similar to the Aurignacian of western Europe. In addition, Mr. Leakey has lately excavated in the Kenya Colony caves several deep culture deposits exhibiting as many as eight successive occupation levels, beginning at the bottom with a distinctly Aurignacian industry and ending at the top with modern or Post-Neolithic relics. All of these culture horizons include faunal remains, living or extinct, which latter, taken together with the geological evidences of climatic fluctuations, will ultimately serve to date the archaeological findings. Rhodesia and South Africa have also furnished flake implements of Upper Paleolithic type, but until very recently these promising items were mostly of surface origin.

To date, the most complete inventory comes from the Kenya Colony caves and includes the following typical items; hammerstones of subspherical form; rubbing or grinding stones of lava, used for grinding paints and suitable also perhaps for smoothing and sharpening bone awls; "sinew frayers," adapted from flint flakes; "pressure chippers," likewise adapted; knives with straight edges and bluntly chipped arched backs; perforators, or drill points; gravette points, or incising tools; burins, or engraving tools of several different forms; sidescrapers with either convex or concave edges; single and double endscrapers; geometric microliths (triangular, trapezoidal, semilunar, etc.); awls of bone; and, finally, numerous beads and pendants of shell and ivory. Traces of pottery were also found, but these may perhaps be explained as intrusions from the Neolithic levels above. The inventory given by A. Pond for his Algerian sites is slightly richer in bone implements, exhibits no pottery, but otherwise is nearly the same. In conclusion it should be pointed out that the Upper Paleolithic in at least some parts of Africa ended with a microlithic industry in some respects identical with the Azilian-Tardenoisian of Europe. There is this important chronological difference, however, that whereas Europe's microlithic stage ended some eight or nine thousand years ago, in Egypt certain of the traits (for example, semilunar arrow points) held on down into Dynastic times and have been retained in the Bushman's implemental outfit practically to our own day.

As supplemental to the indicated industrial remains, Africa is characterized also by numerous and widely distributed animal pictographs, both painted and sculptured, which are at least in part of Paleolithic date. Their general style and mode of execution bear a strong resemblance to the Paleolithic cave art of Europe, especially to that of the rock shelters of eastern Spain. But while some of the African representations are of extinct creatures and therefore presumably ancient, others are not; and of the latter not a few are attributable to the Bushmen of comparatively recent times.

Africa's Neolithic stage is comparatively unknown. Surface collections are available from such scattered localities as Mauritania, Egypt, Kenya Colony, and the Vaal River valley in South Africa. But aside from a few excavations in minor Nile valley shell heaps and in some of the Kenya Colony caves, very little, if any, unmixed material has been obtained. Consequently the purely Neolithic inventory is as yet uncertain; likewise its geographic and chronologic ranges. However, it appears to have included spear and arrow points, celts, mortars and pestles, perforated stone rings, simple stamped or incised pottery, as well as ordinary bone awls and disk beads of shell and other materials. In Egypt alone, where much work has been done of late, the Neolithic inventory seems fairly complete, and here also there are indications of considerable antiquity. Thus Breasted states that broken pottery has been obtained from wells, driven through the Nile valley silt, at depths ranging close to ninety feet below the present surface. From this fact he has calculated that the Egyptian Neolithic culture may date back all of 20,000 years. But while this conclusion as regards ceramics is strengthened in one sense by the suggestive pottery finds in the Aurignacian of Kenya Colony, other indications from all around the eastern end of the Mediterranean would seem to call for a lapse of not more than about 12,000 years since the beginning of the true Neolithic.

When we turn to Africa's metallurgical stages there is still less to be said. The Mediterranean coastal zone may be assumed to have shared the products found in Egypt and Spain, though little information is available on the subject. Elsewhere, as in scattered localities south and southeast of the Sahara, copper seems to have been worked during Pre-European times, and at least some uncertain alloys were made even as far south as the Orange Free State. But very likely all of this work was of relatively late Arabic introduction. Iron, on the other hand, is positively known to have been smelted from early times in many localities outside the Sahara and central Congo regions; and when the Portuguese first began to circumnavigate Africa, during the latter half of the fifteenth century, its products were already being traded practically throughout the entire continent. The only places, in fact, where stone implements were found still in use were among some of the Bushmen in the south and on the Island of Fernando Po off the Guinea coast. The investigation of Africa, outside of Egypt, is still in its infancy. Nevertheless, enough is known to warrant the current opinion that man is as old here, probably, as in Europe itself, though apparently his culture has not everywhere undergone so many sharply marked changes.[8]

Southern Asia. The mainland of India has yielded many cave and open-air indications of the Lower, Upper, and Final (Tardenoisian) Paleolithic industries; also a crude cave art resembling that of southeastern Spain and Africa. In addition, numerous sites representative of the Neolithic and iron-working techniques have been found, and these are associated with megalithic structures, some of which, like the dolmen, are still being erected in places. The copper and bronze industries are only faintly indicated, and current opinion is that India passed directly from the Neolithic to the Iron stage. To date, the extensive collections made appear to be mainly of surface origin; but many workers are now active.[9]

Farther India is less well known but has been sampled in every part, sufficiently to indicate several peculiarities. The only thoroughgoing work, executed since 1902 by H. Mansuy and his co-workers of the Geological Survey of French Indo-China, has been concentrated on the caves and shell heaps of Tonkin, which have yielded data ranging back to a primitive Neolithic culture called Bacsonian.[10] A somewhat similar industry is also reported from the Malay peninsula. The region as a whole exhibits at least some megalithic monuments and is noted especially for its historic ruins, like the great Angkor-Vat in Cambodia. The general results for southern Asia go to show that this part of the world, at least as far as India, shared all the major culture stages revealed in northern Africa and western Europe.

Central Asia. Being comparatively difficult of access, central Asia has until lately been left practically untouched by the archaeologists except for its marginal areas. It is only recently that finds have been made which reveal the importance of this whole vast district for an understanding of earliest human prehistory. The finds include skeletal and cultural remains, some of which date back to the early part of the Pleistocene epoch, thus rivaling European discoveries in respect to both antiquity and primitiveness of culture status.[11]

Northern Asia. Northern Asia, or Siberia, contrary to theoretical expectations, has also yielded important antiquities. The first important discovery was made by I. T. Savenkov in 1884 near Krasnoyarsk in the upper Yenisei country. This revealed implements of Upper Paleolithic aspect associated with bones of the mammoth, the rhinoceros, and other extinct mammals. Not until 1923 were the authenticity and character of the finds made generally known.[12] In the meantime G. P. Sosnovski, B. E. Petri, and other Russian investigators have uncovered similarly associated remains, not only higher up in the Yenisei valley toward Minusinsk, but also to the west, near Biisk in the upper Ob basin, and to the east along the Angara River as far as Irkutsk, near Lake Baikal. However, this primitive culture phase is not necessarily as old as its European counterpart, because the accompanying fauna here, as in America, may have survived until fairly recent times. The types find their parallel in the typical Mousterian and the transition to the Aurignacian of Europe. A more recent type, Petri's Siberian Magdalenian, was found near Irkutsk.[13]

In the same general latitude — that is, throughout the steppe zone between fifty and sixty degrees north — numerous Neolithic stations have also been worked at points ranging all the way from the Ural mountains to the mouth of the Amur. A few stray sites are known even along the Arctic coast, particularly at the mouth of the Ob River and at various points near Bering Strait. Finally, the North Pacific shore is represented by recently worked Neolithic locations, with pottery, on the Kamchatka peninsula.[14] Indicative of the later culture stages, a rich and unique bronze-working center [15] has been made known in the Minusinsk region and elsewhere since about 1860; while evidence of an iron industry is marked, for example, in the upper Lena valley, northwest of Lake Baikal. These two metal stages, however, according to Radloff, are widespread in south-central Siberia, as well as in Outer Mongolia, and are marked by burial sites in the form of both mounds and cairns.

Summing up for Asia, it appears that in spite of practical difficulties much sound archaeological work already has been done and that the scattered and disconnected results demand further investigation. To date, perhaps the most important general conclusions that have emerged are the three following. It appears tolerably certain that the Lower Paleolithic phase, as characterized in western Europe and Africa by the coup-de-poing, is confined to southern Asia and that therefore the available traces of contemporary stone-working techniques north of the Himalayas correspond to the Pre-Mousterian flake industry of central Europe. It appears equally certain that, as in South Africa, so in various parts of Asia — India, Manchuria, Siberia — the Iron Age followed directly upon the Neolithic without the intervention of the Bronze stage. Finally, it appears more than probable that western Asia and adjacent Egypt mark the locality in the Old World where early man made the first successful transition from the primitive mode of subsistence based on the hunting and gathering of natural food products to a life sustained mainly by artificial production through agriculture and animal husbandry.

Indonesia. In the not very distant geological past a subsidence of southeastern Asia produced the series of islands variously known as the East Indies, Indonesia, and the Malay archipelago. This insulation of the outlying high portions of the mainland took place presumably before man arrived on the scene; yet today these islands are all more or less densely populated by an invading series of racial types, of which the Negritos are the most primitive though not necessarily the most ancient. Just when they or their predecessors arrived is uncertain; but the discoveries in Java since 1890, by E. Dubois and others, of primitive skeletal remains (Pithecanthropus erectus, Homo wadjakensis, etc.) of Pleistocene date suggest that members of the human and protohuman stocks reached this part of the world perhaps even before implements were invented. In keeping with this idea, Paleolithic culture remains are lately reported from Java, and indications of similar finds are alleged for the Philippines. Whatever the truth, the cousins Sarasin in 1903 excavated a number of caves in Celebes, obtaining a stone industry which, as in the case of Ceylon, they regarded as of Magdalenian affinities.[16] On the other hand, the caves of Borneo appear to have yielded nothing particularly ancient, and the same seems to be the case with Sumatra, Formosa, and far-away Madagascar. Shell heaps, strange to say, are not reported from the region except in Formosa. Pottery is extremely rare. Implements of the polished stone type are everywhere present in limited quantities and varieties, while chipped arrow points are absent — for example, in Formosa and apparently also in Borneo and the Philippines. Associated doubtless with this prehistoric semi-Neolithic horizon are old mining shafts and agricultural terraces; also a scattered sprinkling of megalithic features, such as monoliths, human images, circles, dolmens, platforms, and some peculiar great circular stone urns. Several of these items are identical in type with those of the adjacent continent; but apparently, excepting Madagascar, such cyclopean works are no longer being produced. Architectural ruins of pretentious order are seemingly confined to Java and, like those mentioned in Cambodia, are of Indian origin, dating from the latter half of the first millennium of our era. Ceramic and other evidences of Chinese contact, confined mostly to the northern islands, are traceable also to about the same period. The final noteworthy fact about the Malay archipelago is that since the first arrival of Europeans the native inhabitants, in spite of inequalities of status, have all employed metals as the basis of their material culture.

Australia and Tasmania. Passing southeast beyond the "Wallace Line," which by a deep and ancient ocean channel has effectually separated the continental and island faunas, and also come near to marking the boundary between the metal-working and stone-working cultures in the Pacific region, we may turn our attention first to Australia and Tasmania.

Archaeologically the Australian-Tasmanian realm is of more than ordinary interest. Being an extreme border region, comparatively unfavorable climatically and zoölogically, it may have been the place of retreat of primitive forms. Professor Sollas, for example, has ventured to compare the Tasmanian flint-flaking technique with the facies of European eoliths and the Australian flaked and chipped stone industry with that of the European Mousterian stage. In short, he has sought to identify these isolated peoples as truly living representatives of the fossil men of the Old World mainland. These resemblances are real enough as far as they go, but their chronologic significance in the absence of stratigraphic investigation is doubtful because Australia, like America, yields a mixture of implements, some of which, measured by European standards, are of ancient form while others are presumably of relatively recent invention.

Since most of the recovered Australian implemental data unfortunately have been obtained from living tribes or merely gathered from the surface of old workshops and camp sites, including rock shelters and minor shell heaps, the material may consist of mixtures dating from widely separated periods of time or stages of technique. Too little is known about observed time sequences to allow us to determine a succession of industries. The recent excavation of two stratified culture deposits in South Australia,[17] a rock shelter accumulation fully six meters deep and an open-air site of earlier date with about three meters of debris, do not give any clear evidence. The two sections together exhibit a slightly changing fauna and also four or five distinguishable implemental phases, the lowermost of which is in general very similar to the crude stone and bone industries of Tasmania. In other respects the excavated section exhibits rather unexpected sequences. There are no definite examples of the coup-de-poing, of the geometric microliths, or of the ground stone axe; the technologically late oblong pointed flake comes early and shortly disappears; and what is equally remarkable, bone implements are more abundant in the middle and lower levels than in the upper. Clearly, these chronological results add new problems in place of solving old ones, and we must accordingly await further excavation, perhaps of the shell heaps, which in places are said to reach a height of thirty feet.

Melanesia. Until recent years the natives of Melanesia had a more or less advanced Neolithic culture except in parts of New Guinea where the influence of Malay and Chinese culture is noticeable. As to human existence here during the distant past, archaeology has so far revealed next to nothing beyond superficial observations. Certain monumental features are found, such as upright stones with and without carvings, stone circles, ruined megalithic structures, old mining pits, as well as irrigation terraces and aqueducts. This last group of traits, together with the polished stone implements, has induced some recent students to assume the very unlikely migration of a mysterious early historic people who came from the west, and who in their search for gold and pearls spread over the entire Pacific and even reached America.[18]

The old native types, found in part by excavation, include club heads, celts and adzes of jade, etc.; spear points and knives of obsidian and other flintlike substances. Certain Paleolithic indications have been alleged for the Solomon Islands, but the oldest form here positively known is a flake tranchet or adze, nearly identical with the Northwest European form of the Campignian culture stage.[19]

Stone structures of megalithic character are especially numerous and widespread in Melanesia. The general forms include monoliths, trilithons, carved images, small dolmens, pyramids, buildings, platforms, fortifications and agricultural terraces. In places like the New Hebrides these structures are regarded as of ancient date; in New Caledonia some of them continue in use; and in the Solomon Islands construction is said still to be kept up.

Micronesia. Archaeologically considered, Micronesia can scarcely be very important, at least so far as human antiquity is concerned. Stone implements of the commoner types are rare in the area, their purposes being served by substitutes made mostly of sea shells and shark teeth. Nevertheless, the carriers of the early, relatively advanced culture successfully worked several kinds of rock for a variety of constructional purposes. The remains of these activities include pretentious buildings, pyramids, truncated cones, platforms, terraces, stairways, gateways, cyclopean walls and ramparts, harbors or canals with embankments, paved roads, etc. — much as in Melanesia and the Malay archipelago. The majority of these features are now in ruins, or at any rate are regarded as relics of the past. Perhaps the most unique holdover trait is the use of the so-called "stone money" made in the shape of perforated disks like Chinese "cash," and ranging in size from ordinary disk beads to specimens resembling millstones as much as nine feet in diameter. All of these lapsed cultural elements of the late prehistoric past were presumably derived from various South Asiatic centers by way of the Malay archipelago, and their degeneration is a subject of considerable interest.

Polynesia. We come at last to what seems the final outpost of prehistoric migration, the easternmost Pacific island group called Polynesia. This immense ethnographic area approaches the shape of a great scalene triangle the base of which coincides largely with the

180th degree of longitude, along which it extends from Hawaii to New Zealand, a distance of seventy-five degrees of latitude or over 5000 miles. The apex of the triangle, marked by Easter Island, lies near the Tropic of Capricorn in west longitude 109 degrees (that of the Utah-Colorado boundary), or nearly 4000 miles above the base.

Barring a few minor shell heaps in New Zealand and some scattered monumental remains not now claimed by native residents, there is little for the archaeologist to investigate. This barren condition may conceivably have been brought about by an allegedly recent subsidence of the island realm. On the other hand, the Polynesian migration legends and their accompanying genealogical tables, if they were to be considered of historical value, would give a nearly complete and approximately datable account of the whole immigration episode and limit it to the last two and a half millenniums.[20]

Turning now to the limited aspects of Polynesian culture which by courtesy may be considered archaeologic, we find a series of traits in all main essentials much like what has been indicated for Melanesia and Micronesia. That is, we have a somewhat unevenly distributed variety of monumental remains, partly of megalithic character; and we have a similarly sporadic occurrence of somewhat unique portable artifacts. Fortunately, for reasons both climatic and economic, as well as sociological, we are far better informed about the imperishable handiwork of Polynesia than about the corresponding remains in any other sector of Oceania. Both general treatises and special reports exist; and the available collections, while not large, are sufficiently complete to characterize widely separated sections of the area.[21]

The Polynesian monumental remains, as stated, correspond in large part to those observed elsewhere in the Pacific islands, and mere enumeration of the principal types must here suffice. Included are rock carvings or petroglyphs and sculptured monolithic idols; a large trilithon of dressed stone; circles, platforms, terraces, pyramids, tombs, altars, substructures with low walls for temples and secular buildings, fortifications, roads, fences, gateways, and stairways — all constructed for the most part of natural boulders and basaltic blocks, but in some places supplemented by cut and dressed rectangular slabs. In addition, idols carved of wood and simple earthworks, including agricultural terraces, irrigation systems, and a few mounds are found in certain scattered localities. Easter Island carries the unique distinction of having furnished a number of wooden tablets inscribed with semiconventionalized pictographic characters which presumably served as mnemonic devices rather than as truly phonetic writing. As indicated, not all of these features are everywhere equally profuse or even present. Stone idols, for example, are absent in Samoa, where they might have been expected, while abundantly present in distant Easter Island. Similarly, stone structures, though fairly common everywhere else, are rare in New Zealand and the Chatham Islands. In both these cases wood was employed as a substitute. In brief, the utilization of stone for constructional or monumental purposes, while well-developed, is not a distinctive Polynesian trait and, as one investigator has put it, may often have been resorted to merely because the material was plentiful and in places where tillable land was scarce had to be disposed of in some fashion, as in the case of our ubiquitous New England stone fences.

Polynesian implements and utensils, as well as some of the ceremonial objects, were necessarily made for the most part of various kinds of volcanic rock. However, sandstone and nephrite were used wherever present, as were also to a limited extent such raw materials as coral, shell, and bone. Barring the sandstone, these last-mentioned substances served mostly for the refined types of implements and for ornaments. In working stone all the usual methods such as pecking, grinding, and polishing were employed; only true pressure chipping was conspicuously absent.

The actual inventory of stone objects is limited as to number but is correspondingly interesting as regards unique or specialized forms. Typical among them are natural stones used as hammers, rubbers, grinders, and polishers, as well as boat anchors and sinkers for net, line, or hook fishing apparatus. Outstanding among the forms prepared by pecking, grinding, etc., are grooved sinkers, plummet-shaped slingstones, grooved club heads, sword-shaped clubs, mullers, food pounders of various pleasing shapes, pestles, mortars, cups, trays, salt pans, lamps, game stones (spherical, discoidal, and pitted), flat circular rings, plummet-shaped charm stones, pendants of different forms, phallic emblems, fish images and human images, both naturalistic and highly conventionalized. The primary tools, prepared mostly by flaking and partial grinding, include the adze (no less than eight varieties, different in size, general outline, and cross section), the chisel, the gouge, and rare examples of the axe. Finally, there is a small group of roughly flaked core forms and simple flake blades which include chopperlike implements, scrapers, drills, and knives.

Shells of both marine and land species were utilized as scrapers, as tweezers for pulling hairs, as trumpets, as net sinkers, as beads for necklaces, and as ornaments for canoes. In addition, several of the larger marine forms were worked into ornamental plaques, ear plugs, and arm rings. Shell was also on rare occasions used as a medium for adzes, but more often for fishhooks of both the one-piece and two-piece varieties, as well as for a curious form of pendant resembling a nearly closed one-piece fishhook — identical, strangely enough, with specimens found in the shell heaps of southern California. Tortoise shell also served both useful and ornamental purposes, as, for example, for ear piercers and fans.

Bone, though not precisely a scarce article in view of the presence of the domestic pig and fowl, and at all events of the human skeleton, was employed only sparingly. It was, however, wrought into such articles as dart points, barbed on one or both sides; fishhooks of both the one- and two-piece types and also the straight double-pointed form known as the gorge hook. Rare examples of knives and spatulate tools, as well as simple tongue-shaped pendants and beads cut from hollow bird bones, are also extant. In the Marquesas, tubular sections of human bone, plain or carved, were used as hair ornaments. Ear plugs (Marquesan) and a unique hook-shaped pendant (Hawaiian) were made from whale ivory. Lastly, boar tusks were made into bracelets; shark teeth were set into wooden handles to be used as knives and razors; and both whale and porpoise teeth were perforated and strung for necklaces and other purposes.

The other more readily perishable media, such as wood and wood fiber, feathers, skins, etc., are here of little concern to the archaeologist. It must suffice to say merely that they were all employed, most of them for a great variety of purposes, ranging from houses and canoes to articles of furniture, household utensils, musical instruments of various types, toys, weapons — especially clubs and spears — clothing, mats, baskets, fishtraps, and other things, useful as well as ornamental. Clay, strangely enough, was used for pottery in the Tongan and Easter islands; while elsewhere gourds and probably shells, as well as containers made of wood and stone, served all the purposes for which these roaming islanders employed such utensils. Metals, as has been remarked, had no place at all in Polynesian economy.

Summing up briefly for Polynesia, Micronesia, and Melanesia, it may be said that while our information is as yet rather scanty, the vast island region involved is of special interest to us because it was apparently the last habitable portion of the world to be invaded by prehistoric man. Part of it is also the last region to be exploited by modern Europeans and therefore the region where primitive culture is making its last stand. Indications are that while the first comers to Melanesia may have possessed only a late Paleolithic type of hunting equipment, the later invaders who swept over all the remaining Pacific island world brought a fairly advanced food-producing culture of Post-Neolithic or Megalithic affinities which in its new and inadequate setting underwent a general decline, dropping back as it were to a condition resembling in several respects the normal advanced Neolithic status.

Oceanian-American connections. If we seem to have lingered unduly over the Pacific island area there are several reasons for it. In the first place, there has been until recently next to nothing known about the archaeology of this vast region. Then, too, the material traits found here are engagingly easy to understand, being few in number, moderately simple in form, in part very widely distributed, and, above all, nearly free from the complications connected with great antiquity and the resulting succession of chronological levels. But, more important than all this, some knowledge of Pacific island characteristics is made necessary by the fact that this area has long figured in the opinion of some students as the mysterious realm whence the American continent derived all of its advanced traits of culture.[22] To this claim we must now give some consideration.

The suggested transpacific connection between the Old World and the New constitutes a challenging many-sided problem the salient details of which can only be broadly indicated. Offhand it seems absurd to suppose that the navigators who so freely roamed the vast Pacific and Indian oceans, and who are said to have visited even the Antarctic regions, were unaware of the American continent. Obviously they were bound neither by trade winds nor by the ocean currents but knew their stars sufficiently well to steer a course out and back over thousands of miles of open sea. Compared to such bold seamanship contemporary feats of Europeans in the Atlantic seem child's play; and even if deliberate search for new lands had not brought the islanders over the extra two or three thousand miles to our shore, storm or accident sooner or later must have done so.

Indications that the crossing was actually accomplished appear to be numerous. Thus there is at least some general similarity between the platform and pyramidal structures of North and South America on the one hand and those of the Pacific islands on the other; between the simpler sculptured monoliths of Middle and South America, as well as of the West Indies, and those of Polynesia; between Venezuelan and Melanesian pile dwellings; and between certain Oceanian sailing craft and those of the Pacific coast from Alaska to southern California. Coming down to smaller features, a table of about fifty strikingly similar Oceanic and South American ethnological traits is given by Erland Nordenskiöld,[23] and the list, consisting largely of items made of wood, wood fiber, feathers, bone, shell, and stone, could easily be extended. A somewhat shorter and different but equally important series of trait parallels is given in the same paper for Asia and America. These include various technical processes used in metallurgy, ceramics, textiles, architecture, painting, hunting, fishing, etc., as well as specific products of some of these arts and industries. Now the presence in the New World of more than one hundred Old World elements of material culture — not to mention the nonmaterial parallels — is only partly explainable as a dissemination by way of the region of Bering Strait, and the individual traits must therefore be either independent inventions or else transpacific diffusions. Doubtless both modes of origin must be taken into account, for even if independent invention is allowed as probable in many cases, diffusion cannot be ruled out altogether. However, if we inquire as to when the transmission took place, there arise difficulties. Some of the recent diffusionists insist that inasmuch as the Pacific islands were uninhabited until relatively late times, America could not have received her quota of advanced foreign loans until within the last two thousand years. But, unfortunately for that view, some of the American traits in question appear to be very old. Other exponents, however, point out that several of the outstanding Pacific island traits like the domestic pig and fowl, the cultivated banana, sugar cane, taro, and breadfruit, and especially the unique contrivance known as the outrigger canoe, never passed beyond Polynesia and that therefore America must have received her accession of Old World gifts at a relatively early date — that is, before these elements of culture were disseminated in the Pacific area. From this they naturally conclude that America was reached from Melanesia rather than from Polynesia. In keeping with this latter view it may be urged also that such demonstrably ancient and important American contributions as maize, tobacco, potatoes, peanuts, beans, and peppers, as well as spinning, loom weaving, pressure chipping, and metallic objects, were not carried back to the Pacific islands. To be sure, vigorous claims have been made for the Pre-Columbian transplantation of the banana to America, of the sweet potato to the Pacific islands, and of the coconut palm either one way or the other; but the facts do not appear to be adequately substantiated. At best, therefore, the only conclusion warranted by the ethnological evidence is thàt intercommunication between Oceania and the New World must have been of a sporadic and more or less accidental character.

When we turn to the archaeological parallelisms it becomes necessary to group the available data under several separate headings in order that we may fully appreciate the significance of such trait identities as may exist. Thus, to begin with the broader aspects, it is a conspicuous fact that the prehistoric peoples of the western hemisphere, like those of the eastern, made use of all types of readily accessible raw materials. Even iron of meteoric origin was utilized in America, though the smelting of its ores was not achieved. Moreover, examination reveals that both peoples employed, though not in equal measure, all the same basic handicraft processes. In short, the major arts and industries of the Old and New Worlds were identical. But striking as these similarities may seem, their significance is more apparent than real, for, on the one hand, the general classes of raw materials furnished by nature are so few that duplication in use was unavoidable; and, on the other hand, while doubtless the elementary working processes reached America from without, the shaping arts are also limited in number and their later refinements were therefore bound, independently, to take more or less the same course.

When we concentrate on the forms of handiwork produced, the similarities, though relatively fewer, have much greater significance, because here the maker's creative ingenuity had wider play. Nevertheless, it is a demonstrable fact that more than two hundred varieties of implements and ornaments found in the New World are duplicates of Old World forms.

These inventions are not only similar as regards the purposes they served and as to general typology, but they are to a large extent identical in form. Incidentally, the list of parallelisms could be lengthened not a little by adding basketry, matting, textiles, and feather work; and if we topped off with geometric ornamental designs our total would be nearly doubled. But here again there are limiting conditions which tend to discount the significance of parallelism. Elementary human activities do not vary greatly. The problems to be solved, the forces to be overcome, the raw materials to be dealt with, are much the same the world over. Under these circumstances, if similar solutions, similar methods, and similar devices for executing particular types of work have made their appearance in widely separated regions of the world we need scarcely be astonished. Independent duplication of inventions, the Patent Office assures us, is a common occurrence today and doubtless was so in the past. And what is true about contrivances serving practical ends is surely true also for geometric ornamental designs. For here, too, duplication is unavoidable, inasmuch as the various patterns are made up merely of dots, straight lines, and curved lines which can be combined in only a limited and more or less obvious number of ways.

This being the case, when or how can we be reasonably certain of diffusion as opposed to independent invention? Obviously only in cases where controlling circumstances can be largely eliminated, or where, in other words, human fancy has had free play and where consequently "style" or uniqueness of some sort has resulted. Conventionalized representative art, therefore, would seem to be a valid standard; likewise utilitarian objects of unusual or highly specialized design. Whenever such traits or, better still, particular combinations of traits, are found in widely separated localities, no matter what the distance, we are justified in suspecting genetic relationship, though our judgment in such cases may often rest on subjective rather than objective criteria.

Now, to come to the point at issue here, it so happens that Polynesia and North America, in spite of the three thousand miles that separate them, share a number of cultural traits of precisely this specialized character. Full details cannot be given, but the essential point is that the Pacific coast region from Costa Rica to Alaska exhibits sporadic occurrences of a variety of stone, shell, and bone objects peculiar to Hawaii and other sections of marginal Polynesia, ranging even to New Zealand. Of special interest is the presence in southern Alaska, British Columbia, Oregon, northern California, and Costa Rica of several forms of the unique food pounders which are typical mostly of Hawaii and which as implements are put to somewhat different uses in America. Equally noteworthy is the sword-shaped stone club shared by New Zealand and the Pacific coast from Oregon northward. Lastly, the coast region of southern California yields a peculiar circular one-piece fishhook — or a pendant in the shape of a fishhook — made of either shell or bone, which also has its exact counterpart in New Zealand. Parallel items of slightly less significance are stone adzes, chisels, mortars, pestles, discoidal stones, charm stones or plummets, slender oblong pendants with suspension knob or perforation, perforated subspherical stones, grooved sinkers, fish or whale effigies, as well as such bone objects as the straight double-pointed gorge hook and the barbed dart or harpoon point. In wood there are, for example, the rectangular house with gable roof and carved ornamentation, the plank boat, and the grooved or striated tapa or bark beater, which in Middle America is partially imitated in stone. Finally, it is worth noting that the New Zealand method of working nephrite and other hard rocks by the sawing method was practiced also in Mexico and on the North Pacific coast and that in part of the latter section of America the otherwise universal art of pressure chipping is all but absent, as it is in Polynesia.

These and other similarities that might be cited give undeniable proof of Polynesian influence in America, but the real character of the relationship is not so clear as might be expected. For while the indicated parallelisms are far more convincing than the apparent Neolithic similarities between, for example, northwestern Europe and northeastern North America, still, like the later Norse discoverers of America, the Polynesians appear to have left no obvious impressions either on the Indian physique or the Indian languages, whatever be the case with social institutions. Accordingly, whatever the future verdict may be, at present we are warranted only in supposing that from time to time small groups of Polynesians and possibly other Pacific islanders deliberately or accidentally reached our shores and were effectually absorbed in the native Indian population.

America. The first problem of American archaeology is that of the origin of the American Indian. There is general agreement now that the American race is closely related to the Mongoloid and that

s origin must be looked for in the Old World. Contrary to this
iew, F. Ameghino tried to prove that man originated in South
merica. His views were based on his own explorations and the
bservations of the Danish paleontologist P. W. Lund in the province
f Minas Geraes of southeastern Brazil between the years 1835 and
844. Lund is said to have investigated more than eight hundred
aves. In six of these, located in the vicinity of Lagoa Santa, were
und about thirty human skulls, as well as parts of skeletons and
races of artifacts, in some cases seemingly associated with extinct
Quaternary animal remains, but under conditions, nevertheless,
hich did not warrant the finder to claim geologic antiquity for
hem. Ameghino's own investigations were begun about 1870 in the
rgentine Republic.

Argentina, topographically and geologically, resembles our west-
rn prairie and Rocky Mountain states in being made up largely
f a vast alluvial plain known as the Pampas which slopes gently
rom the Andes to the Atlantic. This Pampean formation is made
p chiefly of water-borne and wind-borne (loess) materials, inter-
tratified here and there with lake deposits and near the Atlantic
order with traces of marine beds. In the coast region this loesslike
lanket, as in middle Europe, is separable into two major horizons,
he Lower and Upper Pampean, known also respectively as the
nsenadean and Bonarean formations. Beneath these two charac-
eristic strata lies an older Pre-Pampean formation called the Her-
osean; and above them, along the stream course and in the lake
asins, there are superficial Post-Pampean or Recent deposits, while
he Atlantic coast belt is marked by sand dunes, both fixed and
oving. Until very recently students were at odds concerning the
spective ages of these formations, except the sand dunes. Ameghino
imself held some of the latest coastal surface deposits to be late
liocene, the Pampean horizons to be middle and early Pliocene,
nd the underlying Hermosean to be Miocene. Later investigators
or the most part agree in regarding the Hermosean as Pliocene
nd the two Pampean levels as Pleistocene. Ameghino's "late Pli-
cene" horizon has been demonstrated to be of modern origin. The
etermination of the geological age of these deposits is chiefly due
o two paleontological facts: first, that the native mammalian fauna
haracteristic of all the later Argentinian formations was of a curi-
usly primitive type, distinguished by giant sloths and great arma-
illolike creatures; and, second, that the mastodon, saber-toothed

tiger, horse, and cloven-footed animals, typical of the North Amer
can Pleistocene, did not appear as migrants in South America unt
very late and persisted for only a brief period. Now that the lat
survival of essentially Tertiary species in South America — as
Australia — has been fully recognized, the discovery of archaeolo
ical remains associated with them in these same deposits no long
means what it once did for the antiquity of man in America.

The archaeological discoveries in question range geographical
all the way from Paraná in southern Brazil to the Strait of M
gellan — chiefly, however, along the Argentine coast; and geolog
cally they are said to have come from all the indicated deposit
Thus, while most of the available artifacts have actually been four
exposed on the surface of the sand dunes and especially on th
Pampean surface, a considerable number of isolated finds were d
rived from both the Upper and Lower Pampean and even from th
Pre-Pampean or Hermosean formation below. These latter fin
have all been questioned and for the most part discredited; b
some apparently remain to be accepted. Skeletal finds, single an
multiple, total up to thirteen for the Upper Pampean, four for th
Lower Pampean, and two for the Hermosean; but these also k
some have been largely disposed of either as recent burials or a
non-human remains, and for the rest as scientifically unacceptabl
It must be remarked, however, that the credibility and significan
of certain of these discoveries have not yet been generally agree
upon. The affirmative view is still to some extent upheld by I
Outes, R. Lehmann-Nitsche, and others, while the negative ha
been presented most forcefully by A. Hrdlička, Bailey Willis, an
W. H. Holmes.[24] At best, however, little remains today of Am
ghino's theory that man and culture originated in South Americ
and from there spread over the rest of the world.

One reason for delaying judgment on the questions of both rel
tive and absolute chronology of human remains and implements
Argentina inheres in the typological character of the artifact. U
fortunately, as indicated, all the available collections — flake
chipped, and ground stone, with a few potsherds — appear to k
surface pickings and not excavations from stratified deposits. Bu
even so, the inventories from the widely scattered coastal sites
the four southern provinces differ somewhat, so that, natural
enough, some students have suggested contemporary local variatio
while others have inferred chronological sequences. Thus, whi

Irdlička inclines to see only one culture of recent date, Holmes avors two, likewise late but somewhat localized variations, and)utes postulates four successive stages, one of Paleolithic and three f Neolithic aspect. The partial explanation is that Outes appears o have found isolated sites characterized exclusively by: (1) flaked ore implements of the coup-de-poing type; (2) flake implements ⁻ith marginal pressure chipping on one face, typical of the Middle nd early Upper Paleolithic; and (3) completely pressure-chipped nplements together with pecked and ground stone forms, as well s pottery. Then, too, in the Paraná region roughly flaked core nplements have been found in isolation in the upper levels of the)ess, while the true surface deposits of the region yield the normal Jeolithic inventory, including bone implements, which appear to ave completely decayed in the south. In short, the indications of tratification and gradual technological evolution in Argentina tally ⁻ith those found by Uhle both superficially and in the shell heaps f Peru, and are further strengthened by stratigraphic data recently btained from the shell heaps of Tierra del Fuego. What this seria-ion means in chronological terms it is impossible to say at present; ut it is at least certain that man was present in South America, as ₁ North America, in time to witness the extinction, for example, f the mastodon, some of the giant sloths, and the horse.

While in earlier years there was a strong inclination to parallel ne Paleolithic development of Europe by means of typological omparisons with that of America, a critical examination of the nds has not so far yielded anything that can conclusively be proved o be of the same antiquity as the earlier Paleolithic remains of :urope. Geologically datable remains from North America show in very case man, not only of the modern type of Homo sapiens, but xhibiting characteristics that do not allow us to assume a race ɪndamentally different from the modern Indian. The industries of hese early periods are mainly, if not entirely, of typical Neolithic haracter. Particularly the lately discovered Folsom types, which elong to a period when man lived with some of the now extinct pecies of animals, show a highly developed and highly special-ɪed stone technique. Thus the data available at the present time ɪdicate the absence of an earlier race of man, corresponding to ne Neanderthal or other early forms, and likewise the absence of he most primitive forms of artifacts.

It would seem likely that man immigrated into America at one

of the periods towards the end of the Ice Age when the continen
was accessible by way of the Bering Strait region. Since, accordin
to geological evidence, the way was open toward the end of th
Ice Age for a migration from Siberia to America along the ice-fre
regions east of the Rocky Mountains, it does not seem unlikely tha
the western continent was reached by man about that time. Th
earliest finds in North America seem to be located on the wester
plains and may belong to this early wave of migration.[25]

This view of the early history of man's migration to Americ
necessitates the assumptions of a very rapid movement from th
extreme north to the southernmost extremity of South America
his adjustment to all the many types of climate, from arctic t
tropic and again to that of the temperate zone; and the develop
ment of many well-differentiated local types and of many culture
and languages. The last named might be explained by a long-con
tinued immigration of different linguistic stocks, but of these w
have no evidence.

It is not possible to follow here the development of the numerou
types of later local cultures. It will be sufficient to indicate that th
immigrants must have been hunters and that agriculture as a
essential foundation of existence must have developed in Centra
America, whence it gradually spread in both directions, north an
south, but without covering the entire area in which climatic condi
tions made agriculture possible. With it the more advanced arts
such as pottery, spread over the continent. Metal-casting was con
fined to narrow areas in Central and South America. It seems tha
all these steps in cultural development occurred in the New Worl
later than in the Old. A connection between them cannot be estab
lished. The question of possible relations between Polynesia an
Melanesia and America has been discussed before.[26]

General world considerations. From our brief survey we have no
only learned something of the varied outstanding archaeologica
features of different habitable portions of the globe, but we hav
discovered, incidentally, that long as prehistoric man has been o
earth and far as he has roamed, he did not, for obvious geographical
climatic, floral, faunal, and cultural reasons, complete its occupatior
At least as far as is now known, he never reached either Antarctic
or the outlying portions of the Arctic; and aside from the closel
strung West Indian chain, none of the distant Atlantic island group
— not even Iceland — was ever occupied. Equally illuminating i

our realization that during what is at present called the Paleolithic culture stage human distribution was confined to limited and contiguous parts of Europe, Asia, including Java, and Africa. Omitting England, Sicily, Malta, and the Canaries as until recently more or less completely connected with their respective continents, all other closely adjacent islands like Ireland, the Balearics, Corsica, Sardinia, Crete, Cyprus, the Aegean archipelago, Ceylon, Japan, and Sakhalin have not yet been definitely proved a part of the early Paleolithic domain; and presumably the ill-favored mountainous and glaciated regions, as well as the densely forested and swamp-covered areas like southeastern Asia and the Congo basin, remained largely uninhabited until comparatively recent times. Whether or not Australasia and America were invaded during the Paleolithic culture phase depends largely upon our definition of the word "Paleolithic"; and necessarily, therefore, what migrations took place during the Neolithic stage becomes correspondingly uncertain. As further examples of the difficulties created by mere words, it might be pointed out that the aboriginal inhabitants of the marginal Pacific and Indian oceans, who, as we have seen, arrived there in post-Neolithic times and who, when discovered in the fifteenth and sixteenth centuries, subsisted mainly by agriculture, have consistently been regarded as living in the so-called Neolithic stage of culture, while the same rating or status is given to the Indians and Eskimo of northern North America, who live entirely by hunting, fishing, and food-gathering. Our understanding of the situation as now developed by archaeological investigation clearly calls for an examination of these two important stumbling blocks.

The terms "Paleolithic" and "Neolithic" as now used are sources of much confusion, for the simple reason that they have double and sometimes even treble meanings. Thus, "Paleolithic" refers to a definite geological time period in the Old World and it denotes also a much less definite type of physical man and a similarly less definite stage of cultural development — namely, the stage especially marked by flaked and chipped stone implements. Similarly, and by contrast, "Neolithic" stands at once for a new or later time period and for a stage of culture characterized in part by ground and polished stone implements. At first sight nothing seems simpler or more explicit. But actually, except in a very broad or general sense, time and culture have no necessary connections. Time proceeds inexorably in one direction while culture rises and falls, owing to a

variety of historical circumstances essentially independent of time
Our world culture distribution problem would therefore be muc
simplified if once for all we boldly divested the expressions "Pale
olithic" and "Neolithic" of their precise chronological connotation:
By doing so the term "Paleolithic" would be broadened and thereb
become parallel to what the ethnologists call the hunting or food
gathering stage of culture; while the term "Neolithic" would b
narrowed and come to be parallel to the first phase of the food
producing culture stage as founded mainly upon the artificial culti
vation of selected plants and animals. So defined, there is no diffi
culty about admitting the presence now or formerly of Paleolithi
man, for example, in Australia and America, or in any other par
of the world where the strictly hunting mode of life prevails. I
would still be true that certain early and characteristically primitiv
Old World features of the Paleolithic are missing for instance i
the New World; but their absence here is what we should expect i
man and culture first arose in some other distant time and place

To complete our world picture of the origin and spread of materie
culture we might now very properly introduce a time-and-spac
chart giving the details of the story in more nearly graphic form
Several such diagrammatic presentations exist for Europe, and other
have been attempted for the world as a whole [27]; but all are defective
either because of inadequate knowledge about many of the area
considered or because of lack of harmony in the interpretation
placed upon the available data. For that reason, as well as for lac
of space, it seems best here not to add to the existing confusior
But the ideal chart would consist of a series of vertical column
representing the geographical divisions of the world arranged a
far as possible in conformity with the actual juxtaposition of th
countries concerned. Beginning with the formerly glaciated portio
of northern Europe, the most feasible order would be central, west
ern, and southern Europe; the various sections of Africa; souther
Asia, Australasia, and the Pacific islands; northern Asia, Nort
America, and finally southernmost South America. The world'
land forms not being arranged in a single continuous strip, as woul
be nearly the case if southern Africa, Australasia, and the Pacifi
islands were omitted, excursions, as it were, become necessary i
these directions. But even so, the indicated arrangement throw
most of the earliest inhabited countries toward the center of th
chart while the countries on the left and right received their huma

opulations in relatively late times. Our chart would also have to
e ruled horizontally to represent geologic time divisions, which in
urn would be subdivided to provide for the successive and approxi-
ately dated culture levels. The frame completed, it would remain
o check, in the proper rubrics, the demonstrated culture stages for
ach country. Such a chart, here only broadly visualized, is one of
he first great desiderata of prehistoric archaeology and one which
annot be adequately realized without prolonged coöperative effort.
nce achieved, we shall have a solid foundation showing when and
here the basic culture complexes first arose and the approximate
outes by which they spread. We shall then at last be in position
o write the permanent outline of human culture history.

As a partial substitute for this desirable two-dimensioned detailed
ulture chart, we may sum up on broad lines the present state of
ur knowledge by indicating the approximate limits of the successive
ulture stages on an ordinary world map (Fig. 37). For this purpose
e shall accept the newly suggested definitions of Paleolithic and
eolithic; we shall combine the early work in copper, tin, silver,
old, and their various alloys as a separate preliminary stage in
etallurgy; and we shall indicate work in iron only in so far as it
volves the art of smelting.

Now such a graphic presentation necessarily embodies compro-
ises and generalizations and must therefore be viewed in the light
f what has been previously said about distributional irregularities.
o indicate the difficulty of laying down precise cultural boundaries,
will be illuminating merely to recall that modern industrial out-
uts more often than not find markets far beyond the actual manu-
acturing centers and to suggest that to a limited degree the same
ust have been true also in the past. Iron implements, for instance,
ere apparently in use all over Africa, even to some slight extent
the Bushman territory of the extreme southwest, when first ex-
lored by Europeans; but smelting was naturally confined to regions
here ores and fuel were plentiful and where the requisite technical
kill had been acquired; while smithing or forging had a much wider
ange. For the rest of the continent barter served as the means of
istribution, the peoples of the marginal areas receiving the trait in
ttenuated form only and at appreciably later dates than the cen-
ers of origin. The Bushmen, therefore, though benefiting by the
ndustry, can scarcely be held to have risen to the Iron Age status.
he same must be said also of the nomadic reindeer herdsmen of

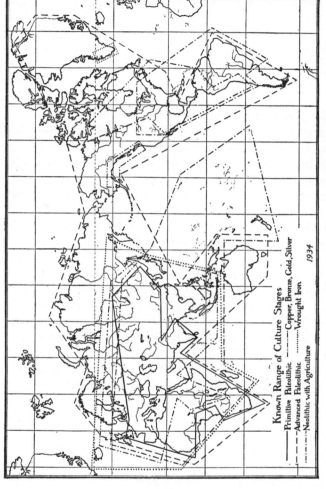

Fig. 37. Map showing known geographic range of culture stages. The Lower Paleolithic range now (1938) includes Farther India and Java.

northern Europe and Asia, who doubtless obtained a few metallic implements from the south but took no real part in their production. An essentially reversed mode of distribution is represented by the preceding copper-bronze stage of metallurgy; for during this relatively long double-process phase, while nuggets of copper, gold, and silver (to a slight extent also meteoric iron) were at first — and in many widely separated regions of both hemispheres — shaped by simple hammering, with or without heating, the melting and casting of such metals, as well as of bronze and other alloys, were not achieved until comparatively late, and then only in a few centralized localities of advanced states of culture, beyond which the articles produced had not, at least in Africa and America, been transmitted very far. Indeed, if the size of the map permitted, the early transitional stage of forging, commonly called the Copper or Chalcolithic stage, should be indicated separately from that of casting. However, the two related processes continued on, independently, side by side, and it is by no means certain that ore reduction, melting, and casting arose in the place or places where cold-forging was first practiced.

A similar condition is presented by the Neolithic-Agricultural areas. The science and art of plant cultivation were far from equally intense or on the same level throughout the indicated ranges, let alone the fact that the plants used varied from place to place and sometimes, as on the North Pacific coast, amounted to nothing more than the growing of tobacco and planting of cinquefoil and clover. But, regardless of the status and character of this key industry, true agricultural produce, owing to its bulky nature, is not likely to have been transported to any great distance outside the actual areas of cultivation, so that the indicated geographic limits may be considered as relatively exact. On the other hand, products of the sedentary activities commonly associated with agriculture, as well as the activities themselves, such as pecking and polishing of stone, pottery-making, weaving perhaps, and even the crude fashioning of metallic implements, were so transmitted (or else were independently invented), some of them far beyond the range of genuine agriculture. The outstanding case in point is that of northwestern North America, where the Pacific coast tribes, independent of agriculture if not exactly of animal domestication (the dog being utilized), reached a status of development in some respects equal if not superior to the contemporary agriculturists or horticulturists farther south and east. With the so-called Paleolithic stages, however, the case is different, for here the few natural raw materials employed were almost everywhere available, so that the geographic limits of production and utilization were more nearly the same. Finally, it must be observed that the map is not a self-explanatory chronological guide, because the boundaries marking, let us say, the more advanced or later stages do not fall regularly either within or without the boundaries of the earlier phases of development, but cross each other, as in the case of agriculture bursting out over Polynesia. The map is still more disappointing in that it cannot very well bring out the important fact that in some regions, like parts of eastern and southern Asia, as well as in the Malay archipelago and probably over most of Africa, the iron-working technique was apparently mastered before that of bronze or its equivalent alloys.

For the rest, the map may be said to speak for itself as far as it goes. It reveals that human culture began in the Old World and that the earliest and most primitive phase was confined roughly to the central and at the same time doubtless the most favorable or most accessible portion of that hemisphere. It reveals that the second or advanced Paleolithic phase swept practically over the entire earth and was stopped only here and there by natural boundaries requiring artificial means of transportation not developed until a later date. It suggests that most of the initial steps toward artificial food production and the subsequent development of the more highly specialized arts and industries, such as agriculture, ceramics, loom weaving, and true metallurgy, were taken supposedly at particularly favorable spots in the tropical and subtropical belts, whence they gradually spread to the more temperate zones, there to undergo further specialization. The map does not, unfortunately, take account of more or less purely nomadic herdsmen cultures, still typical of northern Europe, northern and central Asia, parts of Arabia and the Sahara, as well as of extreme southwestern Africa. The origin of this mode of subsistence, in point of time approximately contemporary with the beginnings of agriculture, presumably was mainly in the steppe regions of the temperate zones, though the colder and warmer belts cannot be entirely excluded. In later times these two culture complexes, presumably not developed in entire independence, came to supplement each other.

In conclusion we must take a last look at the map for tangible suggestions inherent in the spatial culture picture with respect to time relationships. Viewing the American continent for the time being as an independent unit, wc observe that the three grand developmental stages — that is, the late Paleolithic, the Neolithic-Agricultural, and the Copper-Bronze — occupy successively less and less territory and that their respective boundaries are approximately concentric. This condition, regardless of whether or not the two final phases were introduced from without, the same as the first, can mean only one thing; namely, that the two advanced stages began somewhere in the central region, whence they gradually spread over the previously laid Paleolithic foundation, the builders of which for the most part adopted the new traits, while some of those who did not accept them may as a result have been pushed out into the marginal areas north and south or southeast, as well as into the barrens of Lower California. Such a geographical or horizontal presentation can readily be converted into a chronological one by exhibiting, as it were, a geological or vertical north-south section of the continent, taken along a line that shall intersect all three culture boundaries at both extremities. A section so constructed would reveal the successive culture levels stacked up in the shape of a stepped pyramid, provided we could be certain that the later trait groups everywhere overlie the earlier ones and that the earlier ones are nearly if not quite as old along the margins as they are in the center. But while the answer to the first of these two questions seems affirmatively established, we have as yet no positive indications that man has occupied for long either northeastern North America (including Greenland) or the extreme southern and southeastern portions of South America, and it may well be that the late Paleolithic peoples entered those distant regions in relatively late times. In other words, time was passing while culture was spreading. Were we to present this most probable state of affairs in America graphically, our horizontally ruled time section would exhibit the beginnings of the Upper Paleolithic by a slanting line rising gradually from left to right — that is, from Bering Strait to Tierra del Fuego, while the two succeeding culture stages would be represented by inverted pyramids having their apexes located approximately midway on the section or at points corresponding to Middle America and north-Andean South America, as in Figure 38.[28]

The geographic boundaries of the cultural succession as presented by the Old World portion of the map are far less definite and orderly. Thus the beginning phase — that is, the primitive Paleolithic —

fails to attain the widest distribution, as does the oldest stage in America. Moreover, its range does not lie central in the triple-continental area but favors the west and southwest. This eccentricity may, however, be more apparent than real; for, very likely, environmental conditions at this time prohibited or discouraged occupation of the north and the southeast. Then, too, we have as yet no clear proofs that the early Paleolithic culture entered extreme South Africa until relatively late and therefore probably in a modified or improved form. The advanced Paleolithic, on the other hand, sooner or later reached all continental limits and even passed beyond. The Neolithic-Agricultural complex for various reasons, climatic and

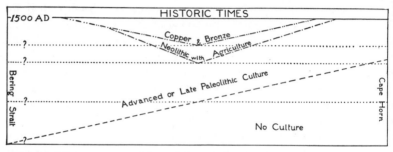

Fig. 38. Diagram representing section of the American continent from north to south, giving hypothetical time range of the known culture stages. Compare Figures 37 and 39.

cultural, failed to expand as far as was possible either north or south, but instead spread suddenly out over the entire and hitherto uninhabited central Pacific island area.

Parenthetically, it becomes necessary here to call attention to the fact that the habitable world was now nearly populated and that as an indirect result a new factor, trade, entered into all the later stages of progress. Up to this point in the development and dissemination of material culture traits, slow migration and simple borrowing had largely sufficed as the agencies of dispersal, commerce in the strict sense having been of only slight importance. It could scarcely have been otherwise, because, as previously suggested, the arts and industries that had been achieved, regardless of their ultimate points of origin, were of the types that could readily take root in all the new home soils. In other words, hitherto the *production* and the *utilization* of specific artificial means of livelihood enjoyed very nearly the same geographic range, no doubt for the simple reason that the natural raw materials employed were almost everywhere present. An inevitable change was brought about, however, by the discovery of the practical usefulness of natural metals and above all by the gradual perfection of processes for their artificial recovery from ores. For metals and ores were not found everywhere, and consequently the uniquely efficient implements produced from them naturally became objects of mutually profitable trade, a form of interchange which has since become the principal agent in the diffusion of material culture.

Returning now to the map, with the preceding remarks in mind, it will readily be understood that the early metallurgical (copper and bronze) range is extremely difficult to bound because, in the Old World as in the New, it apparently had several separate centers of origin, both within and without the agricultural domain, as, for example, up and down the inner portion of East Africa, southwestern Asia, southeastern Asia, and possibly north-central Asia, some of which were chronologically early while others were undoubtedly late. But the extreme diffusion of this trait complex falls well within the earlier boundaries on the south and east, while in the north it extends, at least in central Asia, somewhat beyond the borders of agriculture. Finally, the use of iron has the same range as that of copper and bronze on the east and west, but extends beyond it on the south and to some extent at least also on the north. Were we, however, to ignore the distribution due to trade and instead to lay down the borders of true metallurgical production, it is probable that we should obtain a more nearly concentric or pyramidic arrangement of boundaries, except for the primitive Paleolithic, which in most directions was overtaken and outdistanced by the more rapidly moving advanced Paleolithic.

In the light of the preceding explanations and interpretations there is little need of demonstrating the Old World chronology in graphic form. Besides, no cross section that might be chosen would be universally applicable because, as indicated, the successive boundaries are not uniformly concentric nor do they form a pyramid in an orderly way. There remains, however, the desirability of presenting a generalized sectional diagram to illustrate our chronological deductions for the world as a whole. Such a section might be taken across the map, say along the thirtieth parallel of north latitude, or it might follow a broken line stretching from South Africa via the Levant to Bering Strait and thence via Panama to Tierra del Fuego.

The latter alternative is the more attractive because it conforms more nearly to the supposed major routes of cultural transmission and in addition offers certain other advantages.

Accepting, then, for the present purposes the ascertained sequence and chronology of cultural happenings in Europe as applicable in the main to the entire world; and assuming that in the Old World the successive steps in the inventive process originated in nearly one and the same roughly central region represented by the eastern Mediterranean lands where Europe, Asia, and Africa meet; and assuming also that they spread over the world at an approximately uniform rate, let us plot our section. By actual measurement the distance from the Cape of Good Hope to Palestine is found to equal 46 units; that from Palestine via central Asia (Lake Tsagan Nor in the Gobi desert) to Bering Strait, 66 units; and that from Bering Strait via Panama to Cape Horn, 100 units; and we proportion the vertical divisions of our section accordingly. Incidentally we may also note the locations of the various cultural boundaries, as given on our map, and so place them approximately where they belong on the section. We must next provide for the incorporation of the equally necessary geological or time factor. Practical considerations here compel us to scale down the approximately one million years since material culture began, and we may do this to best advantage by giving the last few thousand years their properly equalized values and the early and less important time span an arbitrarily reduced allotment of diagram space. Taking A.D. 1500 as the most suitable upper datum to mark the end of prehistoric times for the world at large, and using 1500 years as the most convenient time unit, we may rule the section horizontally, adding dates as far as necessary, and our plotting frame is ready, as in Figure 39 (p. 228).

There remains the dubious task of diagramming the selected human events. To do this with care a moderate show of precision calls for the exact dates at which the successive culture stages began. As these are not ascertainable in most cases, we can do no better now than to rely on the approximations given in our chronological chart (pp. 174–75) for western Europe. However, as we perforce are seeking merely to express the relations of the various culture complexes in general terms of time and space, absolute dates, however desirable, are not indispensable. If we but succeed in all the main essentials, the future will doubtless supply greater mathematical exactitude.

Commencing then, for reasons that will presently appear, with the Upper Paleolithic and selecting Palestine as the point of origin, we may, in conformity with previous determinations, place its beginning at about 25,000 B.C. Its entry into America is placed at 12,000 B.C. as about the earliest likely date considering the presence of hindering glacial conditions in the north and the apparent state of the flint-working technique (Solutrean?) at the time of entry. These two dates supply the approximate rate of geographical dispersion and enable us to calculate that the culture in question reached extreme South Africa about 16,000 B.C. Advancing at the same rate, the Upper Paleolithic would not reach Tierra del Fuego until about A.D. 7700; but inasmuch as man was there when the region was first visited by Magellan in 1520 and evidently had been there for some time, it must be either that he entered America before 12,000 B.C. or else that, owing to the narrowness of the New World in places, he moved forward at a correspondingly faster pace. Of the two alternatives the latter is the more probable; accordingly, if for a close approximation to the known facts we double his speed, he should have arrived shortly before 2000 B.C., a not unlikely date. Having connected these time-and-space points on the section by the necessary "commencement" lines, we are able to enter the corresponding lines indicating the progress of the Lower Paleolithic phase. In doing this we may give some latitude to the beginning date — roughly indicated as 1,000,000 B.C. — and for the closing date rely on the apparent fact that the culture did not arrive (if it did arrive) in South Africa much before the coming of the Upper Paleolithic. The time-and-space values thus determined for Africa may be regarded as approximately true also for the spread of man and culture across Asia and are so indicated, the two uniformly diverging commencement lines being broken at the 25,000 B.C. date level in partial conformity to the expansion here introduced in the chronological scale. Incidentally, it is worth noting that the point in central Asia at which the Upper Paleolithic overtakes the Lower Paleolithic agrees fairly well with the ascertained facts as given on the map.

The next succeeding commencement dates are likewise none too certain in the absolute sense. For instance, published opinions concerning the dawn of the Neolithic-Agricultural stage for Egypt and Mesopotamia range all the way from about 6000 B.C. (Peake and Fleure, Childe) to 18,000 B.C. (Breasted, Montelius, de Morgan) and we shall simply strike the average and take 12,000 B.C. as the

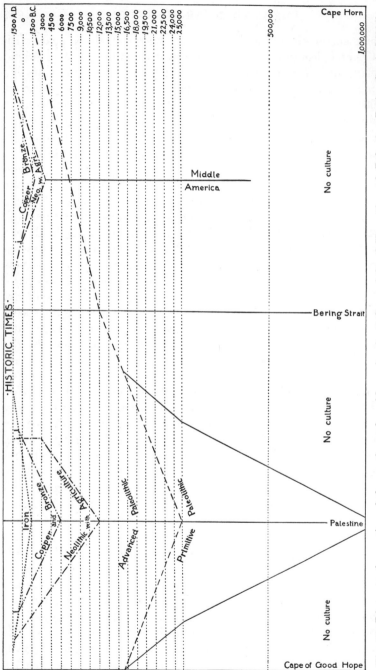

Fig. 39. Diagram of a section of the continental world ranging from Cape of Good Hope through Palestine, Bering Strait, Middle America, to Cape Horn, and showing the estimated space and time distribution of the successive culture levels.

safest estimate. The beginning of the Copper-Bronze stage has by several writers (Pumpelly, Peake and Fleure) been placed between 5000 and 6000 B.C. for Turkestan and Egypt; while the start of the Iron Age proper (that is, ignoring the early use of meteoric iron during Pyramid times) has of late been provisionally placed for Asia Minor at about 1500 B.C. by T. A. Rickard. With these approximate beginning dates fixed on the section, we may plot the commencement lines, beginning with those pertaining to the Iron stage by bringing them up to the A.D. 1500 date level at the limits of distribution indicated on the map. We are now in position to add the commencement lines for the Copper and Neolithic stages, again using the given map limits for space values and bringing them at these points up to the commencement lines for the Bronze and Iron ages, which will give us the approximate date at which the Neolithic-Agricultural and Copper-Bronze complexes were overtaken by the products of the iron-working industry.

There remains the even more hazardous venture of introducing the origin and general distributional behavior of the post-Paleolithic culture stages on the American portion of the section. Figure 38 gives a freehand presentation, or merely a setting up, of the general relations; but an attempt at something more precise seems justifiable. To begin with, unless all the known facts belie the antiquity of man in America, all our culture stages arose at a later date than did the corresponding phases in the Old World. If in conformity with this notion we assume that the corresponding steps from the beginnings of the Upper Paleolithic onward occupied about the same proportionate lengths of time in the New and Old Worlds, and accept the middle point in the Americas as the starting point (with date therefore of about 7000 B.C.), simple calculations give about 3400 B.C. and 1700 B.C. as the respective dates for the commencement of the Neolithic-Agricultural and the Copper-Bronze stages in America. For the upper limits on the A.D. 1500 date level we may consult the map as before and plot the two pairs of commencement lines, and our visual representation of culture in relation to time and space is complete as in Figure 39.

Now such improvisation is not of course to be regarded as equivalent to scientific demonstration. In viewing the diagram, all the assumptions involved must be borne in mind and the apparent conclusions accepted with corresponding reservations. For fear of misleading anyone, all the facts taken for granted and all the steps made in constructing the plot have been stated in full. The resulting picture is intended merely as a crude approximation to the probable happenings, some of which still remain to be proved.

General conclusions. The attempt has been made in the foregoing pages to present an outline treatment of prehistoric archaeology. The result is little more than a bare skeleton of the subject and might perhaps with greater propriety be labeled "the mechanics of the inventive process" or "a brief account of the inquiry into the origin and development of material culture." Within prescribed limits the task has been to set forth what seemed most essential to a sound general understanding of the subject. In judging the presentation, it must be borne in mind that the subject is overburdened with undigested facts and therefore also with loose, ever-changing speculative theories. So much so is this the case that, even if it were possible for one person to examine all the evidence, it would scarcely be worth the while for present purposes, which are not those of a descriptive manual but rather a digest of general features together with a presentation of methods and principles by means of which it is hoped the vast multiplicity of facts, known and unknown, may be made more intelligible.

The purpose has been to define the nature, scope and general aims of prehistoric archaeology; to name the principal objective features with which it has to deal; and to indicate the important time and place connections of these features with other pertinent facts of natural history. Some attention has also been given to the methods employed in both the field (stratigraphy) and the laboratory (typology and technology), with a view to bringing out of the chaotic mass of details a reasonably clear account of early human progress. Lastly, maps and charts have been introduced, not merely to summarize past accomplishments in convenient form but also to indicate present problems and thus in a measure to suggest future procedure.

And what, it may be asked, are the broad outstanding achievements of prehistoric archaeology to date? The most convenient answer is threefold: there is the growth or organization of the science itself; there is the accumulated body of facts from all parts of the world about early man as proof of his contribution to our present civilization; and there is the growing body of interpretations and its obvious influence on modern thought.

From what has been stated directly and indirectly it must be apparent by this time that we owe a vast deal to our prehistoric ancestors besides life and limbs. The main essentials may be summed up under a few general headings. Early man explored and settled nearly all of the habitable world. He located most of the places since found suitable as great centers of population. He opened trails and used waterways connecting many of these settlements, which to some extent have since been taken over as avenues for modern trade and intercourse. He identified and brought into use most of the ready-made natural resources — animal, vegetable, and mineral — either as foods or as materials suitable for implements. He discovered fire as a source of warmth and protection as well as its serviceability in the preparation of food; and by means of fire and other agencies he converted or reduced additional resources, like clays and ores, into equally useful products. He converted or brought under cultivation most of our cultivated plants and domesticated animals, training the latter to carry his burdens and otherwise help him in his labor. He founded most of our basic handicrafts, devised the tools that served them, and with these in time produced clothing, shelter, and gear for all of his varied activities. He made at least good beginnings with medicine and surgery, as well as with astronomy and mathematics in their practical application to the calendar, to architecture, to agriculture, and to navigation. In addition to all these practical endeavors, considerable advance was made also along several esthetic lines. Those attested by archaeological remains include decorative and representative art, executed in every available medium; music, games, and sports expressive partly of individual temperament and partly of the community spirit; and, finally, dances, ceremonies, and rituals to suit, we may suppose, every critical occasion in the group life. In short, primitive man, as we are pleased to call him, is seen to have laid the foundations of practically all of our present-day activities.

Our inductions based on the interpretation of archaeological material must concern the nature of culture as such — its origin, its nature and mode of behavior, its practical use and ultimate value.

The question of primal origin need not detain us long. About all that can be said is that material culture is a spontaneous phenomenon foreshadowed in the behavior of many of the lower animals. How it was that only one member of the primate group came to succeed with it we shall probably never know. At all events such questions cannot be settled by archaeology alone.

As approaches to the essential nature and behavior of culture, on the other hand, archaeologic findings are obviously of the highest importance. On the first point nothing more need be said than that material culture is a new way of adapting inner life forces to external nature or, to be more exact, adapting external conditions to the rule of mind. By means of implements — mentally created external accessories — new and otherwise unattainable advances have become possible. This unique mode of progress has several advantages over organic evolution, which to some extent it actually replaces. Thus it is governed from within rather than from without. It is far swifter in achieving lasting results and, above all, it enables the individual for the first time really or consciously to take part by affording him personal opportunity and thus lending him a sense of endless adventure in an otherwise seemingly meaningless humdrum existence.

With regard to the second point, the behavior of culture, it is possible to be more specific. Not many years ago it was taken for all but granted that material culture had grown, as it were, always from the bottom up. That is to say, whatever was found to have happened, for instance in France, was assumed to have happened also by sheer inner necessity in every other part of the world. This would be a situation such as could be diagrammed by a simple stepped pyramid or cone the top center of which would represent the latest high level not yet reached by the surrounding zones. At present, culture is conceived not as a merely static but rather as a dynamic phenomenon; it is actually perceived as a diffusional phenomenon and one which in a certain sense may be said to have grown from the top down. This condition has been diagrammatically represented by a succession of inverted pyramids; but, as must be apparent, such schematization oversimplifies the process involved and does not tell the whole story even as to all the known but scattered primary centers of invention; much less does it take account of the unknown secondary centers. The diagram does, however, convey two fundamental suggestions worth noticing. One is that the advanced centers of culture literally radiate traits or influences in every direction, influences which in time tend to raise all the recipient areas to new and higher levels, perhaps even high enough to become in turn new centers of radiation, as in the actual case of Europe and China superseding the Near East. The other important fact revealed by the diagram is the ever-accelerating speed of the culture process — that is, the gradual shortening of the time interval which separates the successive stages. The final and chief conclusion yielded by archaeological studies, as here conceived, is that the origin, the development, and the diffusion of the long lines of discoveries and inventions which go to make up the entire modern material culture complex constitute a genetically connected whole; or, stated in other words, the various artificial contrivances in question are the visible manifestations of a great continuous creative process which serves to reflect the growing mentality of their creator, man.

Broadly viewed, this material culture process appears to us as an orderly succession of related events with few upstarts or erratic phenomena in evidence. Studied in detail, it is seen as a mode of origination by more or less gradual specialization or improvement, brought about in the course of time as the result of human ingenuity at work adapting the few material resources to all the numerous desirable ends that necessity or fancy suggested. It is seen as a natural process with rhyme as well as reason in it; for the steps, as shown, follow each other in due order: first the ready-made raw materials, then the derived ones; first the quick but clumsy methods of manufacture, then the slow and painstaking ones; first the crude generalized implements, then the refined and specialized ones; and first the crude utilitarian forms, then the addition of esthetic embellishments. Further scrutiny reveals what may be regarded as occasional mistakes and lapses, in places even revolutions now and then; but these are comparatively insignificant and tend to fade out when attention is focused on the general trend of development and might disappear entirely if we knew the whole history. The final and seemingly inevitable conclusion is therefore that cultural growth is continuous, undergoing change or growth by gradual modification, usually in the direction of higher specialization or greater adaptiveness toward any given stable type of environment. Just what "growth by modification" means in the case of material culture — in short, how new or improved inventions really come about — is a problem we must leave for the present to the psychologist.

New questions face us on every hand. For with all that has been done there is as yet scarcely a country in the world, not even in those most thoroughly investigated in northwestern Europe, that can be said to have completed its preliminary field studies. For the rest there are many more countries where the investigation is hardly well under way, and still others where it can scarcely be said to have been more than begun. Our own richest and well-worked high centers of prehistoric culture, like the Ohio basin, the Southwest, Middle America, and Andean South America, still offer problems for solution; and as for the rest of the two Americas, we have only partial notions of what secrets they hold. In short, systematic accumulation of field data must continue.

In the laboratory and study other tasks are awaiting solution. Typological work — that is, identification, classification, and general systematization of many lines of evidence — is still necessary for most culture areas and culture stages, with a view to establishing true, historically valid series, as well as to eliminating nondescript artifacts that now pass as implements. Comparative studies of adjacent culture areas and continents are required to determine mutual influences and time relationships. Also, we need a simplified but more adequate terminology. If we have properly identified the full-fledged stages in the culture process, we are still not clear about the origin of some of the transitional phases. The main steps now named as indicative of the course of development are at least partly arbitrary and do not in all cases furnish a true estimate of the carriers or producers concerned. For example, the division between Paleolithic and Neolithic is highly artificial, especially as applied to America, and requires modification.

Then, too, there are larger questions that demand answers. When, for example, did man actually enter the New World? And are his higher achievements here truly independent developments or not? Still broader and more fundamental problems loom up in the Old World. Granted that our chronology is approximately correct and that our typological subdivisions of culture stages hold true in a general way for the world at large, we still do not know for certain that the main succession of steps were all taken in one and the same general region, or that they were everywhere taken in the same order. Chance traits were surely invented or discovered in various out-of-the-way places where they remained relatively unimportant until taken up, improved, and fitted into the centralized vanguard culture complexes, thence to start out anew on their diffusional careers. We have therefore to ascertain the time and place of origin of many important single inventions as, for example, the bow and tailored clothing. Incidentally we shall presumably always have with us the tantalizing ultimate question of how, when, and where — if not why — human culture arose in the first place. In conclusion then, prehistoric archaeology calls for workers along several different lines: field study perhaps for only a few generations and the laboratory study for a much longer period. The museum will continue to require and to furnish endless opportunity for improved realistic demonstrations of various lines of development to answer temporary or permanent public interests. And in the meantime the teacher will have his task of exposition and application cut out for him as long as learners retain a spark of interest in how human affairs came to be as they are.

FOOTNOTES

1. Kidder, A. V., *An Introduction to the Study of Southwestern Archaeology* (1924).
2. See articles "Typenkarte" and "Typologie" in Max Ebert's *Reallexikon der Vorgeschichte*, vol. 13 (Berlin, 1929).
3. Moir, J. Reid, *Antiquity of Man in East Anglia* (Cambridge, 1927), p. 35.
4. For special treatment of the subject see MacCurdy, G. G., "The Eolithic Problem — Evidences of a Rude Industry Antedating the Paleolithic," *American Anthropologist*, vol. 7 (1905), pp. 425–479.
5. Menghin, O., *Weltgeschichte der Steinzeit* (Vienna, 1931), p. 130.
6. *Ibid.*, pp. 17 ff., 23, 32, 274, 327.
7. For the most recent digests of European prehistory, see: Peake, H., and Fleure, H. J., *The Corridors of Time* (Oxford, 1927–33); Childe, V. G., *The Dawn of European Civilization* (1925); Leakey, L. S. B., *Adam's Ancestors* (1934).
8. As introductory to the archaeology of Africa, see: Breasted, J. H., "Origins of Civilization," *Scientific Monthly* (1919); Pond, A. W., *A Contribution to the Study of Prehistoric Man in Algeria*, Logan Museum Bulletin, vol. 1, no. 2 (Beloit, 1928); Jones, N., *The Stone Age in Rhodesia* (London, 1926); Burkitt, M. C., *South Africa's Past in Stone and Paint* (Cambridge, 1928); Leakey, L. S. B., *The Stone Age Cultures of Kenya Colony* (1931); *Adam's Ancestors* (1934); Sanford, K. S., and Arkell, W. J., "The Nile-Fayum Divide" and "Paleolithic Man and the Nile Valley in Nubia and Upper Egypt," vols. 1 and 2 of the *Prehistoric Survey of Egypt and Western Asia*, Oriental Institute Publications, vols. 10 and 17 (1929 and 1933).
9. Mitra, P., *Prehistoric India* (Calcutta University, 1928).
10. For a summary of southeastern Asia see: "Zur Steinzeit Ostasiens" by O. Menghin in *P. W. Schmidt Festschrift* (Vienna, 1928).
11. For a brief summary see: Nelson, N. C., "Archaeological Research in North China," *American Anthropologist*, vol. 29 (1927), pp. 177–200.
12. von Merhart, G., "The Paleolithic Period in Siberia," *American Anthropologist*, vol. 25 (1923), pp. 21 ff.; "Neuere Literatur über die Steinzeit Sibiriens," *Wiener Prähistorische Zeitschrift* (1924), pp. 139 ff.

13. See also "Sibirien" in Max Ebert's *Reallexikon der Vorgeschichte*, vol. 12 (Berlin, 1928), pp. 55 ff.
14. For this and for general distribution of sites, see Jochelson, W., *Archaeological Investigations in Kamchatka*, Carnegie Institution of Washington Publications, no. 338 (1928).
15. von Merhart, G., *Bronzezeit am Jenisei* (Vienna, 1926).
16. Sarasin, P. and F., *Die Toala-Höhlen von Lamontjong* (Wiesbaden, 1905).
17. Hale, H. M., and Tindale, N. B., *Notes on Some Human Remains in the Lower Murray Valley, South Australia*, Records of the South Australian Museum, vol. 4, pp. 145–218. For illustrations of Tasmanian stonework and a key to the literature, see Hambly, W. D., "Types of 'Tronattas' or Stone Implements of Tasmania," *American Anthropologist*, vol. 33 (1931), pp. 88–91.
18. Perry, W. J., *The Children of the Sun* (1923).
19. Ivens, W. G., "Flints in the Southeast Solomon Islands," *Journal of the Royal Anthropological Institute*, vol. 61 (1931), pp. 421–424.
20. Smith, S. P., *Hawaiki: The Original Home of the Maori* (4th ed., Auckland, N. Z., 1921). See especially pp. 283–284.
21. Brigham, W. T., *Stone Implements and Stone Work of the Ancient Hawaiians*, Memoirs of the Bernice P. Bishop Museum, vol. 1, no. 4 (Honolulu, 1902); Bennett, W. C., *Archaeology of Kauai*, Bulletin 80, Bernice P. Bishop Museum (Honolulu, 1931); Linton, R., *The Material Culture of the Marquesas Islands*, Memoirs of the Bernice P. Bishop Museum, vol. 8, no. 5 (Honolulu, 1923), and *The Archaeology of the Marquesas Islands*, Bulletin 23, Bernice P. Bishop Museum (Honolulu, 1925); Buck, P. H., *Samoan Material Culture*, Bulletin 75, Bernice P. Bishop Museum (Honolulu, 1930); Routledge, S. and K., *The Mystery of Easter Island* (London, 1920); Best, E., *The Stone Implements of the Maori*, Bulletin 4, Dominion Museum (Wellington, N. Z., 1912).
22. For bibliography see Perry, W. J., *op. cit.*
23. Nordenskiöld, E., *Origin of the Indian Civilizations in South America*, Comparative Ethnographical Studies, vol. 9 (Oxford, 1931).
24. Outes, F. F., *La Edad de la Piedra en Patagonia* (Buenos Aires, 1905); Outes, F. F., and Bruch, C., *Los Aborígenes de la República Argentina* (Buenos Aires, 1910); Hrdlička, A., Holmes, W. H., etc., *Early Man in South America*, Bulletin of the Bureau of American Ethnology, no. 52 (1912); Lothrop, S. K., *Indians of the Paraná Delta, Argentina*, Annals of the New York Academy of Sciences, vol. 23 (1932).
25. Nelson, N. C., *The Antiquity of Man in America in the Light of Archaeology*, Annual Report of the Smithsonian Institution (1935), pp. 471 ff.; Howard, Edgar B., "An Outline of the Problems of Man's Antiquity in North America," *American Anthropologist*, vol. 38 (1936), pp. 394 ff.
26. For a summary of American archaeological features, problems, etc., see Wissler, C., *The American Indian* (1938 ed.), chapters 15 and 16.
27. See for example Burkitt, M. C., and Childe, V. G., "A Chronological Table of Prehistory," in *Antiquity* (London, 1932), pp. 185 ff.; Nelson, N. C., in Wissler, C., *Man and Culture* (1923), p. 218.

28. For a slightly different but more detailed diagram, see Spinden, H. J., *Ancient Civilizations of Mexico and Central America*, Handbook of the American Museum of Natural History (1928).

GENERAL REFERENCES

EUROPE, ASIA, AND AFRICA:

Burkitt, M. C., *The Old Stone Age* (Cambridge, 1933).

Cambridge Ancient History, vols. 1 and 2 (Cambridge, 1924).

Childe, V. G., *The Bronze Age* (Cambridge, 1930), *The Dawn of European Civilization* (1925), and *The Most Ancient East* (1929).

Ebert, Max, *Reallexikon der Vorgeschichte*, 15 vols. (Berlin, 1924–32).

Kühn, Herbert, *Kunst und Kultur der Vorzeit Europas* (Berlin, 1929).

Leakey, L. S. B., *Stone Age in Africa* (Oxford, 1936).

Macalister, R. A. S., *A Textbook of European Archaeology* (Cambridge, 1921).

MacCurdy, G. G. (Ed.), *Early Man* (1937) and *Human Origins*, 2 vols. (1924).

Menghin, O., *Weltgeschichte der Steinzeit* (Vienna, 1931).

Obermaier, H., *Fossil Man in Spain* (1934).

Peake, H., and Fleure, H. J., *The Corridors of Time*, 9 vols. (1927–36).

AMERICA:

Holmes, W. H., *Aboriginal Pottery of the Eastern United States*, Annual Report of the Bureau of American Ethnology, vol. 20 (1903); *Handbook of Aboriginal American Antiquities*, Bulletin of the Bureau of American Ethnology, no. 60, Part I (1919).

Howard, E. B., "Evidences of Early Man in North America," *The Museum Journal*, vol. 29, nos. 2–3 (University of Penn., Phila., 1935).

Jenness, D. (Ed.), *The American Aborigines* (Toronto, 1933).

Joyce, T. A., *Central American and West Indian Archaeology* (1916), *Mexican Archaeology* (London, 1914), and *South American Archaeology* (1912).

Kidder, A. V., *An Introduction to the Study of Southwestern Archaeology* (1924).

Kroeber, A. L., *Handbook of the Indians of California*, Bulletin of the Bureau of American Ethnology, no. 78 (1925).

Mead, C. W., *Old Civilizations of Inca Land* (1924).

Parker, A. C., *The Archeological History of New York*, vols. 1 and 2, New York State Museum Bulletins, Albany, 1922.

Roberts, F. H. H., Jr., "A Folsom Complex," *Smithsonian Miscellaneous Collections*, vol. 94, no. 4 (1935) and *A Survey of Southwestern Archaeology*, Smithsonian Institution, Publication no. 3373 (1936).

Shetrone, H. C., *The Mound Builders* (1930).

Spinden, H. J., *Ancient Civilization of Mexico and Central America* (1928).

Strong, W. D., "An Introduction to Nebraska Archaeology," *Smithsonian Miscellaneous Collections*, vol. 93, no. 10 (1935).

Willoughby, C. C., *Antiquities of the New England Indians* (Cambridge, 1935).

CHAPTER VI

INVENTION

FRANZ BOAS

Discovery and invention. Even in the simplest stages of culture man does not obtain his living without providing, no matter how inadequately, for future needs. He does not live without the help of some simple utensils, and nowhere is he without some kind of protection against the inclement weather and without some sort of ornament.

Some of these achievements are shared by man and animals, particularly the habit of storing supplies and of providing artificial shelter. There is no reason to suppose that they originated in man in any way different from the manner in which they developed among animals. Among lower animals, particularly insects, these devices have most complicated forms, and examples are found even of an artificial control of food supply.[1]

But whatever the origin of these devices may have been, however much or little man's achievements may be due to his animal nature, the varied use of implements fashioned by human hands, the gradual changes in their form, the ever-increasing extent of modifications of products of nature, and the use of clothing set off man definitely from animals.

The sources of these characteristically human traits may readily be observed since they continue to function even in our present stage of culture. Many are due to the observation of an unexpected phenomenon that challenges attention, or to the discovery that some object or some method of handling objects can be made to serve a desired end. Others are due to a conscious endeavor to find the means for achieving a purpose, such as the search for adequate materials or for methods of handling them. Often these are based on previous discoveries which are combined in new ways. In other cases they require the discovery of new materials and of new methods.

Although we shall never be able to explain the ultimate sources of inventions, it seems more than plausible that in the early history

of mankind discovery played a most important part and that the
essential element was the recognition of the applicability to human
needs of observed phenomena. The observation that a falling stone
crushes things must have preceded the use of a stone as a hammer
for breaking bones or nuts. How far a conscious recognition occurred
in earliest times cannot be decided. In modern man we may observe
both tendencies: the sudden recognition of the usefulness of some
material, form, or activity, and the intensive search for means of
reaching a desired end.

Discoveries can be made only in the environment in which man
is placed. Nature offers the opportunities of which man avails himself. Stone, wood, and shell are found to be useful materials; the
branches of trees or caves offer shelter. Inventions or discoveries
are based on the observation of the qualities and behavior of objects exhibited in the course of natural events or when handled by
man.

Fire and cooking. The discovery and the use of fire [2] will illustrate
the complexities of early achievements. Clear evidences of the use
of fire are found as early as Pre-Mousterian times. It is difficult to
say how much earlier its usefulness may have been discovered.
Since the remains of fire were found in caves, it must have been
carried there from the outside or been artificially started. It is not
easy to understand how man was induced to domesticate fire, which
must have appeared to him in nature as a terrifying phenomenon.
Burning woods, grass fires, volcanic eruptions, are all of a kind to
frighten man, not to attract him. It is impossible to tell whether
the dead animals that were found scorched after a grass fire, the
fish that were killed in hot or boiling water, attracted his attention
and induced him to keep smoldering roots or rotting trees in order
to start a new fire whenever he wished to do so, but some such
reason must have induced him to preserve fire. It seems plausible
that long before the art of fire-making was discovered, burning logs
and roots were carefully preserved and means were found to preserve fire even when traveling about. Among many primitive people
every village has its permanent fires which, when properly covered
with soil or ashes, keep glowing for many weeks; and various kinds
of slow matches that can be carried along are in common use.

The step from preserving fire to starting a new fire is also difficult. The two essential methods of fire-making were by friction and
by the strike-a-light. We must necessarily assume that some kind

of experience must have preceded the invention of these devices.[3] The most common form of the friction apparatus is the fire drill, an implement consisting of a wooden base, the "hearth," and the wooden drill which is rapidly rotated with some pressure. Generally the hearth has notches through which the wood dust produced by drilling falls upon tinder. Since in early industries there certainly was no drilling of wood in wood, it seems not unlikely that the fundamental experience was that wood dust was produced by friction and that this dust was known to be useful for rekindling the smoldering fire. Then it may have come to be known that the rapid turning motion produced plentiful wood dust, particularly when a little sand was put in the drilling hole, and accidentally the first

Fig. 40. The fire drill (after Hough).

spark may have been produced in this manner. Considerations of this kind suggest at least a possible way in which this fundamental invention may have been made. While the fire drill is well-nigh universal, the fire plow, a board in which a stick is rapidly pushed back and forward, is confined to islands of the Pacific Ocean. In this case also the production of wood dust is essential. The fire saw is used in Malaysia. It consists of a split bamboo which is sawed through so that the dust drops down and is finally ignited by the heat produced by the rapid friction.

It is equally difficult to understand the origin of the strike-a-light. The observation may have been made that flint striking another hard stone, particularly pyrites, produced sparks; and since the art of procuring fire from an ember by adding appropriate tinder was known, the same experiment may have been made with the sparks obtained from the strike-a-light. At best all such assumptions cannot be more than guesses that can neither be proved nor disproved. All we can do is to try to reconstruct conditions that seem possible in the state of cultural development of these early times.

Fire was presumably used at an early time for roasting food, either on spits by the side of the fire or in hot ashes. Much more difficult to explain is the origin of steaming and boiling. The conditions under which the effect of steaming may be observed are hardly ever realized in nature. Still we find almost everywhere the art of making underground ovens. Red-hot stones are placed in the bottom of a pit and covered with leaves or branches. The food to be steamed is placed on top, covered with a new layer of leaves, and finally closed with a layer of soil. Water is poured in, and the steam generated when the water reaches the red-hot stones is kept in long enough to cook the food.

The discovery of boiling food is also difficult to understand. Boiling water is rarely observed. If occurring after a great conflagration, man would hardly approach it until after the water had ceased boiling. It may be seen when a stream of lava reaches a pond, or in geysers. Rare as these two experiences are, they may have been important elements in the invention of cooking, since the earliest method of cooking employs red-hot stones thrown into water. It is difficult to conceive how the use of fire could have led to the observation of boiling and to the experience that boiled food is palatable. Furthermore, all boiling requires vessels, and these would have had to be invented before the art of preparing food by boiling as practiced by the tribes of simplest culture could develop.

Mechanical principles. The handling of materials acquainted man with a number of physical and chemical facts [4] that found application in many inventions. The strength of the blow of the hand was increased by holding a hammerstone or a club which offered the added advantage of hardness of the striking object. The principle of the lever must have been discovered at an early time. It may be presumed that wherever heavy objects are moved the lever came into play. The heavy trees used in traps may have been moved by the coöperation of many hands without implements, but heavy posts and stones can hardly be raised without some mechanical help. Shore poles or other devices like inclined planes and levers were necessary for accomplishing these ends.[5] The lever is used extensively in the construction of deadfalls in which it serves as a release.[6] The South American Indians use it for bringing a strong pull to bear on elastic basketry tubes [7] used for squeezing the juice out of pulp. The Eskimo use it for twisting the strands of sinews [8] with which they back their bows. By being twisted the sinew strands are shortened and give the necessary elasticity to the bow.

Torsion is also used in other ways to obtain strong pressure. In Samoa torsion is used for squeezing out the juice from shavings of the bark of *Bischoffia javanica,* which is used for painting bark cloth (tapa).[9] The shavings are placed in a bag-shaped mat ending in ropes. One end is suspended from the branch of a tree; the other has a loop through which a stick is passed, serving as a lever. By twisting the stick the mat bag is compressed. The striking part of certain traps[10] used by the Eskimo, Chinese, and Egyptians is held by tautly twisted sinews or cords which when released snap back with great force, like the twisted cords used for spanning woodsaws.

Knowledge of movements due to the disturbance of equilibrium is utilized in traps consisting of a pit or cage concealed by a cover

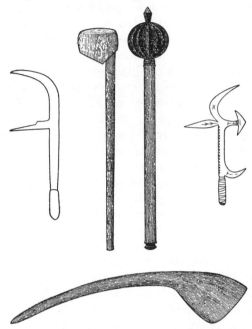

Fig. 41. *Top center.* Throwing clubs of the Kafir (after H. P. N. Muller). Throwing knives from Africa: *left,* Adamaua; *right,* Mbum (after H. Schurtz). *Below.* Throwing club, Australia (after Ratzel).

which is so supported that it tips over as an animal steps on it and then reverts to its original position. Such knowledge is also implied in the game of seesaw.

The resisting power of hard surfaces is made use of in shields and shelters.

Rollers for moving heavy loads were used here and there, for instance by South American Indians in moving their canoes over portages. The Eskimo, whose mechanical genius is quite exceptional, even use pulleys for hauling ashore heavy sea mammals.[11]

Mechanical principles used in implements. Many mechanical devices are in use to increase the force with which a projectile is thrown. When man used for this purpose sticks held at one end, he must have discovered at an early time that those heavy at the far end flew farther and with deadlier aim than those of equal thickness. From this observation must have developed the numerous forms of throwing clubs with thin handles and a heavy knob at the end.[12] Among African tribes this led to the invention of elaborate throwing knives which are hurled like clubs.[13]

The stick used for striking is made still more dangerous when the striking end has sharp edges or when a heavy sharp stone is inserted in the end. These forms occur, for instance, in the tomahawk.

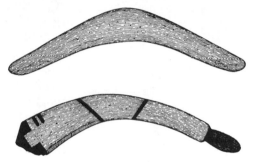

Fig. 42. Australian boomerangs.

Two other inventions are based on centrifugal force, the sling and the bola.[14] By the rapid rotation of the sling and the sudden release of one end of the string the stone is given a much greater impetus than can be given by the hand alone. In the bola several small stones or other heavy objects are attached to strings which are swung around and thrown, and entangle the animal that is hit by them.

A highly specialized form of throwing club, based more upon the cutting effect of striking sharp edges than upon the impact of the heavy end, is found in northeast Africa, southern India, and among the Pueblo Indians of North America. It is a flat carved board for throwing. In the Australian boomerang its wings are slightly twisted; this has the effect that the weapon, if it misses its aim, rises and returns toward the place from which it was thrown.

Increased initial velocity of the thrown lance is also secured by an artificial lengthening of the arm by means of a wooden implement, held in the hand, which ends in a peg or groove — an artificial hand that holds the end of the spear. This point, being farther removed from the shoulder, moves more rapidly and gives to the weapon an increased impetus.

The throwing board is probably a very ancient invention. It is used, for instance, in Australia and by the Eskimo. It survives in Mexico. In some regions a loop made of cord is used in a similar manner. Instead of being attached at the far end of the missile, it is placed near the center of gravity, where it is loosely held by a notch.

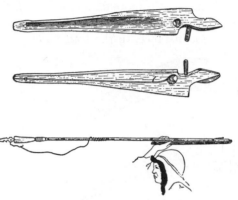

When wound around the shaft it gives a rotating motion to the weapon.[15]

Centrifugal force was also used in the rapidly revolving spindle whorl, in bull-roarers, and in tops.

The effectiveness of a straight forward thrust of a stick depends upon the straight line and strength of the shaft and the sharpness and hardness of the point. An

Fig. 43. Eskimo throwing board (after Otis T. Mason).

attack on large animals with an unhafted cleaver would have been an exceedingly hazardous undertaking. It became less dangerous when the point of a stick was hardened in fire and then sharpened, or a sharp stone or bone was attached to a straight shaft which made it possible to direct the thrust or throw with accuracy.

The elasticity of wood was used in the invention of spring traps and of bow and arrow.[16] The spring trap consists of a branch or sapling which is bent down and held insecurely by a holder. A noose is attached to the holder. In the simpler form of these traps the animal which is caught in the noose loosens the holder by its efforts to free itself, so that the elastic sapling springs back and pulls it up. In more complicated forms there is a mechanism by which the animal steps on a stick which releases the sapling.

It seems very likely that the invention of the spring trap and of the bow are somehow related, although the transition is not easily understood. The two have in common the use of the elasticity of wood and the taut strings, but the use of the latter for propulsion is foreign to the simple spring trap. More complex forms of the spring trap which make use of the arrow are undoubtedly late inventions. Bow and arrow were in use in late Paleolithic times, for rock paintings of this period represent hunters using them.

The further development of the bow presupposes very specific knowledge of the materials that man was handling, for wherever elastic wood was not available complicated devices were used to increase the elasticity of the stave by combining materials of different elasticity. The wood or bone was backed with sinew, whalebone, or some kind of wood of different elasticity. The sinew was glued on or tied on in braids. All these methods are so complicated that they presuppose close observation based on experiences in handling materials. Playful handling may have played an important part in accumulating this knowledge. It is not unlikely that some of these inventions were made at one place and were gradually learned by neighboring tribes and thus spread over a wide area. The distribution of the compound bow favors such a theory.

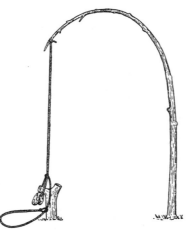

Fig. 44. Noose trap of the Kwakiutl Indians.

The development of the arrow proves also that it is based on experience in handling materials. The distribution of weight in point and shaft, the form of the notch and particularly the steadying of the flight of the arrow by means of feathering, flat or straight and varying in number of feathers, must be the results of experience in handling.

The local absence of the bow and arrow in Australia is a curious anomaly because the invention goes back to Paleolithic times. It seems likely that among the Polynesians and Micronesians and a few African tribes, who otherwise have an advanced inventory of inventions, its use has been lost.

An entirely different method of propulsion is used in the blowgun which is found among the Malays, Melanesians, and South American Indians. The light arrows are said to carry up to one hundred feet. Their effectiveness is due to the poison in which they are dipped.

Both air pressure and suction are employed in the bellows of Asia and Africa.

The effect of suction is used by the Bushmen for obtaining water. A hole made in the ground reaches down to the water table. A tube is inserted and the water is sucked up with the mouth and then squirted into ostrich eggs, the contents of which have been sucked out, and which serve as receptacles. The same principle is used in cupping, which is widely known in Africa and America.

Friction is utilized in all forms of tying and joining. Diminution of friction plays an important rôle in transportation. Examples are the careful icing of sledge runners by the Eskimo, which allows the sledge to slide easily over the hard snow, and the rollers which are placed under canoes.

Watertight and airtight materials are used for many purposes. Stone, wooden, and basketry vessels — the last-named sometimes made tight by a covering of pitch or clay — serve as containers of liquids. Intestines and bladders are used when airtight receptacles are needed. Hides are also prepared so as to become watertight and are employed both as clothing and as covers of canoe frames. Waterproof garments are also made of intestines.

In hunting fish and sea mammals and in transportation the knowledge of the floating of objects of low specific gravity, and of the sinking of those of high, is utilized. Light wood and bladders filled with air are employed as floats holding up the tops of nets while the lower part is held down by sinkers. Floats are also attached to harpoon lines or shafts which prevent the escape of the game or the loss of the shaft. The light weight of wood is employed in rafts. The observation that hollow vessels placed on water are less deeply immersed than solid wood and are capable of carrying heavier weight is utilized in the making of canoes. Other types of canoes consist of frames covered with watertight skins. The canoe is anchored by means of a stone sinker.

The mechanical knowledge displayed in canoeing is remarkable. Paddles are used like levers — one hand serving as fulcrum, the other as the moving force. The Eskimo use oars in their large boat and substitute a rowlock, consisting of two interlocking loops of thongs, for the fulcrum. In steering, a single paddler will turn his paddle so as to counterbalance the one-sided impetus that drives the anoe in one direction and to steer a straight course. The Eskimo uses instead of this the double-bladed paddle which propels his kayak first to one side, then to the other. When an equal number of paddlers are on each side, the steersman controls the direction of the canoe by turning the blade of his paddle or by paddling on one side or the other as conditions demand. Steadiness of the canoe is

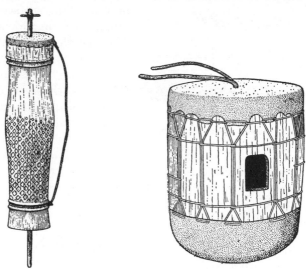

Fig. 45. Friction drums (after Balfour).

obtained by using ballast, in the South Seas by joining two canoes side by side but some distance apart, or by use of the outrigger. Sailing before the wind was known to the Eskimo and Northwest Coast Indians. The Micronesians and Polynesians sailed close to the wind and some of them had even learned to give to their canoes a slightly asymmetrical form in order to avoid leeward drift.

The acoustic effect of beating and rasping strengthened by the resonance of a hollow space was utilized in drums and other instruments. Notched bones or sticks were pulled over the edges of resonance boxes, or an elastic stick was rubbed over a gourd provided with notches. In the friction drum, the drum was made to vibrate by means of a stick or string passed through a perforation in the center of the drumhead. The vibrations are produced either by passing the stick up and down or by rubbing it. The whizzing sound of rapidly moving objects is utilized in the bull-roarer and similar instruments.

The observation that objects of different size produce different tones was made use of in some types of musical instruments. The two-tongued drums of Mexico and the West Indies, the slit drums

Fig. 46. *Top*. Musical instrument, New Ireland (after Ratzel). *Bottom*. Mexican two-tongued drum.

of South America, and the wooden blocks of New Ireland that are played by rubbing over the surface of the tongues are simple examples. The length of bamboo or iron rods is made use of in the African zanza and marimba; the thickness and size of drumheads are varied to obtain pitch. Modification of tension is used for the same purpose. The length of the vibrating column of air determines the pitch of trumpets, and in flutes a number of sounds are obtained by the use of stops. The strengthening of sound by resonance is used in various types of drums, particularly in box drums and water drums, in string instruments, and marimbas. In monochords and marimbas gourds are often placed under the strings and sounding boards for intensifying the sound.[17]

Chemical, or at least partly chemical, processes are also used extensively. They enter into the preparation and preservation of foods and the manufacture of paints and dyes. Leaching serves the purpose of separating soluble substances from pastes. Fer-

Fig. 47. Bushman gora player and end of gora (after Wood).

mentation is used in the preparation of drinks. Poisons are extracted Various kinds of material are dyed by boiling or soaking in decoc tions of bark and the like. Suds for washing are secured from roots

Shells are burned for preparing lime. Ochre is burned for paint.
Most important of all is the reducing of iron ores for obtaining
metallic iron.

In the selection of materials for various purposes the most intimate knowledge of their properties is found. Tough stones are

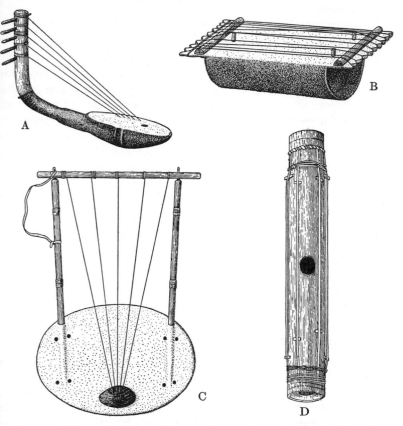

Fig. 48. *A*. Harp; *B*. zither; *C*. lyre — Congo (after *Annales du Musée du
Congo*). *D*. Bamboo zither, Nias (after Modigliani).

selected for pecking, brittle ones for flaking, soft ones for carvings.
Woods of various kinds are chosen according to the purpose they
are to serve: ash, yew, betel palm, Casuarina, etc., on account of
their elasticity for making bows; easily splitting wood for making
planks or for bending; hard, insect-resisting woods for building;
fine-grained wood for carvings; hollow stems for blowguns, and wider

ones, like bamboo, for receptacles. Hard-shelled gourds and fruit
like the coconut or tree calabashes as well as shells serve as water
tight receptacles. Tough twigs, bark, and fiber are employed in
tying and rope-making. It would lead too far to describe man's inti
mate knowledge of the faunal and vegetal products of his home tha
serve as food.

Compound implements. It seems likely that all the earliest imple
ments used by man were objects that were made more handy by
modification of natural forms. Stones, sticks, shells, and jaws may
have been so used. It must have been a great step forward when
two objects were combined to form one implement. Some of these
modifications, like wrapping with skin or covering with pitch the
part of a sharp-edged stone knife held in the hand, served merely as
a protection making possible the employment of greater force. More
important was the discovery of the usefulness of handles to tools
for cutting, piercing, breaking, or scraping. This may have been
suggested by stout sticks with an attached branch, with which a
much stronger blow can be given than with the branch alone. It is
not saying too much when we claim that the invention of the handle
was a step as important as the discovery of the usefulness of a tool
One aspect of the advance of invention consists in the perfection o
the handle. The difficulty of this step should not be underrated
and its importance was pointed out years ago by Daniel G. Brinton.
There is no phenomenon in nature that would suggest the combina
tion of different materials into a whole so as to form a handle. I
may happen every now and then that a stone is inclosed in a root
but I doubt whether this is frequent enough to give the necessary
stimulus. If the connection between handle and working part of the
tool is not secure, it is useless. Therefore many additional experi
ences were required before an efficient handle could be made. In
cutting tools the working edge must remain free. The handle end
must be attached by being united securely with the handle. Archae
ology does not give us information in regard to the earliest stage
of this process, because the connecting material is necessarily perish
able. From modern specimens we may infer that tying was one o
the methods most frequently employed, but tying presupposes the
invention of tying materials, thongs or strings. Tough stems o
fibrous strips torn off from young trees may have furnished material
but the question remains: What suggested the idea of tying? May it
be that the firm encirclement of stems or branches by winding

plants gave the suggestion to use them for holding parts together?
Or may it have been suggested by playing with strips, winding them
around hand and fingers or around objects? However this may be,
it is clear that a great step forward was taken when the art of tying
two objects together had been learned. When the stone was to be
used for clubbing animals, it might be entirely encased, and for this
purpose a piece of skin wrapped around and twisted so as to form a
handle would be adequate.

Cement was also used at an early time to unite separate pieces.
Blood and various kinds of pitch, sometimes mixed with beeswax or
powdered stone, are used by American Indians as well as by Australians. Arrowheads were thus glued to shafts. Cements are used
for calking canoes and wooden vessels. The Eskimo use a cement
made of mixed blood and fat for joining the stone slabs forming the
sides of a rectangular cooking pot to one another and to the bottom.
The South American blowgun, which is made of two parts fitted
neatly together, is made airtight by being covered with cement.

Pieces of wood or thin stone slabs are also joined by sewing with
roots, withes, whalebone, or other strong materials. Holes are drilled
along the edges of the parts to be joined, and the strands are pushed
and pulled through these holes. Sewing was done at an early time
in a similar manner; holes were made with an awl, and the thread
was pulled through the holes. The invention of needles with eyes
seems to have been made in late Paleolithic times. Other methods of
joining materials, like pegging and weaving, are also late inventions.

In Neolithic times we find stone blades driven into a socket in a
piece of antler which forms the handle or part of it. This method requires knowledge of the effect of heat upon antler. The stone tool can
be driven into the soft central part and after cooling is held firmly.
Such handles are found in pile dwellings in Switzerland * and were used
until recent times by the Eskimo.[19] In still later times blades were
riveted to handles, the rivets requiring a perforation of the blade.

Search for materials. Man was not always satisfied with the materials near at hand. There is early evidence of deliberate search for
useful materials. In Mesolithic times there is already evidence of
the mining of flint which was carried on in regions where there was
an ample supply of surface material. The flint embedded in chalk
was mined because it is better adapted for work.

The search for materials is also proved by the occurrence of

* See page 190, Fig. 34.

objects carried over long distances. In the younger Paleolithic times shells from the Atlantic Ocean were found among the remains of the caves of Grimaldi near Mentone and in Cro-Magnon in the Dordogne. Mediterranean shells appear in Switzerland and southern Germany about the same period.

Stone. The fundamental discoveries and inventions relate to the modifications of form of natural objects that make them more available to use. The observation that brittle stones when broken form sharp edges, added to the experience that sharp edges cut, has led to the intentional flaking of brittle stones. This development is proved more or less stringently by archaeological evidence (see pages 176 ff.). The degree and refinement of intentional flaking increased slowly during early Quaternary time. To the process of breaking by strokes was added the shaping by pressure with a sharp bone, small fragments being split off from a core.

Of different origin is the shaping of tough stones, which are worked by battering the surface until the desired shape is attained. This art may well have been discovered by the effect of pounding with a tough grained pebble the striking surface of which was gradually worn down. The time sequence of these achievements has been described before.

Extensive use of polishing flaked stones belongs to a later period, and is characteristic of Neolithic times. Drilling and scraping of wood and piercing and scraping of skin were also practiced in early times. Drilling of stone and bone, particularly of large holes, was not used until Mesolithic and the beginning of Neolithic times. Stones are cut by a sawing motion performed with thongs or thin pieces of wood combined with sharp sand and water. When the cut is deep enough the pieces of stone are separated by a blow or by means of a wedge. Soft stones, like slate, are ground into shape and provided with sharp edges on gritstones.

In one series of tools the blade is attached so that it forms the continuation of the axis of the handle, the cutting edges being on the sides, as in a double-edged knife; it may be pointed for piercing like a dagger, or provided with a cutting edge at the end like a chisel. In another series the blade stands at right angles to the handle, the cutting edge being either in the same plane as the bent handle, as in our axe, or at right angles to it, as in our adze. All these forms must be considered as the results of processes that were gradually developed by the use of stone tools.

While the blades of all these utensils are in principle alike, the handles show great diversity according to the technological development of each people. Special blades and attachments, such as gouges and crooked knives made of stone, and slanting attachments were also developed.

The toothed saw does not appear until Neolithic times, although some irregularly toothed blades of the late Paleolithic period may have been so used. The saw is not universal among primitive people. The Eskimo, for instance, cut large bones by means of a line of drill holes placed in close proximity. The two parts thus produced are then broken by means of a wedge, and the ridges left by the drill holes are rubbed off with a rough stone. Thinner pieces of bone and deep grooves are probably cut by them with rough-edged thin flint blades.

Wood. Wood for making large objects required a high development of stone, shell, or bone tools, for trees had to be felled and the wood worked with chisels, axes, or adzes. Wood is shaped by means of implements of stone, shell, or teeth. It is cut into shape or reduced to the desired form by means of gritstones. The surface is smoothed with rough skin or with leaves or stems containing silicious deposits. Large blocks of wood used as receptacles or canoes are hollowed out by means of fire and finished with axes or adzes. Bending of wood and bone by steaming is known to many tribes.

Food. Even in Paleolithic times man secured food by hunting large animals, infinitely superior to him in strength and speed; also by using fruits, roots, grubs, shellfish, and the like that could easily be procured. The hunting of large game required coöperation of hunters and devices for killing that would not necessitate a hand-to-hand encounter with animals of a strength like that of the cave bear. The simple stone tools would hardly be adequate for this purpose. Hunting with an unhafted cleaver would have been an exceedingly hazardous undertaking, and probably inclosures, pitfalls, and other trapping devices were used by the early hunter. This seems the more likely since in the early Paleolithic period the large pachyderms such as elephant, rhinoceros, and hippopotamus were the principal animals hunted. These could hardly be killed by a cleaver. Most of the bones are those of young animals which were more easily driven into inclosures or pitfalls.[20] Some paintings of the late Paleolithic period seem to represent inclosures and traps.[21] As soon as a reasonably long shaft allowed an attack from a point beyond the reach of the teeth and paws of the animal, hunting became safer. Cave animals may also have been smothered by smoke in their dens; animals of the steppe may have been killed by fires — all methods employed nowadays by primitive tribes.

The invention of implements and devices for hunting and for obtaining vegetable foods will be described later (see pages 282 ff.). The meat of animals, fresh or preserved, is roasted, boiled, or steamed. In Arctic climates frozen meat may be kept throughout the winter. In other regions it must be specially prepared. Knowledge of the anatomy of the animal is generally accurate. The muscles are split into thin sheets according to definite rules and dried in sun and wind or in smoke. Sometimes the dried meat is powdered and kept mixed with fat. Fish are also cut and sun-dried or smoked. The intestines of larger animals, so far as they serve as food, are eaten fresh, roasted, or cooked. Blood is used in the preparation of soups.

Plants are also eaten raw or cooked. Many bulbs, roots, and fruits are preserved and used as staples for seasons in which no vegetable products can be gathered. Bulbs and roots are generally sun-dried. Dry seeds may be kept without any preparation. They need only protection against predatory animals, particularly rodents, and insects. Seeds are broken up either by pounding in a mortar or by grinding on a millstone. Berries and other juicy fruits are boiled to a jam and then dried.

One of the most puzzling facts is the frequent use of plants which in their natural state are either unpalatable or actually poisonous. Among the former may be mentioned the bitter acorn and buckeye of California. These are ground by means of a pestle in a basket mortar, and the meal is leached until the bitterness is removed. In Australia, also, many acrid or poisonous plants are used which require a most elaborate treatment before they become edible. Best known among the poisonous plants are the manioc of South America and the potato, which in Peru, before being used, was exposed to frost and used only after the fluids had been removed by pressure. Complicated methods of preserving food and making it palatable are universal.[22]

The methods of preparing meals from the raw or preserved food products are principally roasting, boiling, and steaming. Roasting is generally done in ashes, broiling by the fire, boiling by throwing red-hot stones into appropriate vessels filled with water (see pages 239–241). Sometimes the fluid to be boiled is placed over a fire in stone kettles, as among the Eskimo, or in wet skin or bark receptacles which withstand the fire long enough to permit the contents to simmer or even to boil. Steaming in earthen ovens is widely practiced (see page 240). Baking on hot stones is found rarely; the Pueblo Indians, who bake cornmeal wafers in this manner, present one of the few instances. Meal obtained from ground or pounded seeds, bulbs, or roots is almost universally used for preparing mushes.

Intoxicants and narcotics. The use of intoxicating drinks and foods is widespread although not universal. Alcoholic drinks made of grain, roots, or tubers, juices of fruits, sap, milk, and honey are found in Africa, South America, Polynesia, and southeastern Asia. They were also known in ancient Europe. In the extreme northeastern part of Asia fly agaric is eaten to produce intoxication. The use of peyote spread widely among North American Indians and goes back to pre-Spanish times. Narcotics which are chewed are the betel, the coca of South America, and the pitcheri of Australia, to name only a few. Hemp, opium, and tobacco are smoked, chewed, and eaten. South American Indians use powdered seeds of an acacia as an intoxicating snuff.[23]

Medicine and poison. It would lead too far to enumerate the medical uses of plants. Every tribe has discovered the effects of many plants upon the human body and these are extensively used.[24] Animal and vegetal poisons are used. Putrid tissues, snake and insect venoms, as well as poisons obtained from plants, are applied to points of arrows and to blowgun darts. Poisonous plants are thrown into the water to kill or benumb fish. Poison is also used in ordeals to detect guilt.

Preparation of skins. The progress from tearing up or cutting up animals to careful skinning was certainly not easy, but we may safely assume that the discovery of the skinning of whole animals was made in early Paleolithic times. The elaborate process of curing the heavy hides of reindeer, bear, bison, and deer is probably a later achievement. It requires the careful scraping of the inner side. This is done either with a stone scraper or with a hoe-shaped stone implement. After this has been done many tribes work the inner surface with a grainer, which is applied until the skin becomes flexible. Generally the skin is rubbed with brains and fat to make it more flexible. Rawhide is obtained by drying the skin and scraping off the hair. Tanning was invented at a very late period. Skins are allowed to putrefy until the hair can be removed. The same end is attained by soaking the skin in lye from ashes or some other alkaline fluid. In Africa dung of cattle is used for this purpose. After being properly scraped and softened the skins are often smoked.[25] Clothing and bags are made of skins.

Bark cloth. The art of obtaining large sheets of material by felting fibers is used in Polynesia, Melanesia, southern Asia, and South America. The bark of certain trees (*Broussonetia, Ficus,* etc.) is carefully peeled off, cleaned, and beaten with a mallet with a cor-

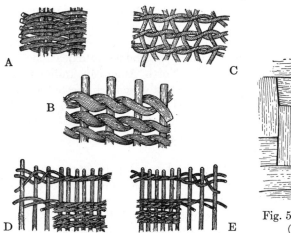

Fig. 50. Twilled matting (after Mason).

Fig. 49. *A.* Wicker work. *B.* Single-strand twining. *C.* Twined weave. *D.* Three-strand braid and twined work, outside; *E.* inside (after Mason).

rugated striking surface. By this process the fibers are felted, and in the Polynesian bark cloth they are beaten down to the thickness of a tough paper. Finally it is rubbed with the hands until it is soft and pliable. In Africa the pieces of bark cloth are rather small and are sewed together, while in Polynesia large sheets are manufactured. The bark cloth is often painted by hand, or colored designs are applied with stencils.[26]

Basketry and mat weaving. The simplest form of weaving consists of the intertwining of pliable branches or twigs between stiff rods. Such watling is used for fish traps and for the construction of shelters; later on it was filled with clay to form permanent walls. Closer weaving of pliable materials between warp strands is employed in the manufacture of coarse baskets. When a twist is given two adjoining strands of the woof, twined weaving originates. In a more complicated form of twining these strands are twisted around the warp so that every strand passes in front of two and behind one warp strand. The same technique is used with pliable warp. In plain up-and-down weaving, warp and woof are of the same width and pliability. This type of weaving is used for mats and to a lesser extent in baskets.

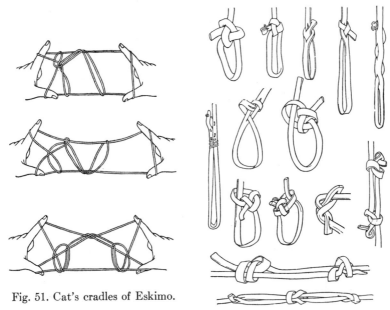

Fig. 51. Cat's cradles of Eskimo.

Fig. 52. Knots used by Eskimo.

These fundamental types of basket weaving lead to an infinite variety of forms, partly by skipping of warp strands in twining, so-called twilling, partly by varying the method of twining — for instance, by braiding woof strands instead of simply twisting, by introducing overlays or embroideries into the single meshes, or by wrapping the twining strands around a cross woof. These variations may have originated from the pleasure enjoyed when playing with strings and from that of mastery of a complex technique; perhaps also from the enjoyment of the figures resulting from the most complex forms of this technique. It would seem that the play with strings has been a most important element in the development of weaving and sewing. String games like cat's cradle are found all over the world, and knots of the most varied kinds are used everywhere. Tricks of opening apparently firm knots play an important part in the shamanistic procedure of many countries.

Spinning. The step from basket- and mat-making to weaving is not sudden. In North America woven blankets are found which are technically analogous to twined baskets. Skins are cut into narrow strips and dried so that they become twisted and have the hair everywhere on the outside. These are united by twining with a warp made of vegetable fiber. In the same manner soft bark is used as a warp and made into blankets by twining. All these manufactures depend upon the art of spinning, of making strong and sufficiently long threads of material such as vegetable fiber or hair. The general principle is that the fibers are twisted together and that new fiber is so introduced that it becomes interwoven with the material previously twisted together. A common method of securing this

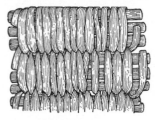

Fig. 53. Coiled basketry (after Mason).

result is by rubbing the fiber, hair, or feathers on the thigh or on some flat surface, attaching the end to a spindle which revolves rapidly and twists the material into a stronger thread. Stronger threads are secured by twisting two or more such threads together.

Weaving. The methods of mat weaving may be transferred without change to spun material. The simplest form of weaving is done by hand, one set of threads being hung up as warp while another set of threads is passed with the fingers up and down the warp threads. Simple looms were used in many parts of the world although the art of weaving is not by any means universal.

Sewing. Sewing of skins and of wood has been referred to. After the invention of the needle the variety of stitches increased considerably and various methods of embroidery developed. Sewing is also employed in the manufacture of coiled basketry. Bundles of material are wrapped with tough strands and twisted into coils which are sewn together with the wrapping strands. The coils vary considerably. Generally they consist of bundles of fibers, but in some cases single rods or a small number of rods are substituted. Great varieties of sewing are used, and the pleasure of play is expressed in this technique no less strongly than in the woven baskets. The stitches are so arranged as to produce varieties of patterns, and embroideries are added.

Pottery. The art of pottery did not develop until Neolithic times. Its present distribution suggests that it was invented independently in the Old World and in the New World, for an extensive area in northwestern America separates the regions in which pottery occurs in the two hemispheres. The knowledge of plastic clay goes back to Paleolithic times. In Neolithic times earth ovens appear. When made in clayey soil or lined with clay, the sides are hardened by fire. The time to which these pits belong is uncertain, but considering the wide distribution of cooking in pits it seems likely that the effect of fire upon clay may have been discovered accidentally, particularly if it happened that the same pit was used several times. During the period to which the Neolithic pits belong, elaborate pottery was in use so that the knowledge of firing clay must have been much older. Besides this, clay is being used for making baskets and canoes watertight.[27] After drying, the clay lining may have separated from the basket. Tylor [28] has assembled evidence in favor of the theory that the making of pottery developed from the custom of protecting basketry or gourd vessels from being burned over the fire by covering them with clay which became fired when the fire was hot enough. While this did not often happen, the knowledge of the firing of clay in the earth oven together with the exposure of lined baskets to a hot fire, perhaps during a conflagration, may have given rise to the art.

Generally the natural clay is fine-grained; and unless tempered by the addition of sand, pounded shells or stones, or pulverized pottery, the fired pot is fragile. The knowledge of tempering is found wherever better grades of pottery are made.

Pots are shaped in various ways. They are moulded with the fingers out of a lump of clay. The walls are finished by being beaten flat with a light spatula while they are supported on the inside by a smooth stone. Vessels were also moulded in or over baskets, as is evidenced by the impression of the fabric on the outer side, or over gourds. In more advanced stages of pottery, moulds of fired clay were made, into which was pressed the clay for the objects to be manufactured.

An entirely different method of making a clay vessel is by coiling. The process is strictly analogous to the manufacture of coiled bas-

ketry, only the coils of the plastic clay are merely pressed together
and do not need sewing like the basketry coils. In all the more elaborate forms of pottery both the inner and the outer side of the pot
are polished with some smooth material.

Metal work. The use of metals which occur in pure state is probably contemporaneous with the development of Neolithic industries.
In America pure copper was used in the region of the Great Lakes,
in the Mackenzie area, and on the North Pacific coast. It was ham-
mered out into daggers and other weapons. The Eskimo used also
meteoric iron, small blades of which were inserted in the edges of
bone implements in the same way as pieces of flint were used when
it was desired to obtain sharp cutting edges. According to tradition
copper was heated on the Northwest Coast to make it more malleable. Pure gold was worked into ornaments. In Mexico it was
melted and cast in lost forms. For instance, small bells were made
by making a form of coils of beeswax which was covered inside
and outside with clay. Then the
whole was heated until the wax
ran out and the molten metal
was cast in the hollow form. The
heat of the fire used for melting
the metal was increased by means
of a blowpipe.

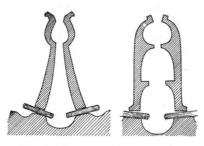

Fig. 54. Cross section of smelting
furnace (after Schweinfurth).

The reduction of metals is a
much later invention which was
presumably made in Asia or Africa. Bog iron (limonite), mag-
netic iron ore, and brown iron ore
when mixed with charcoal and sufficiently heated are easily reduced
in a simple smelting furnace to loupe (or bloom) which can be ham-
mered out. The reduction of the ore requires an adequate supply
of oxygen, which is secured by means of bellows. It may be presumed that the possibility of reducing iron ores was discovered accidentally in conflagrations. The whole process is so complicated that
it must be based on many diverse experiences. The addition of charcoal as one essential had to be discovered. The necessity of increasing the heat of the fire by an artificial supply of oxygen had to lead
to the development of the bellows, for the blowpipe did not furnish
a sufficient amount of air for this purpose. First of all the usefulness of the iron which was obtained by this complicated process

had to be found. Just how this came about can hardly be surmised. In the earliest finds iron serves merely as material for ornaments. It is soft and as material for cutting tools is much inferior to copper and bronze.

The invention of bellows presupposes also many experiences. In this case it would seem that we may speak of an actual purposeful invention. It was necessary to obtain a continuous supply of air. First it may have been blown out of a single skin bag with attached tube, but then the bag had to be refilled. The possibility of speeding the filling of the bag through a slit which when pressed can be closed with the hand, and even the invention of the valve, may have been an accidental discovery, but the combination of two bags with connecting tubes which are filled with air and compressed alternately, thus securing a steady flow of air, was certainly a deliberate invention.

Fig. 55. Wolf trap (after Lips).

Application of inventions. Although in the preceding pages the relation between discoveries and their uses, or the application of inventions, has been touched upon, it seems desirable to summarize briefly a few of the most important uses to which they are put.

Devices for obtaining food. Weapons and mechanical traps have been described before. It remains to mention the various devices used for capturing animals. The simplest of these is the pitfall dug on the trail of animals and hidden by branches. Sometimes sharp posts are set in the bottom so that the animal falling into the pit becomes impaled. In both land hunting and fishing, devices are used that lead the game into a trap from which it cannot escape. Wolves are caught in a double circular enclosure of posts driven into the ground (Fig. 55). The wolf enters through a door that opens only inward, and finds himself in the narrow space between the two circles, in which he cannot turn. Running around, he closes the door and cannot escape.

Fish are caught in traps based on a similar principle (Fig. 56). They consist of a long basket into the opening of which a short inverted basket is inserted, open at the end, through which the fish can enter but which prevents their escape. They are connected with weirs that lead the fish into the basket trap. In a similar way land animals are driven by a group of hunters towards converging nets that have a narrow outlet, or they are driven into a converging enclosure of bushes closed at the narrow end by a net. Here hunters are stationed who kill the animals. Herds of game animals are also surrounded from one side and driven towards a precipice. They kill themselves by jumping over, or are dispatched by the hunter. Others are driven into the water and killed while swimming. Nets spanned over a large frame are thrown over birds. Fish are caught with hooks, in bag nets and drift nets. Hunting in disguise is much practiced. The Eskimo in sealskin clothing imitates the movements of the barking seal and thus approaches it. The Indians used to conceal themselves under com-

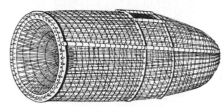

plete skins of deer, and stalk the game in this disguise. The Bushmen dress themselves like ostriches and thus stalk their game.

Fig. 56. Fish basket.

Tribes that have no agriculture, or only the most primitive methods of cultivating plants, use the digging stick for gathering roots or tubers. The digging stick is made of hard wood and provided with a sharp point. The Bushmen increase its effectiveness by the attachment of a perforated stone. In other cases a crossbar is attached, on which the worker steps. The New Caledonians use the digging stick in preparing their fields. These men work in a line, push down their digging sticks to a depth of more than a foot, and jointly turn over the soil, which is then broken up by the women. The spade must be considered as developed from the digging stick.

The most important implement of primitive agriculture is the hoe, which is either formed like a pick or has a broad blade, often running into a point. While the workers who use the digging stick shove the tool forward, those who use the hoe pull it towards themselves.

The difference is worth remembering when we try to understand the origin of the plow. The simplest forms of plows seem to be digging sticks pulled forward instead of being shoved forward. The uniformity of the principle employed in the plow, the range of its distribution in the Old World, and its absence in all the outlying parts of the Old World as well as in the whole New World make it certain that it is a single invention which has spread at a late period from a single center. In Egypt the plow was known in the Old Empire.

Grass seeds are cleaned in flat winnowing baskets. The seeds are tossed up and the chaff is blown away by the wind. Berries are cleaned by being rolled down along wet planks, the leaves adhering to the plank while the berries roll down on a mat or into a receptacle.

In several parts of the world gardens are irrigated by a system of ditches. These were found in the southwestern parts of the United States. In Malay countries and elsewhere in Oceania terraces are built on steep hills to retain the soil and to regulate irrigation. (See also pp. 294 ff.)

Protection against attack. In treating of the methods of increasing the natural strength of the hand in striking or throwing, their application in various tools and weapons has been mentioned. A word may be added in regard to the invention of the shield. The simplest protective shield consists of a staff or a narrow piece of wood, with a handle in the middle, which is used for parrying the thrust of a spear or the blow of a club. Such shields are found for instance in

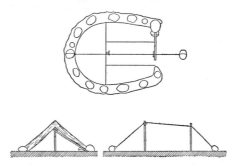

Fig. 57. Plan and sections of Eskimo tent.

Australia and on the upper Nile. For protection against rapid projectiles such as lances and arrows it is useless, and wide shields made of wood or thick hide are in use. The body is also protected by armor made of heavy hide, of slats or rods of wood or bone tied together, or of closely woven heavy fabric. The head is sometimes protected by a wooden helmet or one woven of tough fiber.

Shelter. Protection against climate is afforded by the house. The earliest house was probably the cave, which is still used in some parts of the world. The simplest structures are windbreaks made of branches of trees. Other simple huts or tents consist of frames which are covered with mats or skins. Some Eskimo tribes use as support a single pole over which a thong is stretched, the ends being held by heavy stones. A tent cover made of skin is thrown over the thong and held extended by stones. More complicated tents have the form of a gable roof, front and back each being formed by a pair of poles tied together near the top and spread apart at the bottom. The two pairs are connected by a ridge pole. Simple lean-tos are constructed in similar manner. Sometimes these are very long, serving as ceremonial or communal houses.

The frames of round huts are often made of saplings which intercross and are buried at both ends. This structure is covered with matting or similar material. When necessary, the hut is further protected by a covering of brush, sod, and the like. Round tents

are also constructed over converging poles, often leaning against a central tripod. They have an opening on top for a smoke escape and a flap which serves as a door.

Underground houses or those built in a pit are of frequent occurrence. They

Fig. 58. Menominee hut (after Hoffman).

are generally of more solid construction than the tents. The walls of the pit are supported by wood, bone, or stone. When such houses are built on a slope a frame is erected for the front part, over which poles are laid as supports for the roof. In other houses of this kind four posts are erected in the pit, which support heavy rafters slanting upward from the sides of the pit to the center. Over these, horizontal poles are laid, which in turn are covered with dirt or other material. The entrance is often through an opening in the center of the roof, a ladder reaching from the middle of the pit up through the smoke hole. In other cases the entrance is at one side. In Arctic climates it is further protected by a tunnel.

Large wooden houses are rather rare. They occur on the Northwest Coast of America. In the region of northern Puget Sound they reach enormous size, many sections being joined so as to form a single structure which is used as a communal house. The corners are made of posts which are connected by beams. The sides are made of boards which are tied between pairs of holding posts. The roof is either a shed or a gable roof. Whenever boards or horizontally placed poles or logs are used in house-building, the ground plan is necessarily rectangular. Houses built in shallow water are on platforms supported by piles; others, built on the slope of hills, are on a foundation of crossed logs. Large rectangular houses are also common in southeastern Asia, the Malay Archipelago, and Melanesia.

In arid areas houses are also built of clay or of sun-dried bricks covered with some kind of rain-resisting plaster. Buildings of this type are strengthened when the foundations of the work are straw, wattling, or the like, which is filled with clay.

Stone architecture is a late invention. In early Europe it is confined to the Mediterranean and later on to the Atlantic coastal region. In America it is confined to the advanced people of the Andean plateaus and to Mexico and part of Central America and to rather weak beginnings in the southwestern deserts of the United States.

Special mention should be made of the Eskimo snow house, a true vault constructed of spirally arranged blocks of snow.

Villages are protected against hostile attack partly by being built in inaccessible places, like the tops of steep hills, even on ledges or in recesses of steep cliffs, or by being surrounded by palisades or walls.

Clothing. Protection against the rigors of the climate was in early use. It is probable that we overestimate the need of clothing

Fig. 59. Eskimo snow hut and section.

for people living in climates like that of Tierra del Fuego or of the Northwest Coast of America. The Indians of the Mackenzie valley are scantily clad. The difference in the desire for protection between them and the neighboring Eskimo is particularly striking. Skins were presumably the earliest kind of clothing used. Many of the Paleolithic scrapers and awls were presumably used in the preparation of skins. It is unlikely that the hides of the large pachyderms, cave bears, and lions gave impetus to the preparation of skins. It seems more likely that we have to assume that birds and small mammals, the skins of which require for their preservation only drying and rubbing, were attached to the most sensitive parts of the body. The attempts of apes to cover themselves with leaves suggest the beginning of the use of more permanent coverings.

The problem of the invention of clothing cannot be answered with any degree of certainty. It is not self-evident that man on account of the loss of hair of the body was compelled to seek for an artificial covering. He may well have lived during the warm periods of Paleolithic times without any covering. However, at the beginning of the younger Paleolithic period we find evidence of the use of ornaments. The conditions under which man lived at that period did not make it absolutely essential for him to have more protection than a blanket, for besides the reindeer there lived other animals, like the deer, that require a temperate climate. The scrapers and awls found at this time make it probable that skins were prepared and sewed.

It has been suggested that all clothing developed from ornament. This does not seem plausible, because the desire for ornamentation and that for protection are based on entirely different mental attitudes. Apes enjoy carrying flowers or other attractive objects as ornaments. This desire has nothing to do with the protection they seek in covering their bodies with leaves. On account of the limitations of clothing among the most scantily clad tribes to the regions of the sexual organs it has been claimed that the origin of clothing is due to a peculiar inborn modesty, to the aversion to expose the organs of sex.[29] It seems impossible to reduce the origin of clothing to a single cause, for need of protection, fondness of ornament, and modesty — whatever its origin — must each have contributed its share.

In the development of clothing we may distinguish between the simpler forms, which consist of some kind of material cut into suitable form so that it can be wrapped around the body, and tailored clothing. The former type includes loin cloths, aprons, blankets, wrappings around the legs, and simple sandals. Tailored clothing includes shirts, leggings, moccasins, and caps, all of manifold forms.

Ornaments. A variety of materials, techniques, and objects of manufacture are used for ornamenting the body. The body is painted or tattooed. Among people with dark skin ornamental scars are more frequent than tattooing. The teeth are filed or knocked out, among some people even inlaid. Ears, nose, cheeks, and lips are perforated for the attachment of ornaments such as plugs, strings, rods, or the like. The head is deformed by pressure. The faces of infants are moulded in the expectation that permanent effects will result. Thus Negroes flatten the noses, Indians try to shape the cheeks. Other parts of the body are deformed according to local customs. The Indians of Vancouver Island tie the ankles of women so as to secure slim ankles. The Chinese used to deform the feet of women.

Painting, carving, inlaying, and artistic wrapping are used for obtaining artistic effects on objects of use. In weaving, twilling of colored materials gives rise to a wealth of artistic forms.

Transportation. Ease of locomotion is secured by a variety of inventions. For travel by foot, protection of the sole is obtained by means of sandals, and of the whole foot by various types of shoes with hard or soft soles. For climbing and for support when carrying heavy loads, staffs are used. Travel over soft snow is facilitated by the use of snowshoes — in the Old World skis, and in the New World generally netted frames. Swimming is to be considered a means of locomotion in a limited sense only. Almost all primitive people living near water are good swimmers.

Loads are transported by being carried on the head or on the back. Head loads, particularly pots with rounded bottoms, are supported on stuffed rings or pads which are laid on the head. Back loads are held in place by a packstrap passing over the forehead or over the chest. The ends of the straps are attached to loops at the top of baskets or bags, or slung around the load.

Branchless thin trees are climbed by the Aëta of the Philippine Islands by clasping the trunk with the hands and placing the soles of the feet against the trunk. Then the climber walks up the tree. Malay tribes and South American Indians climb larger trees by passing a rope around the tree and over the small of the back, thus forming a loop. Pressing the soles of the feet against the trunk and holding the loop tightly, they walk up the trees. The tribes of the North Pacific coast of America add to this loop a wooden seat through which the rope passes. Trees are also climbed by means of pegs driven into the wood as the climber ascends.

Ladders are made of the trunks of trees notched on one side.

Trails are kept open by frequent traffic. In South America and Indonesia, rivers are spanned by suspension bridges (Fig. 60). In the Malay Archipelago the footway of bridges is sometimes laid over a series of supports, each consisting of two converging stakes, driven into the river bed and tied together near the top.

Other means of transportation by land are tied up with the use of domesticated animals. The most ancient domesticated animal is the dog, and it is used for carrying and hauling loads. The loads to be carried by the dogs are tied on like saddlebags. On the North American plains the dog is used to drag a small travois, an arrangement consisting of two poles which are attached to a simple harness and to the middle part of which, as support for the load, a netted frame is attached. More important is the use of dogs with the sledge for transportation over snow. A number of dogs are attached to the sledge, either fanlike or tandem. The sledge itself in its simplest form is a toboggan; in more complex forms it is built upon a pair of runners. The use of the dog as a draft animal for small carts has

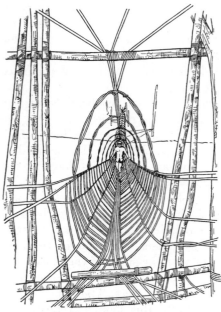

Fig. 60. Suspension bridge of rattan, Celebes (after Grubauer).

survived in Europe up to the present time. After the introduction of the horse the North American travois was enlarged and used for transportation of goods by horses. In South America the llama was used as a pack animal.

A most important step forward in the art of transportation was made with the invention of the wheel, which in an open, level country took the place of more primitive means of hauling loads. It is probable that this invention was first made in Neolithic times in Asia. It is absent in Africa south of the Sudan and had not been invented in America at the time of the discovery. Both the sledge and the wheeled cart provided a means of more rapid transportation of man himself.

The oldest monuments show the warrior drawn by horses on a chariot, not riding. It seems that the art of riding is more recent than the carrying of loads on the backs of animals and the hauling of vehicles. It probably originated somewhere in central Asia.

The simplest method of transportation by water is by means of floating logs. Simple canoes are made of a large piece of bark, held spread by means of thwarts, or by hollowing out a tree. The former type is common in South America and Australia; the latter is widely distributed over all the other continents. Much more complex are bark and skin canoes stretched over a wooden skeleton — like the birchbark canoes of North America and Siberia and the kayaks of the Eskimo. Skin-covered round tubs, like the Welsh coracle and the bull boat of the Mandan Indians, are used locally.

Rafts are made by tying together bundles of reeds or logs. Much more complex is the boat built of timbers. A gunwale raised by sewing a narrow board on to the dugout occurs in British Columbia. Boats with keels consisting of hollowed trees and sides built up of boards are found in Polynesia. Greater steadiness is secured by connecting two canoes by means of a platform or by attaching an outrigger — a swimmer held firmly by means of crossbars at some distance from the body of the canoe. These forms are characteristic of the islands of the Pacific and Indian oceans. Double canoes are also used on the Northwest Coast of America.

Fig. 61. Dog travois (after Wissler).

The art of sailing before the wind is known to the Eskimo and the Northwest Coast Indians. The former used sails made of thin skin, the latter those made of thin boards sewed together. Sailing close to the wind is known to all the maritime people of the Pacific Ocean.

Games and tricks. Many inventions are used in games of skill.[30] Almost all kinds of weapons like spears, bow and arrows, and blowguns are also used in playing. Skill in throwing and hitting is trained in ball games, in catching or hitting objects that are swung suspended from a string, and in hitting rolling rings with spears. For ball games a variety of types of bats have been invented, each serving a particular purpose. String games are played almost everywhere.[31]

Technical knowledge plays an important part in tricks performed in ceremonials. One of the best known is the handling of knots. The performer is apparently firmly tied but frees himself by opening the knots. Other tricks are based on the skillful handling of invisible strings, on ventriloquism, and the use of speaking tubes. Devices for deceiving the uninitiated are innumerable. Among tribes that use fire tricks it seems to be known that stones or metals in white heat can be handled with impunity.

Medicine.[32] The knowledge of the properties of poisons and of plants of medicinal values has been mentioned. Here we have to refer to the use of mechanical devices. Massage is widely practiced. It is reported from Easter Island [33] and Samoa.[34] The Indians of Vancouver Island massage the abdomen in cases of constipation; the Crow Indians against stomach-ache.[35] It is also commonly practiced in connection with shamanistic procedure. Its use for bringing about abortion is probably known everywhere. Pressure by means of circular bandages is used to alleviate headaches and pains in the stomach. Perspiration is produced by placing the patient in a heated ditch or in a steam bath. The latter is widely used in North America,[36] where it is often followed by a plunge in cold water. In Australia the affected part of the body is steamed while the whole body of the patient is covered with furs.[37] Scarification is in common use.[38] Generally the blood is sucked out with the mouth. Opening of the veins and cupping are also reported.[39] To stop bleeding, powdered charcoal,[40] bird's down, and other similar materials are used. Abscesses are cut and the pus is removed by sucking or washing. The wounds are protected by poultices. In case of snake-bite some tribes make cuts around the bite, or scarify and tie a ligament above the bite.[41] Cauterization is used for treating abscesses and to cure headaches or backaches.[42] Emetics of various kinds are used. Tickling of the throat is resorted to. Enemata are given by means of tubes. Broken bones are set in splints or covered with clay which hardens and forms a protective cover. In other cases a cut is made, a splint is placed alongside the broken bone, and the whole is firmly bandaged. Later the splint is removed.[43] Amputations are undertaken ritualistically rather than for surgical purposes although the latter are not missing. Certain natives of southeast Australia amputate two joints of one little finger, or remove them by stopping the blood supply by means of a tight bandage and letting ants eat off the mortified tissues. The Tsimshian of British Columbia cut off one joint of the fourth finger to put an end to a succession of deaths in a family. Amputations of hands or noses as forms of punishment have been reported from many parts of the world.

The sewing up of wounds is not unknown. In East Africa when the mother dies in childbirth the Cesarian operation is performed in order to save the child. There is also a report of a successfully performed Cesarian operation from Uganda. The incision was closed by needles pushed through the margins of the wound and wound around with thread (sutura circumvoluta).

Trephining is widespread. Trephined skulls from Neolithic graves of Europe have been collected. Numerous specimens from Peru, New Caledonia, and the Loyalty Islands are known.

A number of operative procedures of the sexual organs are customary. Circumcision is most widely distributed. In Australia subincision is practiced, which consists in slitting open the urethra. Excision of the clitoris, sometimes connected with infibulation, is practiced in Africa. The castration of domesticated animals is known to primitive people. Thus the Hottentot castrate their cattle[44] and the Hidatsa Indians their dogs.[45]

Writing. The art of phonetic writing is unknown to primitive man, but he has devices for recording and communicating by means of conventional symbols which are understood by his tribesmen. Many of these are used for counting. The South American Indians use knotted strings which indicate the number of days that are to elapse before a festival. The invited guests open one knot every day and arrive on the day when all the knots have been opened. The Indians of British Columbia indicate the amount owed by a person by small cedar sticks, one length indicating blankets, another canoes.

Another type of communication is by means of conventional signals. The Thompson Indians of British Columbia indicate by four small slanting wands stuck in the ground that four persons had left that camp in the direction indicated by the slant. A larger stick points to where the sun was when the party left. Fresh leaves placed near the sticks give information telling about how many days previously the party had started. A number of hairs from a horse's tail shows the number of horses they had. Deer's hair tied on the horse's hair shows that they were carrying venison. A stick placed apart with a fishbone or a root tied to it shows that they were out of provisions and were living on fish or roots.[46]

Smoke signals[47] are also used as means of communication. By covering repeatedly with a blanket the column of smoke produced by throwing wet grass on a fire, it is interrupted and in this way information is spread. The meaning is either traditional or prearranged.

Other devices serving the purpose of communication or of assisting the memory are numerous. The Australians send messengers with message sticks in which notches are cut, each representing part of the message. The notches are intended as a help to the memory of the messenger.[48] Alone they have no meaning except in a very few cases in which notches in definite places have attained a traditional significance.

Pictographs are used in a similar way. The Ojibwa and other eastern Indians used a series of pictographs marked on birchbark to remember the sequence of songs in a ceremony.[49] Thus the six designs shown in Figure 62 signify the following: (1) The god of thunder and lightning filling all space. (2) A drum. (3) A drum ornamented with feathers. (4) A raven. (5) A crow. (6) A medicine lodge. Each of

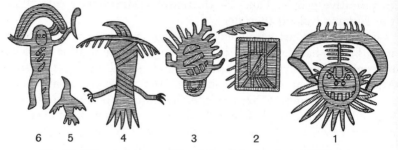

6   5   4   3   2   1

Fig. 62. Ojibwa picture writing (after Schoolcraft and Mallery).

1. The god of thunder and lightning filling all space. 2. Drum. 3. Drum ornamented with feathers. 4. Raven. 5. Crow. 6. Man in medicine lodge.

these recalls a song that occurs in this particular order. Of similar type are the year counts of the Dakota in which an outstanding event of each year is recorded by means of a symbol; for instance, two men in distinctive hair dress holding peace pipes indicate the conclusion of peace between two tribes (Fig. 63, 4). The Dakota also indicate pictographically the name of a person by attaching a symbol of the animal to the head of the person. In Figure 63, No. 1 represents a man called Wolf; No. 2, Eagle Feather; and No. 3, Little Moon.[50]

The use of pictography is widespread. In Africa simple outlines scratched into a gourd are symbolic representations of proverbs. These have been recorded from Togo and the Congo. Thus the design of a double bell means that it may be rung only at the time of the death of a chief. They are also used to record complex events. Most of the latter are probably not intelligible without explanations.

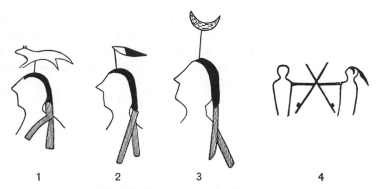

Fig. 63. Dakota symbols of names.

1. Man called Wolf. 2. Eagle Feather. 3. Little Moon. 4. Peace with Crow Indians (after Mallery).

Still more complex is the pictographic writing of Ibo which is used exclusively by a secret society.[51] Figure 64 *a* represents married love; *b* a quarrel between husband and wife; in *c* the man (1) has eloped with the woman (2) and pays compensation (4) on account of the woman (2) to her husband (3) and to her family (5); *d* represents an inconstant heart; in *e* the curved line represents a snake, the dots its poison, and the crossline the knife with which it has been killed.

Cases in which pictures were given phonetic values independent of their significance occur in ancient Mexican writing, particularly

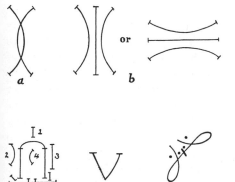

Fig. 64. Pictographic writing of Ibo (after McGregor).

Fig. 65. Mexican picture writing. *Above*. Petlatlan. *Below*. Mapacthepec (after Peñafiel).

in place names.[52] An example is the name *Mapachtepec,* Raccoon Mountain. It is represented by the symbol for *ma(itl),* hand; *pach(tli),* the long lichens Usnea; and *tepec,* in a mountain. In the same way *Petlatlan* is rendered by the syllables *petla(tl),* mat; and *tlan* from *tlan(tli),* teeth.

Science. Man has not only utilized his experience in handling materials but has also, at an early time, learned to observe nature in such a manner as to utilize his experiences in regulating his activities. Astronomical and meteorological observations and those relating to the tides are probably most widely found. Almost all primitive tribes have a lunar calendar. Most of the moons are designated according to the changing aspects of vegetation, the ripening of wild fruits, or the phases of animal life. Thus we find twelve moons among the Hottentot [53] largely named according to seasonal changes of vegetation. The Thompson Indians count eleven months and an indefinite rest of the year. They begin with (1) the rutting season of deer, followed by (2) the moon when people go into their winter houses, (3) the moon when bucks shed their antlers, (4) the spring winds, (5) leaving the winter houses, (6) fishing, (7) root-digging, (8) ripening of berries, (9) summer solstice, (10) salmon run, (11) fish reach the heads of the rivers.[54] The Koryak count twelve months, many of which refer to the phases of the life of the reindeer.[55] The Maori begin the year with June, the rising of the star Puanga, and count thirteen months.[56] The Marquesans counted twelve or thirteen months.[57] Both had names for the days and nights of the month.[58]

Observations of certain phases of the positions of the heavenly bodies are frequent. Among the Hottentot and South American Indians the beginning of one month is determined by the rising of the Pleiades. The Thompson Indians as well as the Coast Indians of British Columbia and the Pueblos carefully observe the summer and winter solstices and readjust their calendar accordingly. The solstice is determined by observing from a definite position the day when the rising or setting sun reaches its most northern or southern point. The Kwakiutl of Vancouver Island determine the time of the arrival of the ʻolachen, a fish that furnishes the indispensable oil, by the relation of high tide and the moon. They set out when the high tide of the second moon after the winter solstice is in the early morning. Wherever the year is counted to have twelve moons there is one long moon to equalize solar and lunar years.

Among the Mexicans and Maya, a calendar had been developed
by the priests based on a combination of divinatory and ceremonial
units of thirteen days adjusted to a solar year. The divinatory cycle
consisted of twenty periods of thirteen days each. Each of the
twenty periods had a name and each of the thirteen days a number.
The year consisted of 365 days divided into eighteen periods of
twenty days each. The remaining five days were considered an
unlucky period. The least common multiple of 20 × 13 and 365
(= 5 × 73) is 52 × 365, so that after 52 years the same divinatory
combination will occur. The combination may also be written as
20 × 13 × 73 so that it contains both
the elements of the divinatory and solar
calendar. The revolution of Venus takes
8 × 73 days. These two periods may also
be brought into relation.

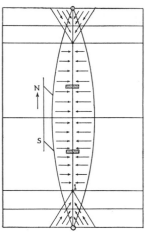

The Micronesians not only used the
constellations as guides in their navigation but also observed the direction of
the swell of the sea. On the basis of these
observations they made sailing charts
consisting of frames of thin rods tied
together.[59] The central vertical line in
Figure 66 represents the course to be
followed. Inside of the lower triangle this
line represents the meeting of the east
and west swell deflected by the island of
Jalut. The sailor follows this line until
he reaches the steady easterly swell north

Fig. 66. Nautical map,
Marshall Islands (after
Krämer).

of point (1). He continues sailing at right angles to the swell.
When he approaches Ailinglaplap he strikes again the meeting of the
deflected swell and steers along the line of meeting of the easterly
and westerly swell.

The boats are so built that the lee side is much steeper than the
gently curved weather side, which is on the side of the outrigger.
This seems to have the effect that the waves pass under the boat
more easily. In sailing, the outrigger is always kept on the luff side
so that the sail has to be taken back or forward on each tack and
the boat goes forward first with one end and then with the other.[60]

Among some of the peoples in whose economic life large numbers
play an important rôle, additions are made without difficulty. Thus

the Kwakiutl in important transactions add numbers of blankets paid, canoes, and other objects the value of which is counted in blankets. Thus in one case a man paid for a valuable object 1000 + 200 + 400 + 1000 + 600 blankets, + canoes worth 300 + 120 + 80 blankets, + 200 blankets, + 2 canoes each worth 50 blankets, + 200 blankets, a total of 4200 blankets which were added after each amount had been deposited.[61] For values borrowed, definite amounts of interest are charged.

The Maya of Yucatan had developed a method of writing numbers, of adding and subtracting. They had also invented a symbol for zero and gave a value to their numbers according to position. The ascending values of digits in their writing are 20 for the first higher unit, 360 for the second, 7200 for the third, 144,000 for the fourth. The numerals up to four are indicated by dots, each five by a bar. Thus the number 19 may be designated by three bars and four dots. The higher units are written so that the highest is on top. Figure 67, for instance, reads

$$1 \times 144{,}000 = 144{,}000$$
$$5 \times 7{,}200 = 36{,}000$$
$$14 \times 360 = 5{,}040$$
$$4 \times 20 = 80$$
$$0 \times 1 = 0$$
$$\overline{\ 185{,}120}$$

Fig. 67. Maya numerals.

The Aztecs indicated 1 by a finger, 20 by a flag, 400 by hair, 8000 by a pouch in which copal was carried. These were written side by side.[62]

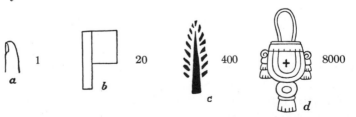

Fig. 68. Symbols of numbers, Aztec (after Spinden).

The quipus of Peru have been proved to be also a system of numerical writing.[63] The quipu consists of a string from which groups of pendants hang down. These are knotted, the knots being arranged in rows. The row farthest away from the main string represents units; the one nearer to the main string, tens; the next hundreds; and so on. To each group is attached one single string which gives in the same manner the sum total of all the knots in the group. The diagram (Fig. 69) illustrates this system.

Measurements are needed for many purposes. The standards of linear measurements are generally taken from parts of the body. On the coast of British Columbia [64] the principal measures were a finger width; a long span (from thumb to tip of fourth finger); a short span (from thumb to tip of first finger); a cubit (from elbow to tip of second finger); half a fathom; a fathom. The Hupa of California measured their dentalium shells by the length of the finger joints and by marks tattooed on the forearm according to certain accepted standards.[65] In southern California the measures are rather based on the length of the second finger and the circumference of the hand and forearm.[66] I do not know of any kind of hollow measures except clam shells for medical administration of fluids and buckets or vessels of fairly standardized size.

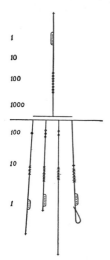

Fig. 69. Quipu (after Locke).

The Peruvians had invented beam scales [67] with an original method of determining equilibrium.

When exact forms are to be made, measurement becomes indispensable. As an example I give a method used by the Kwakiutl of Vancouver Island in laying out the lines for a square house. A rope is run from the center of the line where the front is to be to the center of the rear, and the ends are staked off. Then the rope is halved. One half-length is stretched to the right, the other to the left of the middle front stake. Next another rope is used to measure the distance from the rear stake to the ends of the front rope, which is adjusted until these two distances are equal. In this way the front line is made to be exactly at right angles to the medial line. The rear corners are determined in the same way in reference to the stake in the middle of the front line.

Another example of the application of geometric principles is found among the same tribe, who make square boxes by bending a board. The board is cut by making one edge straight by sighting along it and cutting off all irregularities. The width is marked at two points (a and b) by means of a strip of cedar bark, and the opposite side is cut along a straightedge of yew wood. Next a central line is determined by folding over the cedar strip used for determining the width and from one point of this line, by means of a piece

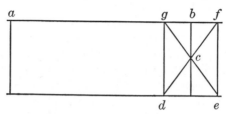

Fig. 70. Diagram showing method of squaring sides of a box.

of cedarwood, a half diagonal, running from the center (c) to what is to be the corner of one side of the box (d) is determined. By turning it the other three corners (e, f, g) are marked, and thus an exact rectangle is obtained. Then kerfs are cut along the end of each side. After the four sides have thus been marked out the superfluous part of the plank is cut off; the kerfs are steamed and then bent until the two ends meet. To make the box itself rectangular a cross of two pieces of cedarwood of equal length is inserted in the box, which is twisted until the cross is parallel with the upper edge.[68]

FOOTNOTES

1. Alverdes, Fr., Social Life in the Animal World (1927), p. 96.
2. Tylor, E. B., Researches into the Early History of Mankind (London, 1878), pp. 229 ff.
3. Mason, O. T., The Origins of Invention (1895), pp. 84 ff.
4. Weule, K., Die Anfänge der Naturbeherrschung (Stuttgart, 1921, 1922).
5. For instance: Boas, F., The Kwakiutl of Vancouver Island, Jesup Expedition, vol. 5, Part II (1909), p. 338.
6. Lips, Julius, Fallensysteme der Naturvölker (Leipzig, 1926); also in Ethnologica, vol. 3 (1927), pp. 123 ff.
7. im Thurn, E., Among the Indians of Guiana (London, 1883), pp. 260 ff.
8. Mason, O. T., North American Bows, Arrows and Quivers, Annual Report Smithsonian Institution, 1893 (1894), pl. 74.
9. Krämer, A., Die Samoa-Inseln, vol. 2 (Stuttgart, 1903), p. 304.
10. Lips, Julius, op. cit. (1926), pp. 118 ff.; (1927), pp. 234 ff.

11. Mason, O. T., *The Origins of Invention*, p. 61.
12. For instance: Muller, H. P. N., *Industrie des Cafres du sud-est de l'Afrique* (Leiden, 1893), pl. III, figs. 6, 7.
13. Schurtz, H., "Das Wurfmesser der Neger," *Internationales Archiv für Ethnographie*, vol. 2 (1889), pp. 9 ff.
14. Murdoch, J., *Ethnological Results of the Point Barrow Expedition*, Annual Report of the Bureau of Ethnology, vol. 9 (1892), p. 244.
15. Krause, F., "Schleudervorrichtungen für Wurfwaffen," *Internationales Archiv für Ethnographie*, vol. 15 (1902), p. 121.
16. Lips, Julius, *op. cit.* (1926), pp. 52 ff.; (1927), pp. 168 ff.
17. *Annales du Musée du Congo, Ethnographie et Anthropologie*, Série III, vol. 1 (Brussels 1902–06), pp. 7 ff., pls. 1–21.
18. Brinton, D. G., *The Subdivisions of the Palaeolithic Period*, Proceedings of the American Association for the Advancement of Science, 1887.
19. Boas, F., *The Eskimo of Baffin Land and Hudson Bay*, Bulletin of the American Museum of Natural History, vol. 15, Part I (1901), p. 381.
20. Soergel, W., *Das Aussterben diluvialer Säugetiere und die Jagd des diluvialen Menschen* (Jena, 1912).
21. Lips, J., *op. cit.* (1926), pp. 132 ff.
22. Hahn, Ida, "Dauernahrung und Frauenarbeit," *Zeitschrift für Ethnologie*, vol. 51 (Berlin, 1919), pp. 243 ff.
23. Sumner, W. G., and Keller, A. G., *The Science of Society* (1927), vol. 3, pp. 2080 ff.
24. Bartels, M., *Die Medicin der Naturvölker* (Leipzig, 1893).
25. Mason, O. T., *Aboriginal Skin Dressing*, Report of the United States National Museum, 1888–89 (1891), pp. 553–589.
26. Krämer, A., *op. cit.*, vol. 2, pp. 299 ff.; Weiss, M., *Die Völkerstämme im Norden Deutsch-Ostafrikas* (Berlin, 1910), p. 440.
27. von den Steinen, K., *Unter den Naturvölkern Zentral-Brasiliens* (Berlin, 1894), p. 216.
28. Tylor, E. B., *op. cit.*, pp. 270 ff.
29. Schurtz, H., *Grundzüge einer Philosophie der Tracht* (Stuttgart, 1891).
30. Culin, S., *Games of the North American Indians*, Annual Report of the Bureau of American Ethnology, vol. 24 (1907), pp. 383 ff.
31. Jayne, C. F., *String Figures, A Study of Cat's Cradles in Many Lands* (1906); Haddon, K., *Cat's Cradles from Many Lands* (1911).
32. Bartels, M., *op. cit.*
33. Thomsen, W. J., in Report of the United States National Museum for 1889 (1891), pp. 470–471; Krämer, A., *op. cit.*, vol. 2, p. 117.
34. Turner, G., *Samoa* (1884), p. 141.
35. Lowie, R. H., *The Crow Indians* (1935), p. 63.
36. For instance, *Maidu, California*, University of California Publications in American Archaeology and Ethnology, vol. 20 (1923), p. 53; "Tillamook," *ibid.*, p. 4; Speck, *Naskapi* (1935), p. 212; Lowie, R. H., *Shoshone*, Anthropological Papers, American Museum of Natural History, vol. 2, Part II (1909), p. 228.
37. Smyth, R. Brough, *The Aborigines of Victoria* (London, 1878), vol. 1, p. 261, note.

38. Man, E. H., *Aboriginal Inhabitants of the Andaman Islands*, Royal Anthropological Institute (1932), p. 17; Howitt, A. W., *The Native Tribes of South-East Australia* (1904), p. 385; Ehrenreich, P., *Die Karayastämme am Rio Araguaya (Goyaz)*, Veröffentlichungen aus dem Königlichen Museum für Völkerkunde (Berlin, 1891), vol. 2, p. 32.

39. Ehrenreich, P., *op. cit.*, p. 32; Sumner, Keller, and Davie, *The Science of Society* (1927), vol. 4, p. 800; Czekanowski, J., *Deutsche Zentral-Afrika-Expedition*, vol. 6 (1917), p. 326.

40. Ehrenreich, P., *op. cit.*, p. 32.

41. Howitt, A. W., *op. cit.*, p. 19.

42. Man, E. H., *op. cit.*, p. 19.

43. Parkinson, R., *Dreissig Jahre in der Südsee* (Stuttgart, 1907), p. 114.

44. Schultze-Jena, L., *Aus Namaland und Kalahari* (Jena, 1907), p. 202.

45. Wilson, G. L., *The Horse and the Dog in Hidatsa Culture*, Anthropological Papers, American Museum of Natural History, vol. 15 (1924), p. 201.

46. Teit, J., *The Thompson Indians of British Columbia*, Jesup Expedition, vol. 1, Part IV (1898–1900), p. 287.

47. Mallery, G., *Sign Language among North American Indians*, Annual Report of the Bureau of Ethnology, vol. 1 (1881), p. 536.

48. Howitt, A. W., *op. cit.*, pp. 691 ff.

49. Mallery, G., *Pictographs of the North American Indians*, Annual Report of the Bureau of Ethnology, vol. 4 (1886), p. 82, pl. IV.

50. *Ibid.*, pls. XXVI, LXXVIII.

51. Macgregor, J. K., "Some Notes on Nsibidi," *Journal of the Royal Anthropological Institute*, vol. 39 (1909), p. 214.

52. Danzel, Th. W., *Die Anfänge der Schrift* (Leipzig, 1912).

53. Schultze-Jena, L., *op. cit.*, p. 371.

54. Teit, J., *op. cit.*, p. 237.

55. Jochelson, W., *The Koryak*, Jesup Expedition, vol. 6, Part II (1908), p. 428.

56. Taylor, R., *Te Ika A Maui* (London, 1870), p. 362; Best, E., *Astronomical Knowledge of the Maori*, Dominion Museum Monograph, no. 3 (Wellington, 1922).

57. Handy, E. S. C., *The Native Culture in the Marquesas* (Honolulu, 1923), p. 350.

58. Taylor, R., *op. cit.*; Handy, E. S. C., *op. cit.*; Firth, R., *Primitive Economics of the New Zealand Maori* (1929), p. 63.

59. Schück, A., *Die Stabkarten der Marshall-Insular* (Hamburg, 1902); Krämer, A., *Hawaii, Ostmikronesien und Samoa* (Stuttgart, 1906), p. 419.

60. Krämer, A., *ibid.*, p. 417.

61. Boas, F., *Social Organization and the Secret Societies of the Kwakiutl Indians*, Report of the United States National Museum for 1895 (1897), pp. 348 ff.

62. Spinden, H. J., *Ancient Civilizations of Mexico and Central America* (1922), pp. 106, 204.

63. Locke, L. Leland, *The Ancient Quipu or Peruvian Knot Record*, American Museum of Natural History (1923).

64. Boas, F., *The Kwakiutl of Vancouver Island*, Jesup Expedition, vol. 5, Part II (1909), p. 410.

65. Goddard, P. E., *Life and Culture of the Hupa*, University of California Publications in American Archaeology and Ethnology, vol. 5, no. 1 (1903).

66. Kroeber, A. L., *Handbook of the Indians of California*, Bulletin of the Bureau of American Ethnology, no. 78 (1925), p. 565.
67. Nordenskiöld, E., *Origin of the Indian Civilizations in South America*, Comparative Ethnographical Studies, vol. 9 (Oxford, 1931), p. 46.
68. Boas, F., *The Kwakiutl of Vancouver Island*, p. 411.

GENERAL REFERENCES

Alverdes, Fr., *Social Life in the Animal World* (1927).
Annales du Musée du Congo, Ethnographie et Anthropologie, Série III, vol. 1 (Brussels, 1902–06).
Bartels, M., *Die Medicin der Naturvölker* (Leipzig, 1893).
Danzel, Th. W., *Die Anfänge der Schrift* (Leipzig, 1912).
Mason, O. T., *The Origins of Invention* (1895).
Tylor, E. B., *Researches into the Early History of Mankind* (London, 1878).
Weule, K., *Die Anfänge der Naturbeherrschung* (Stuttgart, 1921, 1922).
Wissler, C., *The American Indian* (1917).

CHAPTER VII

SUBSISTENCE

Robert H. Lowie

General categories. All complex societies gain their food supply by farming, by stock-breeding, or by a combination of the two. Simpler peoples derive their sustenance by hunting, fishing, and the gathering of wild roots and seeds. This dichotomy has chronological significance, for tillage and animal husbandry invariably succeed the simpler economic activities. There is no convincing proof that cultivated plants or domestic beasts existed anywhere until after the end of the glacial period. The archaeological remains of the Paleolithic period include the bones of wild game species, but neither indications of livestock nor of cultivated grains appear before some time after the beginning of the Neolithic. This Paleolithic "hunting stage," as we may conveniently label the stage of hunting, fishing, and gathering, has persisted to the present day. The recently extinct Tasmanians, the Australian aborigines, the pygmies of the Congo and the Andaman Islands, the Bushmen of South Africa, the Shoshonean Indians of our Basin states, all Californians except those on the banks of the Colorado, and the Tierra del Fuegians are conspicuous samples of such backwardness. We shall see presently that notwithstanding the indubitable inferiority of their status, even *their* economic labor involves undreamed-of complexities that lift them immeasurably above, say, the anthropoid level.

While hunting, then, represents the earliest food-getting stage, the relative priority of herding and farming is a moot question. Eduard Hahn [1] has illuminated the problem by sharply distinguishing two forms of farming: culture by means of the hoe, which may be designated as horticulture since the same methods are still used in the private garden, and culture by means of the plow, which we will designate as agriculture in a restricted sense. The former depends on human hands wielding a hoe, dibble, or mattock; in the latter a plow is drawn by a domestic beast. Thus, by definition agriculture involves antecedent stock-breeding, while horticulture does not. As Hahn, and Alexander von Humboldt, as well as I. Iselin before him,[2] pointed out, some primitive tribes farmed without ever having owned a single head of stock. In other words, they advanced directly from hunting and food-gathering to farming. The pastoral stage is not a necessary condition for tillage. Instead of the traditional three types — hunting, herding, farming — we are thus obliged to recognize four categories — hunting, farming with hoe or dibble, farming with plow and livestock, and stock-breeding without farming (pastoral nomadism).

The chronological position of pastoral nomadism remains a subject of discussion. Hahn finds it inconceivable that roaming hunters should be capable of raising wild animals so as ultimately to get them to breed in captivity. He assumes rather that the earliest domestication was achieved by horticulturists and that subsequently some tribes simultaneously practicing horticulture and stock-breeding completely abandoned the former pursuit, thus turning into herders pure and simple. On the other hand, as G. Hatt[3] points out, inclosures are often constructed by hunting peoples (see below), so that their ability to impound and raise captive beasts as raw material for domestication is vindicated. Hatt himself, speaking of the reindeer only, rather stresses the hunter's desire to use tame animals to decoy their wild fellows, the former being attracted by human urine; and some such symbiotic arrangement is accepted by Schmidt and Koppers as foreshadowing domestication in the hunting stage.[4] Up to date no decisive evidence has been brought forward in favor of either theory. It is, however, unquestionably true that Hahn exaggerates the primitiveness of the hunting stage and thus underestimates its potentialities.

To return to our four categories, even these represent no more than a very rough scheme of classification, which fails to do justice to the multiplicity of actual developments. For one thing, the higher activities may be coupled in such varying degrees of relative significance with the lower as to yield quite different economic patterns. The Hopi of Arizona depended almost wholly on their maize crops; with the Ojibwa around Lake Superior maize was auxiliary to hunting and fishing. Horticulture is not the same thing in these tribes. Again, in our own culture, farming has pushed the chase and angling completely into the background: they are gentlemanly pastimes but not vital pursuits. Not so in South Africa. There, for one thing, the rearing of cattle never led the Bantu to harness an ox to a plow; they remained horticulturists. But unlike other peasants they were far from giving up the chase; so long as big game still abounded in their country they continued hunting on a large scale. This is doubtless to be linked with another distinctive trait of their culture: they make abundant use of milk, but they do not slaughter their cattle except for very special occasions. In other words, the normal meat supply had to be provided in other ways, and there was but one other source, the *wild* fauna of the region. On the other hand, the Chinese, like ourselves, are agriculturists no longer largely dependent on the chase. But unlike ourselves they make little use of beef; and unlike both ourselves and the Bantu they disdain all forms of dairying. These cases exemplify, then, a second principle: the totally different use made of the same economic possibilities.

Clearly enough, the mere statement that people keep stock is inadequate. It does not tell us what they keep stock for; it says nothing about the relative economic importance of animal husbandry and farming or hunting. But apart from such differences there are still other points to consider. Pigs are livestock, but the implications of pig-raising are utterly distinct from those of rearing cattle, horses, and sheep. Pigs cannot be driven over large tracts of land; hence they are characteristically lacking among pastoral nomads. The Kirghiz of Turkestan and southern Siberia herd cattle, sheep, goats, horses, and camels, but have no use for pigs. These are typically linked with sedentary cultures, such as those of Oceania and China.

"Horticulture," "agriculture," and "stock-breeding" are obviously catchwords, convenient enough for a rough characterization but far from telling us all we need to know. The same holds for "hunting." Wahle [5] objects to the term as applied to the earliest economic stages, on the ground that primitive man invariably eked out his flesh diet with vegetable substances. But his substitute, "gathering stage," errs in the opposite direction. What primitives, no matter how vegetarian, forego the flesh of their fauna? All these terms should be taken for what they are — makeshifts to cover a variety of activities not included in their etymological meanings.

Adhering, then, to the traditional "hunting stage," we must merely stress the astonishing diversity covered by the concept. For one thing, we cannot too vigorously reject the absurd, though still prevalent, notion that "hunters" were uniformly rovers ad infinitum. Even Australian hordes wandered within narrowly circumscribed limits, and maintained a sentimental attachment to their hereditary tract; and the Bushmen of South Africa exhibited "an almost passionate fondness for the rocks and glens in whose caves they and their fathers had lived," clinging "to their ancient haunts . . . against all odds and all dangers." [6] The Arctic sea-mammal hunters live in permanent settlements, and fixed villages are characteristic of the Amur River fishermen, of most Californians, and of natives of the British Columbia coast. Some "hunters," it is true, like our northern Plains tribes, covered considerable territory. Others, like the northwestern Californians, lived in fixed hamlets and virtually never traveled except to their immediate neighbors. [7]

Apart from this difference in mobility, the "hunting" category can be unified only in contradistinction to the herding and the two farming categories. Positively, a chasm yawns between the Eskimo or the Yukaghir of Siberia and, say, the South Californian Cahuilla. The two Arctic peoples do not despise what vegetable food their environment offers, but this is of the most meager nature; the upper Kolyma Yukaghir, for example, are restricted to berries and roots and extract the lichens from reindeer paunches. [8] What is significant for these Siberians is the supply of fish, reindeer, or elk meat, while most of the Eskimo specialize in sea mammals. In the "forbiddingly desert" stretches of Cahuilla territory such sustenance was, of course, barred. Inhabiting a country poor in game, the natives enjoyed a compensatory abundance of wild plant life. They made a staple of the mesquite, grinding the fruit in mortars; and they roasted the sweet stalks of agaves and yuccas, ate the seeds of *Pinus monophylla* and other conifers, and reduced to flour the parched seeds of various species collected with the help of a special beater. [9]

Appraisal of the hunting stage. Nothing is easier than to exaggerate the difference between the simpler and more advanced economic activities. Mr. Perry has set off the "food gatherers" from the "food producers," and Professor Childe adopts the distinction, contrasting the "purely parasitic" existence of early man with the "productive life" of his successor, who "became a creator emancipated from the whims of his environment." [10] But this conceptual dichotomy holds only for the two extremes of the series: namely, the lowliest hunters imaginable and the scientific agriculturists of the most progressive nations. It is true that agriculture gives man control over certain aspects of "the whims of his environment."

Potentially it supports a vast population while the same number of hunters would require ten times the area even in early times when an abundance of game animals existed. But what of the herders on a simpler plane whose maintenance is periodically jeopardized by plagues — who, like some Lapp bands of the nineteenth century, were obliged to fall back upon fishing? What of the primitive peasants who clear and till without compensation of the soil, exhaust one plot and pass on to the next, and are threatened by famine with every drought? Are they any more in control of misfortune caused by natural conditions than the hunter-gatherer?

Without minimizing the important step involved in the intentional cultivation of plants and domestication of animals it may be recognized that the battle against the forces of nature was won when the storing of supplies enabled man to survive seasons of starvation. The beginnings of such provision are found even among animals who store food for the winter. The complicated methods of preservation and the quantities of food stored show an equal understanding of economic needs among both hunters and food gatherers on the one hand and early horticulturists on the other. Both the acquisition of the food supply and its preservation among hunters and food gatherers imply a considerable amount of ingenuity.

As the pastoral and farming tribes are not necessarily masters of their destiny, so the hunters and gatherers of historic times are far removed from the parasitic appropriation of natural resources. Early travelers may have pictured the Californian natives as browsing in the field like so many head of cattle. We now know that they took fish in weirs and nets and by harpoons as well as by stupefying them with special preparations of ground buckeye nuts fed into small streams. They drove rabbits into nets and decoyed deer. Above all, they made acorns a palatable staple by a lengthy process that leached them clear of tannin.[11] This last-mentioned technique was as genuine and literal a form of food production as any on record. It certainly involved more labor and experience than many types of farming.

This often holds for the securing of food even when it requires no actual transformation. The Vedda of Ceylon eat honey fresh, wax and all, but the method of obtaining it is hazardous and implies a number of adjustments to the situation. Descending precipices by means of long cane ladders, the natives cut off the combs from the sides of the rock, preferably at night when the bees are less ferocious, and after first stupefying them with smoke. There is a four-pronged stick to remove the comb, which is carried off in a container of hide to prevent breakage against the rock as the gatherer swings to and fro on his flimsy ladder. No wonder that the procedure is systematically taught to the younger generation and that the right to take rock honey from a particular spot is jealously guarded and transferred to a son-in-law as part of his wife's portion. And when we learn of gourds hung up as hives for colonies of stingless bees, we have an actual case of food production.[12] Equally important are the rules limiting the number of animals that a hunter is allowed to kill within a given time, a precaution that serves to maintain the food supply.

But a fair comprehension of the economic life of our rudest peoples can be gained only by viewing it as a unit. Let us note the relevant practices of the South African Bushmen, one of the very rudest of known peoples.[13] Like the Vedda, they prized the honey of wild bees, and in order to find a nest they observed the antics of the honey bird, which guided them to a nest in a rock cleft or a hollow tree. Again, like the natives of Ceylon, the Bushmen often risked their necks to gain the coveted delicacy, scaling the giddy heights of decayed tree tops or precipices by means of sharpened wooden pegs driven into the bark or crevices. In districts harboring fish these were shot with bow and arrow, struck with bone-headed harpoons, or caught in baskets set at intervals where the fish were known to ascend the streams at certain seasons. To prevent escape, the victims were hemmed in by obstacles that inevitably forced them into the basketry traps. Wolves are caught in a double circular inclosure of posts driven into the ground. A bait is placed in the inner circle. The wolf enters through a door that opens only inward and finds himself in the narrow space between the two circles in which he cannot turn (see page 261). Running around he closes the door and cannot escape. So long as South Africa swarmed with game, the Bushmen proved expert sportsmen. They stalked elephants, quaggas, hippopotami, and ostriches in suitable disguises. One of the best-known Bushman rock paintings shows the hunter approaching the ostriches as though himself a member of the species. A hunter donned an ostrich skin, keeping the head erect with a long flexible stick run through the neck, and imitated the bird's movements. Picking at bushes, rubbing his head against the feathers, standing still to gaze about, he gradually sneaked close enough to

discharge his dart with telling effect. The Eskimo in sealskin clothing imitates the movements of the basking seal and thus approaches
it. The Indians used to conceal themselves under complete skins of
deer and stalked the game under this disguise.

At other times the hunters collectively assaulted a big pachyderm
till it succumbed to the wounds or was hamstrung by a harpooneer.
Again, there was the device of suspending a poisoned shaft from a
tree so that the animal returning from its watering place released
the block with the venomous blade, which was driven deep into its
flesh. Still more remarkable was the construction of pitfalls. Not
only were the natives obliged to make enormous excavations with
their crude digging-sticks in order to hold large beasts, but they
forced the animals to their tomb. Having constructed fences converging toward the pitfall, the hunters scared the game with blazing
torches so as to close all paths but that toward the fatal apex of the
funnel; guards on either side prevented the quarry from breaking
the fences. The animals tumbled into the pit "into which they
were precipitated one upon another, until the whole presented an
indescribable chaos of writhing, smothering, tortured animals," of
which fifty to a hundred head might then be safely speared by the
natives.

But this does not yet exhaust Bushman food habits. They collected grass seeds for winter storage, fed on bulbs, took the chrysa-
lides of ants from the nests, and did not disdain lizards, grasshoppers,
and locusts — the last mentioned being dried in the fire and pulverized with muller and metate.

The tactics enumerated obviously imply a wealth of concrete
knowledge as to fauna, flora, and topography; the ability to produce
suitable weapons of the chase; and the skill requisite for successful
manipulation of such implements; not to forget such industrial
processes as the plaiting of fish baskets.

It is perhaps less manifest that such economic procedures also tie
up with social arrangements. On the lowest plane now under consideration, class distinctions are not pronounced, but individual
differences and special privilege begin to loom on the horizon. Prestige goes to the expert hunter, and he it is that is sought as a son-
in-law by ambitious parents, as among the Athapascans of northern
Canada. Bushmen who had the good luck to discover a beehive
claimed it as their inalienable property, to be transmitted to their
descendants; and they so marked the spot as to "detect any attempt

that might be made during their absence to pilfer from the hives."
The comparable Vedda customs have already been noted.

But the concerted effort imperative for effective hunting on a
large scale might also lead to definite assertion of authority. The
Washo and Paviotso of western Nevada recognized as a "rabbit
boss" the Indian most competent to direct a rabbit drive; and in
organizing an antelope *battue* on Bushman principles they had an
"antelope boss" who not only wielded temporal authority but was
invested with a sacred character. The Plains Indians, whose very
existence hinged on their communal bison hunt, went further and
delegated supreme authority, for the time being, to a constabulary
force. This "buffalo police" literally exercised dictatorial powers.
If anyone prematurely started to hunt or otherwise acted in con-
travention of the rules of the chase, the police whipped him, confis-
cated his ill-gotten game, and might even destroy the offender's
lodge. The custom is an ancient one, being characteristic of most of
the Plains tribes and reported by Hennepin for the Santee Dakota
as early as 1680.[14] Economic pursuits may thus culminate, even in
the hunting stage, in the temporary development of centralized
political authority.

Similar restrictions are found in regard to fishing and berrying.
In British Columbia, for instance, one particular hereditary officer
indicates the time when olachen fishing may begin; and on the
northern plateaus of British Columbia nobody is allowed to pick
berries until a certain old woman, to whom belongs this privilege,
indicates that the proper time has come.

Another interesting concomitant may be the foreshadowing, if
not complete realization, of unilateral clans. Suppose that a patch
of shrubs is valued as the Vedda value their beehives. A natural
consequence will be the desire to transmit such property according
to definite rules of descent, and since exploitation is usually sex-
linked as a result of the conventional division of labor, a man will
transmit his rights to his sons, a woman to her daughters. In Queensland a woman individually owns patches of plants and her prerogative is acquired by her daughters.[15] The Washo transmit clumps of
pine-nut trees from father to son. Hunting territories are perhaps
still more rigorously inherited in the paternal line among the northeastern Algonquians.[16] Thus patrilineal or matrilineal lineages are
outlined in the most natural manner by the alignment of kin in
consonance with customary rules of inheritance.

The attempt of man to control the wild growing food supply does not necessarily begin with actual sowing and planting. We find a number of cases in which man endeavors to make the conditions of growth more favorable. Thus all along the North Pacific coast of America woods are burned to improve the conditions of growth of berry-bearing bushes. On Vancouver Island this process is regulated in such a way that every social group claims the right to those berry patches which are burned over every third year and used in turn for picking berries. The same people use the roots of cinquefoil for food. These grow in estuaries exposed to floods. The women clear away pebbles so as to cause the roots to grow larger and more regularly. Each little garden is the property of a woman. It is surrounded by boards put up on end, and the pebbles are thrown up around them like little fences. There is little planting, but care of the plants.[17]

It is noticeable in the cultivation of plants and in the domestication of animals that by far the greatest number of both, at least in temperate climates, are gregarious. The grasses which are among the early cultivated plants of a large part of the Old World, as well as maize, occur in large masses, covering extended territories. Most of our domesticated animals, cattle, horses, sheep, goats, are gregarious. It seems justifiable to suppose that there is a certain relation between this and their early selection for cultivation and domestication. While it is impossible to prove the steps that may have led to this, it might be supposed that the association of individuals or social groups with certain fields or certain herds from which they obtained their sustenance led to protection of the field by refraining from gathering in too much seed, and to protection of the herd against wild animals that might disperse it and thus endanger the food supply.

Cultivation. If we keep in mind the frequently sedentary existence of "hunting" peoples and the often complicated devices by which they exploit the flora of their habitat, the first step toward the deliberate cultivation of plants will no longer loom as a complete break in the continuity of cultural development.

The earliest attempts at cultivation need not have been made with our common cereals. It is true that the first more or less datable evidence for farming comes from Badari in Egypt, where emmer wheat is said to have been raised about 5000 B.C.[18]; and that possibly a thousand years later Babylonia and Egypt are both found dependent on cultivated barley, wheat, and millet. But this may be a sheer accident.* For all we know the first efforts at husbandry may have been made in southern Asia and with species of a quite different order. As Werth has argued, members of the banana family probably have been cultivated in these regions from very early times, which on geologico-meteorological grounds he places about the close of the Pluvial period.[19] There is no reason to suppose that the technique of sowing seeds is more obvious than that of inserting into the ground the side shoots of a plantain, the only method ever followed in cultivating bananas.

Plate III shows that artificial pollination of the date palm was practiced in Assyria as early as the ninth century B.C.

Irrespective of this hypothetical point of relative chronology, the phenomenon has an important bearing on other historical problems. "Cultivation" is a convenient catchword but it represents no real unit as applied to methods so diverse as the sowing of wheat and the propagation of the plantain, which is invariably not from the seed. The two processes cannot be derived from each other. In other words, the congeries of practices we oppose as "farming" to "hunting" and "herding" have a diverse origin and it is idle to determine a single center of diffusion.

On the other hand, the careers of distinct cultivated species are indubitably often intertwined, and it seems unlikely that the planting of each one constitutes a separate invention. Thus, rye crops are a by-product of wheat-growing. Botany tells us that "the varietal riches" of wild rye are concentrated in parts of western Asia where "as a cultivated plant [it] is either of secondary importance or no importance at all." In Persia and neighboring areas it "is simply considered a nuisance jeopardizing the real crops of wheat or barley." But in the mountain districts of Bokhara, Afghanistan, and Anatolia it changes its character from a weed into that of an independent crop, being sown pure at an altitude of about 2000 meters and upward. "It is a curious fact, that at the border line of the struggle between winter rye and winter wheat it is an ancient custom . . . to sow out a mixture. . . . Not expecting to obtain a return of wheat every year, the farmer sows out the mixture of rye and wheat on purpose, hoping that if the wheat is killed by an adverse winter, rye will stand it and produce at least half of the expected yield."[20]

* See also page 263.

PL. III. Winged Being Pollinating Sacred Tree

Frieze from the Palace of Ashur-Nasir-apal II (885–860 B.C.), King of Assyria
at Kalhu (modern Nimrud). Courtesy of the Metropolitan Museum of Art.

This incidental creation of new crops from weeds holds for oats, originally a weed linked with emmer; *Eruca sativa*, at first a concomitant of flax; and other species. It implies the successful extension of a planting *pattern*. Apart from such special association, a pattern of this sort may even be applied to species without economic value. When the Hidatsa men planted tobacco seed, they followed the devices perfected by their wives in planting maize; they hoed and raked the ground and hilled up the earth about each plant with a buffalo rib "into a little hill like a corn hill." Similarly, Linton suggests that the American Indians had evolved various devices for the treatment of indigenous species and applied them to maize when this cereal reached them.[21] The development of tobacco-growing may be visualized as follows. At one time in the past the Indians employed only wild species of tobacco, as some tribes had done until recent times. Horticultural tribes experimented with *planting* it by methods familiar to them from corn-growing, succeeded, and in course of time made the minor variations in procedure suggested by experience. In some cases hunting tribes, like the Crow of the western plains and the Yurok of California, borrowed the farming technique only with reference to tobacco and thus present the anomaly of growing nothing but a useless weed. The Kutenai may have learned the planting of tobacco from the Plains tribes. It is more difficult to understand the origin of tobacco-planting among the Haida of British Columbia, particularly since it was not used for smoking but for chewing with burned shells, somewhat like the betel-chewing of Malaysia.

The example of rye illustrates the influence of accident on the creation of a new crop. Chance may operate in the same direction through other factors. Some species — wild hemp, for example — settle and thrive on rich fertilized soils. Thus they naturally follow man, "keeping near his dwelling places, settling on rubbish and everywhere where the soil was manured. . . . During famines, when man turned to the seeds and fruits of wild plants, he naturally chose hemp." Later hemp was used for fiber and oil.[22]

We have thus gained a number of significant propositions bearing on the early history of farming. In many cases the cultivation of a plant represents not wholly independent invention, but merely the extension of an established planting technique. On the other hand, there is no reason to suppose that such wholly distinct operations as those connected with banana- and wheat-growing constitute a single historical unit. It is inevitable to assume several distinct centers for "farming" operations.

Where, precisely, the line is to be drawn in the absence of clear-cut evidence is another matter. For example, shall rice be conceived as a crop of wholly independent origin? At the present stage it is less important to insist on a definitive conclusion than to realize the criteria that should throw the balance in favor of either alternative theory. In the case of rice, the innumerable variations of the plant fall broadly into two categories with corresponding techniques of husbandry. "Swamp rice" can be grown only in marshes or under irrigation. "Mountain rice" yields smaller crops but can be grown anywhere with normal precipitation.[23] Considering that irrigation is a highly complex invention, that it was demonstrably practiced in Babylonia in ancient times, and that Babylonia and India — the most probable center of rice cultivation — had ancient contacts, the transfer of irrigation methods from other cereals to rice is plausible enough even if mountain rice is supposed to have previously been grown by the simpler process. But it is probable that all rice-planting was a mere extension of, say, the practices used in the cultivation of barley. Wild rice,* specifically indistinguishable from the cultivated species, occurs among African tribes,[24] and under stress of similar circumstances a South Asiatic people already familiar with tillage may have tried sowing the wild form. The factor favoring the theory of such extension of the knowledge of the cultivation of cereals is the continuity of the areas involved, which permitted the ready transmission of ideas, tools, and techniques. Moreover, though rice is generally associated in our minds with India and southern China, it can be grown in conjunction with the more northerly cereals or in proximity to them. The Kirghiz visited by Radloff raised wheat and millet in the central steppe, rye in the north, and in Tashkent rice also; while in Persia wheat was the ancient staple, with rice gradually coming in during our era and not yet of prime importance a thousand years ago.[25]

The case of New World tillage is fundamentally different. No important Old World crop was raised in pre-Columbian times along with the distinctive native crops of maize, manioc, and potatoes. If the knowledge of farming came from the Chinese or outposts of Egyptian civilization, why was not the plow brought in, which in these regions dates back thousands of years, but was wholly un-

* This bears of course no relation to the "wild rice" of our central states.

known in America? How would the broadcast sowing of Old World cereals suggest the typical American method of heaping earth around the growing maize?[26] Still more, how could the process of *sowing* suggest the technique of raising potatoes or manioc (cassava)? "Cassava can be propagated from seed, but this procedure is not practiced" by the Indians of Guiana.[27]

It has been argued that the Polynesians are responsible for at least part of American husbandry. The Maori kumara, for example, is equated with the American sweet potato by Rivet, who derives it from New Zealand.[28] But this is a more than doubtful case. De Candolle, arguing from the botanical evidence, arrives at precisely the opposite conclusion: to wit, that the New Zealanders obtained their kumara from the American Indians, a conclusion in which Dr. E. D. Merrill concurs; and Dr. Laufer challenges the identification itself.[29]

If the Polynesians introduced any food plant, we might expect them to have brought in the banana, which they actually disseminated over immense distances in Oceania and which has been thoroughly acclimatized in the western hemisphere since 1492. But the historical, linguistic, and botanical evidence conclusively proves that the banana is post-Columbian.[30]

The Polynesians may furthermore be eliminated as apostles of farming in America on chronological grounds. Their occupancy of Polynesia itself is so recent that we should have to assume a beggarly few centuries of occasional contacts with the New World. Indeed, Professor Elliot Smith and Mr. Perry insist that the American Indians until certainly two thousand years ago were "food gatherers" little superior to anthropoid apes in their economic activities.[31] If so, they manifested a rapidity of development subsequent to Polynesian contacts that is miraculous.

Let us visualize clearly what is involved in the hypothesis of a Polynesian origin for American husbandry. Maize is descended from a wild grass indigenous in parts of Mexico. It has developed in such manner that without transportation by man it cannot spread over long distances. Still, at an early prehistoric time it was cultivated over a large part of North and South America. We have seen that it is grown by distinctive methods. But these methods are not and could not have been uniform throughout America. The Hopi of northern Arizona, for example, had to adapt cultivation to arid conditions of their region, while the Mandan and Hidatsa of North

Dakota were obliged to reckon with the shortness of the season. Furthermore, it is not a question of a single form of maize, but of a number of diverse varieties, which could not possibly be produced in the twinkling of an eye from a wild prototype. Indeed, in the older Basket Maker sites of our Southwest only "a single and apparently fairly primitive variety" appears.[32] But maize represents only a part of the total problem. By A.D. 1500 the Aymara of Bolivia had developed 240 varieties of the potato along with methods of preserving them by a special process of freezing and drying in the sun.[33] Then there is manioc, the more common variety of which becomes a food plant only after the elimination of the deadly prussic acid from its roots. In Africa, where the plant was introduced in post-Columbian days, a Bongo in Schweinfurth's party died from eating of the unprepared manioc,[34] for it requires an intricate series of operations to convert manioc into food. Besides these the American aborigines cultivated the peanut, tomato, pineapple, and a number of other indigenous species. It seems, therefore, quite impossible that American agriculture was introduced from Polynesia.

The only sane inference is that "farming" or "gardening" had a multiple origin in the world, though the number of truly independent efforts at cultivation is disproportionately small when compared to that of cultivated species; and, specifically, American husbandry is preponderantly an indigenous growth.

The extreme diffusionist position on this question seems to derive support from the indubitable fact that certain cultivated plants have in recent centuries spread with amazing rapidity. Thus, maize and manioc have rapidly usurped the place formerly held by other plants cultivated by African Negroes; the potato is often associated with Ireland by the unsophisticated, as the pineapple is with Hawaii. Deliberate commercial exploitation of geographical possibilities has indeed greatly altered the original distribution of plants. Who connects the coffee tree with its Abyssinian center of origin? One links it ordinarily with Brazil or Java, or at best with Arabia, from which it was first vigorously disseminated.

But it should be noted that it is not a question of merely putting two peoples into juxtaposition and thus automatically precipitating an osmosis of cultural goods. Cultivated plants, like arts and ceremonies, are accepted selectively. Indian corn revolutionized the economic life of many African tribes, but it barely affected that of the Baganda: "Maize was never grown in any quantity; it was only eaten while still young, either between meals, or as a relish after the meal; no one called the two or three cobs which he ate a meal." [35] Here, presumably, the intensive cultivation of the plantain (banana family) precluded substitution of the newcomer. Equally instructive is the case of the Nilotic Lango. As among so many African tribes, millet is the outstanding crop. Through raids into Bunyoro the Lango became familiar with the banana and sweet potato, but their response to these two potential staples was quite different. "The former has not found much favor, and although here and there a tree is put in near a village the banana cannot be said to be cultivated, and owing to their migratory tendency is not likely to become popular. With few exceptions, where it is planted it almost seems as if it had been planted for aesthetic effect. The sweet potato, on the other hand, is being planted in large quantities every year; such was its early popularity, in fact, that when it was first discovered and brought back in triumph from Bunyoro, a bundle of runners for planting was actually sufficient dowry for a wife." [36] Within our own culture sphere millet has been ousted from its ancient position as an important human food crop, while even the stress of war times failed to popularize Indian corn in Great Britain and France.

In other words, diffusion is a most capricious phenomenon and its psychology merits study in this as in other departments of culture; the spectacular historical cases of maize, manioc, etc., should not blind us to the ever selective and often nonrational tendencies of the human mind.

When all qualifications are made, however, the distribution of cultivated plants remains a most valuable index of historical connections, and while the state of our knowledge often leaves important problems undecided, other instances provide us with quite definite results. It is clear, for example, that wheat, barley, and millet could not be first cultivated in central Europe where the corresponding wild forms are lacking. If, then, prehistoric sites in Switzerland harbor grains of these cereals, there must have been trade routes connecting the Alpine region with the Near Orient, where botanists discover the wild ancestral plants. Similarly, though maize was grown in North Dakota, its occurrence there is due to diffusion from the south, since the ancestral form is found in Mexico.

A somewhat different problem is offered by the geographical range of the banana family. In part, indeed, it coincides with the foregoing; since the *Eumusa* subgenus occurs in wild state only as far east as Tahiti but was grown in Easter Island, eastward diffusion of the cultivated plants is proved. But in Africa a wild banana, *Musa ensete*, occurs, from which *a priori* the cultivated forms might be derived. But botanical examination shows that that is impossible: the wild African form lacks the side shoots from which all cultivated bananas are grown; its seeds are large and hard, whereas the seeds of cultivated bananas are mostly nonexistent; and the fruit is small and inedible. The *cultivated* African forms are therefore one and all traceable to the South Asiatic bananas, which in a state of nature produce shoots, are small-seeded, and bear soft, fleshy fruits.[37]

Eduard Hahn coupled his luminous discrimination of hoe tillage and plow tillage with the theory that these two forms of husbandry were quite distinct; that the former is historically associated with women and still remains so, while the plow is essentially a masculine implement; and that the former correlation naturally grows out of women's economic labors in the hunting stage. The elements of this theory are best considered separately.

The view that farming by means of the hoe is conducted by women can be illustrated by many striking examples. The Bánaro of New Guinea depend on their women for all horticultural products, the men merely making a clearing.[38] In Uganda "the garden and its cultivation have always been the woman's department. . . . When a man married he sought a plot of land for his wife in order that she might settle to work and provide food for the household." Other Negro tribes, for example, in southeastern Africa and Nyassaland, conform to this pattern.[39] Among American tribes may be cited the Hidatsa, among whom maize, beans, and squashes are raised by women, men taking charge only of the tobacco gardens.[40]

These instances are sufficiently numerous to have betrayed the present writer into acceptance of Hahn's generalization.[41] But closer study shows that among tribes with more complex culture there are far too many exceptions to warrant this conclusion. In all three areas mentioned there are many instances of masculine horticulture. A familiar picture shows Maori men pushing their dibbles into the ground; and for the Tongans even Captain Cook in 1777 noted that the men were the tillers, the employment of the women being mostly domestic.[42] In Unyoro, next door to Uganda, men assist the women and among the Lango the heaviest share is theirs; in Bornu the two sexes are said to be equally busy in attending to field and garden

with the hoe; among the Nuba of southern Kordofan and the Lake
Chad tribes masculine tillage predominates; and it is exclusive
among the Lakka of the Logone-Shari districts. In ancient Egypt
the hoe was invariably associated with men.[43] In the New World
men bear the brunt of hoe tillage from the Pueblo area southward
throughout the region of intensive cultivation. In these cases the
correlation of horticulture with the female sex is thus far less intimate than Hahn supposed. On the other hand, he seems to have
been essentially correct in asserting the almost invariable linkage of
the plow with the male sex. Where that implement occurs in ancient
Egypt, Babylonia, India, or China, it is operated by men, and the
rare exceptions, as in modern Kafiristan,[44] hardly militate against
the generalization.

The question arises how the data just presented affect the theory
of farming origins. They obviously complicate matters: it would be
much simpler if women invariably were the dibblers and hoe tillers,
as Hahn supposed. Shall we, then, abandon the view not only of
Hahn but of virtually every writer on the subject, that the beginnings of cultivation must be credited to women? By no means. In
order to judge of these ultimate origins we must envisage the conditions which characterize tribes unequivocally in the hunting stage.
Among the Semang of the Malay peninsula the men traverse the
woods with their blowguns in search of small game, while the women
dig up wild roots with pointed sticks.[45] Though men sometimes get
yams among the Vedda of Ceylon, "hunting is essentially their
work, and yams were usually dug by the women." [46] In New South
Wales women dig up all sorts of esculent bulbs for the household,
having been trained from infancy to recognize edible plants.[47] To
turn to America, the Nez Percé of Idaho are typical: "Camas, as
well as the other food roots, was gathered entirely by the women,
the men at this time being busied with fishing, hunting, and war
parties." [48]

In short, in the hunting stage the providing of vegetable food
devolves on the women. Hence, they were naturally the first to note
the potentialities of seeds dropped by chance, or of shoots planted
without definite purpose, and thus inaugurated the era of gardening
or farming. Particularly in those cases in which definite areas served
as a harvesting ground for the family, sib, or tribe opportunities
may have arisen when the harvesting field was not only exploited
but also tended — like the berry patches of the North Pacific coast.

How, then, are we to account for the fact that even the hoe tillers of Egypt were uniformly men and that men do the farming in the more advanced American tribes? We must assume that the gradually increasing dependence on cultivation in some regions decreased the importance of the chase and induced man to take over the activities that formerly constituted the exclusive domain of the other sex.

The hoe is either formed like a pick or has a broad blade, often running into a point. While the worker who uses the digging-stick shoves his tool forward, those who use the hoe pull it toward themselves. This difference is important when we try to understand the origin of the plow. The simplest forms of plows seem to be digging-sticks pulled forward instead of being shoved forward. The uniformity of the principle employed in the plow, the range of its distribution in the Old World, and its absence in all the outlying parts of the Old World as well as in the whole New World make it certain that it is a single invention which has spread at a late period from a single center. In Egypt the plow was known in the Old Empire.

These considerations support Hahn's opinion of the genetic independence of plow and hoe. To this view Dr. Laufer has given his assent, though he points out instances of degeneration in which Asiatic populations relapsed into the use of the hoe. "There is a sharp line of demarcation between tillage by means of the hoe and the plow, each being a well-defined sphere in itself, the latter not being developed from the former." [49] This position of Hahn's seems to rest on two grounds. On the one hand, he insists that the technological derivation of the plow from the hoe is inadmissible; on the other hand, he stresses the correlation of the hoe with the female sex. It may be argued against this that, whatever else the plow may signify, it represents a technological achievement that must have arisen out of some earlier tool. The hoe does represent a simpler device serving the same purpose, and Egyptologists have endeavored to trace its evolution into the plow [50] (see, however, page 262) Secondly, the ethnographical data cited above show that a sexual division of labor as to tillage need not be so absolute that the hoe ancestor of the plow could not have been used by men. Therefore the maize-growing of the eastern Indians of the United States which is carried on by women cannot be considered as independent in origin from the masculine husbandry further south. Similarly we cannot imagine that Egyptian women at one time came to grow barley and that, independent of this, Babylonian men at some other

time and in complete ignorance of all cultivation of barley took to
raising the same cereal with the aid of the plow. The definite cultivation of any plant from the wild state is too difficult a matter to
be lightly assumed as being accomplished over and over again.
Here, as in other fields, it is much easier to borrow than to create.

Though we have suggested possibilities for the earliest gardening,
it should be noted that a number of favorable circumstances must
combine. The seed or shoot must get into proper soil, some primitive
gatherer must observe the effects, and there must be an adventure-
some spirit willing to try deliberate planting. While it is obvious
that plants must have been first raised where they occurred in a
state of nature, it is never safe to infer that because a plant occurs
wild in a certain region the people resident there must have been
the first to cultivate it. No one has more convincingly exposed this
error than Laufer. It does not follow that the Italians raised olive
trees at an early date because there is some evidence of a wild olive
in the Pliocene of the peninsula; we know from historical sources
that the *cultivated* olive was brought to Italy from Greece at a relatively late period. So China had a wild grapevine but viticulture
started there only after 128 B.C. through the importation of *cultivated* vines from the west; and similarly the wild walnut indigenous
in China was never grown there, another species being introduced
from Iran as a cultivated plant.[51] That is to say, even expert farmers
having an agricultural experience of millennia may fail to detect the
potentialities of wild species of their flora.

Primitive husbandry is certainly crude when gauged by modern
standards. It is "predatory" in the sense that there is little, if any,
systematic practice of crop rotation or compensation. The consequence is naturally exhaustion of the soil, involving removal to a
new plot, where a new clearing is made with much wastage of tim-
ber, as among the Lango. But positive achievements merit equal
attention. The Kwakiutl, whose weak beginnings of agriculture are
confined to the care of clover gardens, burn over berry patches in a
rotation of three years. Tribes like the Hidatsa, who were not even
preponderantly dependent on tillage, knew enough to put away
seed enough to last for two years.[52] The Lango do know that it is of
advantage to burn over the ground; that the growing corn must be
protected from weeds and birds; that millet must be harvested in
time lest rainfalls cause the ripe grain to rot. They will construct
stout palisades two miles in length to ward off the invasions of

hippopotami and other large beasts.[53] Again, the Jagga inhabiting the slopes of Mt. Kilimanjaro not only fertilize their banana groves but lavish infinite pains on eleusine, which is grown on the steepest declivities and requires careful irrigation.[54] The American Indians fertilized their maize with fish and in some places with manure.

Certain social and political institutions are intimately linked with primitive farming. Among the frequently shifting Lango we could not expect rigorous principles as to land ownership. Land is not alienated or bequeathed, and this holds for the community as well as for individuals. "Any alien . . . who with its inhabitants' permission settles in the village may cultivate the common land on exactly the same temporary terms." A village may retain its right to cultivate old sites for a year or two, but these are open to occupancy by others, who cannot be ousted. Within the village anyone may take up what unused plot he desires, "the appropriations being made by mutual agreement and the village headman deciding any dispute." [55]

In many other horticultural tribes, however, the arrangement is different. The chief allocates the land to each family and thus may become master of his subjects' destiny. For parts of Fiji a suggestive development has been described. The chief originally wielded only a modicum of authority, but had the right to allot unused land. As tribal representative he thus came to assign plots to fugitives from other tribes. For these newcomers, however, he was naturally the dispenser of life; he became their overlord — a position he had not held toward his own people — and with the aid of these henchmen he could arrogate to himself a status originally alien to the aboriginal polity.[56] Through some such process we can conceive a chief turning into a truly dominant figure even without actual conquest of a neighboring group. The acme is reached when, as among the Baganda, the feudal scheme was fully developed, the king being sole owner of all land, the chiefs his delegates, and the commoners holding the land from these superiors "on condition of doing work for them, especially building work, and rendering military service." [57] In the less pretentious monarchical system of the Jagga the ruler was likewise the sole landowner, who assigned to each subject a residence, determined the time for sowing and harvesting, exacted service in his plantations, and transmitted through headmen his orders for constructing and repairing irrigation canals.[58]

Domesticated animals. According to Hahn's classical definition,[5]

domestic animals differ from corresponding wild forms by some
hereditary traits; and they differ from merely tame animals by
freely propagating in captivity. The latter point is a crucial one.
In Indo-China, India, Ceylon, and Java young elephants are trained
to do the work of domestic beasts; and Chinese chroniclers of the
ninth century of our era picture the aboriginal peoples of Yün-nan
harnessing elephants to plows and using them to transport loads
over long distances.[60] But unlike horses and cattle, these animals
will not breed in captivity; hence have to be caught and tamed
individually.

The revulsion against natural breeding habits in confinement is
the chief barrier against the multiplication of domesticated species.
For at least two thousand years no species of economic value has
been brought under domestication, and our main livestock animals
have been living in symbiotic partnership with man for more than
five thousand years. Francis Galton [61] even believed that man un-
consciously experimented for millennia, keeping all manner of animals; that a very limited number proved capable of such association,
particularly without diminished fertility; and that this remnant
represents all the domesticable species.

The determinants of a permanent partnership from the animal's
point of view varied with the species. The ancestor of our dog is
supposed to have been attracted by the protection of a fireplace and
the temptations of refuse heaps.[62] Reindeer have an inordinate craving for human urine, and even individuals not especially tame have
been known to approach Lapp settlements in search of this coveted
delicacy.[63] From the human point of view, the psychology of domestication seems obvious — economic exploitation. Nevertheless, this
entirely utilitarian explanation is insufficient. It is one of Hahn's
great contributions to have consistently emphasized the irrational
factors connected with incipient domestication; and in this conten-
tion he has been ably seconded by Laufer.[64] These authors rightly
emphasize the fact that wild sheep have no wool; that wild cows
yield milk only adequate for their calves; that wild fowl lay only
a modicum of eggs. It is a commonplace of the history of culture
that the Chinese have kept cattle for millennia yet never milk cows
or females of other species of livestock. Laufer points out that the
same people are likewise sheep-breeders of long standing yet have
never made woolen textiles. He shows that in Burma and in its
vicinity — the probable ancient center of chicken-raising — poultry

are "not primarily kept for utilitarian purposes, and the eggs are hardly, if ever, consumed." What the natives mainly want is to use the thighbones of the cock for divination: bamboo splinters are thrust into the foramina and the future is divined from the various angles at which the splinters project. This practice is recorded by Chinese observers going back to 110 B.C.

This conception of poultry-raising is supported by African data. In Unyoro fowls and eggs are never eaten by the dominant pastora. population and rarely by the peasants. Herders keep fowls, nevertheless, partly to sell to other tribes, but also for magico-religious purposes, for by inspecting the entrails of a chicken they determine the cause of a person's death. Elsewhere in the interlacustrine region poultry are kept solely for sacred uses. The eggs are abhorred as excrements and less squeamish tribes are treated with contempt The Baganda did not allow women to eat eggs or poultry flesh, and associated their consumption by men with such occurrences as the birth of twins, the cementing of blood brotherhood, and the termina-tion of the mourning period. The Bongo of the upper Nile, on the other hand, considered fowls as proper food for women only. Ii Kamerun and Spanish Guinea the Pangwe abstain from eggs and reserve chicken for special and ritualistic occasions. To take the comparable case of another bird species, the Bambala take good care of their pigeons and build cotes for them, yet "they serve no utilitarian purpose. . . . The only reason ever given is that the people like to see them." [65]

The pig also, as Laufer points out, figures as an animal used for divinatory purposes, its gall bladder being examined by the Karen of Burma and the Khasi of Assam. In this connection it is most important to note that while swine appear as domesticated animal in prehistoric Egypt, not one practical purpose for their keeping ha ever come to light: they were neither eaten nor worked in any way until a relatively late period.[66]

This nonutilitarian position is further borne out by observation as to animal treatment by tribes the world over. Whether they do or do not rear domestic species, they lavish an enormous amount of affection and care on utterly useless pets. The pigeon cotes of the Bambala have already been cited. The Bakairi of Brazil keep parrots, macaws, herons, and lizards but breed none of them and find the notion of eating a pet abhorrent. The Guiana Indians shoot monkeys with arrows to stupefy the animals, and then raise them a companions. The Taulipang, a Carib tribe of northern South America, catch and carefully tend parrots, mice, turtle, and deer. Further south Nordenskiöld saw a Choroti woman suckling an infant at one breast, a puppy at the other; the children made playmates of storks and ostriches. The Australian kept his dog, the dingo, without training it to catch game or render any service whatsoever. With the coming of the Whites European breeds superseded the dingo and the native transferred his affection to them. Each family is accompanied by several dogs, which are never killed. The blackfellow 'tosses to them a portion of all his food, and at night he sleeps with them in his bosom to keep him warm.' [67]

Nonrationalistic motives persist even in sophisticated civilizations that are well able to exploit some of their animal species. The reasons for the existence of lap dogs, race horses, and bulls for the *plaza de toros* are sentimental and sportive. The Chinese have kept crickets partly in appreciation of their music, partly to train them for the cricket arena. [68]

The conclusion is thus inevitable that the peculiar symbiosis under discussion was not entirely effected through deliberate human aiming at exploitation of beasts, but was due to a variety of reasons still powerful alike in tribes lacking all domestic beasts and among peoples well versed in animal husbandry.

But though practical considerations are not primary, they often assert themselves and exert a potent influence on primitive economics, sometimes in ways no longer familiar to us. To the hunter, for example, the dog, the earliest animal domesticated, was often of vital importance. The Tierra del Fuegians used him against otters, the Hottentot against antelope, the Shoshone of Idaho in bringing to bay mountain sheep, the Eskimo for scenting the seal's breathing-holes. Here and there, as in New Zealand, he was eaten for food, and sometimes, as among the Dakota, at ceremonial festivals. In New Zealand he also furnished hair for weaving, and so did the long-haired breeds of Puget Sound and Chile. Dog traction gave the primeval hunter a mobility that made it possible to exploit a much larger territory, as when the Yukaghir of northern Siberia move in dog sledges to the upper courses of the Kolyma River in search of wild reindeer and other game. The Kamchadal, too, in their present habitat, could not do without driving-dogs, every family owning from eight to fifteen. [69] Among the Eskimo the dog sledge played an important part, and the Plains Indians at least harnessed a dog to a wheelless dray of two poles lashed to each side of the animal's back, the butt ends dragging along the ground, and with a netted frame connecting the converging poles to bear the load (see page 269).

Wherever the larger livestock species were added, man acquired at least potentially further aids in transportation, vital sources of food, and materials for containers, tent covers, and other necessaries. Some districts are opened to human settlement or at least temporary occupancy solely through the possession of certain animals. In the Arabian desert, for example, the camel is indispensable as pack or mount. For several weeks it will keep up the even pace of five or six kilometers an hour for eight or ten hours a day. No horse could stand this; on the second day of such a journey the camel will catch up with his competitor, leaving him behind with the pack camels on the third, while on the following day the horse must be led. If saltless pasturage is available, the camel owner need not worry about drink or fodder; his beast finds its own provender and can go without water for a long time. In fact, it feeds its master, who can shift very well with camel's milk, which is very thick and nutritious and yields butter superior to that from a sheep's or goat's milk. At a pinch the Arab traveler may even extract water from his beast. "If hard pressed the Rwala kill the fattest camel, cut out the paunch, place it on a cloak, and squeeze the liquid from it into a leather bag, allowing it to cool and settle. They either drink it or, if it is too thick, they suck it into their throats through the nostrils." Professor Musil's guide had drunk such water on eight occasions, "and there is nobody among the Rwala who has not tasted it at least once." In addition to all this, the camel provides fuel in the form of dung. Finally, the hair is made into cordage and sewing thread, is spun into yarn woven into cloaks, or serves as a padding for winter garments.[70] In the Arctic the reindeer gains comparable significance, supporting itself where dogs have to be fed; carrying loads and riders on its own back or on sledges, irrespective of winds that make travel impossible for the dog; adding milk and flesh to the larder of some tribes and elsewhere at least enlarging the compass of their hunting trips.[71] The more common uses of cattle, sheep, horses, and donkeys are too well known to require exposition.

However, it should be once more emphasized that even where practical considerations play a dominant rôle capricious irrationality checks the full and rationalistic exploitation of domestic beasts. We expend thousands for breeding race horses but have never taken up the milking of mares. Yet in Turkestan "people of means live almost exclusively on kumiss, consuming it in enormous quantities," during the summer time; and Rubruk reports of his Mongols that so long as they had mare's milk they cared little for other food. The ancient Egyptians, we have already noted, originally made no use whatsoever of swine; neither did they use wool, though they kept sheep from at least 3000 B.C. Negro stock-breeders prepare no cheeses, which seem a unique achievement of the pastoral nomads of Eurasia; and there are African tribes that churn butter only to smear it as a cosmetic over their bodies. The Lango of the upper Nile are more reasonable and use it for food; but they will milk neither sheep nor goats. Again, the idea of regularly eating beef is quite remote even from experienced cattle-breeders. The Bantu as a rule eat only the flesh of cattle that have died of disease; slaughter is peculiar only to great festive occasions or looms as the prerogative of chiefs. The Kirghiz ride oxen on domestic errands or harness them to a plow in farming; they milk cows and work the hides into leather containers; but they will never eat beef if well-to-do, and even in destitute circumstances with the utmost reluctance. For them mutton is infinitely preferable, while the sheep-raising Baganda taboo it. Most amazing of all, from our point of view, is the attitude of the Chinese. Familiar with cattle for several thousand years, they not only prefer pork to beef, but they have never conceived the idea of milking their cows. As Laufer points out, this is all the more remarkable because they have long been in intimate contact with nomads who largely depend on milk for their sustenance and who do not scruple to milk the females of all their livestock. Apparently severed from other protocivilizations at an early time prior to the invention of dairying, the Chinese maintained unaltered the cattle complex that had evolved before their separation; the ox was a beast for drawing a plow, and there its uses ceased.[72]

Finally, another aspect of irrationalism is significant. Irrespective of the measure of recognizing the possibilities of their animal species, people from sheer acquisitiveness will accumulate vast herds that cannot be economically exploited. The stock-breeder develops not only an inordinate love for his beasts, but also a fantastic craving for larger and larger herds. There are tales of Negroes who committed suicide over the loss of a favorite cow. The Pangwe[73] keep sheep and goats not to eat them, which they rarely do, but mainly for the pure pleasure of possession. So, as Hatt explains, the Lapps[74] are prompted by "the lust of ownership." Reindeer-breeding might be most profitable if they limited their herds in accordance with available pasturage and bred to produce meat. But "such modern rationalism is foreign to old Lapp ideals." Again, though the horse is of little use to the Bedouin he will take infinite care to raise a mare and disregard the comfort of the household in her behalf. "The whole camp may suffer from thirst, and the children cry for a drop of water, but the master, unmoved, will pour the last remnants of water into a dish and set it before the pampered mare." [7]

The tremendous difficulty of making animals breed in unnatural confinement must affect our attitude toward the problem of independent development. It will prevent us from assuming an indefinite number of separate centers. The case of the oldest domestic animal, the dog, is instructive in this regard. The pre-Columbian American Indians had at least three main and sixteen lesser varieties, and it seemed plausible at one time to regard them as derived from such indigenous Canidae as the fox, wolf, and coyote. But Glover M Allen's anatomical comparison rules out all such hypotheses and proves that all American dogs are traceable to a single Asiatic type of wolf, their ancestor being brought from Asia in domesticated form. Indeed, Allen and Antonius derive *all* dogs the world over from a single wolflike ancestor, and Hilzheimer assumes but one additional ancestral type, the jackal, for African dogs. [76] Like other semidomesticated forms the dog interbreeds with wild, closely related species. Thus the Eskimo dog frequently interbreeds with the wolf.

Indications of bones gnawed by dogs or of dogs themselves occur in early Neolithic or even Epipaleolithic times; therefore the earliest domestication of a wolf may have been achieved toward the close of the Paleolithic period. The hunters possessed of this companion brought him with them on their migrations, for example across the Bering Strait region, and in the course of millennia the observed diversity arose in different local centers. In some cases the dog, like other cultural goods, might be lost, as happened in some parts of Brazil. In a few instances extraneous evidence suggests that the lack is due to the crudity and isolation of the aboriginal culture. This holds especially for the Tasmanians.

Zoölogists who happen to be unfamiliar with the cultural aspect of the problem are liable to serious error in assuming that every *biologically* diverse origin has equivalent culture-historical implica-

:ions. For instance, Feige argued that "the variations of form, as
among the various races of cattle, always indicate diverse descent."
In the same way the author infers several separate centers for
domestic swine.[77] Of course, breeds that are not zoölogically traceable to a common ancestor must have originated independently.
But that is beside our point. Let us take the zoölogist's moot ques-
:ion whether the humped ox or zebu of India is descended from
:he banteng of Indonesia and Indo-China or from some wild form
:losely related to the urus.[78] What interests us is, first of all, the
apparently unanimous judgment of the specialists that the zebu of
Africa is derived from India, that one of the taurine breeds of that
:ontinent definitely indicates contact with southern Asia. So far the
:oölogical difference is also historically significant. But it does not
mean that the first zebu-breeders domesticated their beast in total
gnorance of the occurrence of other taurine cattle. What they evidently did was to apply the domestication pattern observed among
heir neighbors — or preëxisting among themselves — to a related
orm. They succeeded, and added a new breed to the list of domestic
animals. So with the more remotely related buffalo of India (not to be
:onfused with our American "buffalo," the bison): its utilization
was modeled on that of cattle. This is neatly demonstrated by the
attitude shown as to milking buffalo. In Indo-China and Indonesia
— that is, in the culture sphere of eastern Asia where dairying is
acking — buffalo are not milked but are employed in agriculture, as
he ox is in China. In India, however, where dairying flourishes, the
preparation of milk products is practiced even by the comparatively
primitive Toda.

The question is how far this view can be safely extended. Schmidt
and Koppers assume that an Asiatic tribe in the vicinity of Lake
Baikal domesticated the reindeer as the earliest species of livestock;
:amels and horses were domesticated in imitation of reindeer; and
ultimately all other forms of stock, including the Peruvian llama,
'o back to this primary stimulus.[79]

Let us consider first the Peruvian data. The llama and the alpaca
are derived from the guanaco and vicuña, respectively — the recent
American representatives of the camel family. The llama was used
primarily as a beast of burden, being able to carry a load of 100
pounds a distance of ten or twelve miles a day. Its flesh was used
only to a moderate extent; the dung served for fuel in timberless
districts, but there was no attempt at milking, in striking contrast

to the utilization of Old World camels. The coarse wool of the llama was sheared for textile purposes, as was the finer wool of the alpaca and vicuña.[80]

Considering these facts, the Polynesians are immediately eliminated as possible stimulators of guanaco domestication. At best they had only the fowl, the dog, and the pig, and none of these is in the least capable of serving as a model. But neither can the Indonesians have played the part. Their buffalo, used either with the plow in rice culture or for sacramental slaughter, seems an impossible starting-point. The Peruvians' abstention from milk has been cited as a link with eastern Asia, but this purely negative feature has no evidential value: milking is obviously an artificial process, and its practice, not its lack, is what requires explanation.[81]

We shall therefore conclude that llama domestication was achieved independently of non-American cultures.

But even in the Old World several independent origins must inevitably be assumed, at least in some instances, if several species were domesticated by the same people. Let us assume, for the sake of argument, that cattle, sheep, and goats were domesticated by the Egyptians. Can we, then, derive the domestication of the nongregarious cat, which is generally credited to the Egyptians, from an imitation of cattle domestication? The notion is not tenable, for there is no *tertium quid comparationis*. If ox and cat were both domesticated on the banks of the Nile, it was on the common basis of keeping tame animals for social and religious reasons, not because the ancients detected a similarity between cat and cattle potentialities.

To take a less extreme instance: as Laufer and others have pointed out, and as Schmidt and Koppers admit, swine and poultry appear in a wholly different setting from that of the larger stock animals "Both pig and chicken are nonmigratory animals and consequently make their domicile only in sedentary, never in migratory communities." Hence the pastoral nomads uniformly lack swine, and even in modern Turkestan hog-raising is confined to the Russian colonists.[82] How sedentary horticulturists would conceive the notion of domesticating wild pigs and jungle fowl by watching the cattle- and horse-breeding nomads of the Asiatic steppes, as Schmidt and Koppers seem to suggest,[83] is difficult to imagine. To sum up, we shall do well to assume several, though not many, independent achievement of domestication.

In agreement with all authorities we may put the almost universal dog first in order. Beyond that it is not safe to make definite chronological statements. Domestic cattle, sheep, pigs, and donkeys appear in Egyptian pictures dating back to the fourth millennium B.C. Cattle and sheep bones are reported from early Neolithic North European kitchen middens, and a vast number of pig bones were found in Neolithic Chinese sites, but it is not easy to assign definite dates to these finds. The domestic horse does not appear in Egypt until approximately 1700 B.C.; in Babylonia it is mentioned as the possession of rude nomadic tribes in about 2300 B.C., though it remained rare until after Hammurabi's reign (ca. 2000 B.C.). Camels are mentioned in Mesopotamia about 1100 B.C., the one-humped dromedary as an Arab introduction in 854 B.C. The earliest mention of the domesticated reindeer — as a South Siberian beast — occurs in a Chinese source dated A.D. 499.

The dates given are, of course, not conclusive as to the period of earliest domestication: they merely tell us that at such and such a period the Babylonians encountered horse- or camel-breeders and that the Chinese first became cognizant of domestic reindeer toward the end of the first half of the first millennium of our era. Nevertheless, they are the best information we at present possess. Extravagant estimates have been made as to the Paleolithic antiquity of the reindeer; the ox has been vigorously declared and vehemently challenged as the earliest livestock species; southern Turkestan has been acclaimed as the fountainhead of all domestication; but so far as I can see, none of these assertions can be accepted at present as more than guesswork.

Some other conclusions seem more tenable, even though not strictly demonstrable. Thus, wild horses evidently were not the easiest of beasts to tame, and Hahn's hypothesis seems highly probable, that its tamers followed the pattern offered by the closely related and gentler ass, for whose domestication there is much earlier datable evidence. Breaking the horse in as a mount must have been a late achievement. In Babylonia it appears originally only harnessed to a war chariot, equestrianism not being mentioned until roughly a thousand years later (ca. 1130 B.C.) and Assyrian cavalry not until about 860 B.C. In Egypt the horse is also linked with the chariot. It was ridden only in exceptional cases and never harnessed to a common wagon or plow.[84]

The history of the reindeer is beset with moot problems; yet on a number of points there is fair agreement. Whatever may have been the first attempts at the domestication of the beast, special features of its utilization are patterned on the complexes developed with other species. The reindeer sledge was a "conscious and rational imitation of driving with dogs." The use of reindeer as mounts by the Tungus and some other Siberians is clearly modeled on the practice of South Siberian equestrians. Similarly the milking of reindeer by a few tribes is an imitation of the dairying customs of cattle-breeders. Indeed, the Lapp vocabulary itself for milk, cheese, and the correlated implements, betrays the Scandinavian origin of the technique.[85]

When people simultaneously own several species of livestock nothing is more natural for them than to transfer techniques perfected for one type of animal to another. This leveling may stop short of completeness from reasons inherent in the nature of the beasts, from aboriginal caprice, or from wholly obscure causes. However this may be, the tendency must be recognized. The Yakut, a Turkish tribe, driven northward by political disturbances retained their horses and cattle in northern Siberia, and even where they abandoned these for reindeer they applied to the new species their traditional experiences as to selective breeding. On the other hand, there is a reason why even the Kirghiz, who milk camels, goats, sheep, and mares as well as cows, do not produce other dairy products from mare's milk. "It is poorer in fat, casein, albumen, and salts, but much richer in milk-sugar, than cow's milk, and therefore is not adapted for butter and cheese making." [86]

Pastoral nomadism. The mere possession of livestock does not constitute pastoral nomadism. Our Plains Indians remained hunters after they had obtained horses from the Whites. They neither milked their mares nor took to eating horse flesh. The horse was to them quite different from what it was to the Kirghiz — not a direct economic asset but a means of transportation that facilitated the chase and thus indirectly affected the food supply. If the Arabs had nothing but their horses, they, too, would fail to pass muster, for it is the camel's milk and flesh that make their existence possible. On the other hand, the southeastern Bantu practice garden culture and rear cattle as sedentary farmers, so that they likewise cannot be regarded as nomads; and the same holds, of course, for all the higher agricultural civilizations that rest on field agriculture bound up with animal husbandry.

But where pastoral nomadism appears in typical form — in Mongolia, Turkestan, Arabia, or among some East Africans — hunting and farming recede into the background and may even be completely superseded. The Masai neither hunt game nor eat the flesh of wild beasts; in the midst of their cattle wild gnu can be seen peacefully grazing. With the Kirghiz of seventy years ago hunting was practiced by individual amateurs and mainly as a sport and a test of horsemanship. Falcons were trained to soar into the air and swoop down upon their quarry while their master followed their movements on horseback, possibly at the risk of his neck. Or an equestrian might crush a fugitive wolf's skull with a stick while galloping past his victim.[87]

The relations with farming are more intricate, and Hahn goes so far as to deny that nomads represent an independent economic condition. In his view they are degenerate horticulturists. They retain the livestock which, he assumes, they had brought under domestication while still tilling their gardens, but they are unable to subsist except by auxiliary farming or by sponging on the neighboring peasantry. This view is demonstrably inaccurate. In the first place, a glance at the Turkish tribes of southern Siberia and Turkestan dispels the notion that their existence depends on alien tillage. The Altaian Turks cultivate a quite negligible acreage of barley and buy flour only in years of dearth. The Kirghiz east of the Caspian raise barely enough grain for a dish of porridge, and only the well-to-do import flour for bread. Farther east, to be sure, they did devote part of their energies to growing wheat, millet, rye, and rice; but their agricultural technique, which included large-scale irrigation, was the result of contacts with higher civilizations and remained unessential. People with ample supplies of mutton, beef, and horse flesh; of cow's, sheep's, goat's, camel's, and mare's milk, and with a variety of cheeses to boot, were not likely to starve. The Mongols whom Rubruk encountered in A.D. 1253 had access to millet and rice, but so long as they had kumiss in the summer they cared not for other kinds of food. The Rwala Bedouins live exclusively on camel's milk for months at a time, and the Kababish camel herders of Kordofan thrive on it from November until February. It is true that great Mongol lords had their villages in the south, from which they could import flour and millet in the winter, and that even the poorer classes secured cereals in exchange for hides. In Arabia, too, the Bedouins, before setting out into the interior, coerce the settled fellahin into supplying them with wheat. But all this is doubtless due to the common human craving for a varied diet. In North America pure hunters like the Crow were glad to obtain from their semihorticultural fellow-Siouans, the Hidatsa, supplies of maize, but if they had no opportunities of visiting them they went without as all American aborigines had to do in prehorticultural days. Contrariwise, such inveterate farmers as the Hopi did not scorn venison and rabbit flesh, an indulgence which by no means implied backsliding into the hunting stage. And if the Bedouin takes the fellahin's wheat, the latter looks to the Bedouin for camels to pull his plows, so that the relationship, however abused by the stronger party, is not that of one-sided economic parasitism. Finally, it is worth noting that the "Hamitic" herders of interlacustrine East Africa not only despise the peasant race but vegetable products as well, to which as a rule they resort only in times of stress.[88]

The significant thing, then, is not the rearing of livestock, which is often coupled with a sedentary farming life; nor whether or not a tribe obtains grain in the interests of a more diversified bill of fare. What determines classification under the head of pastoral nomadism is whether people depend mainly, and potentially altogether, on their flocks and herds. The medieval Mongols used cereals as they wore costly furs from Russia and silken stuffs from Cathay, but these were luxuries they were able to forego; and as their true costume was of skin and felt, so their true and sufficient food was the produce of their livestock.

But in order to subsist on what their livestock provides it is necessary to maintain large herds and flocks — whence the contrast between the pastoral nomad, with his need of abundant grazing lands, and the sedentary stock-breeder. Even the reindeer, under suitable circumstances, can be kept in stables, as in parts of northern Russia and Siberia, but obviously this is possible only where there are, say, but three to five head to be tended. A large number of beasts inevitably creates for them and their masters a migratory existence and considerably less individual attention. Beyond supplying young lambs and fall calves with hay, the Kirghiz make no provisions for sheep and cattle, which are obliged to seek their own subsistence even during the cold season. There is also a dearth of winter stables.[89]

Nevertheless the animal husbandry of such peoples betrays a considerable degree of knowledge. To prevent the death of newborn fall lambs from the inclemency of the weather the northern Kirghiz employ contraceptives of felt during several months of the year. The Bedouins fully recognize the difference of thoroughbred and common camels and carefully watch pregnant she-camels lest they pasture on noxious plants or give birth in gullies or on sand drifts where the young animals would be devoured by wild beasts. A milking Tutsi keeps up a smudge of cow dung to ward off troublesome flies, and in case of illness there are veterinaries who specialize in bleeding the beasts. Herders generally make allowance for the female's reluctance to yield milk except in presence of her offspring. Nearly seven hundred years ago Rubruk noted how the Mongols tied colts in sight of their mothers. "Then the mares take a stand next to their foals and allow themselves to be milked." Similarly, the Kirghiz allow a calf to suck a little first, then tear it away, milk the cow, which is quite tractable after the process is once inaugurated, and finally again permit access to the calf. Among the Bedouins the milker stands on one side while the calf tries to suck from the other: "The camel gives her milk when she sees that the young one is approaching the udder." In this context some widespread deceptive devices merit attention. The Arabs kill a newborn weakling, draw the mother's nostrils together with a rope so that she cannot smell, and make her yield milk to another sucking camel. The Tutsi and other Africans stuff the skin of a dead calf and with it dupe the cow into being milked by the herder. The same ruse is reported for the western Kirghiz in connection with mare-milking.[90]

The pastoral nomad, by the necessities of the case, is not an aimless wanderer. If he and his herds are to survive there must be adaptation to the pasturage required by each species and migrations determined by their interests. When the Kababish Arabs first encamp, the cattle feed near by, "but soon every blade of grass in the neighborhood is devoured and nothing but sand and dry thorn bushes remain." Then the beasts go farther and farther away until they run risk of capture by the enemy. A wealthy Kirghiz herder is compelled to divide his herds according to the fodder best suited to the palate of each species. In winter they require protection in low, wooded tracts or low valleys not exposed to gusts of wind and with ample pasturage. The summer calls for open, well-watered plains or mountainous districts free from gnats and other insects. In the fall the narrower valleys and ravines make an appeal, because there the sun has probably failed to destroy the rich verdure, while in the spring the livestock browse on mountain slopes where the melting snow fosters the growth of vegetation. Since suitable winter quarters are much the hardest to secure, their control often precipitated warfare in the past, and in contrast to the summer pastures they are individually owned, marked off by topographical features or appropriate boundary signs.[91]

The inordinate passion for stock that develops among herders fosters various interesting social and political developments. A cattle plutocracy is likely to develop, with the poorer men sinking to the status of mere attendants or vassals tending the herds of their betters. This condition, however, may be prevented from taking the form of a fixed class system by the vicissitudes to which livestock is subject. When Radloff visited the Altai in 1860, there were men owning several thousand horses; ten years later anyone owning fifty head ranked as wealthy. The change was locally explained as due to the rinderpest. The depletion of some Kirghiz herds and the increase of others lead to a constant shift in the possession of the coveted winter grounds, since an impoverished herder naturally disposes of the superfluous pasturage. In one district the Kirghiz once lost eighty per cent of their stock through a hard winter.[92]

One aspect of the proprietary sense linked with pastoral nomadism is the elaboration of property marks. The Altaian Turks brand their horses' thighs; the western Kirghiz mutilate the horses' ears, cut triangles out of the lobes of sheep's ears, and brand their camels; and among the Bedouins every clan and tribe has its distinctive brand.[93] The Wahuma and their interlacustrine congeners in East Africa have even developed a cattle feudalism. The king is owner of all the cattle in the realm and the chiefs receive herds as fiefs. By parceling out herds and land — the latter being prized only as pasturage by the ruling class — the king exercises supreme control. In Ruanda the provincial princes received 10,000 head apiece, and their vassals from one to several hundred cattle; members of the next order in the feudal hierarchy had ten each, and the peasants had to content themselves with one or two.[94]

The basic requirements of extensive pastoral nomadism bring the herder into conflict with the sedentary farmer, whence one of the most significant and typical antitheses in human history. Usually better organized and possessed of greater mobility than neighboring peasant populations, the herders enjoy definite advantages and frequently gain the upper hand even in opposition to old and stable civilizations. Thus, from about 1400 B.C. the Chinese were constantly harassed by the mounted Turkish and Mongol hordes to the north. "These ever restless hordes perpetually poured over the Chinese frontiers and raided and pillaged the villages of the farmers." The Great Wall was constructed to ward off these depredations, but for a long time it was of doubtful value. The Hiung-nu (Huns) had developed a formidable type of warfare based on their general mode, of life. "The Chinese armies in the beginning were usually the losers as they opposed their infantry to the mobile cavalry and mounted archers of their enemies." Only in 307 B.C. Wu-ling, the ruler of Chao, took a leaf out of the Turks' book by adopting the horseback archery of the nomads along with their tight-fitting costume. Subsequently, under the Han dynasty, the Chinese at last took the offensive and to secure their frontiers carried the war into Hiung-nu territory. But this by no means solved the problem once and for all. The Chinese were again troubled by such nomadic peoples as the Kitan; in 1215 Peking was occupied by the Mongols, who founded a new Chinese dynasty; and in 1644 the Manchu, a Tungus tribe from the north, similarly gained control over the empire. Of these, the Mongols are noteworthy for the amazing extent of their conquests, under Jenghiz Khan and his successors, who not only subjected China but also such countries as Persia, the principality of Kiev, and other parts of Russia. In fact, it was a mere chance that the Mongols failed to exploit their crushing defeat of the German and Polish army at Liegnitz.[95]

The sudden appearance of the Arabs on the scene of world history and their rapid conquest of enormous areas in North Africa and the Iberian peninsula form another example on a large scale. In miniature the antithesis is still illustrated by the attitude assumed by the nomads toward the settled population of Arabia. "The Bedouins are convinced that the *fellahin* are obliged to supply them with food. . . . If the *fellah* does not give it to them of his own free will, they have the right to take everything they find." [96]

This typical relationship is nowhere more amply illustrated than among the natives of Africa. In the west the Fulbe, who had been herders in the Sudan for centuries, conquered the Haussa states in 1806 and reorganized the political order. In East Africa the pastoral Masai lift the cattle of neighboring peasant communities and massacre those who resist their inroads. In the interlacustrine states, such as Ankole, Unyoro, Ruanda, and Urundi, the herders conquered an alien sedentary population and made themselves into an upper caste, despising the farmers and obliging them to render tribute and to perform menial tasks. Even where the direct economic exploitation is limited by the aristocratic herders' contempt for vegetable food, the economic results may be fatal to the development of farming. In Ruanda the Tutsi chiefs drive their herds into the plantations at will, and the peasants are not permitted to drive them off irrespective of the damage caused. "In the aristocracy of herders of Ruanda the Muhutu is compelled to give way to the cattle. The cows have driven the Bahutu from certain parts of Ufumbiro. They also destroyed completely the peasants of the lava plain of Mulera. They transformed the region of Niansa into a wilderness. It may therefore be said that the cattle were a powerful element in shaping the landscape of Ruanda." In this respect the tillers share the fate they themselves have meted out to the hunting Twa (Batwa), whom they have expropriated by the growing necessity for deforestation in order to create horticultural plots. Deprived of his retreat, the hunter sinks to the level of a pariah.[97]

Economic determinism of culture. The examples cited above seem to prove the ultimate dependence even of nonmaterial culture upon the food-getting activities of the people concerned. But the matter is not nearly so simple as that. Certain truisms of course admit of no argument. People must gain a livelihood in order to maintain any culture at all; and those economic patterns which allow seasonal leisure or free some individuals for productive specialization in other than merely food-producing lines offer more chances to exceptional individuals. This condition is further emphasized in regions in which lives a denser unified population the existence of which is entirely tied up with the development of agriculture. But within this general framework an extraordinary diversity is possible, and we are driven to the conclusion not that economic conditions determine the rest of culture, but rather that between the economic and all other phases of communal life there are functional relations, in which the noneconomic may play the active and the economic the passive rôle.

Even in so extreme an instance as that of Ruanda the subordination of the peasantry into a class of commoners did not follow automatically from the contact of herders and farmers. The Tutsi, numbering barely 120,000, were able to conquer a million Hutu, because of the peasants' separatism, a feature not of economic but of political culture, which made it possible for the cattle-breeders to overcome one small community after another and to play off peasant groups against one another. These conditions have repeatedly occurred, but they are not inevitable; and in Uganda we find that the same people who elsewhere represent a privileged nobility form merely the specialized occupational caste of herders.[98]

Some writers hold that the low social position of woman among pastoral nomads is economically determined. Men, so the argument runs, were the first domesticators of livestock; accordingly women are tabooed from any connection with stock, are not allowed to own the most highly prized form of property, and automatically assume a lower status. This theory rests on a number of indisputable facts. Among an appreciable number of peoples women are either wholly excluded from dairy tasks or relegated to a humble place in the dairying economy. Thus, the men milk among the interlacustrine herders and perform all the relevant work except churning; and among the Lango, Baganda, and southeastern Bantu, who combine millet-raising with stock-breeding, no woman is permitted to milk. Further, among a number of Siberian tribes women are precluded from inheriting herds, and a remote kinsman may fall heir to the property rather than the deceased man's own daughters.

Notwithstanding these facts, there is no convincing proof that the empirical correlation found is organically fixed. Next door to the southeastern Bantu, the Hottentot women regularly milk cows; the Chukchee women assist their husbands in herding reindeer; and although among the South Siberian nomads the men milk the mares on account of the danger involved, women milk the cows, as Rubruk noted among the Mongols in 1253. It is wholly possible that feminine disabilities over a wide part of Asia and Africa are due not to a natural nexus but to an accidental association of ideas in the remote past which was widely diffused and stabilized within the range of a certain culture sphere. That is why tribes outside that range, such as the Hottentot or the Chukchee, fail to participate in the relevant ideology. On the other hand, this may explain why a theoretically low status is assigned to women by Amur River fishermen, Chinese agriculturists, Turkish stock-breeders, and Ostyak reindeer nomads.[99]

It is certainly not legitimate to assume that the economically productive part of the community is *ipso facto* the ruling class. If this held true, the European peasants of the Middle Ages would loom as the aristocracy of the period! For this reason I am more than skeptical concerning the suggested correlation between feminine garden culture and a gynecocracy.[100] The matrilineal system of *descent* may be functionally connected with cultivation by women, but of a true matriarchate there is virtually no example.[101] Even as regards the universal dependence of maternal *descent* on feminine tillage grave doubts may be entertained. On the one hand, there are tribes like the matrilineal Tlingit and Haida of British Columbia who do not practice any farming; and there are the preëminently matrilineal Pueblo Indians with whom corn-planting is primarily a masculine occupation. Further, a comparison of such closely related tribes as the Crow and Hidatsa shows that both are matrilineal, and women play much the same part in both societies. There is no ascertainable difference that can be traced to the adoption of tillage by the Hidatsa or its lapse or absence among the Crow.

Economic, like geographical, determinism, is part of that rationalistic philosophy which has so often obscured an understanding of human history. Social phenomena are not simple, and accordingly the same condition, owing to an indefinite number of unknown concomitants, will produce quite different results in different areas. If wild cattle exist in a certain country, it does not follow that the natives will domesticate them. If they domesticate them, it does not follow that they will milk cows or eat beef. Religious or dietary preconceptions or sheer ignorance of utilitarian possibilities may play an incalculable part, checking and even precluding economic utilization.

A fruitful investigation of economic causality will proceed by narrowing the field of inquiry and isolating the probable influence of single factors. Is it possible to discover the social status of Navajo women before the introduction of sheep? How do women among the purely pastoral Herero compare in position with those of the neighboring fellow-Bantu who breed stock and raise millet? What changes have been wrought in the ideology of the Chukchee and Koryak by the introduction of domesticated reindeer? How are the social and religious conceptions of the Twa modified when they become sedentary potters and farmers? These questions cannot yet be satisfactorily answered, but they are not inherently unanswerable and their formulation promises more ultimate illumination than the customary vague generalizations.

It is possible to turn the tables on economic determinism and to show how largely economic life is affected by considerations that, although irrelevant from our point of view, are of the utmost importance to the people concerned. Religious ideas, political ideology, notions of prestige (see pp. 327 ff.) intrude where an economist expects nothing but the creation and exchange of economic values, together with their practical correlates. It is presumably no mere chance that, while Melanesians have evolved a variety of currency systems, no equivalent phenomenon is noted for Polynesia. Where a chief could taboo a subject's possessions and make them his own, property was nonexistent, trading was checked, and its concomitants in the form of exchange media were unnecessary. In the Trobriand Islands the production and apportionment of wealth are inextricably bound up with tribal ideology as to the chieftainship and magic. The garden magician interposes at every stage of horticultural activity, and it is he and the chief who jointly systematize the efforts of the whole population. Yet, though the chief may command services, he is obliged to offer compensation. By way of contrast may be cited the condition of various Polynesian groups, where theoretically the soil was vested in a supreme ruler, even great nobles holding their lands from him, so that he was legally entitled to dispossess them as a Ruanda monarch was in principle entitled to deprive his lords of their cattle. The Polynesian commoners had no unqualified rights: "The great chiefs could seize on whatever took their fancy. Besides, the king or his representatives could assess labor upon the whole community whenever he pleased. The chiefs also claimed a share of all the fish taken by their tenants." [102]

Uganda illustrates typical African conditions. The king was a despot owning all the land; the chiefs were his vassals; and commoners held the land from the chiefs "on condition of doing work for them, especially building work and rendering military service." In other words, a feudal ideology was basic to the agricultural efforts of the people. But the mode of production and distribution of wealth rested on further ideologies. Plantains, the staple crop, were raised by women, who in return expected their husbands to plant the trees that provided them with bark cloth. That is to say, there was a definite ideology as to the sexual division of labor. Further, the relationship between a chief and his subordinates was not wholly that of master and slave. As among the southeastern Bantu, there was an appreciable admixture of patriarchal sentiment. A chief had a host of dependent relatives who formed, indeed, a body of henchmen but expected to be rewarded with gifts or minor offices; and unrelated malcontents might leave an unpopular chief and attach themselves to a neighboring rival. In other words, the mores implied the recognition of a supreme overlord but tempered the attitude of the lesser chiefs to the commoners, as they regulated the relations of husband and wife by stressing the factor of reciprocity.[103]

FOOTNOTES

1. Hahn, E., *Die Haustiere und ihre Beziehungen zur Wirtschaft des Menschen* (Leipzig, 1896) and *Das Alter der wirtschaftlichen Kultur der Menschheit* (Heidelberg, 1905).
2. Koppers, W. P., "Die ethnologische Wirtschaftsforschung," *Anthropos*, vols. 10–11 (1915–16); Schmidt, W., and Koppers, W. P., *Völker und Kulturen* (Regensburg, 1924), p. 385.
3. Hatt, G., *Notes on Reindeer Nomadism*, Memoirs of the American Anthropological Association, vol. 6 (1919), pp. 94, 109.
4. Schmidt, W., and Koppers, W. P., *op. cit.*, p. 509.
5. Wahle, E., article "Wirtschaft," in M. Ebert's *Reallexikon der Vorgeschichte*, vol. 14 (Berlin, 1929), p. 324.
6. Stow, G. W., *The Native Races of South Africa* (1905), pp. 34, 452.
7. Kroeber, A. L., *Handbook of the Indians of California*, Bulletin of the Bureau of American Ethnology, no. 78 (1925), p. 13.
8. Jochelson, W., *The Yukaghir and the Yukaghirized Tungus*, Jesup Expedition, vol. 9 (1926), p. 418.
9. Kroeber, A. L., *op. cit.*, p. 695.
10. Childe, V. Gordon, *The Most Ancient East* (London, 1929), pp. 2, 50.
11. Kroeber, A. L., *op. cit.*, pp. 87, 529, 814, 817.
12. Seligmann, C. G. and B. Z., *The Veddas* (Cambridge, 1911), pp. 91, 112, 327.
13. Stow, G. W., *op. cit.*, pp. 54–60, 71 ff., 80–94, 149 ff.
14. Lowie, R. H., in Anthropological Papers, American Museum of Natural History, vol. 11 (1916), pp. 130, 180, 747.
15. Roth, W. E., *North Queensland Ethnography*, Bulletin 5 (Brisbane, 1903); Bulletin 8 (1906).
16. Speck, F. G., *Family Hunting Territories*, Canadian Geological Survey Memoir, no. 70 (Ottawa, 1915).
17. Boas, F., *Geographical Names of the Kwakiutl Indians*, Columbia University Contributions to Anthropology, vol. 20 (1934), maps.
18. Brunton, Guy, "The Beginnings of Egyptian Civilization," *Antiquity* (1929), p. 462.
19. Werth, E., "Zur Natur- und Kulturgeschichte der Banana," in *Festschrift Eduard Hahn*, vol. 14 (1919), pp. 22–50.
20. Vavilov, N., *Studies on the Origin of Cultivated Plants*, Bulletin of Applied Botany and Plant-Breeding (Leningrad, 1926), pp. 196–209.
21. Wilson, G. L., *Agriculture of the Hidatsa Indians: an Indian Interpretation*, University of Minnesota, Studies in the Social Sciences, no. 9 (1917); Linton, R., "The Significance of Certain Traits in North American Maize Culture," *American Anthropologist*, vol. 26 (1924), p. 345.
22. Vavilov, N., *op. cit.*, pp. 221–233. For review of Vavilov, see *American Anthropologist*, vol. 30 (1928), p. 716.

23. Kroeber, A. L., *Peoples of the Philippines*, Handbook of the American Museum of Natural History, no. 8 (1928), p. 86.
24. Schweinfurth, G., *Zeitschrift der Gesellschaft für Erdkunde zu Berlin*, vol. 45 (1910), p. 99.
25. Radloff, W., *Aus Sibirien* (Leipzig, 1893), vol. 1, p. 466; Laufer, B., *Sino-Iranica*, Field Museum Publication, Anthropological Series, vol. 15, no. 3 (1919), p. 372.
26. Cf. Wissler, Clark, *The American Indian* (1917), chap. 1.
27. Roth, W. E., *An Introductory Study of the Arts, Crafts and Customs of the Guiana Indians*, Annual Report of the Bureau of American Ethnology, vol. 38 (1924), p. 216.
28. Rivet, P., in *P. W. Schmidt Festschrift* (Vienna, 1928), pp. 583–586, 603.
29. De Candolle, A., *Origine des plantes cultivées* (Paris, 1883), pp. 36–42; Merrill, E. D., oral communication; Laufer, B., "'The American Plant Migration," *Scientific Monthly* (1929), pp. 246 ff.
30. Nordenskiöld, E., *Comparative Ethnographical Studies*, vol. 5 (Oxford, 1922), pp. 64–76.
31. Smith, G. Elliot, *In the Beginning* (1928), p. 83.
32. Kidder, A. V., *An Introduction to the Study of Southwestern Archaeology* (1924), p. 78.
33. Nordenskiöld, E., "The American Indian as an Inventor," *Journal of the Royal Anthropological Institute*, vol. 59 (1929), p. 275.
34. Schweinfurth, G., *The Heart of Africa* (1874), p. 526.
35. Roscoe, J., *The Baganda* (London, 1911), p. 432.
36. Driberg, J. H., *The Lango* (London, 1923), p. 100.
37. Werth, E., *op. cit.*, pp. 22–50.
38. Thurnwald, R., *Die Gemeinde der Bánaro* (Stuttgart, 1921), pp. 53 ff.
39. Roscoe, J., *op. cit.*, p. 426; Shooter, J., *The Kafirs of Natal and the Zulu Country* (London, 1857), p. 17; Fülleborn, Fr., *Das deutsche Njassa- und Ruwuma-Gebiet* (Berlin, 1906), p. 101.
40. Wilson, G. L., *op. cit.*
41. Lowie, R. H., *Primitive Society* (1920), p. 75.
42. *Captain Cook's Voyages of Discovery*, Everyman's Library, p. 289.
43. Roscoe, J., *The Northern Bantu* (Cambridge, 1915), p. 68; Driberg, *op. cit.*, pp. 96 ff.; Nachtigal, G., *Saharâ und Sûdân* (Berlin, 1879–81), vol. 2, p. 389; Frobenius, L., *Und Afrika sprach* (Berlin, 1912–13), vol. 3, pp. 102, 128, 166; Roeder, G., article "Wirtschaft," in M. Ebert's *Reallexikon der Vorgeschichte*, vol. 14 (Berlin, 1929), p. 369.
44. Vavilov, N. I., and Bukinich, D. D., "Agricultural Afghanistan," in Supplement 33 to Bulletin of Applied Botany and Plant Breeding (Leningrad, 1929), p. 544.
45. Schebesta, P., *Bei den Urwaldzwergen von Malaya* (Leipzig, 1927), pp. 110, 198.
46. Seligmann, C. G. and B. Z., *op. cit.*, p. 87.
47. Fraser, J., *The Aborigines of New South Wales* (Sydney, 1892), pp. 4, 51.
48. Spinden, H. J., *The Nez Percé Indians*, Memoirs of the American Anthropological Association, vol. 2 (1908), p. 201.
49. Laufer, B., *Jade*, Field Museum Publication 154 (1912), p. 48.

50. Ranke, H., article "Pflug," in M. Ebert's *Reallexikon der Vorgeschichte*, vol. 10 (Berlin, 1927), p. 119; Gompertz, M., *Corn from Egypt* (1928), p. 41; cf. Tylor, E. B., "Origin of Plough and Wheel-Carriage," *Journal of the Royal Anthropological Institute*, vol. 10 (1881), p. 74; Leser, Paul, *Entstehung und Verbreitung des Pfluges* (Münster, 1931).

51. Laufer, B., *Sino-Iranica*, pp. 220 ff., 415 ff.

52. Wilson, G. L., *op. cit.*, p. 48.

53. Driberg, J. H., *op. cit.*, pp. 96 ff.

54. Gutmann, Bruno, *Dichten und Denken der Dschagganeger* (Leipzig, 1909), p. 111.

55. Driberg, J. H., *op. cit.*, p. 171.

56. Thomson, B., *The Fijians* (London, 1908), pp. 70, 354–386.

57. Roscoe, J., *The Baganda*, p. 268.

58. Gutmann, B., *op. cit.*, pp. 12, 24 ff.

59. Hahn, E., *Die Haustiere und ihre Beziehungen zur Wirtschaft des Menschen* (Leipzig, 1896).

60. Laufer, B., *Ivory in China*, Field Museum Anthropology Leaflet 21 (1925), pp. 11–14.

61. Galton, F., *Inquiries into Human Faculty and its Development* (London, 1883), pp. 243–244.

62. Hahn, E., article "Hund" in M. Ebert's *Reallexikon der Vorgeschichte*, vol. 5 (Berlin, 1926), p. 403.

63. Hatt, G., *op. cit.*, p. 108.

64. Laufer, B., "Methods in the Study of Domestication," *Scientific Monthly* vol. 25 (1927), pp. 251–255.

65. Roscoe, J., *The Northern Bantu*, pp. 54, 72, and *The Baganda*, p. 423; Evans-Pritchard, E. E., "The Bongo," in *Sudan Notes and Records*, vol. 12 (1929), p. 53; Tessmann, G., *Die Pangwe* (Berlin, 1913), vol. 1, p. 107; Smith, E. W., and Dale, A. M., *The Ila-Speaking Peoples of Northern Rhodesia* (London, 1920), vol. 1, p. 134.

66. Ranke, H., article "Schwein," in M. Ebert's *Reallexikon der Vorgeschichte*, vol. 11 (Berlin, 1928), p. 383.

67. von den Steinen, K., *Unter den Naturvölkern Central-Brasiliens* (Berlin, 1894), p. 210; Koch-Grünberg, Th., *Vom Roroima zum Orinoco* (Berlin, 1923), vol. 3, p. 79; Roth, W. E., *An Introductory Study of the Arts, Crafts and Customs of the Guiana Indians*, Annual Report of the Bureau of American Ethnology, vol. 38 (1924), pp. 551, 555; Spencer, B., and Gillen, F. J., *The Arunta* (London, 1927), vol. 1, p. 15; Fraser, J., *op. cit.*, p. 55.

68. Laufer, B., *Insect-Musicians and Cricket Champions of China*, Field Museum Anthropology Leaflet 22 (1927).

69. Jochelson, W., *Peoples of Asiatic Russia*, American Museum of Natural History (1928), pp. 50, 56.

70. Musil, A., *Arabia Petraea* (Vienna, 1907–08), vol. 3, pp. 140 ff., 254 ff., 263–270, and *The Manners and Customs of the Rwala Bedouins* (1928), pp. 94, 368; Seligmann, C. G., in *Harvard African Studies*, vol. 2, pp. 116–120; Radloff, W., *op. cit.*, vol. 1, p. 455.

71. Cf. Laufer, B., *The Reindeer and its Domestication*, Memoir of the American Anthropological Association, vol. 4 (1917), p. 139.

72. Jochelson, W., *Peoples of Asiatic Russia*, p. 80; Ranke, article "Schaf," in M. Ebert's *Reallexikon der Vorgeschichte*, vol. 11 (Berlin, 1927), p. 221; Driberg, J. H., *op. cit.*, p. 94; Radloff, W., *op. cit.*, vol. 1, p. 439; Roscoe, J., *The Baganda*, pp. 420, 423; Musil, A., *The Manners and Customs of the Rwala Bedouins*, pp. 90, 96; Laufer, B., "Methods in the Study of Domestication," *Scientific Monthly*, vol. 25 (1927), p. 252; Herbst, H. (tr.), *Der Bericht des Franziskaners Wilhelm von Rubruk über seine Reise in das Innere Asiens in den Jahren 1253–1255* (Leipzig, 1925), p. 13.

73. Tessmann, G., *op. cit.*, vol. 1, p. 105.

74. Hatt, G., *op. cit.*, p. 114.

75. Musil, A., *The Manners and Customs of the Rwala Bedouins*, p. 382.

76. Allen, G. M., in *Bulletin of the Museum of Comparative Zoölogy*, Harvard, vol. 63 (1920), pp. 431–517; Antonius, O., *Grundzüge einer Stammesgeschichte der Haustiere* (Jena, 1922), pp. 89 ff.; Hilzheimer, M., article "Hund," in M. Ebert's *Reallexikon der Vorgeschichte*, vol. 5 (Berlin, 1926), p. 408.

77. Feige, Ernst, "Motive der Haustiererwerbung," *Archiv für Anthropologie*, N. F., vol. 22 (1930), pp. 7–28.

78. Lydekker, R., *The Ox and its Kindred* (London, 1912), p. 147; Antonius, O., *op. cit.*, p. 185.

79. Schmidt, W., and Koppers, W. P., *op. cit.*, pp. 506, 514, 518, 608.

80. Mead, C. W., *Old Civilizations of Inca Land*, Handbook of the American Museum of Natural History, no. 11 (1924), pp. 26, 38, 65.

81. Kroeber, A. L., *Peoples of the Philippines*, Handbook of the American Museum of Natural History, no. 8 (1928), p. 84.

82. Jochelson, W., *Peoples of Asiatic Russia*, p. 82.

83. Schmidt, W., and Koppers, W. P., *op. cit.*, p. 506.

84. Ranke and Meissner, article "Pferd," in M. Ebert's *Reallexikon der Vorgeschichte*, vol. 10 (Berlin, 1927), pp. 113, 115.

85. Laufer, B., *The Reindeer and its Domestication*, pp. 138 ff.; Hatt, G., *op. cit.*, pp. 86, 89, 96.

86. Jochelson, W., "Kumiss Festivals of the Yakut," in *Boas Anniversary Volume* (1906), p. 260.

87. Routledge, W. S. and K., *With a Prehistoric People, the Akikuyu of British East Africa* (London, 1910), p. 345; Radloff, W., *op. cit.*, vol. 1, p. 466.

88. Radloff, W., *op. cit.*, vol. 1, pp. 297, 463; Karutz, R., *Unter Kirgisen und Turkmenen* (Leipzig, 1911), pp. 42 ff.; Herbst, H., *op. cit.*, pp. 8–20; Musil, A., *The Manners and Customs of the Rwala Bedouins*, pp. 90, 348; Seligmann, C. G. and B. Z., "The Kababish, a Sudan Arab Tribe," in *Harvard African Studies* (1918), vol. 2, pp. 119, 152; Roscoe, J., *The Northern Bantu*, pp. 77–79, 103.

89. Jochelson, W., *The Yukaghir and the Yukaghirized Tungus*, pp. 360 ff.; Radloff, W., *op. cit.*, vol. 1, pp. 423 ff., 437.

90. Musil, A., *The Manners and Customs of the Rwala Bedouins*, pp. 87 ff., 332 ff.; Czekanowski, Jan, *Forschungen im Nil-Kongo-Zwischengebiet* (Leipzig, 1917), vol. 1, pp. 141 ff.; Radloff, W., *op. cit.*, vol. 1, pp. 437, 445; vol. 2, p. 264; Karutz, R., *op. cit.*, p. 52; Routledge, W. S. and K., *op. cit.*, p. 45; Roscoe, J., *The Baganda*, p. 419.

91. Seligmann, C. B., and B. Z., "The Kababish, a Sudan Arab Tribe," p. 118; Radloff, W., *op. cit.*, vol. 1, pp. 414–420.
92. Radloff, W., *op. cit.*, vol. 1, pp. 284, 416; Machatschek, Fr., *Landeskunde von Russisch-Turkestan* (Stuttgart, 1921), pp. 153–155.
93. Radloff, W., *op. cit.*, pp. 279, 455; Karutz, *op. cit.*, p. 50; Musil, A., *The Manners and Customs of the Rwala Bedouins*, p. 312.
94. Roehl, quoted by Spannaus, G., *Züge aus der politischen Organisation afrikanischer Völker und Staaten* (Leipzig, 1929), p. 89.
95. Laufer, B., "The Early History of Felt," *American Anthropologist*, vol. 32 (1930), p. 4; Wilhelm, R., *A Short History of Chinese Civilization* (1929), pp. 179, 253.
96. Musil, A., *The Manners and Customs of the Rwala Bedouins*, p. 90.
97. Spannaus, G., *op. cit.*, p. 134; Merker, M., *Die Masai* (Berlin, 1904), pp. 110, 170, 196, 207, 246; Roscoe, J., *The Northern Bantu*, pp. 77 ff., 103; Czekanowski, J., *op. cit.*, pp. 143, 132.
98. Czekanowski, J., *op. cit.*, p. 50.
99. Cf. Lowie, R. H., *Primitive Society*, pp. 193 ff.
100. Schmidt, W., and Koppers, W. P., *op. cit.*, p. 266.
101. Lowie, R. H., *Primitive Society*, p. 189.
102. Gifford, E. W., *Tongan Society*, Bernice P. Bishop Museum Bulletin 61 (1929), p. 171; Malinowski, B., "The Primitive Economics of the Trobriand Islanders," *Economic Journal*, vol. 31 (1921).
103. Roscoe, J., *The Baganda*, pp. 13, 268, 233, 426.

GENERAL REFERENCES

Forde, C. Daryll, *Habitat, Economy and Society; A Geographical Introduction to Ethnology* (London, 1934).
Thurnwald, Richard, *Die menschliche Gesellschaft in ihren ethno-soziologischen Grundlagen.* I. "Repräsentative Lebensbilder von Naturvölkern" (Berlin and Leipzig, 1931).

CHAPTER VIII

THE ECONOMIC ORGANIZATION OF PRIMITIVE PEOPLES

RUTH BUNZEL

Introduction. Economics, literally "household management," is the total organization of behavior with reference to the problems of physical survival. Fundamentally the function of any economic system is to maintain some kind of equilibrium between material needs and the potentialities of the environment. What these material needs are conceived to be, and by what processes and for whose benefit the equilibrium is maintained, are matters subject to endless variation among the peoples of the world. As in the study of any other part of culture, the uncovering of the basic assumptions underlying economic institutions of a people leads us to the very heart of culture. Every economic system has a certain degree of unity and integration, no matter how diverse the origin of its elements or how checkered its history.

The economic functioning of any group shows a constant interplay of three complementary principles, which may be characterized briefly as the material, the formal, and the psychological.

The material principle deals with the physical relationship to the environment and with the classical anthropologist's "material culture." It concerns such problems as: What does the environment offer? What is utilized? What techniques are employed to acquire and transform the materials at hand, and what forms are given to them?

The formal principle is, roughly, "social organization" — the structure of the group, the organization for production, the network of economic obligations between individuals, the position of each individual with reference to a group.

The psychological principle is concerned largely with the general question of value in its widest sense, the structure of the personality that determines choice, and the attitudes that animate institutions.

In these three aspects of economics we find the answers to the three questions: What is done? Who does it? Why is it done?

This interrelation will be made clearer by a simple example. A man — an Eskimo, let us say — requires food; so he goes out to harpoon a seal. The habitat, the season, the technological means at his disposal, determine the nature of the food quest. The social structure of the Eskimo camp, the ideal of manhood which requires that each man must be a good hunter, determine the fact that he goes himself and that he goes alone, perhaps borrowing a dog or a kayak or a sledge, instead of taking food from another, or requesting it as a gift or in trade, or demanding it as a right. When he has caught his prey, he does not consume it on the spot, leaving behind what he does not need, but takes the animal back with him to his hut. The hut is not merely a shelter from the Arctic storm, but a home which he shares with other individuals to whom he is bound by ties of economic obligation. The pot of soup which his wife prepares provides the occasion for assembling the inhabitants of the camp, who linger until morning, eating, discussing the events of the day, singing, telling stories, in an atmosphere of warm sociability. The whole complex of behavior involved in this relatively simple act must be referred to other concepts besides a direct response to an instinctive drive.

The interplay of these three principles in shaping economic institutions is not the whole story by any means. There is a fourth factor, that of historic accident. The position of a tribe in relation to other tribes contributes its share to the building up of its economic institutions. Traits of material culture spread from one tribe to another, and the whole technological development of a people may depend upon phenomena of contact. The Chukchee learned reindeer-breeding from the Tungus, who learned it from peoples to the west; it has not yet reached the Eskimo, despite the fact that they hunt the reindeer (see page 311). Historic accident is evident in the development of certain types of economies. Caste systems are frequently the result of the superposition of alien cultures, but not a necessary result; migrations and aggressive warfare may be followed by inter-marriage, trade, and cultural interpenetration. Africa and Melanesia show both types of adjustment in neighboring groups (see page 373).

The contact of peoples plays its part in less obvious fashion. Large areas of the world are characterized by economic complexes, material, formal, and psychological, developed under influences of contact. Throughout Africa, from Morocco to the Cape, some form of the bride price occurs, carrying in its wake a whole complex of structural consequences. It is found among agricultural as well as pastoral people. Just as conspicuous is the distribution of exchange between groups related by marriage as an important economic mechanism over the whole Pacific area. On the other hand, the absence of important property rearrangements in connection with marriage throughout the greater part of North America is equally significant.[1]

The classification of peoples according to the dominant method of getting food is implicit in most ethnological thought, but the widely used categories such as *hunting, harvesting, horticultural, agricultural, pastoral,* must be qualified. It is insufficient, even in simpler economies, to classify a tribe as "hunters." The inquirer must know the habits of animals that are hunted, whether they are solitary or gregarious, sedentary or roving, whether they are tracked in the forest or ambushed at water holes, before it is possible to form any conception of what mode of life the food quest entails. The Australian aborigines form relatively permanent settlements near water holes, with strict property rights (see page 342); the Kaingang of Brazil, at the same "stage" of economic development, range freely through the forest, erecting rude shelters wherever night overtakes them.[2] The attempt to correlate these gross classifications with forms of social structure and economic ideals is of limited value.

Certain correlations between habitat, food supply, and mode of life seem obvious: hunters of solitary animals live in small groups, widely dispersed, highly mobile, with fluid social forms; garden people live in fairly permanent settlements, for considerations of land tenure and other property rights produce greater fixity of social forms. However, the Arapesh, a garden people of New Guinea, have all the mobility and looseness of social structure that we ordinarily associate with primitive hunters. They are agricultural nomads. Although they depend almost entirely on garden produce and pigs, they spend a third of their time "walking about"; they plant their crops in other men's fields and have only the most tenuous ties to their own homes.[3] Australian aborigines, on the other hand, although they derive their sustenance entirely from wild game and uncultivated plants, are relatively sedentary. In their waterless country each small group must stay in territory which it knows, and remain close to water holes to which it has rights of access. The Australian aborigines have the most inflexible social structure of any primitive group.[4]

These cases are exceptional, but their existence disproves any theory that derives social forms directly from the problem of subsistence. The *probability* of finding fixed residence, complex social organization, and the development of luxury is greatest among agricultural peoples. But it is not upon the growing of food alone that these developments depend. It is not the source of supply, but the existence of surplus, that is most significant for social forms. Hunting and fishing people with reliable and abundant food supplies, such as the peoples of the Northwest Coast of America[5] and the western prairies, when buffalo were still plentiful, have developed the elaborate social and religious institutions which are usually associated with agricultural economics.[6]

If the character of the food quest does not determine even such a closely related phenomenon as permanence of residence, it is not surprising to find a similar lack of determinism in such matters as mode of descent, totemic organization, the relations of the sexes, and religious ideas. Within any society social and material phenomena influence one another, but the search for general correlations has been unrewarding. Patriliny, patrilocal residence, bride purchase, polygyny, inferior status of women, and ancestor worship are frequently found in association with pastoral life. Matrilineal descent and inheritance are difficult to maintain in a pastoral community where animals are cared for by men. But the Herero[7] and the Ba'Ila of South Africa[8] and the Navajo[9] of America are pastoral and still have strong matrilineal institutions.

Comparative study shows that the pastoral configuration holds together somewhat better than any other similar configuration. A certain number of traits are found together often enough to give a typical picture to which many pastoral tribes conform, at least on the formal side. The unformalized aspects of such cultures are less readily comparable. The Herero, Ba'Ila, and Navajo are "special cases," with special historic backgrounds which we can trace in part. But every culture is a special case, as unique as an individual human being, and every event has an infinite multiplicity of causes. No aphorism could be more untrue than the famous one that history repeats itself. History never repeats; it is impossible for history to repeat itself, since the cumulative effect of the past is never at two moments or in two places the same.

Value. Even if it were possible to isolate causes, any general theory of determinism would hamper our understanding of cultural phenomena. Underlying all deterministic theories is the general concept that culture is adaptive behavior, each item of which aims at the maximum economic efficiency in a given environment. Efficiency in the sense in which we conceive it is conspicuously lacking in many primitive societies. The Lango [10] become involved in endless litigations in order to recover the particular cows paid for an absconding wife; the Mafulu [11] give pig feasts of such dimensions that they devastate their villages; the Kwakiutl deliberately break and throw into the sea articles of great value acquired after much difficulty; the Arapesh travel for days over slippery mountain trails to harvest crops in the hamlets of relatives, only to find the crops eaten by the pigs. In the face of such evidence of economic inefficiency we must abandon the concept of "economic man" grimly making the most of his environment and his techniques. Nevertheless primitive man is not a creature of whimsical impulse, without foresight or sense of order, unable to make any consistent attempt to control his environment. The material problem is always part of a greater whole, a cultural economy that aims at the good life, however differently it may be conceived in different cultures. This cultural economy has its own laws of efficiency; frequently "the good life" can be maintained only at the sacrifice of material efficiency. Each of the seemingly inefficient arrangements which we have mentioned serves some purpose in the total culture of the people who perpetuate it. The Arapesh, for instance, value wide social contacts as the most reliable guarantee of security. The conditions of life in their rugged and infertile mountains make it impossible for many people to come together at one time; social relations and economic sharing can be maintained only by the cumbersome method of individual wandering, and at the sacrifice of agricultural efficiency.

One of the characteristics of the psychic economy of culture is that a single act may serve many functions. It is easy to illustrate this from our own culture. A man gives a dinner party. He is paying off social obligations, indulging his taste for conviviality, exhibiting his possessions and his attractive wife, furthering his cousin's matrimonial schemes, and over the brandy and cigars he ferrets out important trade information from an unwary guest.

Examples of such multiplicity of aims can be drawn from any primitive society. One may safely assume that a feast is always complex in motivation. Among the Quiché, feasts are sacramental meals to honor the ancestors; among New Guinea cannibals, they are celebrations of revenge. At Zuñi, house-building forms part of the preparations for the harvest rituals; it is the occasion for important property distributions, a social obligation of the wealthy, and a mechanism for social integration. Among the Trobrianders [12] the building of a seagoing canoe fulfills much the same sociological function.

This multiplicity of function is not the only or by any means the most important way in which the psychic economy of culture manifests itself; for, in all societies, the whole structure which we call economic serves other purposes besides that which we have defined for it — the satisfaction of material needs, food, shelter, clothing, transportation. After these requirements have been met the economic structure is turned to the service of other needs or pursues a fantastic career of its own quite independent of the material needs which gave rise to it.

A certain minimal requirement must be met, notably the need for food and, in Arctic and sub-Arctic climates, the need for clothing and shelter. Accustomed to our own high standards of comfort, even among the poorest of our population, we are constantly astonished at how little is actually needed to maintain life. Discomfort is often accepted where a simple and known expedient might avert it. The Kaingang, a tropical forest people, do not like the rain and the mud; they know that they are uncomfortable if they have to sleep on the wet ground. Nevertheless they wait to erect their crude shelters until the tropical rain is actually upon them. The Arapesh are constantly and, to our way of thinking, unnecessarily tramping around in the rain and the cold, and they do not like it, but constant visiting is part of their scheme of life. Other peoples are able to achieve considerable comfort under the most difficult conditions. The Central Eskimo [13] manage to be comfortable even in winter. If a man finds himself away from his camp at nightfall he can in half an hour build himself a snow house in which he can remain snug and secure until morning, while the Reindeer Chukchee,[14] caught in a storm on the tundra, lies face down on the ground, waiting for it to pass, or else trudges on to keep from freezing to death.

Different valuation of comfort is found even within the economic framework of our own civilization. The French peasant does not do without sanitary plumbing, central heating, telephones, and automobiles because of ignorance, innate conservatism, or inability to see the advantages; nor, necessarily, because of poverty; but because he regards them as luxuries bought too dear at the price of security. Many small American farmers have all these conveniences because they value them more highly than savings. The choice of values is not individual. The spending habits of Americans are part of a social philosophy based on the relative fluidity of our social forms and on our traditional belief that future security is guaranteed by our unlimited opportunities.

The question of general standards of value is not only a question of what things one acquires, or even whether surplus wealth is used for present enjoyment or future security. There is the further question whether, after all, it is desirable to accumulate wealth. We believe in the fundamental desirability of more and more things. Our hero is the man who makes two things grow where one grew before.

Yet it is obvious that, beyond a certain point, the possession of wealth can be of no direct and material advantage. There is a limit to the amount of food one can eat, the clothing one can use, or the number of horses one can ride. Among primitive peoples with relatively simple material possessions the saturation point is soon reached. Beyond this saturation point of direct usefulness wealth assumes secondary values, as validation of things in themselves impalpable — security, prestige, power, achievement, love. In almost all human societies wealth has taken on some of these secondary meanings. In such societies individuals tend to accumulate surplus wealth provided there are institutions within which wealth can be accumulated.

There are, however, certain primitive societies where the accumulation of wealth is considered undesirable and where this principle is reflected in economic institutions. The pursuit of this aim means either that the society remains at a subsistence level or, if a surplus is actually produced, that the economic organization provides means for liquidating it. The Samoans live in an environment especially favored by nature, and their technological achievements are not to be despised. They are expert gardeners and fishermen; they build excellent canoes and make fine mats and bark cloth. Yet they are not addicted to luxury and they accumulate no property. With slight exertion and the help of relatives anyone can gather whatever is needed for an occasional feast or a marriage gift. The few articles of permanent value, fine mats and bark cloth, are continually circulating, passing lightly from hand to hand in a diffuse system of gift exchange.[15]

In Zuñi we have the same principle worked out at a higher economic level, with more wealth, which here is harder to get, and there are more complex institutions for keeping it fluid.

To value present wealth as a guarantee against future want is a reasonable idea and the first step in economic planning. It is certainly an idea with which we are very familiar. In our society the craving for security drives men to accumulate and hoard far beyond any realistic need. This craving for security is perhaps as universal as hunger or love, but it belongs to a wholly different level of psychic phenomena. Hunger is a mental state induced by a physical condition of the organism, and it is removed by the restoration of the bio-chemical balance. Anxiety about the future has no such identifiable physical cause; it originates wholly in the mind and is built out of such impalpables as emotions, intuitions, memories, projected hostilities. It is protean and, therefore, insatiable. The burned child fears the fire — sometimes. The man who has once been hungry will provide against future hunger — sometimes. Some hoarders have never known hunger and some men become misers without ever having experienced poverty.

It is difficult to tell from the accounts of primitive peoples how much of their feeling of economic insecurity, where it exists, is realistic. We find peoples who feel insecure without economic justification and, conversely, peoples who have no material guarantees for the future quite free of any comparable feelings of insecurity. The Trobrianders, living in the midst of plenty, practice the strictest frugality, hoarding food in order to throw it away at the next harvest.[16] It is impossible to guess whether it is insecurity, vanity, or some more deeply hidden motive that impels them to such behavior. In nearby Dobu it is clearly insecurity that produces the identical attitude toward food stores. But the insecurity of the Dobuans is not primarily economic. Although Tewara is not fertile and yam seed is scarce, the island exports sago; and Dobu itself is extremely fertile and exports its surplus of yams and sago. The insecurity that pervades Dobuan life is the terror and insecurity of a sorcery-ridden culture in which each man fears his neighbors.[17]

The Chukchee of Siberia are also a people who are fundamentally insecure in their environment, their social relationships, and their relationship to the supernatural. Away from their own hearths and the sacred fire of their ancestors, everything is hostile and bent to destroy them. The fundamental emotional insecurity of the Chukchee [18] is shown in such obvious facts as the extraordinarily high incidence of insanity, alcoholism, homicide, and suicide. Their whole economic system is an attempt to build up some security in this hostile world. They acquire great herds of reindeer, sometimes more than can be conveniently herded or economically exploited. They use the surplus to hire poor young men to herd for them, and then try to marry these dependents to their daughters in order to strengthen their camp. Their feasts, at which they distribute large amounts of property, serve to strengthen remote kinship ties, the only ties upon which they can count. Here wealth, power, and such poor security as they know go hand in hand. Possibly the unfriendly environment plays some part in their anxiety. Certainly there is nothing helpful in the environment.

But that it is not in itself the cause of the Chukchee temperament is shown by the contrast with the Eskimo. In an equally inhospitable environment, without even such security of food supply as the Chukchee have in their reindeer herds, the Eskimo present a picture of a secure, self-reliant people, confidently facing the struggle for existence. They make only slight attempts to lay up food stores. When they have food they share liberally with their fellows. They are hospitable. They know scarcity and starvation that even leads to cannibalism. But they do not put their faith in stores of food; they think strength and skill are better guarantees against calamity than wealth. No insanity has been reported among the Central Eskimo; their suicide pattern is different from that of the Chukchee; they commit suicide when they are old and sick, no longer able to cope with the environment. Moreover a comparison of the Maritime and Reindeer Chukchee shows that the stabilization of the food supply among the latter has not served to mitigate their feelings of insecurity. Rather the acquisition of property and its use for exploitation has intensified their violence and anxiety.

The Chukchee are not the only people who use wealth for power. This identification seems so obvious to us that we are inclined to think that wealth *is* power, or automatically gives it. Wealth can give power only under certain frequently developed conditions of ownership.

The desire to control others belongs to the aggressive side of our nature. Power, which is the ability to control, is free-floating in human society, and may become associated with any one of many distinguishing attributes — with physical strength (Eskimo), age

(Andamanese), with being the firstborn son of the firstborn son (Polynesia), with knowledge (Zuñi), psychic gifts, skill, or valor in war, or with being born with a caul. Often it becomes associated with wealth, and economic institutions take on an exploitive character. Capitalism is the most extreme expression of this identification.

There is no full capitalism among primitive peoples; but there are many societies where wealth and power are at least partially identified. The Ifugao are partial capitalists. Their wealth is rice land. It is prepared at enormous labor, limited in quantity, and belongs to a class of rich men. They have all the comfort, honor, prestige, and the choice of mates. Through a system of usury the rich become richer and the poor poorer. Still the poor are not entirely destitute. Yam gardens are by definition not "wealth" and cannot be permanently owned. Anyone may plant as much as he wishes and manage to live after a fashion, but he will never be able to pay his debts, give a feast, or meet the requirements of marriage and funeral payments without further borrowing.[19]

Wealth serves the drive for power differently in Africa. Here wealth, usually consisting of cattle, buys women. Women do the greater share of the work, practically all the agricultural work, and produce children to build up the political, military, and economic power of the husband and father or of his clan. Because women are limited the bride price is the keystone of African economic systems.

There are many societies where wealth brings power of a very limited kind. In Buin the two upper classes theoretically own all the wealth, of which the most important forms, next to land, are pigs and shell money. But land cannot be alienated and shell money can be exchanged only for pigs and special services, and pigs can be exchanged only for shell money, and all such transactions can be conducted only between people who stand in a certain complementary relationship to each other. Wealth validates status, status confers certain rights over persons, and there is a good deal of scrambling for wealth and power, but this is very different from our kind of unlimited identification of wealth and power.[20]

Because of the frequency with which wealth and power are identified, it is important to remember that there are societies, like Zuñi, where wealth and power are kept distinct. Wealth is desirable there because it contributes to comfortable living. It gives no control over others. Power, by which is meant always knowledge ritualistically acquired (the word for *power* means "that which is told to him"), is supernatural and dangerous, and its exercise may be a great nuisance. A man is afraid of his own power. Since men shun power there are devices for bribing, cajoling, and even kidnapping the unwary into positions of power, just as there are institutions to facilitate the sharing of wealth.[21]

We find among many peoples that although wealth gives no power in the sense of control over persons, the possession (or control, as in giving away) of wealth confers prestige. Veblen was the first economist to be impressed by the use of wealth for this purpose, and to point out the parallels between our own and primitive societies.[22] The psychological mechanism behind this formulation of the significance of wealth is not primarily aggression against another, but the glorification of the self. There are certain institutions connected with this attitude: the development of giving away as an important economic mechanism; the display and destruction of property. The most extreme example of this is to be found among the Kwakiutl. Wealth confers privileges, the right to sing songs, perform dances, boast publicly, and insult others. None of these privileges have any relation to power over others; they relate entirely to the self. When used against another the point is prestige, not factual power. This attitude toward wealth is common to all American Indians in a greater or less degree. Even the Zuñi, with their predominantly realistic attitude toward wealth, show traces of it. It is common also in Melanesia where it forms the basis of potlatching, which occurs sporadically in this region. In this undisguised form it is not characteristic of African or Polynesian societies, except the Maori.

There are peoples among whom wealth takes on a very special and personal symbolism. Among the Quiché of Guatemala, for instance, wealth is a symbol of (or substitute for) sexual capacity. "A man, if he is truly a man, will not bring into his house corn that is grown on the field of his wife. He sells it and gives her the money for her clothing. But this is bad, for it is the duty of a man to provide the food of the house, and if the woman has money she will not respect the man." [23] They explain the bride price the same way; it is "to make the woman respect the man." These statements can be fully understood only in relation to the total picture of Quiché married life, with the incidence of impotence, frigidity, refusal of conjugal rights, rejection, infidelity, and a crushing sense of guilt. The reasons for the failure of Quiché marriage lie far back in the

organization of family life, and are not immediately relevant. Frus-
trated in marital relations, the Quiché Indian has seized upon the
fertility of his field as a symbol of his masculine potency. This is
not the only value that wealth has to the Quiché, but it is this
peculiar valuation of it that is used to justify and make more dynamic the arrangements of household economy. Like all other institutionalized wealth symbolism this too can be paralleled in our own
society.

In our society we often make gifts directly to a person, or in his
name as proof of love or veneration. We give such things as "loving
cups" that are quite useless, are never sold, but are treasured "for
sentimental reasons," and become heirlooms. Or else a gift is given
publicly in the name of a relative, frequently after his death, as evidence of the love in which he was held, and we often measure love
in terms of the size of these gifts.

The Dakota have made this into one of their major economic
institutions, which finds its extreme expression in the child-beloved,
the child who from birth is especially privileged in all things and
whose position is maintained by the large amount of property which
is constantly given away in his name. He is expected to maintain
this position by continued generosity, but because of the large
amount of property that has been given away in his name and because, as the Dakota phrase it, "everyone has been benefited by his
mere existence," he has special claims upon the loyalty and support
of his tribesmen. Nothing could be more explicit than the symbolic
importance of wealth conveyed in these words of a Dakota informant.[24]

There is a strange contradiction in our own attitudes toward
wealth. We have been called "the acquisitive society." [25] Certainly
the outstanding feature of our civilization and the feature upon
which we most often pride ourselves is the quantity and complexity
of our material possessions and achievements. Nevertheless philoso-
phers in all ages have questioned the value of riches and have even
declared that wealth is the root of all evil. Official Christianity, as
well as other philosophic systems, has declared unequivocally against
the accumulation of riches. These strictures have had little effect
upon our institutions.

There is no better description of the dynamics of acquisitiveness
under modern capitalism than that given by a leading German
economist:

There are no absolute limits to acquisition and the system exercises a psychological compulsion to boundless extension. . . . Activity in the capitalist system is no longer determined by the needs, quantitatively or qualitatively limited, of one person or a group of persons. Profits, no matter how large, can never reach a level sufficient to satisfy the economic agent. The positive drive towards boundless acquisition is grounded in the conditions of management. . . . Any enlargement of business reacts to its own advantage. . . . This provides the stimulus to continuous expansion of a business, often contrary to the expressed wishes of its owners and managers. In this peculiar orientation of human activity upon an infinitely removed goal lies the reason for the dynamic potency of the capitalistic system, a potency which renders intelligible all its remarkable achievements.[26]

The reason for the contradiction between our ethics and our behavior, and the resulting tension in individual lives, lies in this "psychological compulsion" exercised by our institutions. The intense desire for profits as an ultimate aim rather than actual needs is the outcome of an attitude toward wealth which no longer permits us to regard it realistically in terms of things to be obtained and enjoyed for their intrinsic value, but as food for insatiable psychic drives toward power, prestige, and security.

In our civilization the identification of wealth with power or aggression is made on two levels: under the present form of our property institutions wealth becomes an instrument by which one can exercise control over others; but in addition to this the accumulation of wealth often is a substitute for direct aggression against individuals. This, perhaps, is the source both of the compulsive character of our pursuit of wealth, and of our recognition of its antisocial elements, and the tendency to say that it is wealth which is evil, rather than the use which we make of it.

The few examples quoted show some of the more obvious meanings which wealth may take on in different cultures. The relative importance which is attached to wealth in the psychic life, and the particular symbolisms which cluster about it, will color and animate all economic institutions. In analyzing that part of the economic life that is not directly concerned with the control of the environment, the first question which we must ask is: What does wealth mean to these people? Only when we have answered that question — and it is not always easy to answer it — do economic institutions become intelligible.

Property. The relation of man to wealth is expressed in his system of property, which is a channeling of the relationships between men and things that has the same structural and dynamic significance in the material field that kinship has in the field of relationships between individuals. The more we try to isolate the concept of property from social structure and general philosophical attitudes, the more the concept eludes us and becomes a meaningless abstraction like "totemism," while we are left with a miscellaneous collection of equities, rights, interests, claims, privileges, and preferences. In each society these are arranged into some kind of system for regulating man's relations to his environment and his fellow, and it is the underlying principles of this system with which we must concern ourselves. No group lives in a wholly diffuse, undifferentiated relationship with the environment which furnishes the wealth upon which survival and comfort depend. There is always some selection. The relationship may be as slight and tenuous as the sentiment of an Eskimo for the locality where he was born, and to which he hopes some day to return, or it may be as specific as the feeling of a Dakota for a favorite horse, a feeling so strong that the meanest revenge one can take on a man is to kill his favorite horse. When such relationships between men and the external world are differentiated in favor of certain individuals or groups we have the institution of property. The direction, depth, and permanence of these channels of ownership vary from one group to another, and always they exercise their subtle influence upon social relations and psychological attitudes.

This is not a definition of property that would satisfy lawyers who try to define property in terms of abstract rights rather than in terms of the dynamics of human behavior. A legal definition of property based on our categories and involving such concepts as exclusive rights, absolute control, and right of disposal, which differentiates property from usufruct, is liable to obscure other and more vital problems of proprietorship. Many primitive societies give scant recognition to such concepts. Yet such people have a clear concept of their own of what property is and what rôle it plays in human affairs.

The recognition of the dynamic aspect of the relationship of man to his environment makes it unnecessary to assume the existence of a special "acquisitive instinct," or any primordial concept of animism, or the extension of the personality, or "libidinal interest" n the products of the body to account for the universal existence of differentiated attitudes, such as a desire to control, for one's own benefit or pleasure, in relation to inanimate objects.[27] Such special ideas may dominate the property institutions of any people. Property rights among the Maori are based on their theory of personality. The chief has *mana*, power inherent in his personality, greater than that of others. Whatever he touches or even names as his becomes invested with the taboo that surrounds his person and becomes dangerous to others.[28] This idea is found in more or less attenuated form in all aristocracies when property rights are felt to be inviolable in proportion to the length of genealogies. The Zuñi have no such theories of personality. They are inclined to assume a more or less dependent, or at least a reciprocal, attitude toward things "owned." They have no word that denotes possession; the word by which they express ownership means merely "to be with." Marriage is "to be with" a person of the opposite sex; membership in a society is "to be with" that society; one "is with" a field or a house or a silver necklace. They sing to the corn in their storerooms so that it may not feel neglected. This concept of property is part of their total unaggressive, receptive attitude toward the universe. From this it follows that there is no tendency to retain control of things that are not in use. There is, indeed, little understanding of such "ownership." Under the influence of Whites they are being educated to it.[29]

The Dobuans, on the other hand, conceive their relationship to material objects as one of domination. Yams in the gardens like to go visiting and must be kept at home by magical spells.[30] They must be controlled and also defended from other men's aggression. Though we do not formulate it animistically, this is substantially like our own conception of the relation between men and things. We speak of "conquering nature," "controlling the environment," "wresting a living from the world." Life is a struggle, and property represents the spoils of battle.

The most important part of man's environment is the land. In approaching the general problem of land tenure it must be recognized from the outset that the relation of people to the land is never solely economic. The farmer whose family has resided for long periods on the same spot has not only an economic but also a sentimental attachment to the land he tills. In our modern states there is a feeling of "ownership" of a different character regarding

the territory of the nation, infringement of which arouses, evei
among the most peaceful, warlike sentiments and deeds.

We might expect that these attitudes which so strongly influenc
our own thinking would exert a still more profound influence on th
lives of primitive peoples, and in general this is the case. Man under
stands very well that he does not "own" the everlasting hills in th
same way as he owns a spear or a blanket or even an animal. H
may hotly defend against others his right to exclusive occupancy
but toward the land itself there is always a feeling of dependence
slight or strong. This feeling may be expressed symbolically in th
concept of the Earth Mother, with its mythological corollaries re
garding the origin of life. Such myths are of very general occurrenc
and exist independently of any earth fertility cults. The Eskimo, a
truly maritime people in their principal food dependence, hav
transferred these feelings to the mother of sea mammals.

Strong feelings of dependence on the land are not characteristi
of agricultural people only. Among the Arunta and other tribes o
central Australia each patrilineal band inhabits a territory to whicl
it feels bound by mystical ties. This relationship is expressed in th
veneration of sacred places, centers of totemic worship. These place
are at the same time the sources of their own life, since it is at sucl
places that women conceive by the spirits of the dead, and th
shrines at which they renew the fertility of the land. The native
belong to the land as much as the land belongs to them, and the
cannot be induced to leave the source of their life.[31]

The existence of such mystical conceptions of man's connectio:
with the land will influence the nature of occupancy and the theorie
of ownership; but such ideas are not universal among peoples at th
same economic level. In some regions the Ojibwa have toward thei
territory the predatory attitude so familiar in our own culture. Th
land is there to be despoiled. They stake out huge tracts for trappin
grounds, blaze their boundaries, and defend them against trespas
openly or by magical spells. These trapping grounds are owned b;
individuals, without any restrictions even on rights of disposal. A
lad will not hunt on his father's trails without permission, nor
woman on her husband's. It is up to each man to conserve th
resources of his land by moderate hunting, or to keep moving on t
new tracts after the old one is impaired. This is possible because o
the vast tracts of uninhabited land, but it results in the wide scat
tering of the group.[32]

On the other hand, there are people like the Eskimo who, in spite of a considerable sentiment for the place of their birth, have absolutely no idea of permanent residence or exclusive rights. A man hopes to return to die at the place of his birth, but meanwhile he wanders over thousands of miles, joining up with groups of equally unanchored individuals. These groups have no great permanence, no place of residence, no hunting grounds to which they claim any rights. The fact that a man is challenged when he comes to a strange camp is due to suspicion of personal aggression, and to a wish to test and rank the stranger's strength; it is not in any sense a defense of territorial claims against trespass.[33]

In these three tribes we have three completely different attitudes in relation to the land among people at the subsistence level who gain their living by hunting and collecting; and these three attitudes are cast into very different property institutions. The Australian concept of ownership is by far the most complex and subtle. It is relevant that of the three the Australians have also the most complex social forms. Among the Eskimo there is no group sufficiently cohesive to maintain territorial jurisdiction, and the lack of a common stake to be defended keeps the groups fluid. Among the Australians the sense of belonging to the place where one was born or conceived, and of having claims upon that territory, supports the patrilineal and patrilocal social structure, and the cohesiveness of the band as a social unit upholds the territorial claim.

We are not trying to answer the question about the priority of individual or collective ownership of land among hunting peoples, which is unanswerable. All kinds of property institutions exist among very simple people, and property institutions must be understood not with reference to a general economic level but with reference to specific problems of survival. The Ojibwa trap nonmigratory animals; the Eskimo are essentially maritime; the Australians must exploit and they know or perish of thirst; but the Kwakiutl also are primarily maritime and have rigid concepts of property in fishing grounds; the Yukaghir trap the same kinds of animals as the Ojibwa and have no private trapping grounds, only a right to the trap line. In property as in everything else we must return to the same general truth, that there is no single cause of any item of behavior.

Even if it were possible to answer the question concerning the earliest form of property, it would not tell us very much. The title of owner is not of the same importance everywhere. It is perfectly correct to point out that there is no collective ownership of tilled fields among the Zuñi; all fields are owned by individuals, practically without restrictions; a man has even limited testamentary rights, neither clans nor other groups having any jurisdiction. It is also correct to point out that hunting and fishing grounds are not individually owned among the Kwakiutl, but are owned collectively by "clans." But such formulations refer only to the legal forms of property rights. They tell us very little about the dynamic functions of property in either tribe. We must know how property is used; inquire whether there is a real or artificially created scarcity of necessities; whether all individuals have free access to the main sources of food supply; whether the control by certain groups of all or an important part of the food supply can be used as a means of class exploitation; whether there is any special form of wealth the unequal distribution of which places certain individuals or groups in positions of control.

In answering the first of these questions we must not be naïve about the concept of scarcity. In discussing wealth and security we pointed out that there can be a feeling of scarcity where no real scarcity exists, as among the Trobrianders, and, on the other hand, an actual scarcity without the existence of competitive pressure within the group, as among the Central Eskimo. But the Eskimo scarcity is never conceived as absolute — it is no limitation of potential wealth, but human limitations that create the temporary shortage. The sea is full of seals waiting the spear of the fearless and skillful hunter. When we turn to people like the Ifugao there is an acute and irremediable scarcity of rice land. Rice fields must be level and abundantly supplied with water. The whole Ifugao territory consists of precipitous mountains, and level fields must be created by terracing, an enterprise requiring enormous expenditure of labor. There remains the problem of water, which must be obtained by irrigation from permanent sources at a high altitude, which makes most of the land unavailable for this type of cultivation. In any event, a rice field cannot be made overnight, and the capitalistic tendencies of the Ifugao — their acquisitiveness, the development of interest, and the use of property for power — must always be seen against this real situation. The Quiché Indians have a real land problem also. Such absolute limitation of resources is extremely rare in primitive society. Usually, in more thinly populated regions scarcity merely means that one must go farther afield to hunt or to pasture one's animals or to stake out new gardens.

Artificial scarcity can be brought about in many ways, by many kinds of taboos, restrictions, and monopolies. Among the Maori the sea and the forest are taboo at times until certain magical rites have been performed; some plants are taboo to all except members of definite clans. Such limitations may be regulative and aimed at a conservation of resources for the common good; others are protective of property rights in certain goods; there are some few that are definitely restrictive. The Trobriand chief kills by sorcery any man whose garden excites his envy or threatens his power.[34] Men are therefore careful not to make their gardens too productive. In the neighboring island of Dobu there is no chieftainship, but the same attitude is diffused through the whole population, and every man fears the envy of his neighbor. It is probable that fear of envy tends to inhibit activity among all peoples where wealth symbolism is strongly developed, and is accompanied by in-group sorcery. Where there are class distinctions, this attitude may become economically and politically dynamic, as it has among the Trobrianders.

Ideas of ownership may become associated with any object, animate or inanimate, tangible or intangible. We have excluded slaves, usually regarded as property, from this consideration of property because slavery is an institutionalized relationship between persons, involving maximum control. It has its economic aspect, as have all status relationships and, as we shall see, relationships within the family and between the sexes. Whatever the legal status of slaves may be, from the sociological point of view it obscures rather than clarifies issues to regard slaves (or women) as property.

This leaves three important classes of objects which may be owned: natural objects, the land or sea, and all the animals, fish, and growing things which it sustains; man-made objects; and incorporeal property. In general — there are exceptions — the rights to natural and intangible objects are more restricted, especially as regards rights of disposal, alteration, or exclusive possession. Food occupies a special position, sometimes falling into one, sometimes another class. Among ourselves food supplies are chattels over which we have absolute rights of ownership. However, most primitive peoples tend to regard food as a part of nature over which only limited control can be exercised. The Zuñi believe stored corn has a will and runs away if the laws of hospitality are violated.* Restric-

* The Zuñi family with whom I lived would never accept direct remuneration for food. They would sell almost anything else, but to sell food violated their

tions on the ownership of food may be nothing more than rules of hospitality, the requirement to feed every visitor, or to give food to whoever requests it, or it may be a requirement to share in time of need, or it may be full communality of food among members of the same camp or village or compound. Among the Kaingang [35] every large animal is divided among the women of the camp; among the Vedda [36] one woman cooks for the whole settlement; in Lau [37] one earth oven serves a sib group; among the Bathonga [38] the women of the compound exchange cooked food at each meal. Communality of food is not restricted to people at the subsistence level. The Dakota feel that food actually cannot be owned. This attitude is expressed in their language. The possessive pronoun cannot be used with reference to food. One can say "the meat that is in my tipi," but one cannot say "my meat," any more than one can say "my mountain" or "my buffalo." "My horse" always means my favorite horse, regarded almost as a member of the family. Other animals cannot be mine or thine. The attitude revealed in language is substantiated by behavior. They interpret very broadly the requirements of hospitality. One must be prodigal with food. On the hunt old men or women without male providers go along and ask for whatever portion of the kill they desire, and self-respect demands that it must be given. Anyone may ask for anything as a gift, and it may not be refused. Refusal would brand one as "not a true Dakota."

The right to demand gifts, usually restricted to certain relatives tempers the absoluteness of ownership among many people. Another limitation on ownership is the right of usufruct without compensation. At the simplest levels this is usually the right to borrow, either with or without permission and for an indefinite period of time surplus hunting equipment. Among the Kaingang an article may be "borrowed" without the permission of the owner. The borrower may recognize that he does not own the object; eventually he may even return it to the man to whom it "belongs." The owner may even claim it, but such demands are not made within the group unless one is looking for trouble.[39] The Eskimo, however, feel that if the owner gave another man permission to use his harpoon it was because he did not need it, and therefore there is no urgent necessity

---

deepest sentiments. They were insulted if offered money for food, but would accept "presents" of money offered as "remembrances" of a visit.

for the borrower to return it while he still has need of it.[40] The Zuñi have exactly the same attitude about land. A has let a field go out of cultivation. If B wishes to plant in it A cannot refuse. Although it still belongs to A it would be "mean" — and unavailing — to assert his claim so long as B is using it. It is perfectly clear to any Zuñi that B needs the field more than A. Isn't he using it? If A presses his claim, as he has a legal right to do, B offers another field in exchange. If he has no other field that he can spare, that proves that he needs this one. So then A compromises by offering a field in exchange. *B now has clear title to the second field.*[41] We have quoted this example in detail to show that although the Zuñi have perfectly clear ideas about land tenure and what constitutes title, they are not fanatics about it. Title they regard as a rather shadowy factor compared to a present need. The strength with which in some societies abstract rights are defended in the face of reality is a measure of the symbolic importance of wealth. Men for whom property has great symbolic value as evidence of security, achievement, or power will die defending their possessions from desperate men.*

There are many kinds of restrictions upon ownership of real property. A commoner in the Trobriands owns his fields; they cannot be alienated from his lineage, but the chief claims an overlordship which entitles him to tribute in the form of first fruits. So does the garden magician who performs growth magic for all the gardens of the village. Since he makes it grow it is "his" garden. The chief also owns the coconut trees on other men's lands.[42] A district chief among the Lango may grant large tracts of land to a subchief. These grants cover nothing but hunting rights, and in no way interfere with the occupancy of peasants who are cultivating fields within the area.[43] Ancient Hebrew law reserved for the poor the right to glean in rich men's fields. Among primitive peoples there are many special rules and guarantees regarding water rights, access to wells and springs, and access to special kinds of trees and shrubs. Certain Maori clans have the right to gather the berries of certain shrubs, regardless of where they are growing.[44] Among the Quiché the most important of all shrines, which is visited by everyone, is in the

---

* A rhyme current a few years ago expresses the idea perfectly:
"Here lies the body of Jonathan Gray
Who died defending his right of way.
He was right, dead right as he rolled along,
But he's just as dead as if he were wrong."

middle of someone's cornfield. Moreover it is the rare exception among primitive peoples for the owner of land to have free rights of disposal. Often the land is entailed within the kin group, and the rules of succession are fixed by custom. Testamentary powers are rarely accorded the owner, and often the land can be alienated during the life of the owner only with the permission of the heirs. Among the Quiché to alienate land from the male line of primogeniture is a great sin against the ancestors as well as the heirs, and carries a burden of guilt. Still a man may legally sell land, but the sale is not valid without the permission of the neighbors on all four sides, given before official witnesses.[45] These restrictions are commonplaces. The limitations of ownership must be constantly redefined. But the problem of land tenure goes far deeper than a definition of limitations.

The idea of incorporeal property is not unfamiliar to us. We recognize that "good will" has a cash value; shopkeepers can get injunctions against pickets on the grounds that they are impairing a value. Property interests in knowledge are protected by patents, and the words of songs and stories by copyright. Even names are property. The Kwakiutl Indians pawn their names when they have no other way of meeting their debts. A Polish immigrant in Massachusetts was enjoined from changing his name to Cabot on the complaint of the Cabot family that he was infringing on a vested right.

So when we say that among certain peoples intangible properties like names, myths, songs, vision prayers, and magical formulas are the most important form of property, we are not dealing with wholly unfamiliar categories, although we rarely phrase it quite that way. Among the Kwakiutl, the right to names forms the great point of rivalry [46]; among the Dobuans one of the bitterest conflicts is between cousins over the rights to magical formulas.[47]

Rights to incorporeal property merge imperceptibly into various social privileges. The courts of the African kings contain innumerable functionaries such as the Keeper of the King's Umbilical Cord, the Custodian of the Royal Tombs, the cooks and drummers and gatekeepers (in other courts the Knights of the Bath or the Garter), whose posts are hereditary within certain clans, although not necessarily in any one line, and which carry with them estates large or small. The title to all land is vested by divine right in the king, who parcels it out among those who perform personal services or who guarantee military support, or who keep his storehouses filled.[48] This is an essential feature of the feudal state wherever it is found. The other aspect of this relationship is the responsibility of the king for the welfare of his subjects. Hence the right to take care of the king's umbilical cord, or to give a daughter to make the king's bed, has more than honorific importance. The elaborate ritualism of the African potentates serves as a mechanism for administering property. It gives the feudal lords something to do to justify their tenure of land; and the peasant who brings a basket of grain to help keep this structure going is justifying his occupancy. Partial feudalism, in the form of local feudal chiefs, not headed up into a state, is found in Buin and other parts of Melanesia; strong chieftainship with overlordship that gives the right to demand tribute, but no control of succession or occupancy of the land, is found in Polynesia and the Trobriands. There are no traces of feudal institutions in America north of Mexico.

Monopolistic control is found in many places — especially in Africa where iron work and the manufacture of salt are often restricted to certain clans. It is not a question merely of learning a skill; one must be born into the proper clan in order to share in their vested interest. There is a tendency all over Africa for all industries to become organized into monopolies; it has gone farthest among such people as the Bakitara and the Banyankole [49] among whom the basic occupations of agriculture and dairying have become the vested interest of certain clans, and the whole society has become an intricate structure of interdependent monopolistic groups. We must not lose sight of the fact of this interdependence, which is the basis of feudal economic relations. There is another point about East African feudalism, and that is the absence of the profit motive, since there is no way in which any group can extend its operations.[50] (This is not true of West Africa, where, apparently, the sky is the limit.) We do not know how these caste monopolies are maintained; we can only guess at the sanctions; but we know how it is done in the Trobriands. Here certain villages maintain a monopoly of fishing. The villages of the interior need fish for their ceremonial exchanges, and the only way they can get it is by ceremonial trade with partners in the fishing villages, who in turn need garden produce. These villages will kill anyone from the interior caught trespassing in the lagoon, but when the Dobuans come on trading expeditions they may fish in the Trobriand lagoon. This differs from the usual property rights of primitive people in its monopolistic character; what these villages are defending is not their food supply, but their vested interest in the production of a commodity for trade. Still there is no capitalism in the Trobriands. Trade is conducted without profit, for profits have no reinvestment value. There is not much that one could do with capital — land cannot be alienated; "valuables" are not for sale; pigs belong to the chief. No man can exploit the labor of another, or make another dependent upon him for the necessities of life.[51]

The use of property for class exploitation which most closely resembles our own use of it is found among the nomadic Reindeer Chukchee. Among them there are men who have no property — the disinherited or those who have lost their herds. The interests of younger brothers are not always respected in inheritance; it is easy to lose a herd through illness, bad weather, or inept handling, or to deplete it through slaughtering to satisfy ritual or daily needs. Such men are in a truly desperate situation. They have no access to any reliable source of food. No one assumes responsibility for them. They wander from camp to camp, until they are taken on as servants by some relative more fortunate than they.[52] The control of land by chiefs in Micronesia has the same exploitive character.

The objects of wealth among primitive people are not always material instruments like land, animals, and food, but articles whose value is culturally determined and purely symbolic, like the blankets and coppers of the Kwakiutl, the valuables of the *kula* trade, the shell money (which is not really money in our sense at all) of other Melanesian islands, the cowrie shells of West Africa. These objects frequently do not have even an exchange value in terms of commodities, but their possession lends prestige. It is about such objects, rather than land or houses or food, that the competitive passions most frequently rage. The fact that their value is subjective does not make it any less real to the people, but their possession does not afford economic security because they have no objective reality. Our symbols have it. "Playing the market" in Wall Street is sometimes called a game, but it is a game in which the stakes involve the livelihood of millions. In this it differs from the potlatch and many other speculative games of primitive peoples.

Attitudes toward wealth and property institutions constantly interact in a powerfully dynamic relationship. The existence of acute anxiety stimulates individuals to accumulate property and use it to control others; the existence of private control of the necessities of life produces anxiety in those who are shut out and also in those who have, but fear to lose. This in turn produces a tension between groups and individuals which serves to increase the rigidity of institutions. This is the dynamic character of Chukchee or Ifugao civilization, where it is based on a real inadequacy in the environment, and of our own.

The dynamic trend may also be in the opposite direction; institutions which permit free access to the necessities of life to all promote a sense of security. People with no worries about the future see no need to accumulate to the exclusion of others. This is the Zuñi or Samoan picture. How these tendencies get started we do not know, although we can see how, under cultural pressure, they are built up individually in children. Once started the process pursues its course, sometimes with increasing intensity, or with diminishing vigor, until some new element is introduced. In Zuñi the introduction of strict property rights and profit in sheep-herding has altered the direction of economic development. It will be interesting to see whether the socialization of wealth under Soviet régime will diminish the Chukchee manifestations of anxiety.

Types of economic structure. Let us now describe briefly three economic systems as illustrations of ways in which primitive people have worked out the problems which we have been discussing. The choice of examples has been dictated partly by the availability of the material, since very few primitive economies have been completely described, partly for their complexity and partly for variety of motivation. These are societies well above the subsistence level whose economic institutions have been subjected to considerable elaboration but with very different aims.

The Zuñi.[53] The Zuñi in western New Mexico gain their sustenance primarily from agriculture, with sheep-herding as a secondary source of income, but one that is increasing in importance. They live in one compact village with three outlying hamlets occupied during the crop season. They inhabit a terrain that on account of climate and the character of the soil is conspicuously unsuitable for agriculture. Game is of no economic importance at present but probably was important in the past.

In a singularly inhospitable environment the Zuñi Indians have built up an economy with relatively high standards of living, considerable surplus wealth, and a maximum of security for everyone.

There is a surplus of corn sufficient to carry the village through a bad year, and there are large herds of sheep. Each individual possesses surplus clothing and valuable ornaments of turquoise and silver; many have automobiles. All this wealth is derived from native agriculture and stock-raising.

The outstanding characteristics of the economic system are the strong development of coöperative attitudes and techniques, the corresponding absence of competition and aggressive behavior in general, the dominant rôle of women in economic affairs, the fluidity of wealth, which implies the absence of acquisitiveness, and a thoroughly realistic attitude toward property, which is valued for direct use and not as an instrument for power or prestige. Power and authority are vested in the possessors of nonmaterial privileges, rituals, songs, fetishes, and war honors, and these are never used for economic ends. The "poor man" at Zuñi is one without ceremonial connections. These economic principles are related to the general attitude toward the universe, which is one of great security. The Zuñi believe themselves part of a thoroughly benign universe in which the supernaturals and especially the deified ancestors are concerned with supplying man's material needs. Their religion consists of an elaborate system of collective ceremonies, the purpose of which is to keep these pleasant relationships active. In these ceremonies everyone participates according to his social position and shares in the collective blessings thus attained. Their optimistic fatalism encourages unaggressive, uncompetitive, and generous economic behavior.

The tribe forms an exceptionally cohesive unit, bound together in a network of cross-cutting groups. In this mesh an individual's place is fixed by varying affiliations with different groups and corresponding responsibilities. Although in all matters of ultimate importance the tribe must be regarded as the economic as well as the sociological unit, in the day to day business of living the functioning unit is the household. The core of the household is a maternal lineage, a woman or group of women and their descendants through females. The men of the household are those who have married in and those born in the house who have not yet married or who have returned "home" after being divorced or widowed. Even married men consider the house of their mother or sister as "home," and contribute occasional labor to its support; but the household is supported chiefly by the labor of men who have married in. Marriage is monogamous, but readily broken. Young people change mates frequently before settling into permanent unions, and even then the marriage tie is tenuous compared to the tie of blood. Until his children are grown no man has status or security in his wife's home, where he lives and labors. This gives to women tremendous economic and emotional security in spite of the fact that men do all the productive work and hold all the positions of ceremonial and political importance. Men raise the crops and build the houses; women own them. Men speak of "owning" fields. Actually the title is entailed in the maternal lineage, passing from mother to daughter, and exploited, according to expediency, by brothers and husbands. This is the Zuñi theory of land tenure, but its strictness is tempered by the Zuñi insistence that property is for use, not for power. Therefore surplus land is freely loaned, bartered, or given away. Surplus land is that which the household cannot cultivate. There is no labor for wages — only invited assistance of neighbors, which is uneconomical for the host; therefore there is no incentive to increase the area under cultivation beyond actual needs.

In all transfers of land — in fact, in all transactions within the tribe — there is a complete absence of the profit motive. Objects have no fixed exchange value; there is no such thing as a "sale"; there are simply transfers of property within the framework of personal relationships. In "selling" a field, the size and location of the field are less relevant than the kinship ties and relative ages of the individuals concerned. "I bought this field (a good cornfield) for a piece of calico because he was an old man" (and presumably would not use the field). Although good land is actually scarce, land has no scarcity value because, according to native theory, it is labor to till the land that is scarce and expensive.

The household group may include as many as twenty-five individuals occupying a single house of several rooms, using a common kitchen and drawing upon a common storehouse. Agricultural work is done jointly on fields scattered in many places and "owned" individually by male members. The stores are pooled as the collective property of the women. For any large task like planting, harvest, or house-building the men invite a miscellaneous group of blood and affinal relatives, ceremonial associates, and neighbors to assist. They come if convenient, or they stay away. The men who respond work in the fields; their wives come also to help the women of the house in their work. After the day's work all are feasted and the women receive gifts of food. These combinations for mutual help are not partnerships with definite obligations. They are not permanent or even reciprocal. There is no compulsion on anyone to respond, nor is the man who refuses penalized in any way. If he systematically refuses aid he is regarded as uncoöperative, but he can always get help when he needs it; for a feast with meat, a day of sociability, and the opportunity to flirt with a pretty girl make helpfulness a pleasure rather than a tedious burden. Also a man, by helping a neighbor, conserves his own stores and avails himself of the neighbor's surplus. This is the chief economic point of tribal feasts.

The herding complex that has been superimposed upon the old agricultural base has a somewhat different ideology. Sheep are individually owned by men; they are earmarked and are inherited in the male line. But this rule, like that of land tenure, may always be set aside in the interests of expediency. A group of male relatives herd their sheep together at a distance from the village, and take turns in watching them, theoretically on a strictly reciprocal basis, each man going out for a month. But the whole system of reciprocity is unbalanced by the feeling of social responsibility on the part of the old toward the young. If a boy goes to herd for his father, the whole coöperative group assumes responsibility for him, giving him presents of animals; the leader, who is also richest in sheep, gives the most, so that the young man soon has a herd of his own. Direct reciprocity between individuals obviously is not a principle of Zuñi economic structure.

The varying composition of households and differentials in skill, industry, and intelligence have resulted in great inequalities in the distribution of wealth at any moment, but these inequalities are not permanent. There is only one recognized "rich" family at Zuñi, and they are half-breeds. The rest of the population rides a seesaw of slow accumulation and rapid dissipation of surplus wealth. This redistribution is accomplished by two mechanisms: institutionalized gift-giving and the ceremonial extension of the work-party system. Both of these institutions depend on attitudes of social responsibility — individual responsibility to one's relatives, and collective responsibility to the tribe, directly and through the performance of religious duties.

Within the family there is a constant giving of presents, quite spontaneous and carrying no obligations to make any return. Parents give presents of all kinds, even fields, to their children; women give presents, usually clothing, to their brothers' sons, men to their sisters' daughters. Manufactured articles like pottery are rarely sold. If the maker is poor he "gives" the article to a relative and receives for it more than its current trade value in food or clothing or store goods. There is also a ceremonial friendship of which the most conspicuous feature is the exchange of presents. But in this relationship, the motive of which is frankly economic, strict reciprocity is avoided. "It would be like trading, and one does not trade with one's ceremonial friend." Gift-giving runs through the religious system also. The rich man who undertakes to finance a ceremony gives presents of food to all who come to help, and the priests who take part in the ceremony receive valuable gifts. One rich man gave away sewing machines in this ceremony. There are "give-away dances" in which food and trinkets are thrown from the housetops, and ritual games in which individuals are singled out to receive presents.

The giving of a present requires no occasion. It is always done with the maximum of publicity. This is flattering to the giver and to the recipient who has been singled out for such distinction. Since no one is ashamed of poverty, no one feels embarrassed at receiving gifts. On the contrary, it is proof of the fact that his relatives love him. The donor values prestige more than property, and shows that he knows how to treat his relatives. This is a point of honor. Stinginess is the one unpardonable offense — much more disgraceful than adultery and worse even than surliness.

Among the most important of Zuñi ceremonies to ensure tribal well-being is the great annual harvest ceremony in which supernaturals visit the village to bless it with fertility. Each year eight wealthy men undertake to finance this ceremony. This involves building a large new house, which means calling many people to help, which in turn means planting additional crops to feed the workers, and calling in more help for this extra work. For those who undertake this responsibility the months from July to December are a continuous work-party. The building of these houses is a "good work" and everyone rushes to participate and share in the blessing. The last weeks are a frenzy of activity; the house goes up; all day and late into the night groups of women grind to song. The ovens go day and night, great bins are erected to hold the bread, and back rooms are piled high with the carcasses of slaughtered sheep. All this is distributed to those who have helped. In all this festivity there is no waste; the only display is the quantity of shawls, embroidered robes, and strips of calico which are hung on the walls of the ceremonial room.

These feasts are costly. One family who had underwritten this ceremony three times in twenty years estimated that each time it cost nearly $1000 in sheep and store goods in addition to field produce. There is little prestige attached to this since it is something that everyone does sooner or later. It is a social responsibility to the tribe and to the supernaturals from whom all blessings come. The higher a man's position in the ceremonial aristocracy, the more often he will undertake this responsibility. There are other forms of ceremonial participation that involve large expenditures; they are the same in principle, but less striking in organization.

The Zuñi are not unappreciative of beauty and physical comfort. But they have no use for excess wealth except to give it away in this somewhat diffuse system. It is useful to support and adorn social position, but it does not buy status or prestige; the prestige comes from the position itself, which is acquired through inheritance, personality, and knowledge. Commodities are used to buy knowledge; they cannot buy the position through which power is exercised. Material wealth is conceived as unlimited; a person who wants more things has only to work harder. Power is limited in amount to that given by the supernaturals at the beginning of the world, and is attenuated by sharing. Therefore a man who parts easily with economic goods, and even lends sacred possessions like masks to those qualified to use them, is "stingy" with knowledge and will not divulge the words of a prayer unless he is amply compensated. However, the powers so jealously guarded are never used for private ends.

The Zuñi system is in the process of change due to contact with Whites. The profit motive, so foreign to the aboriginal system, has been introduced into the sheep-herding. There is also a new emphasis on wealth, since only men who own sheep can get credit at the store. But up to 1929 these attitudes were confined to dealings with Whites. The profits were all made from selling to traders. Within the tribe the old attitudes and values still ruled. But there are signs of change in the frequency of litigation over inheritance of sheep. Quarrels over land are practically unknown. This conflict may be due to the fact that male ownership and inheritance, taken over from the Whites, cut across the main stem of economic structure, the solidarity of the female line. It is also an indication of increasing interest in the acquisition and retention of property, now that they have come to realize its possibilities in relation to Whites.

The Kwakiutl.[54] The Kwakiutl inhabit the coast and islands of British Columbia, a region where the struggle for existence is not too arduous.* The people have developed techniques whereby they can exploit the generosity of nature with the greatest economy. The sea and the forest supply abundant materials for comfortable living. Salmon, halibut, and shellfish are plentiful. The woods are rich in roots and fruits. Goats live on the high mountains.

Dependent on natural sources of food, the Kwakiutl have nevertheless built up a rich material culture with the surplus wealth and leisure necessary to develop an extraordinary superstructure of manipulation of symbolic forms of wealth in a game of prestige and rivalry. This fantastic game, fiercely played out to the death, is but lightly tied to the realities of life; or rather, it constitutes a wholly different order of reality.

Fishing and food-gathering are seasonal occupations. The principal food dependence is on salmon, which are trapped in great quantities as they ascend the rivers to their breeding grounds. Salmon are dried and packed away in huge wooden chests. The oil of the candlefish is tried out in canoes and stored in bottles of kelp. Berries and roots are dried in summer for winter consumption. After a brief busy season the people have ample leisure for more amusing pursuits.

The Kwakiutl live in large plank houses, each housing several families. In the ordinary pursuits of life these family groups are independent, each having its own apartments, fireplace, food stores, and other movable property. In the struggle for prestige these household groups are united under the leadership of the household chief. Several such households are grouped together in lineages claiming descent from a supernatural ancestor.† The villages, built along the shore, contain several lineages, which are the property-holding units. Among the forms of property which they control are hunting and berrying grounds and fishing territories in the rivers

* The Northwest Coast civilization collapsed in the latter half of the nineteenth century with the establishment of industrial fisheries and repressive legislation. The description refers to the period immediately preceding the collapse.

† The word "clan" is not strictly applicable to these groups, since they are not unilateral. Order of birth rather than sex determines succession. They are not mutually exclusive; a man may claim and validate his claim to membership in several such groups.

and in the sea. These properties are often situated far from the present site of the villages, sometimes in different inlets; yet trespass on them is severely punished.

The most important form of property is quite intangible, consisting of names, which are really honorific titles, and the privileges, songs, dances, myths, and crests that appertain to these titles. Although these titles are hereditary, their ownership must be constantly validated, and the glory of the name renewed by the distribution and destruction of wealth. These property distributions take place in ceremonial feasts known as potlatches.* The ultimate motivation of the potlatch is rivalry, not profit. Profit enters into many of the transactions, but only as a means to an end, not as an end in itself. Honor comes not from the possession of wealth, but from giving it away. Property is given on many occasions, but principally to rivals. Such a gift must be returned in due time by a gift of greater value. The initial gift may therefore be regarded as an interest-bearing investment. But this is a shortsighted view, for with the liquidation of the investment the original creditor is in the position of debtor, and beholden for an amount much greater than that of the original gift. So the battle of property goes on, with no quarter asked or given, until one rival is eliminated in defeat, or is able to withdraw honorably from the contest by yielding his name and position to his son.

Some of these transactions are carried on in commodities — small articles like mats and paddles and dishes, and great ones like canoes. These are used principally in life crisis potlatches. But by far the greater part of the potlatching is done with symbols of wealth. The unit is the cheap blanket of the Hudson Bay Company, valued at fifty cents. Certain transactions involve the transfer of coppers, engraved shield-shaped sheets of copper. The coppers are ranked valuables, each with a personal name and individual history. They are exchanged for blankets and increase in value with each transfer. To honor his name, a person "buying" a copper must pay more for it than its last owner, who is always a rival. Sometimes coppers are broken and the pieces given away and scattered, and later reassembled and riveted together, and this also greatly enhances their value. Although these two forms of currency exist, most of the transactions are conducted on credit. There are not

* The word "potlatch" comes from a Chinook jargon word meaning "to give." In the jargon an outright gift is called "kaltas potlatch," a gift for nothing.

enough blankets in existence to cover the collective indebtedness, but the credit structure is never menaced. It has, after all, little to do with life. No one depends on blankets for food. The fantastic character of the whole procedure is brought out by the fact that since potlatching has been forbidden by the Canadian government, it is carried on surreptitiously with "cheques" on nonexistent bank accounts, and some of the coppers that are still being paid for have been peacefully reposing for years in the Ottawa Museum.

Such, in brief, are the principles of the potlatch. The actual working of the system is anything but simple. One of the complicating factors is that these exchanges are not carried on freely between individuals, but between groups in which individuals hold fixed positions symbolized by the names, which are limited in number, and no two of equal rank. Although the structure is fixed, the personnel changes, and the same individual may occupy positions in two rival groups and, like Pooh Bah, conduct business with himself. Furthermore these titles are inherited in the line of primogeniture, regardless of sex. Moreover, vaulting ambition, backed by wealth, cuts across the rules of inheritance and bends the structure to its uses.

Potlatching is the prerogative of the class of "nobles"; that is, the holders of titles in the closed aristocracy. They are assisted in their undertakings by their untitled kinsmen, who derive vicarious pleasure from the glories of their chiefs and profit from their own share in his investments. The dizzy career of the prospective chief starts in the cradle. If it is a firstborn child — girls, if firstborn, are given men's names and function as men in the potlatches — his father begins at once to launch him on his career by distributing "trifles" to his tribe in honor of the child. There is a series of such distributions, at each of which he acquires new status symbolized by a new name, until the child reaches man's status, when he really begins his career. He borrows some hundred blankets from relatives and gives a feast to his tribe in which these are distributed. It is a point of honor for his tribesmen to repay this gift within a month with more than the usual rate of interest. When his debts are paid he has a surplus with which to start operations against a rival.

After the youth has acquired by potlatching names of increasingly higher rank, his father may yield place to his son, and the youth assumes his father's name and position, and the father may retire from active participation. Since a tender age he has been pitted against a youth of equal rank, and prodded by his elders into the approved state of rivalry. The same psychological mechanism that makes him eager to humiliate his rival makes him excessively sensitive to insult, disparagement, or the slightest loss of prestige. Having acquired a recognized name, he proceeds to make it great among the tribes, utilizing all the techniques for enhancing prestige. He consolidates his position within his group by giving feasts, acquiring new names of increasing importance, buying coppers. Also "he shows his privileges on the sacred side" — that is, he validates his claims to the songs, dances, religious experiences, that are the prerogatives of his rank, advancing through the graded secret societies at the same time that he builds up his secular position.

Marriage is the most important step in this advance, for certain valued names descend in the female line, and can be acquired by men only through marriage. The gift of blankets which a man makes to his father-in-law at his marriage is less a payment for the woman herself than a payment for position in her clan. In due course, after the birth of children, this obligation is paid off. The father-in-law turns over an amount of property much larger than what he received, and the name and rank. The transfer is symbolized in the presentation of the box containing the dance paraphernalia. The marriage debt having been paid, the marriage is at an end and the woman is free to return home unless the husband keeps her by making another payment, for which in due course he receives another name. The rank of the woman increases with every marriage until she has been married four times, maybe by the same man. Theoretically the names received in marriage should be passed on in time to a son-in-law of the husband, but the husband uses them for his own ends. Marriage has become so completely assimilated to the potlatch pattern that fictitious marriages are arranged between men, or between a man and the left foot of another man, in order to keep active a title that might otherwise lapse or pass out of control. Warfare is part of the same game. The way to get a coveted name which one cannot inherit or acquire through marriage is to kill the owner and appropriate the name and prerogatives. Even fratricide occurs and is condoned if one can validate with property one's claim to the brother's rank.

Direct rivalry is carried on meanwhile by giving feasts to rival chiefs and distributing property to their clans. Since every gift implies a return, the supreme expression of the rivalry of chiefs is the destruction of property. A man who has been potlatching with coppers, and whose rival can overtop him each time with a copper of greater value, may, as a final gesture of defiance, break a copper worth thousands of blankets and throw the pieces into the sea. Unless his rival can throw away a copper of greater value, his name will be forever disgraced. In these acts there is no possibility of profit; they are pure deeds of honor. The destruction of property is not restricted to the symbols of wealth. Slaves may be killed and canoes split in these contests of defiance.

The obligation to repay gifts is not an obligation to the person of the donor, but to the bearer of his name. After the death of a man all debts due him become due to his successor, often his son, so that the outstanding debts enable the successor to carry on the game of potlatching and assure to the heir a standing in the community. The potlatch serves as a sort of life insurance, but insurance that carries obligations.

The destruction of tangible wealth ties the system into the economy of subsistence. It is honorable to destroy a surplus. But should excess of ambition on the part of a chief involve him in undertakings in which he jeopardizes the subsistence of his followers they withdraw their support. Without the support of his followers the most arrogant chief is helpless. The credit structure collapses and he is forever disgraced. The Kwakiutl chief is not a capitalist. He does not own or control the means of production; with all his violence and aggressiveness he has no power, military or magical, which would enable him to seize wealth and impose his will.* Kwakiutl civilization is certainly no place for the meek, the modest, and the mild, but neither is there any place for the ruthless exploiter of his own people. Good will has its place, and the chief who alienates the good will of his followers will be broken by them.

The Trobriand Islands.[55] The Trobriand Islands are flat coral islands lying to the northeast of New Guinea. The climate is mild, the rainfall well distributed, and the soil fertile and well adapted to the cultivation of yams, taro, and coconuts. Within the fringing reef the sea teems with fish. Among their neighbors the Trobrianders stand out as the richest, most aggressive, and most respected; they are skilled gardeners and craftsmen, able navigators and enterprising traders.

Their economy is characterized by great emphasis upon the pos-

---

* As he extends his operations he contracts greater debts to his successors. It is an economic structure in which the rich man is in debt to the poor.

session of wealth. They have a delight in mere possession which is relatively rare among primitive peoples. "To the natives the possession and display of food are of immense importance in themselves. . . . Pride in possession is one of their leading characteristics."[56] At harvest time there are displays of food in the gardens, and everyone goes around to compare the yields of various gardens, as regards quantity and quality. The yams are brought in with great publicity and displayed again in the village. They are stored in open storehouses, and the finest yams are placed at the front and not eaten. In food habits the Trobrianders are extremely frugal. Their "prosperity magic" is aimed at keeping their appetites small and their stores large. Despite the fondness for displaying food, there is no hospitality except at large tribal feasts; it is degrading to accept food in a strange village. They are inordinately pleased if, at the end of the year, their storerooms are half-full of rotten yams which must be thrown away to make room for the new crop. But there is a powerful check upon acquisitiveness — the chief brooks no rivals and can kill by sorcery. Malinowski quotes a number of cases of men who were believed to have died because their gardens were too productive.

The principal food dependence is on garden produce, especially yams. The gardens lie outside the small villages, and men and women cultivate them jointly. They are expert gardeners. They use the most primitive tools, but they take great pride in the appearance as well as the productivity of the gardens. In each village there is a garden magician, working under the direction of the chief, who sets the pace for all garden work. There is no communal work except by decree of the chief in special circumstances. The belief in the efficacy of magic is absolute, and no one proceeds to any stage of garden cultivation until the garden magician has performed the proper rituals on selected plots. This introduces into gardening a degree of organization which the tropical climate does not impose. Everyone has in addition individual magical charms for gardening, fishing, sailing, trade, love. These charms constitute one of the most important forms of property.

Although parents and young children form the household group, work together, live together, sharing a common house and common stores, the chief distributive mechanism of the tribe is the contribution of a man to his sister's household, for his sister's children are his nearest kin and his legal heirs. This payment is conceived in three ways: as part of the marital exchanges between two lines related through marriage; as a man's provision for his minor dependents; as a woman's return on her recognized title to land in her "own" village, where, however, she never lives. A man sends almost the whole of his yam harvest to his sister's husband. For his own use he keeps only seed crop, inferior yams, and supplementary crops like taro and pumpkins. For yams he depends upon gifts from his own wife's brother. The presentation to the brother-in-law is accompanied by ceremony and display of food. "A man's most sensitive point of honor is his sister's position, for his sister is his nearest relative. And since scarcity of food is especially shameful, all his *amour propre* is involved in supplying his sister adequately. Those who neglect their duties to their relatives-in-law or do not strain in their efforts to produce gifts worthy of their dignity sink in public esteem and fear public contempt."

Such a system of indirect reciprocity would result in a circulation of wealth fairly evenly through the community, were it not for the interposition of the principle of rank at the critical point of the social structure, to tilt the balance of reciprocity and build up the power of the chieftainship.

The keystone of the economic structure of Trobriand society is the chieftainship. The chiefs have great power which is exercised economically. They are not powerful because they are rich; rather they are rich because, being born chiefs, they are powerful. A certain sacredness attaches to the chief, shown in the numerous taboos surrounding his person. He may demand whatever he wishes. As titular owner of all land, trees, and animals, he exacts tribute from each household. Only chiefs are permitted to practice polygyny, and powerful chiefs have many wives. Consequently through the mechanism of the unequal balance of marital exchange the chief controls thirty per cent of all the garden produce of his jurisdiction and seventy-five per cent of the pigs, coconuts, and betel nuts. He alone may order to have made for his use the valuables of ceremonial trade; as a result, the chiefs own eighty per cent of these articles. Although it is nowhere explicitly so stated, all the evidence is that only chiefs can employ death sorcery against enemies.* This, un-

---

* Malinowski states repeatedly that chiefs use sorcery against enemies and rivals, but describes as the most drastic mechanism of social control among equals the shaming of offenders into suicide. The restriction of death sorcery to chiefs is explicit in neighboring tribes.

doubtedly, is the real basis of power. The wealth which the chief secures through the exercise of all these privileges is used to consolidate his position and enlarge his activities. Between chiefs and commoners, the relationship is complementary, an exchange of services and support in war against commodities. Payments for services are usually in the form of "valuables," pigs and betel nuts — the forms of wealth of which the chief has virtual monopoly. The surplus of garden food is used for festive and other ceremonial occasions, such as mortuary distributions.

Among equals the relationships are strictly reciprocal, with precise regard for the obligations of kinship. This is not conceived as responsibility for unfortunate relatives who claim relationship, but as a requirement to meet all the payments demanded by their extended system of fraternal and affinal exchange. They are, above all, a tribe of traders, and have very clear ideas about equivalence.

At the height of his power the great chief of the village of Omarakana had sixty wives, selected for economic and political reasons from all the villages of his jurisdiction. Since all were selected from ranking families, the whole tribe was paying tribute to the chief through his wives. From the villages of his wives the chief received annually between 300 and 350 tons of yams. This concentration of wealth enabled him to finance major undertakings, such as the building of seagoing canoes, and to underwrite wars and oversea trading expeditions. The building of a canoe takes about two years and involves the hiring of laborers and skilled craftsmen; the services of a magician are required throughout the work. All these services must be paid for. Various stages of the work are marked by feasts with great food distributions. On such occasions property is exchanged between persons related through marriage. The chief being related by marriage to everyone on the island, is involved in tremendous financial responsibilities. His prestige as a chief depends on his ability to plan and carry through large undertakings.

The exchange between affinal relatives is another institution of major economic importance. Every marriage must be validated by exchanges of property. The first gifts of cooked and uncooked food are returned in kind. The large exchanges begin with the next harvest when the girl's family sends to the man's family a gift of some two hundred or three hundred baskets of the finest yams. This gift is repaid with a suitable amount of fish, pigs, or valuables. These exchanges continue throughout the duration of the marriage.

at each harvest, at mortuary feasts, and at tribal festivals. It is always the man's side that contributes the permanent wealth and commodities difficult to obtain. It is the wife's family that maintains the household. The chief's ability to maintain polygamous marriages is tied up with his control of all unusual forms of wealth. The necessity of maintaining strict equivalence in these exchanges and keeping them at a level suitable to one's rank and dignity serves as a check upon acquisitiveness and maintains a constant circulation of all forms of wealth.

In addition to this flow of wealth along the channels of kinship, there is a great deal of trade, commercial and ceremonial. Different districts of the island, and presumably clans within these districts, are industrially specialized. The central villages have the best gardens. The coastal villages fish; the northern villages engage in industry, especially wood-carving, for which they are famed throughout the region. The inland people own canoes which they keep at the beach. They are good navigators and go on overseas expeditions, but they do not engage in fishing because the coastal villages jealously guard their property rights in fishing grounds. Instead, the inland villages bring garden produce to some coastal village, each man leaving his contributions at the door of his trade friend. Two days later they come back to collect the return gift. There is no bargaining, but plenty of recrimination afterward should the return be considered inadequate. With the industrial clans whom they consider social inferiors, they engage in direct barter, a form of activity which they regard with considerable disdain.

Foreign trade for the most part is carried on according to the nonbargaining pattern of gift exchange between trade friends. The principal export is wood work, which ultimately finds its way all around a ring of islands, and even beyond. The principal imports are greenstone from Murua (northeast), pottery from the Amphletts (south), and sago from the volcanic islands of Dobu. This ring of islands, with a few others, forms a trade area throughout which specialized products of each are diffused.[57]

Overseas trade is undertaken only in connection with the *kula*, a system of intertribal, ceremonial exchange of valuables, which in the eyes of the natives constitutes the real object of an expedition, the trade in commodities being regarded as definitely secondary. Only those who have valuables to exchange engage in any form of overseas trade. Only two kinds of articles are involved in this exchange:

necklaces of red shell disks that move in clockwise direction around a closed circuit, and arm bands of white shell that move in the opposite direction. These objects move continuously in endless circuit, for no one who receives a *kula* article as a gift may retain it, but must pass it on to a partner on the other side, from whom he will receive a counter gift. Only certain individuals take part in this honorific trade, and they exchange with trade friends in nearby islands. There is an inland *kula* also, but the overseas trade is most striking and forms the real focus of interest and excitement in Trobriand life. The *kula* valuables are named and ranked; the history of each one is known. They are neither useful nor ornamental; they are not standards of value against which other articles are measured; they are never sold or directly exchanged for useful commodities. They are symbols of prestige "whose presence in the village is a sign of the importance and glory of the village and of the individual trader who brought it in." [58]

The *kula* exchange is conducted in the form of gift and return gift. There is no direct barter; the return is always deferred, sometimes but a few hours, sometimes for years, but it must be equivalent. It must be carried on without profit. The element of excitement in the *kula* is introduced by the fact that each man has several partners on each side and all islands practice inland *kula*, so that the closed circuits are broken and crossed at many points. There are many kinds of solicitory gifts and *kula* magic to attract desirable objects, and there are opprobrium and withdrawal of support for the man who is slow or niggardly. Every act of the *kula* is surrounded by ceremony and fortified by magic. In the important *kula* villages it is the all-absorbing topic of interest.

The importance of the *kula* in providing a ceremonial framework in which economic trade can be safely carried on among hostile tribes of sorcerers must not be overlooked. [59] This does not, however, explain the overwhelming importance of the *kula* in the lives of the participants, and the intensity, often violence, with which this profitless trade in useless objects is pursued. Why has the *kula* so completely captured the imagination of the Trobrianders? Obviously, it is symbolic behavior, behavior through which they satisfy their conflicting attitudes toward wealth. The Trobrianders display a cupidity that is rare among primitive peoples. To possess wealth is, above all else, honorable. They desire wealth for its own sake, and as a symbol of power. "Wealth, in the Trobriands, is the outward sign and substance of power, and the means of exercising it." [60] Indeed, they have constantly before them the spectacle of a privileged chief whose power is consolidated and augmented through the use of wealth obtained by tribute and supported by sorcery. The forbidden fruit is sweet, but it must be renounced. The completeness of the renunciation is shown in the fact that the chief with impunity may — and, indeed, to preserve the social structure, must — kill by sorcery anyone who seeks to rival him in wealth. In the *kula* potentially dangerous possessive impulses are diverted into channels that are not disruptive of social security. Malinowski, in summing up the *kula*, describes it as follows:

A half commercial, half ceremonial exchange, it is carried out for its own sake, in a deep desire to possess. But here again, it is not ordinary possession, but a special type in which a man owns for a short time and in alternating manner, individual specimens of two classes of objects. Though the ownership is incomplete in point of permanency, it is in turn enhanced in point of numbers successively possessed. . . . And it is just through this exchange, through their being constantly within reach and objects of competitive desire, through being the means of arousing envy and conferring social distinction and renown, that these objects attain their high value. . . . To the native it [the *kula* valuable] is something that confers dignity and exalts him and which he therefore treats with veneration. Their behavior at the transaction makes it clear that the *vayga'u* is regarded, not only as possessing high value, but that it is treated also in a ritual manner, and arouses emotional reaction.[61]

Viewed psychologically, Trobriand economy is a delicate equilibrium between an inordinately developed desire to possess and the need to renounce. Viewed in historical perspective, it is a compromise between two types of society developed among neighboring peoples — the Polynesian-Indonesian structure of fixed rank, firm political discipline, and maximum economic security, and the Papuan pattern of status based on wealth, rivalry, vertical mobility, and reliance on sorcery as the ultimate sanction. Out of such incongruous material the Trobrianders have built a secure society.

Economic mechanisms in primitive cultures. It is generally accepted as axiomatic that economic function can be divided into three separate processes: production, distribution, and consumption. We have organized our own economic life so as to differentiate these three aspects. The line between them is more fluid than is commonly assumed. The same act — baking bread, for instance — may be included in either the productive or consumptive structure, depending upon who does it. If we try to apply these categories to societies that are differently organized with reference to the economic problem, we see at once how inapplicable they are. It is not necessary to go to the simplest societies to see these processes merged. The Zuñi work-party is a definite unit of social behavior that serves many purposes. It is not simply a matter of hiring workers at a certain wage to accomplish a certain end. It is just as fair to regard it as an invitation to participate in a food distribution. It is usual for men to emphasize the former aspect, and women the latter. From the point of view of the host (or employer) the social and ceremonial aspects are of paramount importance.

From the functional or sociological point of view there is only one economic process, the process of providing for material wants and for psychological wants that can be gratified by material objects. It is a process with two aspects, getting and using. Economic function, with all its social implications, is more than the production and consumption of wealth. These are convenient concepts to use in the analysis and comparative study of economic behavior, provided that these terms are always understood as abstractions and not as descriptions of behavior.

From this point of view we may consider the Zuñi work-party system either as a mechanism for utilizing the labor force of the community for the production of vegetable food or as a means for distributing animal food. Either view is artificial. The work-party is one part of a social, economic, and religious structure which binds all members of the community together by innumerable ties of social responsibility. On its economic side the aim of this structure, never fully achieved, is equality secured through fluidity along prescribed channels, and the work-party provides one such channel through which both surplus wealth and labor flow. In the following pages no attempt is made to analyze production and distribution, but rather to describe various mechanisms by which primitive societies achieve their economic goals. It is impossible to discuss all such mechanisms since each society has given the economic function some twist peculiar to itself. It has also seemed advisable to omit certain mechanisms which are fairly familiar in economic history, such as slavery, vassalage, work for wages, but which are relatively rare in primitive societies, and to concentrate rather on those mechanisms which are characteristic of the simpler forms of economic life.

The division of labor. The basis of all economic structure and social structure in general lies in the division of labor. Even the peoples whose material culture is simplest show some system of allotting different tasks to different individuals in the group. Among the simplest hunting peoples the division of labor between the sexes is a necessary condition of life. This is true alike among the Eskimo, the Andamanese, and the Arunta. Among people who hunt large roving animals with spear or bow and arrow women's physical disabilities are most conspicuous. A woman who is carrying a child or nursing an infant cannot pursue animals hour after hour. To women fall the more sedentary occupations, frequently just as difficult and arduous, but requiring less muscular strength and fleetness of foot. While men hunt larger and swifter animals, women care for the home, dress skins, and contribute to the food supply such animals as grubs, shellfish and small fish, and vegetable produce. Traps and fishhooks may be tended by women, but fishing that requires hard continuous labor falls to the share of men. An exception to women's generally sedentary rôle is found among the Northern Ojibwa, where some few women hunt as men do, and even go on the war path with men.[62]

Among pastoral and agricultural peoples there is no obvious biological factor to account for the universal division of labor along sex lines. Men herd larger animals, as they hunt them, and perhaps for the same reasons; however, women herd cattle successfully in Europe, and Navajo women herd their own sheep. Throughout Melanesia women raise pigs. Nor does the division of labor always result in giving men the heavier share of work. Bogoras found that the Chukchee women work much harder than the men.[63] In addition to sharing with men the work of herding reindeer during those seasons when they are restless and hard to manage, the women must prepare all food, dress skins for shelter and clothing, and take complete charge of the house. Chukchee tents are heavy, cumbersome structures, relics of the Chukchee days as a sedentary maritime people. In making and breaking camp the women get no help from the men, although the handling of the tents requires great physical strength in addition to skill.

Where agriculture is the basis of economic life still greater diversity prevails.* Among the Pueblo Indians the men do all the work. The women of the Bathonga and other African tribes do

* For a fuller discussion of the relation of agriculture to the position of women see pages 299, 319.

everything except the first clearing of the bush. The Ifugao men plant and harvest; the women weed and cultivate. The Trobriand men and women coöperate at all stages of the work. All possible arrangements occur. But even among people like the Trobrianders where husband and wife share the work from day to day, going out together each morning to their gardens, they share along sex lines. Certain tasks — notably magic — are for the man; others are for the woman. This seems to be a fundamental condition of primitive life. The interchange of different kinds of work forms the economic basis of marriage. In many places this basic principle is given articulate expression, as among the Quiché Indians of Guatemala. Here the men do all the agricultural work. Although the women accompany their husbands to the fields they sit all day in a brush shelter and weave. "It is the part of a man to furnish food for the household." Marriage is presented to the adolescent youth as an economic contract. "My son, now we shall look for your woman. Your mother is old and has much work, and this woman will wash your clothes and weave your kerchiefs; and when she comes here you will be kind to her, and you will sleep together in the same room." [64]

In Zuñi, when a man returns from his day's work his wife drops whatever work she may be doing and goes to the door of the house to greet him. Whatever he brings she takes from him and carries into the house. Then she sets out food for her husband. These gestures demanded by etiquette symbolize the economics of marriage. The house belongs to the woman and she receives her husband in it as a guest. He in turn brings the produce of fields and ranch; as it crosses the threshold it becomes the property of the woman. Any omission of these formalities on the part of the woman would be interpreted by the man as an indication that she no longer regards him as her husband.

The economic interdependence of men and women is one of the great stabilizing forces in family life. It does not prolong the life of any individual marriage, but it helps to maintain the institution. The Zuñi change mates frequently, but the man-woman-child constellation remains constant. There are no bachelors, spinsters, or abandoned children.

The physical and purely economic aspects of the division of labor are frequently bolstered by supernaturalism. In some places this takes the form of a general fear of the evil influence of women upon the fertility of fields or the abundance of game.[65] In other places it takes the specific form of fear of menstrual blood, which is believed to make fields barren (New Guinea), make cows go dry (Africa), or rob men of their power in war and hunting. Wherever such attitudes exist they effectively bar women from engaging in major occupations. As a corollary of this attitude, certain occupations may be considered inimical to female fecundity.

An interesting parallel is found among the Maori. Men, in varying degrees according to their rank, have a supernatural potency, *tapu*, which can be destroyed forever by certain occupations, notably cooking and carrying burdens on the head. This bars them from these occupations, which fall to the lot of women and slaves, individuals who have no *tapu*.[66]

Industrial specialization on the basis of skill is characteristic of all but the most widely dispersed people. Among the Eskimo there are no specialists, except the specialist in the supernatural. Each man makes his own tools, and his wife makes the clothing. But among most other peoples there are specialists in industrial skills or in knowledge, the professional wood-carver, potter, weaver, tattooer, doctor, or sorcerer. There may also be professional marriage brokers, arbitrators, and orators.

The high degree of specialization which is so marked in the Trobriands is common to all Oceania. In Polynesia experts in woodcarving, boat-building, or tattooing are famed beyond their native villages, and chiefs from distant places will command their services and reward them richly. Here specialization extends to knowledge also. There are specialists in genealogy and in the lore of the forest and the sea. All these specialties are bolstered by supernatural sanctions, by the same belief in *tapu* that operates in differentiating the labor of the sexes. The man who knows the lore of the forest and opens the hunting season is said to own the *tapu* of the forest, and his contribution to the total economy consists of magical spells without which the fecundity of the forest would fail.

Differentiation of skills necessarily accompanies a highly developed technology. Our own industrial civilization represents the extreme development in the direction of complexity and differentiation. Like all functional relationships in economics this is not a simple cause-effect sequence, but a reciprocal relationship. Complex technology makes specialization necessary; on the other hand, the development of highly specialized skills leads to further refinements in technology. This process goes on at a constantly accelerating pace and results in an increasing interdependence of an ever-widening circle of individuals. "Primitivism," the movement in our own society that seeks to reverse this process and attain greater freedom and security by a return to economic self-sufficiency of smaller groups under simpler technological conditions, has always failed, because the social factors involved in specialization are too vast to be ignored. With increasing control of our environment we become more dependent upon effective social integration.

Primitive peoples at the same stage of technological development may be very differently oriented with reference to the degree of specialization. Zuñi and Quiché do not differ much in technological development. Among the Zuñi the economic ideal, now somewhat obscured by the intrusion of White traders, was the self-sufficient household within the self-sufficient tribe, with mechanisms to ensure coöperation and fluidity of wealth. Every man commanded all the major skills, every woman the major female skills. Organized trade and barter were negligible; only the feeble and widowed were forced to exchange manufactures for food. The important property distributions were not exchanges of values of different kinds but simple quantitative adjustments. For all purposes of daily living each household was completely self-sufficient. This homogeneous economy is combined with the most minute differentiation in ceremonial function, which suggests that differentiation may have some other basis than simply technical efficiency.

South of the Rio Grande no such ideal of self-sufficient units prevails. The Guatemalan or Mexican village swarms with specialists; a Quiché family head hires a mason to build his house and a carpenter to hang the doors; he buys the adobe from an adobe-maker and the tiles from a tile-maker, and orders the cloth for his suit from a professional weaver. These are all imported skills, as they are at Zuñi. He buys his pottery and baskets and mats and certain foodstuffs in the market place and hires laborers to till his fields while he himself earns his living as a witness and recorder of contracts, an ancient profession throughout Central America. The family does not constitute a closed economic unit. The same attitude prevails in village economy also. The villages, although socially, politically, and often linguistically distinct, are industrially specialized and mutually dependent, bound together by highly organized trade. This state of affairs existed previous to the Conquest. Traders and trade maps guided the Cortes expedition into Guatemala.[67]

A similar contrast may be seen between the self-sufficient Polynesian communities and the specialized Melanesians, but the contrast is especially striking in these two American communities because these cultures are not only similar technologically but specifically the same and historically related. Obviously in these two areas the division of labor is more closely related to density of population and to ideas of conquest, empire, and political integration than to the demands of technology.

Differentiation of economic function may follow class lines. In many parts of the world we find classes, and usually but not always these classes are economic or make themselves felt economically through control of wealth or power, but it is by no means a usual picture for class structures to be reflected in productive organization.

In certain kingdoms of East Africa, especially the Bakitara and the Banyankole, birth determines occupation. The society is composed of two classes: the nobility, who are pastoral, and the peasants, who are agricultural. The nobility form a hierarchy headed by the king and his court. Theoretically the king owns all the cattle of the land, but for all practical purposes the nobility own their own cattle. He is a divine king; his title to the cattle is vested in his magical control of their fecundity, and his court is a glorified dairy in which minutiae of ceremonial preserve the health and fertility of the cattle of the nation. All matters connected with cattle are carried on under severe restrictions. Only nobles may own cattle or have any share in their care, or in any of the activities of the dairy. They marry only within their own class, thus forming a closed occupational caste. The chiefs hold their cattle in fief from the king, to whom they must make return in the form of women and cows upon the demand of his tax-gatherers, who use this opportunity for a little extortion on their own account. The rule of primogeniture and the favors of the king have resulted in great discrepancies of wealth within the caste of cattle people and have reduced the sons of younger lines to positions of dependency in the kraals of powerful chiefs.

The nobility are stock-breeders exclusively; they raise no crops and engage in no industries. The peasants control agriculture and all industries. Among them are clans of iron-workers, salt-workers, potters, wood-workers, cloth-makers. All skills tend to be hereditary in certain clans. Iron- and salt-working are definitely so. The peasants supply the cattle people with grain, manufactured articles, and services in house-building and public works, in return for feasts, gifts of butter, and protection of their land from predatory beasts. The peasants are bound to no place and no master. Since the cattle people depend on them for the necessities of life and for services for themselves and the king, the power and influence of a chief at court depend on his ability to attract large numbers of peasants to his domain. When the king needs cattle he sends out his tax collector to take them; when he needs services from the peasants, he requests them with gifts. Although the peasants own no cattle, they keep sheep and goats, and altogether form an economically self-sufficient group, which the cattle people most decidedly do not. The one important commodity which they lack is butter, for which they depend on the chiefs.[68]

The class system of the Bakitara is usually described as a phenomenon of conquest. It is unquestionably true that large population movements and wars of conquest have marked the history of southern and eastern Africa. The indigenous populations were agricultural; cattle were probably introduced by warlike invaders who swept down from the northeast. The violent juxtaposition of these two types of economy has led to a variety of economic patterning. Among the Bakitara this has resulted in organization along class lines; the cattle people claim to be the descendants of the conquerors. The neighboring Baganda, also organized into a strong state ruled by a sacred king, show no similar caste division. Here cattle-raising is man's province, agriculture woman's; and there are certain hereditary skills. It is this picture rather than the caste system of the Bakitara that is more general for Africa as a whole. It is not the simple fact of conquest that has produced the caste systems of East Africa; they are one of several possible ways of combining different and complementary economies.

On the whole, caste organization is rare in the primitive world. In most places class systems are maintained by the manipulation of wealth rather than by compulsory occupational reciprocity.

Individualism and collectivism in production. Wherever different tasks are assigned to different individuals and mechanisms for adjustment have been devised, a certain amount of collectivism exists. Even in the most individualistic societies, such as that of the Eskimo, where each man hunts in his own kayak and each woman cooks over her own lamp, the family forms a collective unit, organized for joint effort toward the satisfaction of common needs. Coöperation within the biological family, although occasionally seriously hampered by disruptive forces in the social structure, may be assumed for all primitive peoples. Even the Eskimo sometimes organize into larger coöperating groups. Frequently two men hunt together. When traveling in the large woman's boat, in hunting whales, in the spring hunt of seals, and in the summer drives on the caribou larger groups join forces. These temporary unions are the exception in an economy that is basically individualistic.

Large coöperative hunting and fishing expeditions are common in many parts of the world. One of the most striking from the sociological point of view was the communal buffalo hunt of the Plains Indians, with its penalties against private hunting. The Plains Indians were hunting gregarious animals, and the coöperative organization of the hunt appears on the surface to be an obvious response to the habits of the animals. But the policed hunt was not the only or even the usual method of hunting. It was employed only in connection with tribal ceremonies when large groups congregated and large surpluses were required.[69] The Lango (central Africa) use similar methods in hunting all game, large and small, solitary or gregarious. They have five methods of coöperative hunting, all with appropriate ceremonies. The method involving the greatest number of persons and animals is surrounding with fire. Sometimes an area of forty square miles is thus surrounded; men, women, and children take part, and there is a strict distribution of the catch, specified portions of each animal going to certain individuals. The owner of the hunting rights of the land, who is also the organizer of the hunt and the host at the feast that accompanies it, gets a shoulder from each animal taken.[70]

The extreme collectivism of the Maori, among whom all activities are carried on jointly, is bound up with the development of the hierarchy and the power of the chief. The whole community, under organized leadership, turns out to get supplies for the common stores, administered by the chief. Collectivism in labor can exist also without political organization. The Pueblos, without concepts of rank or authority, and only the vaguest ideas of reciprocity, do all their major tasks in field and herd by a system of informal voluntary coöperation. The same pattern of unformalized helpfulness, differently organized, is characteristic of the Arapesh of New Guinea. But the Quiché Indians of Central America, cultivating the same crops with the same technological equipment as the Zuñi, are grimly individualistic as regards agriculture, although coöperative enough in matters unrelated to land.

As a contrast to the informal groupings of the Zuñi we might cite the permanent combines for mutual help found among the Lango and other African tribes. These partnerships are for definitely specified and named units of work, and are either paid for in food or are strictly reciprocal. Such permanent combines exist at Zuñi also in sheep-herding, but the uncongenial idea of strict reciprocity is completely obscured by the basic Zuñi attitudes of helpfulness and social responsibility. Margaret Mead in a recent study of coöperation and competition has pointed out the lack of correlation between collective mechanisms of production and general coöperative attitudes in social relations, in the economic and noneconomic fields.[71]

There are, indeed, among primitive peoples two types of collective organization of production: the true collectivism represented by the Maori and the Zuñi, and the kind of organization represented by the Kwakiutl, where the magnitude of the task or some other factor makes necessary the collaboration of persons who do not unite into a coöperating social unit. This is the type of collectivism that has its extreme development in modern industry. In a large factory many individuals collaborate for the ostensible purpose of producing automobiles. But the product does not represent the same value to all who are concerned in its production; to most of them it represents no value at all. The interest has shifted from the product, the ostensible common purpose, to the manipulation of the process of production, in which each individual strives for personal advantage, and in which individuals combine only temporarily against an opposing interest, but immediately revert to their former state of internal rivalry. This rivalry is, indeed, part of the coöperative structure. Since it results in increased production, it is encouraged by the management, and any attempt to introduce true collectivism is bitterly opposed.

To the Maori or Trobriand ship-builders a canoe represents the same value as it does to the chief who organizes its production, commandeers labor and goods to pay labor, and provides feasts, and who theoretically "owns" the product. The common stake which all feel in the product makes true coöperation possible.

True collectivism was not absent from earlier American life. It is found in the husking bee, the round-up, even in the volunteer fire corps and countless other institutions of American rural life. Coöperation is not necessarily inconsistent with an individualistic philosophy or any theory of ownership. In fact these truly coöperative institutions flourished especially in that paradise of rugged individualism, the frontier, and in other places where the common purpose had a common value. But no matter what theory of ownership may be held at the top, lack of a sense of reality in the common value will inevitably result in lack of coöperation. In a civilization as complex on the technological side as our own, it is difficult to maintain that sense of reality.

The distribution of wealth. The problem of distribution is twofold: distribution in time, and distribution among the different members of the group. The latter problem is generally held in mind in speaking of distribution, but in any one group it may well be the former that presents real difficulties.

The problem of the distribution of produce over time arises wherever a people relies upon a seasonal food supply. Its solution requires knowledge of techniques for the preservation of food. Such knowledge is basic not only to economic security but to the growth of any complex organization. In most cases leisure is not dependent upon the abundance of nature but upon economic planning and, in particular, upon the ability to utilize one day's surplus for the next day's hunger. When man has once learned to preserve food, he can turn chance and the inevitable procession of the seasons to advantage instead of being destroyed by them.

Leisure and economic security are not the achievements of agricultural and pastoral peoples alone. The Indians of Alaska, with only natural sources of food supply, have greater economic security and certainly a great deal more leisure than the Chukchee with their huge herds of domesticated reindeer. For the herds require constant attention, and even with the greatest vigilance they are occasionally lost in storms or stampeded by the incursion of wild bucks, leaving the herdsman and his family destitute and isolated, with no stores of food and no means of transportation.

Peoples living in the tropics, in so far as they depend on flesh foods, have a difficult problem in food preservation; yet tribes on such low economic levels as the Andamanese [72] and the Vedda [73] have devised means for the preservation of flesh foods. The Arctic supplies a natural cold storage plant; yet it is precisely here that scarcely any attempt is made to preserve meat, even though groups are constantly threatened with extinction through starvation. The

Eskimo, despite their great technological achievements, and though they cache food, make no systematic attempt to lay by sufficient stores to secure them against starvation. The surplus is never great; but what there is, is shared, not hoarded. It is not scarcity but inaccessibility of game that reduces Eskimo camps to starvation and cannibalism.[74] Their failure to anticipate this contingency, so regular in its occurrence, is generally laid to the savage's improvident nature. But the Eskimo is by no means improvident. He breeds dogs and rears the puppies and trains them for the harness; he spends the summer hunting reindeer to make winter garments, and never faces the winter inadequately provided with clothing or with inferior hunting equipment. It is a special attitude toward food which the Eskimo share with peoples as differently organized as the Zuñi, the Bathonga, the Dakota, the Maori, and the Kaingang, and which is found among peoples of all levels of technological development and at all subsistence levels. Not all primitive people are generous and improvident in regard to food, but all have a definite attitude toward food, putting it in a different category from all other forms of wealth. Failure to provide for the morrow's daily bread, which may be institutionalized as hospitality, is a reflection of one such special attitude. Whatever attitude may prevail, there seems to be a regular and necessary correlation between food storage, methods of hunting, and the distribution and stability of population. Furthermore, the idea of laying by food is a necessary precursor to any form of agriculture.

The Plains Indian device of prohibiting solitary hunting (see page 289) in order to preserve the buffalo herd intact for the communal hunt is not the only method used by primitive peoples to insure their food supply. The Northern Algonquian family hunting territories are divided into districts hunted consecutively in different years; there is a central section that is never hunted at all, but is kept as a permanent game preserve. The Northern Ojibwa keep a careful census of the sedentary animals on their hunting territories and restrict the number of traps to the safe yield. The Maori taboo the forest and the sea at certain seasons of the year. Throughout the world there are taboos or supernatural sanctions against the useless slaughtering of game animals. Generally this is conceived as the resentment of the animals or supernaturals at wanton killing. At Zuñi the same sanction is invoked against the wanton waste of agricultural products. The Corn Maidens become angry and run away (that is, crops fail) if their bodies are not respected.

The existence of food stores not only offers some security against calamity, but it profoundly affects the whole rhythm and organization of economic life in such fundamental aspects as distribution of population and the permanence of settlements. Where daily search for food is the rule, each unit must remain near a known source of food supply. This means that either the units must be small and widely dispersed, as among the Northern Ojibwa, or they must be extremely mobile, as among the Kaingang of Brazil, since each solitary hunter frightens off the game and so jeopardizes the food supply.

Food-gatherers, fishing and agricultural people with a single brief seasonal period in which the food supply must be brought in, present the most extreme form of natural maladjustment between the daily demands of hunger and the productive rhythm. Alternating periods of abundance and scarcity are a fundamental feature, and the whole social life of the group must be geared to provide against the threat of those inevitable periods of hunger that precede the harvest. The way in which each group faces this annual crisis is characteristic of their whole approach to economic organization. Among the Dobuans with their grim economy, their almost pathological fear of hunger, and their well-grounded expectation of mercilessness on the part of neighbors and relatives, the period that precedes the harvest is one in which each family tightens its belt and goes on short rations, jealously guarding its stores against any treachery in the form of a generous impulse on the part of one of the spouses. The focus of the struggle is the need to maintain the supplies of seed yams against the demands of hunger. For if these are eaten no others will be forthcoming, and the future will be permanently destroyed, since native theory maintains that only inherited seed can be grown on ancestral lands.[75] The Ifugao of the Philippines also suffer from annual periods of scarcity. At such times those who are out of supplies borrow from their more fortunate neighbors at exorbitant rates of interest that mean mortgaging their whole future security in an inexorable system of debt penalties. Here preharvest shortage is used as a definite means of class exploitation.[76]

At Zuñi, where in spite of entailed lands the whole economy is based on the principle of the fluidity of wealth, the preharvest season, which runs imperceptibly into the season of harvest, is the season of maximum social activity, feasting, and open-handed food distributions. Hospitality and generosity are a social responsibility; so no household need go hungry in the lean months. It is consistent with this negative attitude toward hoarding that in a period of panic following an earthquake, Zuñi housewives gave away all their accumulated stores of food.[77]

There is no universal response to periods of scarcity, even the regularly recurring scarcity which those who rely upon seasonal food products have learned to anticipate. Whatever the economic system may be, pressure clamps it down tighter, and serves to intensify prevailing attitudes.

It has become obvious in the foregoing discussion that the problem of adjusting the irregularities of food supply to the exigencies of daily needs cannot be considered apart from the other great problem of distribution, the flow of wealth among members of the group.

Any joint enterprise requires some formal distribution of the product among those who take part. But distribution does not always bear the obvious and direct correlation to production that we might expect. There may be some purely arbitrary division of the spoils of the chase — an animal taken jointly by several men may belong to the first man who saw it, or the man who shot the first arrow, or the man who first touched it; or it may belong to none of the hunters but may be given to someone who stands in a particular relationship to one of them. The theory upon which all such distributions work is that, assuming fairly uniform skill, it will all come out even in the end. It serves indeed to minimize the effects of striking inequalities in skill; like insurance, it distributes risks.

The way in which such a system of distribution works is well illustrated by the Kaingang of Brazil. The Kaingang camp consists of a small group united by close ties of blood or affinity who habitually wander together. They track large animals with dogs. When a hunter brings down a tapir he does not either keep the meat or distribute it. He gives the whole animal to a close relative, a brother-in-law, a brother, or a cousin, and this man butchers it, giving some to the hunter, some to each pot in the camp, keeping the greater part for his own use. The cleverest hunter or the owner of the best dog has only slight economic advantages, and the camp is bound together and made more secure by this even-handed sharing.

Not every system of distribution is as transparent as this. It is often hard to understand the mechanisms, harder still to comprehend the objectives. For frequently the flow of wealth is the dynamic principle that animates the social structure, and on the other hand economic forces are channeled by social forms.

Kinship claims in the distribution of wealth. Perhaps the most widespread and basic of all methods of distribution among primitive peoples — more important than trade or free gifts or warfare or tribute — is a system of compulsory payments between relatives by blood or marriage. The importance of these payments in relation to the total economy varies greatly from tribe to tribe, but among no primitive people is it wholly lacking, not even among the Eskimo. These mechanisms for the internal circulation of wealth assume many forms — bride price and dowry, affinal exchange, compulsory gifts, contribution at individual crisis ceremonies, and many others* — but some tie-up between economy and the rights of kinship is always present. Among people lacking political organization the economic obligations of kinship form one of the most potent means of preserving group solidarity. In many cases the property exchanges constitute the validation of social relationships, and the flow of property along certain channels forms the strongest bond in that society.

We have already seen how the exchange of products of different kinds is the daily commonplace and necessary condition of family life. This must be assumed for all peoples; we are concerned now with some of the more common forms of distribution outside of the group dwelling together.

These exchanges may be individual or collective, direct or indirect, objects exchanged of similar or different kinds. They are always compulsory, and although the economic motive may be extremely conspicuous, as at Manus and in other Melanesian groups, the social motive of recognizing status or a relationship between individuals is primary. Even where the economic motive is prominent, it is not always a direct economic motive such as that which underlies simple forms of trade. The passage of property, its amount and kind, are strictly defined by tradition without reference to the economic needs of the individuals involved. At a Hopi marriage the man's side contributes ceremonial garments; the girl's side, basketry trays — man's work against woman's work, symbolizing the economics of marriage. But the contribution has nothing to do with the individuals involved. Basketry is a specialty. If the girl does not practice it, she begs the trays from a relative or buys them from the White trader; but the prescribed exchanges must be carried out. Basket trays are prescribed marriage gifts even in Hopi villages that do not make baskets.[78]

---

* Transfer of property through inheritance will be dealt with in another place. See page 423.

The bond between siblings, especially between siblings of opposite sex, is usually a strong one, and although it goes counter to the marital grouping is often singled out for economic importance. The most extreme case of this is the fraternal distribution already described for the Trobrianders.[79]

Other forms of compulsory distribution among relatives exist, but none figure so importantly in primitive economics as the various property transfers that take place as the result of a marriage. Marriage may be regarded as the founding of a new family, which is the way we regard it, or as the passing of an individual from the jurisdiction of one group into the jurisdiction of another, or as a permanent alliance for mutual advantage between two families. Each of these attitudes has its associated economic adjustments: namely, dowry, bride price (or groom price), and affinal exchange.

Dowry. Dowry is sociologically defined as marital property contributed by the relatives of either party to a marriage. The popular limitation of the word to the property brought by the woman is not in accord with the precise definition. Still less justifiable is the extension of the term to include the property that passes from the family of the bride to the family of the groom in the course of marital exchange. Compared to other kinds of property adjustments at marriage, dowry is of relatively rare occurrence in the primitive world. The Quiché man, when he wishes to set up a separate establishment with his wife and children, usually several years after marriage, can demand from his father a piece of land, his share of his inheritance, which is entailed for the benefit of his sons. The Chukchee woman usually, not always, brings reindeer to her marriage, which are returned at divorce. A Hopi woman at marriage is given, by her mother, rights over a portion of the clan lands, which her husband cultivates for her. This is of more theoretical than practical importance since this tribe is matrilocal and the land remains undivided and is jointly administered by the extended matrilineal family. The Ifugao exhibit the nearest approach to our concept of dowry. At a marriage the man and the woman each receives a tract of rice land, agreed upon in advance, usually after long negotiations. These fields constitute marital property so long as the marriage endures. Neither party can dispose of any portion of the land or its produce, but even this is not dowry in our sense of the word, since the rights of the spouses terminate with the dissolution of the marriage by death or divorce, and the property reverts to the lineage from which it came. Dr. Ruth Benedict in a recent paper has demonstrated that however descent may be reckoned, property in primitive tribes is usually transmitted unilaterally, and to the exclusion of spouses.[80]

The bride price. It has been demonstrated repeatedly that the payment of a bride price does not necessarily involve the concept of woman as property. It is not necessary to go into that point here. Nor is the payment of a bride price inevitably associated with curtailment of woman's legal rights or her claims upon her own family. We may assume for the purpose of the present discussion that the bride price is an economic arrangement between the two contracting families, which may or may not accord to the husband and the husband's family certain rights over the woman and certain claims upon her family.

Just as often as not the payment of a bride price is conceived not in terms of purchase or legal claims but as a means of showing respect for the woman (the Crow and other Plains tribes) or of making the woman respect the man (Apache and Quiché), as compensating her family for the loss of her services, or rewarding her parents for their care in her education (Zulu). Or if the bride price is regarded as a payment for certain rights, the rights so acquired may be strictly limited and must be redefined for each group. These may include rights to the person of the woman, to her labor, or to whatever children she may bear, or the right to another woman of the same family should the first prove unsatisfactory. The bride price may be given in exchange for any one or any combination of these. For although bride price is not bound up with the status of woman as woman or her rights or disabilities in the marital relationship, it is nevertheless intimately related to considerations of descent, inheritance, and residence.[81]

In the numerous cases where wife purchase is combined with premarital license for girls, it is obvious that it is not the right of sexual access or even exclusive sexual privileges that are involved. It is frequently in just those. tribes where the bride price is the pivot of the economic structure that the differentiation of woman as an economic asset and woman as a sex object is most complete. Among the Bavenda, marriages are contracted between two women; the "husband" pays the bride price, the "wife" has lovers, but any children born to her belong to her "husband." [82]

The idea that woman is valuable primarily as a producer of children is widespread in Africa. In almost all African tribes a man may repudiate his wife if she is barren, which is regarded as the greatest of all misfortunes, and demand the return of the bride price. Some tribes state specifically that the bride price is the payment for the rights over the children. The Zulu say: "Cattle beget children"; "The cattle are where the children are not." [83] Among the Lango, if a marriage breaks up, the woman returns to her people with her children, and the bride price is returned. The original cattle with their offspring are returned to the husband. The offspring of the cattle represent the woman's real and potential children. But the husband may buy back his children from their mother's people by paying one heifer for each child.

Among African societies like the Bathonga,[84] where there is a strict division of labor along sex lines, where agriculture is regarded as woman's work and cattle-raising is man's province, the need for women in the kraal is the need for workers. But the Bathonga headman is trying to build up the security of the kraal rather than his own power over his brothers and sons. Therefore the headman does not try to corner the women but to secure wives for each of his dependents. He retains for himself as the reward for the bride payment the labor of the woman for the common life of the kraal.

All of Africa must be regarded as a region in which both the father's line and the mother's line are recognized, different kinds of privileges being transmitted in each line. If we recognize this kind of organization as fundamental in Africa, then the bride price represents the compensation which the patrilineal group pays for the rights which it acquires over a woman of another line; and over the children in whom her family also have an interest. In this connection it is notable that throughout Africa part of the bride price goes to the bride's maternal kinsmen, her mother and especially her mother's brother. This is also true of other regions.

But although common and, it would seem, obvious, this attitude concerning the economic value of women and children is by no means universal. In some parts of Melanesia and Papua [85] children are rejected by men and women alike. Barrenness is no misfortune and women practice contraception, abortion, and infanticide without interference from the men. It is perhaps a significant correlation that there is no bride price in this area. It is an area in which affinal exchange is the most important economic mechanism.

Bride purchase is associated with no economic level; it is found among hunting, pastoral, and agricultural people; in homogeneous and stratified societies; but almost everywhere it is associated with patrilocality and some form of patriliny. Among the Navajo, a matrilineal people for whom bride price is reported, the full amount is returned to the bridegroom in the form of gifts. The same thing is true of the Crow, the Cheyenne, and other matrilineal societies.[86]

Although the bride price is definitely tied up with patriliny, there is no corresponding economic expression of matriliny. The most powerful matriarchate of which we have records, Zuñi, has no groom price. The young man leaves his mother's household to work for his wife's. His female relatives lose his services. But Zuñi women do not buy their husbands or compensate their husbands' families for the loss of one of their members. The balance in the ceremonial exchanges at marriage is all in favor of the wife's family. Nor has any case come to notice of a groom price — not dowry, but property paid to the man's relatives — that is not the return of a bride price or a payment to secure lien on a woman of the husband's group.

Among the tribes of central and southern Africa, where the bride price is economically important, it runs like a thread through the society, binding the groups together in a never ending and intricate web of financial responsibility. The thread frequently becomes tangled, and the unraveling fills native courts with litigation. Junod reports that among the Bathonga ninety per cent of the cases concern *lobolo* (the bride price).

The difficulties of the system may be observed among the Lango, where the bride price is still paid in cattle. When a girl is given in marriage the cattle received are distributed among various relatives. But the greater portion is given to her brother and forms the nucleus of the payment for his wife, and is used in turn to provide a wife for a young man of a third family. If now the first marriage breaks up, the cattle that were originally given must be collected again, together with their increase, and returned to the husband, even if it means breaking up the brother's marriage to recover them. If the woman is divorced for adultery, her family try to recover from her lover, so that her brother may keep his wife. It is clear why Africans are constantly in litigation. Between a man and his wife's brother's wife there exists a special relationship. Should his wife desert him he can, legally, claim this woman, since she has been bought with his cattle. The right is never exercised, since it is recognized that such a forced marriage would be disastrous. It is significant that, in spite of bride price and the complex family involvements, fewer than twenty-five per cent of Lango marriages are arranged. The rest follow romantic courtship, including sexual relations, and the marriage is generally negotiated only after the birth of the first child, when the husband takes his wife to his village.[87] The use of the price received from a girl's marriage to purchase a wife for her brother is widely spread in Africa, and the complications that follow from this are general also. It is the economic equivalent of an exchange of sisters, and has much the same social effects. The man without sisters is at a disadvantage, and the kraal without women is poor. Men carry on the line, but only women bring wealth. It is this opposition of male and female principles that is expressed in the different forms of descent in Africa.

A variant of bride purchase is the custom of serving for a wife which is found among many peoples, especially among very simple peoples with little accumulated wealth. Among the Quiché this is an alternative for the bride price. The bride price is the accepted and preferred method, the method which is believed to make the girl respect her husband — always a great point with the Quiché. But special circumstances such as the poverty of the bridegroom or the lack of a male heir in the girl's family may induce a young man to go to the girl's home and work for her parents for a year in lieu of paying for her. "But it is bad," says the Quiché informant, "for the woman will not have respect for the man if he works for her in her house." There are other reasons why it is considered bad, but a man gladly serves for his wife if by so doing he can gain for his children inheritance in their mother's line.[88]

In Siberia service is the regular and approved method of securing a wife. Among the Reindeer Chukchee, the suitor, once accepted, comes to live in the girl's camp and works for her father. During the period of service he has no privileges and may be dismissed at any time — but is not. The father, on the other hand, tries to keep the young man with him, and to defer as long as possible the day when he leaves with his bride for his own camp. One of the preferred marriages is for a rich reindeer-breeder to give his daughter in marriage to one of his poor herdsmen, thus binding the man to him permanently by familial ties. "The man without relatives is a poor man," say the Chukchee. Marital arrangements among the Chukchee tie up with other aspects of their economy — food, animals, women are all used as material out of which to build security in a disruptive social environment.[89]

Affinal exchange. We have said that affinal exchange is the economic aspect of a concept of marriage as an enduring contract between two groups. There are some people like the Cheyenne among whom marriage is validated by a single exchange of gifts between the two families. They are rare. Almost everywhere the characteristic feature of affinal exchange is that it sets up a pattern of behavior between two groups which frequently outlasts the union it was intended to validate.

Even among people who regard marriage as a private affair of the two individuals directly concerned, the passing of property may constitute the formal recognition of the marriage. Such a case is Zuñi. Here marriage is by free choice. After the young people have cohabited for four nights with the consent of the girl's parents, the young man brings a gift of a woman's dress, which traditionally should be furnished by his mother. (In Zuñi the women were the weavers; now he buys the dress from a Hopi.) Next day the girl goes to grind for her mother-in-law, and subsequently brings gifts of corn meal "to pay for the dress." If the youth's female relatives do not wish to acknowledge the marriage, the women tell the girl when she comes to grind that they have no corn, and the young man is shamed out of the marriage. In that case the dress which he has given as a bride gift becomes a present given in return for sexual favors. In former days the mother would have refused the dress to an undesirable bride.

In any event, the exchanges are unequal, the man's family contributing the more valuable objects. But this can hardly be regarded as a bride price, since the articles are given to the girl herself. She in turn, assisted by her mother and sisters, gives to her husband's female relatives. All the articles exchanged are women's goods, and pass directly between women. This exchange between women, apparently unique in primitive society, is an expression of the dominance of women in all domestic and economic affairs. The father's sisters (extended to include all clanswomen) are a child's most important ceremonial relatives. This relationship has its economic obligations; the "aunt" must give gifts and service to her "child," and the pattern of exchange set up at marriage is continued throughout the life of the child. Initiations and other crises are marked by the exchange of women's goods between the women of the mother's line and the women of the father's sister's line.[90]

The Zuñi system is an example of extremely simple marital exchange. For marital exchange full-blown and raised to a position of paramount economic importance, we must turn to Oceania. The general structure of affinal exchange from New Guinea to Samoa is identical. Reduced to its simplest terms the basic pattern is as follows. Whenever a marriage is arranged the extended kin groups of the spouses are involved in enduring contractual obligations of an economic nature. The marriage must be validated by the passage of property back and forth between these groups, and the alliance must be repeatedly reaffirmed by similar exchanges at crises in the lives of the spouses and their children and, in some tribes, at every village event. Barring divorce, these obligations continue until the dissolution of the marriage by the death of one of the spouses, the exchange system frequently reaching its high point in the mourning ceremonies. Upon this identical theme the Oceanic groups ring infinite changes, according to the variations in their basic economies, their kinship structure, and their interests and temperaments.

In analyzing the economics of marital exchange one must consider both the kinds of property exchanged and the extension of the system. Where the kinds of property exchanged are the same, sons and daughters can be equated in the exchange system, which has its effect on the status of women and the economic structure of the family. Where, on the other hand, the property exchanged differs in kind, any inequalities in the sex ratio produce in the economic field the same kind of tension within the family that is produced by a marriage system that requires an exchange of women. This may be eased by borrowing or internal trade, or the sex ratio may be kept evenly balanced by adoption; it becomes critical in case the property paid on one side is rare or even absolutely limited in quantity like the ranked valuables required for bride price on Rossel Island.[91]

The other general consideration in affinal exchange, that of extension, concerns such questions as how often the exchanges are repeated, how many people are involved, and whether the two sides function as groups or as individuals. Samoa represents one pattern, Manus the other.

In Samoan exchange the man's side contributes men's goods — principally pigs, fish, other foodstuffs, and wood work — against women's goods — bark cloth and mats — contributed by the woman's side. This pattern, inaugurated at betrothal, is repeated interminably at each event in the life of the new family and at all visits. It is a point of honor and courtesy not to neglect the economic obligations of remote kinship and to have ready the appropriate gift for the distant affinal relative who comes to call. If a suitable article is not available, it must be bought or borrowed, or requested as a gift from a relative. The exchanges are not individual, and no accounts are kept. The exchanges have a ceremonious character, in keeping with Samoan emphasis on courtesy, graciousness, coöperativeness, and the recognition of the most remote kinship ties. The characteristic economic slant is given by the fact that men's property is largely perishable, women's property permanent. The fine mats given with a girl in marriage are limited in quantity and are individually known. They are valuables. But they pass freely from hand to hand, and since only women give valuables, no object of equivalent value is received in exchange.[92]

Among all the Melanesian-speaking islanders who understand trade and money so thoroughly, marital exchanges are conducted in a far more businesslike fashion, sometimes with profit as a dominant motive. In the Admiralty Islands all events which concern a marriage or the children of a marriage set in motion an exchange of property. As in Samoa there is the side of the man and the side of the woman, each giving its own kind of property. The woman's side gives matting, pigs, garden produce, and pots, which are traded in; the man's side gives dogs' teeth and shell money — the valuables. But here the resemblance to the Polynesian system stops. The exchanges are not courtesy gifts presented on joyous occasions; they constitute the validation of status ceremonies — betrothal, marriage, birth and ear piercing, puberty of children — and culminate in the great mortuary exchanges that are characteristic of this part of the world. Also these exchanges are in specified quantities, and careful accounts are kept over long periods of time. Moreover, they are conducted between individuals. Theoretically, each relative on the man's side exchanges with someone similarly related on the woman's side; actually, he exchanges with any economically competent relative. These two conduct their exchanges in the thoroughly commercial manner of Melanesian trade partners. This exchange partnership continues so long as the obligations set in force by the marriage exist.

A man's wealth, status, and power depend on his ability to keep large numbers of these exchange relationships going. An enterprising man will thus finance the marriage of as many of his young relatives as he can corral. He may correct difficulties arising from the disparity of the sexes in his family by adoption or by simply assuming responsibility for the marriage payments of any person younger than himself who is related to him in any way by blood or marriage.

The motive is, as we have said, profit. But the profit is not in the exchanges themselves, which are strictly equivalent. Nor does the lending of required types of property at interest play any part, as it does in Rossel Island. The profit comes from the relationship between the entrepreneur and the young man whose marriage he is financing. Young men have no property. They are betrothed in childhood and henceforth, until they can assume financial responsibility, must work for the man who has incurred financial obligations in their name. They fish or cut sago for their "benefactor." This is bought and sold in regular trade or traded to the bush people, the profit of these transactions being for the benefit of the entrepreneur. There is no profit, apparently, in girls. They are taken on to keep the balance even. So arranging marriages becomes the principal occupation of the "big man" of Manus.[93]

Out of the variety of material before us, one fact is plain. Marriage has economic repercussions that have nothing whatever to do with the immediate economic problem of rearing a family of children. Among the Kwakiutl marriage is another potlatch involving whole tribes; in Rossel Island a marriage is another kind of pig feast; in Manus another gamble with probability for the enterprising financier. Among the Yoruba it is the road to wealth and power. And at a former time in Europe royal marriages were the quickest, surest, and least costly method of redrawing the map.

Gifts and hospitality. Among the important techniques of distribution among primitive people is institutionalized gift-giving. We ourselves have very special attitudes in respect to gifts. Our giving is almost wholly ceremonial. We give presents only on some occasion in the life of the recipient (except Christmas). Theoretically the gift should be as far removed from the economic as possible; it should be something useless and extravagant; above all, something which the recipient would not think of buying for himself. Except in very special cases gifts of money and necessary objects are tolerated only between close relatives, or to a social inferior. There are therefore "gift shops" devoted to the sale of articles suitable for gifts, most of which never find any other use. The "perfect gift" is something with a wholly fictitious value, like jewels and expensive perfumes. The tactful lover sends orchids, although the lady may need shoes. A gift must be accepted graciously * and should be returned on a similar occasion in the life of the original donor, with something different in kind but equal in value. The one exception to this pattern is the wedding gift, which is given only once, should have permanent utilitarian value, and serves a definite economic function in establishing the young married couple. It is in fact part of the bride's dowry. The conventional attitudes in giving and receiving gifts are known to anyone beyond the age of three.

Gift-giving, among us, has become so exclusively a social ceremonial that we are apt to overlook its important economic function among many primitive peoples. There is a tendency to phrase as "gifts" transactions which have very different characters. A "gift" at Zuñi is a very different thing from a "gift" among the Kwakiutl. It is not true, as has often been stated, that among all primitive people the acceptance of a gift invariably binds the recipient to return something of equal or greater value. This is certainly not true at Zuñi, where the giving of presents is always one-sided, and is a definite and recognized means of redistributing wealth.

Whereas at Zuñi gift-giving, like feasting, is a mechanism for adjusting existing inequalities, the Maori manage their whole economy on the principle of giving presents. The village is the economic unit. In addition to offerings of first fruits, the whole catch of birds or of fish is "given" to the chief. He proceeds to redistribute it, giving to each according to his needs, his rank, and the obligations which the chief may have incurred for services or other presents. A large portion he retains for his own use, for the financing of communal undertakings, for gifts to other chiefs. The occasions for gift-giving are innumerable. Moreover, the giving of presents has been substituted for trade. A chief may demand as a gift anything he desires, and it must be given him. This custom is sustained by supernatural sanctions. But a return gift of greater value is required. Gift-giving is expressed in its most extreme form in the intertribal feast; at such a feast large quantities of food are consumed, and still larger quantities are given by the hosts to their guests to take home, and after

* We make one exception to this rule of compulsory acceptance. A woman may refuse a valuable gift from an unrelated male, for such a gift has a sexual connotation. Among the Ibo, a tribe of West Africa, little girls are warned not to accept gifts from men, for such acceptance, in the presence of witnesses, commits the child to marriage. It is a tribe in which competition for women is acute.

it the community is impoverished in material resources, but enormously enriched in prestige. Such a feast requires years of preparation. The prestige and power of the chief and the pride of a group in its chief depend very largely on his ability to maintain a reputation for generosity at home and abroad.[94]

Among the Kwakiutl the giving of a gift is an aggressive act against a rival, an attempt to outdo him. "Rivals fight with property." This emphasis on the humiliation of the rival is the negative aspect — one might almost say the perversion — of the same sentiment which impels men to make gifts out of motives of self-respect. Among the Kwakiutl gift-giving is no longer truly economic; and it is therefore significant that all the more important transactions are in objects that have only an exchange value, blankets and coppers.[95]

The free giving of presents as an important economic function, in contrast to mere ceremonial giving, is characteristic of all North American tribes and of Polynesia. The African king does not receive presents; he sends out a tax collector armed with royal authority.[96] The Melanesians in general do not understand giving — a gift is the initiation of a series of exchanges.* The efficiency of gift-giving as an economic mechanism depends on the existence in the group of strong inner sanctions — a sense of shame or of personal dignity, and a reliance on the will of each man to act becomingly. It is the economic expression of self-appreciation. Most of the peoples who make much of gift-giving have institutionalized boasting; Zuñi is an exception. But the complacent disdain with which the "valuable" man regards everyone else is the characteristic Pueblo manner of expressing the same state of mind. Extreme sensitiveness to criticism and a tendency to disparage others are the negative aspects of this personality structure, and in these characteristics Pueblo Indians excel.

The Orokaiva of New Guinea, all of whose sanctions are based on motives of self-esteem, reinterpret all of the Melanesian and Papuan property exchange situations as occasions for honorific gift-giving. The usual marriage pattern is that the bride elopes; relatives follow her and humiliate the husband. The husband then collects the bride price, pigs, garden food, and ornaments. All his relatives, male and female, contribute. Sometimes human victims are substituted for pigs, in which case the feather ornaments assume the

---

* Dr. Mead and Dr. Fortune have reported on the difficulty of inducing even small children to accept the gift of a trinket.

importance of homicidal honors. The bride's family comes with a show of force to collect this tribute, and the bride's father immediately gives away all of these objects to his relatives. The return of the bride price is optional; the reason given is that the bride's family "would be ashamed to make no return payment," or that it is to honor the woman so that her husband will treat her kindly. In that case "the girl goes for nothing," and may return home when she will. At initiations various relatives kill pigs in honor of the initiates, boys and girls, and give them the homicidal insignia. The pigs are given to visitors. The child who receives these honorific ornaments is expected to wear them with dignity.

Throughout Melanesia death is an occasion for the most drastic economic rearrangements. The Orokaiva have a series of feasts in which first the family of the deceased, and later the family of the widow, distribute pigs and other property. The motive of reciprocity, if present, is certainly not conspicuous, since Williams, a careful observer, does not mention it. It is viewed as a series of feasts with appropriate victims (again the pig is identified with the human victim) "to wipe out the shame of the widow."

Williams [97] generalizes about the economy of the Orokaiva as follows:

Perhaps the most characteristic of all [their virtues] is liberality. . . . There is nothing, not valor in war nor prowess in the chase, that brings an Orokaiva so prominently into the public eye as the providing of a big feast. Yet no one could deny the existence of true generosity; this is shown in countless details of daily life. . . . Although there is no systematic sharing of food supplies, yet constant gifts and feasts large and small achieve in the long run what amounts to equal distribution. . . . To give freely of one's food is the proper thing to do; it is an elementary virtue in respect of which there are few failures. . . . For his liberality a man receives a reward of honor; but beyond that — and this should not be thought to disqualify it entirely as a virtue — he constantly looks for an equal return in kind. . . . The return may be made long subsequently, but it may be called a matter of honor to equal or exceed the original gift; just as it is a matter of disgrace and lowered self-esteem to fail.

This description, which might do equally well for the Dakota, is striking in the middle of New Guinea.

The foregoing discussion shows how difficult it often is to distinguish gift-giving from exchange and trade, especially where the feeling for reciprocity is strong. The Maori chief who exchanges

gifts with a visitor, or who taboos an article which he desires, is —
from the purely economic point of view — engaging in trade. The
Kwakiutl who gives away blankets on behalf of his son in order
that he may procure a potlatch name and a place in all subsequent
property distributions is really initiating his son into a system of
compulsory exchange in which he will become more deeply involved
with each new participation but in which there is always the possibility of profit. It is a matter of how the actors look at their transactions. The Maori disdains any open consideration of relative values
and relies entirely on the sense of the fitting in his vis-à-vis. The
Kwakiutl aims ultimately to cap his career by giving the gift of great
value which cannot be returned. This is quite different from the
attitude, say, of the Manus entrepreneur if he receives no return
of his exchanges; instead of being proud of having downed a rival
or done a fine thing he is chagrined at having made a bad investment. Giving and exchanging may work out the same way economically, with, however, one important difference. Intentional and conspicuous waste is characteristic of those societies where economic
exchange takes the form of gift-giving and serves as a means of self-
approbation.

In the foregoing paragraphs, we have discussed chiefly the private
gift, made by one individual to another. But what has been said
applies equally to the custom of general giving, the "give-away"
(frequently called the "big feast") that figures so prominently in
the economy of many primitive societies. Among people who go in
for lavishness any private or public event, a birth, a marriage, the
initiation of a boy or the appearance of a girl's menses, the return
from a raid, the ripening of the crop, the annual slaughter of the
herd, the recovery from illness, an embarrassing event, and even
death itself may be seized upon by an individual or a group as an
occasion for wholesale property distribution. Sometimes there is no
occasion; it is simply decided to "give a feast." Sometimes this is
simply an occasion for initiating exchanges or paying old debts. On
the face of it we can never be sure, without going into the economics
and accounting in detail, or unless there is other evidence, such as
lavishness and conspicuous waste.

The great event in the life of New Guinea tribes is the "big feast,"
and perhaps no people carry this form of lavishness to greater excess
than the Mafulu, a mountain tribe living simply in small hamlets.
They have gardens and raise pigs, and plant special gardens of sweet

potatoes to feed their domestic pigs. In addition, the young pigs are suckled at the breast, and tended with such devotion that a woman will kill her newborn infant, in order to suckle the pig, if she has no grown pig to kill for the child's name feast. Then every ten years or so a group of these hamlets of from two to eight houses gives a big feast to a neighboring group of villages. The feast is inaugurated by an exchange of insults. At such a feast as many as 130 pigs may be slaughtered and given to the visitors, who take them away. The pigs slain are used to validate some personal crisis — a birth, marriage, an initiation in the family of the man whose pig is killed. After this slaughter the village is uninhabitable and is abandoned as if in mourning. The whole village goes out to hunt and eat the wild pig ceremonially, and a new village is founded.

Firth has described the big feast of the Maori, with its years of preparation, lavish displays of food, much of which spoils before it is eaten, and the dire poverty that follows in its wake.

The feast plays a very different rôle, as we have seen, in the life of the Reindeer Chukchee. Before the onset of winter there are two large slaughterings of animals, primarily to procure skins for winter clothing — an early slaughtering of young fawns with soft thin skins, and a later slaughtering after the full winter coat has grown. In the camp of a large stock owner many animals are killed, there is a great quantity of meat available, and the occasion is one of great festivity. Invitations are sent out in advance, and friends and relatives come from far away. The slaughtering takes place on different days in adjacent camps, and visitors from afar visit from camp to camp. There are games, wrestling matches, shamanistic performances. And to each guest the host gives one or more slaughtered animals, together with the skins. It would be an insult to the guest not to give him the skin. These feasts mark the high point in the social lives of these widely dispersed herdsmen. They are also economically important to those poor herdsmen who, in their anxiety to build up their economic independence, are reluctant to slaughter animals even for the necessities of life. The Chukchee feast has none of the characteristic features of the Oceanic feast — there is no display of food, no wanton destruction, none of the formalities of insult and retaliation.

Nothing could bring out more strikingly the different psychological aura that may surround institutions called by the same name than to read a description of a Chukchee or Zuñi feast after an Orokaiva or a Mafulu or a Kwakiutl feast.

Intertribal economics. The importance of intertribal relations, trade, and warfare in the economy of any group depends on other factors than accidents of geography alone. One might reasonably assume that poverty of the environment will lead men to establish relationships, peaceful or predatory, with the inhabitants of more favorably endowed regions. Like so many reasonable assumptions, the idea that people trade only or chiefly under the spur of necessity is not supported by the facts. The Eskimo, with the most rigorous environment in the world, managed to survive with a minimum of outside contact until White traders forced their way into the Arctic, and they managed very well indeed, as the age and stability of Eskimo culture prove — better, possibly, than they will manage in the era of communication and trade. Eskimo self-sufficiency was not always the result of geographical isolation; in parts of the area they were near enough to other peoples to engage in trade. Moreover, contemporary Eskimo trade is characteristic; they have not surrendered their economic independence or made drastic changes in their economy. The great majority have not given up aboriginal pursuits to live by the fur trade. They merely trade their surplus for improved tools and weapons, guns and steel knives and iron for harpoon points and sledge runners. This is a substitution of materials that has had but little effect on economic structure. The Eskimo are not a trading people in the way that the Melanesians and Central Americans are trading people.

The fact that the Eskimo have made such a meager environment do, without recourse to hostile or dependent relations with other tribes, indicates that it is not the uneven distribution of natural wealth alone that creates wars and trade. Animals adapt their habits to their environment; so can human beings, unless there is something in their social structure or cultural evaluation that makes the products of another region appear desirable. Moreover, it is frequently not necessities, but luxuries like pottery and copper bells, or objects of nonutilitarian value like large greenstone adzes and spondylus shell necklaces, that form the most important trade articles and that travel farthest. Trade and predatory warfare are alternative reactions to coveting one's neighbor's goods, but they are not mutually exclusive. Trade is often carried on in the teeth of intense hostility, between tribes who customarily war on each other, like the Navajo and the Zuñi, or the tribes of New Guinea who trade in the intervals of head-hunting.

Industrial specialization, concentration of wealth of different kinds in different groups, and social stratification are structural factors that predispose to the development of internal trade. Often, however, these asymmetries of distribution are adjusted by other forms of exchange — marriage or mortuary exchange, "gifts," symbiotic feudalism. Local specialization on the basis of geographical or purely cultural factors such as special skill is a necessary condition of intertribal trade. But the development of intense specialization is contingent upon the existence of a dependable market. The market system of Central America is highly organized and thoroughly dependable. Were this not the case the town of Nahualá in Guatemala could not exist, as it does, by the manufacture of grindstones alone without raising sufficient food to support its own population. Nor could the other towns of this trade area get along without troubling to make this necessary article at home. The case of the Amphletts in Melanesia is even more striking. These coral islands live entirely by pottery, but have to import their clay from overseas. Trade must have been well developed before such intense specialization could grow up. The existence of markets depends on the disinclination of buyers to learn new techniques. In Melanesia local monopolies are bolstered by faith in privately owned magic. In North America, on the other hand, techniques spread readily from tribe to tribe, and trade is consequently of slight economic importance.

In preceding paragraphs we have discussed various forms of internal exchange which result in the redistribution of products — often products of different kinds — but which cannot be called trade. These exchanges are obligatory, or at least demanded by prestige; they follow prescribed channels, without regard for such economic factors as the needs or resources of the individuals concerned. But trade is primarily an economic mechanism. It may have a secondary social function as in the markets of Africa or Central America. Or else the prestige and ceremonial aspects may completely overshadow the economic, as in the *kula* trade already described. However the manner of conducting trade may differ from one group to another, however much the interest in trade may vary, the main economic motivations are clear and everywhere the same: to get a fair return of the things one needs in return for the surplus of the things that one has. Profit is not universally absent from primitive trade, but it is usually very much curtailed. The open market as we know it is practically nonexistent, especially in those places where trade is most important.

There is no open market in Melanesia where most trade is conducted through trade partnerships, or in Africa where the officers of the king supervise the market, confiscating adulterated or overpriced merchandise.

The type of primitive trade that most closely resembles the noncommercial forms of exchange is the so-called "silent trade" reported from many of the simpler tribes, and as a method of conducting trade in the face of intertribal hostility. The Veddas, a hill tribe of Ceylon, trade in this fashion with the Sinhalese. They come down at night and leave meat at the shop of a Sinhalese smith as an advance payment on arrow points. They return some days later for the arrows, bringing more meat to pay for them. The two parties to the transaction do not meet; there can be no bargaining over equivalence or values. Parity of exchange depends on the fear of retaliation through violence, property destruction, or sorcery.[98]

Throughout Melanesia flourishes the institution of the trade friendship, a lifelong relationship between individuals in different, often hostile, tribes or in different divisions of the same tribe, who trade exclusively with each other. This often is a relationship of tremendous social importance. Within the tribe it may carry with it sexual rights, such as rights of access to the trade friend's wife or a lien on one of his sisters. In a hostile tribe the trade friend may be the only guarantee of asylum. From the economic point of view the conduct of trade within this institution channels the movement of wealth, curtails profits, and reduces commercial rivalry somewhat. It also opens the way for transactions requiring long-term credit. This makes it a particularly useful institution among people who have no money.

Typical of Melanesian trade is the relationship between tribes on the southeast coast of New Guinea. There are continuous trade relations up and down the coast. Articles of value from the islands are traded as far as the Purari delta, and then inland, and food products move eastward, but for shorter distances. One of the longest expeditions is that of the Motu for the Purari delta, a distance of about 350 miles along the coast. Each year at the end of the southeast monsoon a fleet of some hundred to two hundred canoes, lashed together in groups and manned by about five hundred men, sets out from Motu. They carry cargoes of pots, necklaces, arm shells, and greenstone adzes, the last two commodities having been imported from the east. They sail with the wind to the mouth of the Purari. Here each man goes at once to his trade friend, giving him his pots, arm shells, and other articles, and receiving from him a tally of palm ribs for each article. They then proceed to the bush, where they work on canoes, logs for which have been cut for them by the bush natives. They remain about four or five months and return with the northwest monsoon. Before leaving they receive from their trade friends sago and betel nuts to pay for the pots and ornaments. This kind of trade expedition is typical for the whole Melanesian area.[99]

The objects traded in this part of Melanesia are of two kinds: objects of utility, like sago, pots, wood work, small greenstone adzes, and valuables, conus arm shells, spondylus shell necklaces, and large greenstone adzes, and, in other trade districts such as the Admiralty Islands, dogs' teeth, boars' tusks, and red feathers. Along the coast of New Guinea commodities may be exchanged for valuables, but in certain districts, notably the *kula* district, the exchange of valuables and commodities is kept strictly apart; commodities are exchanged for commodities, valuables for valuables in a system which admits neither accumulation nor profit. These valuables are not media of exchange or fixed values in terms of which other values are measured. They are not, therefore, "money." There is one place in the Pacific where objects fulfilling these two functions of money are found, Rossel Island. Here there are two systems of shell money, each made up of a number of fixed values, the relations between which are measured in terms of the time required for one to accumulate interest that will raise it to the next value. Individual pieces are ranked and named. This money is fixed in quantity and does not circulate freely. It is used only in certain ceremonial exchanges such as the purchase of pigs, wives, and human victims for cannibal feasts. Rossel Island is isolated and engages in very little overseas trade. The "money" of Buin, which has none of the complexity of grading of the Rossel system, is similar in principle, a permanent object of fixed value exchangeable for certain services and commodities.[100]

The trade picture in Central America is somewhat different. The economic background is similar: regions of different geographic endowment that have exaggerated their differences by the development of special skills localized in villages, with the resulting interdependence of a large area inhabited by peoples speaking different languages. But here trade is conducted entirely in open markets. Each village has a weekly or daily market for the interchange of

local products and imports. The weekly market at the village of
Chichicastenango, one of the great trade centers which draws thousands of visitors weekly, includes local producers of foodstuffs, local
merchants with commodities like coffee or mats brought from other
villages, regular visitors from nearby towns with their local products,
and occasional traders from more distant towns with the produce
of their own or other towns for which they serve as middlemen.
These men dispose of the greater part of their stock to local merchants. They do not return empty-handed, but buy other objects,
such as mats or bags, to sell at home, or else buy foodstuffs to sell
at the railhead where they can purchase foreign wares such as steel
knives and cotton yarn. Chichicastenango is a town of middlemen;
almost every man engages in trade for profit. The town is very
wealthy, and most of this wealth is derived from trade. On the
other hand the industrial towns of the area are poor.

Within the same trade district, markets are held on successive
days in different villages. In addition each village has one large fair
each year on the date of the feast of the patron saint; these in important centers attract thousands of merchants from far and near.
The market plays an important rôle in the social, political, and religious life; it brings large numbers of people together and forms the
necessary contrast to the rather disruptive and unsocial life on isolated farms.* Although the Central American market is formally
open, there is little evidence of competition. Prices are set by custom.
Every commodity increases in price with the distance from the
source of. supply. The roads are open to everyone, and everyone
likes to use them. Moreover, there are supernatural sanctions against
greed and sharp dealing, and fear of sorcery and the envy of others
keeps prices moderate.

Money is used in Central American markets, the usual money
or moneys of the country. In pre-Columbian times the seeds of cacao
served as a medium of exchange. But their perishable nature, their
use as a commodity, and their variation in value in different geographical regions preclude their being classed as money. They still
serve as valuables in ceremonial exchanges.

War. One mechanism of intertribal economics still remains to be
mentioned, war. Predatory warfare was an established part of the
economy of many primitive peoples. Raiding for profit was the

---

* A Guatemalan village is not a place where large numbers of people live; it is
a place where they foregather for religious and commercial activities.

characteristic economic relationship between the sedentary Pueblos and their nomadic neighbors. The popular picture is that of hordes of Navajo swooping down on the peaceable and defenseless Pueblos, and robbing them of their corn. But the reminiscences of elders indicate that the Zuñis at least were no passive victims. Navajo who came to trade peaceably were treacherously killed and robbed, and when things became dull at home the Zuñis went on the warpath with the avowed object of stealing Navajo sheep. After killing off all the inhabitants of a camp, they drove off the sheep. On returning home these were divided among the members of the war party, according to rank, and the rest were turned loose among the people. Warfare has been stopped and its place has been taken by trade in sheep and turquoise in which the Zuñis drive the hardest bargains. Ashamed of sharp practice at home, they delight in cheating the Navajo.[101]

Warfare on the northern plains, while primarily for glory, had its economic side. The Crow raided systematically for horses, their favorite form of wealth, and a stolen horse was the only acceptable bride gift. Here, however, prestige outranked profit as a motive; it was the exploit rather than the acquisition of the horse that was most important. The stealing of a horse under prescribed conditions was a recognized counter in the war-rank complex. Horses stolen on the warpath were generally given away, adding still another cubit to the prestige of the warrior.[102]

On the other hand, the whole economic system of the Kiowa hinged upon warfare. Here also the objective was not food or valuables but horses, the instruments of production in their economy. With the development of buffalo-hunting and nomadic life large numbers of horses were necessary for comfortable existence. Each man required several fast, specially trained buffalo horses for the hunt itself, battle horses, and pack horses for carrying meat, tipi poles, etc. Furthermore, they accumulated wealth in the form of large herds of unbroken horses. A man acquired power by having horses to lend. In this way he could get poor relatives to hunt or raid for him. And he acquired prestige from giving horses away. The best and most honorable way to get horses was by raiding neighboring tribes and Mexicans. Certain seasons of the year were devoted to raiding; parties sometimes stayed out for months and years and drove off large herds of horses. On such raids they killed only when necessary. They also took slaves and sold them to the Comanche.[103]

Almost all North American tribes took captives in war, who were brought back as slaves and frequently adopted into the family of the captor. But for slave-raiding as the aim of war we must turn to West Africa. All the tribes of this region have slavery as an established and important economic institution, and warfare with the avowed purpose of capturing slaves has been vigorously prosecuted even across the Sahara.[104] The desert tribes raided the great kingdoms of the Guinea coast to take slaves to be sold to the North African tribes, and during the period of the American slave trade the tribes of the coast raided the inland peoples with similar objectives. But in addition to these great interracial movements the whole internal economy predisposes to this form of warfare. Among all African peoples women are the most valued economic assets. Women, as we have seen, are capital and build power for their owners, and throughout this part of Africa power rivalry is an important motive. Power built through women, polygamy which creates a shortage of women, the resulting high bride price and strong rivalry, have given special economic importance to the taking of female slaves in warfare. Such captive women become wives or concubines of their masters, and their children are free. In most parts of the world this is the only kind of slavery that is known.

Throughout New Guinea the fact that a human victim can usually be substituted for a pig at a marriage or funeral feast — most of these tribes eat their victims and some kill for food without ceremonial pretext — has given a special coloring to their head-hunting. Or perhaps it is only the substitution of pigs for human victims that has kept these tribes from completely exterminating each other. There is no glory in Papuan warfare. The point is to kill in the safest and most economical fashion, and the usual pattern is to send out an expedition of some fifty warriors against a small isolated and defenseless settlement, or to waylay victims in the bush. In such raids the women and children are often taken as captives.

Marriage with captive women and adoption of captive children is so widespread in parts of New Guinea that whole tribes, like the Marind-Anim, are of mixed descent and sometimes even of mixed language. This fact adds still further complications to the whole head-hunting picture for this area. Head-hunting, adoption, and trade exist side by side between the same tribes.

War for territorial expansion was relatively rare in the primitive world. It must have occurred in many places in the past, but for the most part we can only infer it from authenticated records of population movements such as we find in archaeological remains and from such complexities of social structure as those of the caste states of central Africa. Wars of this kind are very different from the desultory murdering and plundering by individuals or groups of individuals. The war party, even when organized under a leader with supernatural sanctions, is purely individualistic in aim; persons go on war parties for individual honor or profit. Raiding for plunder can and does occur among people with any kind of social or economic structure. But wars of conquest involving whole populations can be carried out only by politically organized groups. It is not merely a question of the size of the undertaking which requires more extensive organization and stronger leadership. There is a difference of attitude. The men who go out to raid expect to come back alive, and almost always do. The loss of life is among the passive defendants. In North America, at least, the leader who loses men on a raid is thereafter disqualified; he has lost his power. But a war of conquest cannot be fought without loss of life. There must therefore be an idea of a commonwealth for which men are willing to risk their lives, or an authority strong enough to compel them to do so — in short, a strong state. A strong state does not necessarily mean a large state. Some of the most outstandingly successful wars of conquest, such as the conquest of Mexico, have been waged by small groups of men with a fanatical singleness of purpose, mowing down unorganized or uncertain populations.

Africa is the part of the primitive world that is characterized by strong political organization. It is not surprising, therefore, that wars of conquest have been waged among the native states of Africa from relatively early days down to the present. In early days there were undoubtedly great population movements; the more recent wars have been waged over the point of extension of political power, which always means tribute to the ruler.

One of the most interesting primitive wars of conquest within historic times was the conquest of the islands of Lau, Southeast Fiji, by a war expedition from Fiji proper some 150 years ago. A relatively small group of warriors conquered the islands, established themselves as a ruling class, and proceeded to acquire title to land by intermarriage with the indigenous population. This process is still going on.

Among the Aztecs of ancient Mexico war was the most honorable occupation and warriors formed a privileged caste. War formed one of the integrating factors of the Aztec state. The whole society was organized along martial lines, the various descent groups forming military units each under a war chief. War was waged with two objectives, tribute and captives. First coming into prominence in the thirteenth century as the boldest of the predatory nomads who preyed upon the civilized peoples of the valley of Mexico, the Aztec kings rapidly built up an empire on the Roman plan, which extended into Central America and included peoples of many languages and diverse cultures. To conquered peoples they extended protection — a sort of *pax Mexicana* — and from them they demanded tribute in the form of food stores, local handicrafts, and precious metals. On this foundation was built up the magnificence of the court of the Montezumas whose splendor so excited the cupidity of the Spaniards, and which ultimately formed the economic basis of Spain's age of glory. But in one respect the conquests of the Mexicans differed from those of any other people. The Aztecs had what is unquestionably the most bloodthirsty religion in all recorded history. The sun required human sacrifices, and blood had to be spilled in connection with all the cults for rain and fertility. To supply the victims for this charnel house the Aztecs waged merciless warfare on all their neighbors. The warriors who brought captives to the altars were upholding the supernatural power as well as the material prosperity of the empire. The Aztecs after they settled in the valley of Mexico had a self-sustaining agricultural economy, handicrafts, and an elaborate system of trade. Warfare was the business of the warrior caste, and it supported the temple and the court, but not the people.

FOOTNOTES

1. See Sumner, W. G., Keller, A. G., and Davie, M. R., *The Science of Society* (1927), vol. 4, index, p. 1274.
2. Henry, J., *The Kaingang of Brazil* (Ms.).
3. Mead, M., *Sex and Temperament in Three Primitive Societies* (1935).
4. Spencer, B., and Gillen, F. J., *The Arunta* (London, 1927), vol. 1, pp. 15 ff.; Radcliffe-Brown, A. R., "Social Organization of Australian Tribes," *Oceania*, vol. 1 (1930–31), pp. 63, 439; Pink, O., "The Landowners in the Northern Division of the Aranda Tribe," *Oceania*, vol. 6 (1936), pp. 275 ff.
5. Boas, F., *The Social Organization and the Secret Societies of the Kwakiutl Indians*, Report of the United States National Museum, 1895 (1897); Swanton, J. R., *Contributions to the Ethnology of the Haida*, Jesup Expedition, vol. 5, Part I (1905–09), and *Social Condition, Beliefs, and Linguistic Relationship of the Tlingit Indians*, Annual Report of the Bureau

of American Ethnology, vol. 26 (1908); Boas, F., *Tsimshian Mythology, ibid.*, vol. 31 (1916).

6. See, for instance, Lowie, R. H., *The Crow Indians* (1935); also in Anthropological Papers, American Museum of Natural History, vol. 16 (1921); vol. 21 (1924); Fortune, R. F., *Omaha Secret Societies*, Columbia University Contributions to Anthropology, vol. 14 (1932).

7. Irle, J., *Die Herero* (Gütersloh, 1906).

8. Smith, E. W., and Dale, A. M., *The Ila-Speaking Peoples of Northern Rhodesia* (London, 1920).

9. Reichard, G. A., *Social Life of the Navajo Indians*, Columbia University Contributions to Anthropology, vol. 7 (1928).

10. Driberg, J. H., *The Lango* (London, 1923).

11. Williamson, R. W., *The Mafulu* (London, 1912).

12. Malinowski, B., *Argonauts of the Western Pacific* (London, 1922), pp. 146 ff.

13. Boas, F., *The Central Eskimo*, Annual Report of the Bureau of Ethnology, vol. 6 (1888).

14. Bogoras, W., *The Chukchee*, Jesup Expedition, vol. 7 (1904–09).

15. Mead, M., *Social Organization of Manua*, Bernice P. Bishop Museum Bulletin 76 (1930).

16. Malinowski, B., *Argonauts of the Western Pacific*, p. 62, and *Coral Gardens* (London, 1935), vol. 1, pp. 218 ff.

17. Fortune, R. F., *Sorcerers of Dobu* (1932); Malinowski, B., *Argonauts of the Western Pacific*.

18. Bogoras, W., *op. cit.*

19. Barton, R. F., *Ifugao Economics*, University of California Publications in American Archaeology and Ethnology, vol. 15 (1922), pp. 405 ff.

20. Thurnwald, R. C., "Pigs and Currency in Buin," *Oceania*, vol. 5, no. 2 (1934), pp. 119–141.

21. Benedict, R., *Patterns of Culture* (1934).

22. Veblen, T., *The Theory of the Leisure Class* (1917).

23. Bunzel, R., *A Guatemalan Village* (Ms.).

24. Deloria, Ella, *Dakota Ethnology* (Ms.).

25. Tawney, R. H., *The Acquisitive Society* (1920).

26. Sombart, W., "Capitalism," *Encyclopaedia of the Social Sciences*, vol. 3 (1930).

27. Beaglehole, E., *Property* (London, 1931).

28. Firth, R., *Primitive Economics of the New Zealand Maori* (1929), pp. 235 ff.

29. Bunzel, R., *Zuñi Economics* (Ms.) and *Zuñi Texts*, Publications of the American Ethnological Society, vol. 15 (1933).

30. Fortune, R. F., *Sorcerers of Dobu*, pp. 108, 128.

31. Radcliffe-Brown, A. R., *op. cit.*, p. 63.

32. Landes, R., *Ojibwa Sociology*, Columbia University Contributions to Anthropology, vol. 29 (1937).

33. Boas, F., *The Central Eskimo*, p. 609.

34. Malinowski, B., *Coral Gardens*, vol. 1, pp. 175 ff.

35. Henry, J., *op. cit.*

36. Seligmann, C. G. and B. Z., *The Veddas* (Cambridge, 1911), p. 86.

37. Tüting, L. T. (Ms.).

38. Junod, Henri A., *The Life of a South African Tribe* (London, 1927), vol. 1, p. 317.
39. Henry, J., *op. cit.*
40. Nelson, E. W., *The Eskimo about Bering Strait*, Annual Report of the Bureau of American Ethnology, vol. 18 (1899), p. 294.
41. Case record from Bunzel, R., *Zuñi Economics* (Ms.).
42. Malinowski, B., *Coral Gardens*, vol. 1, p. 300.
43. Driberg, J., *op. cit.*, p. 171.
44. Firth, R., *op. cit.*, p. 372.
45. Bunzel, R., *A Guatemalan Village* (Ms.).
46. Boas, F., *The Social Organization and the Secret Societies of the Kwakiutl Indians*, Report of the United States National Museum, 1895 (1897), pp. 338–340.
47. Fortune, R. F., *Sorcerers of Dobu*, p. 86.
48. Roscoe, J., *The Bakitara* (Cambridge, 1923), p. 57.
49. Roscoe, J., *The Bakitara*, pp. 176 ff., and *The Banyankole* (Cambridge, 1923), pp. 63 ff.
50. Roscoe, J., *The Bakitara*.
51. Malinowski, B., *Coral Gardens*, vol. 1, pp. 18, 162.
52. Bogoras, W., *op. cit.*
53. The analysis of Zuñi economics is based chiefly on the author's intensive study of the functioning of ten Zuñi households over a period of eighteen months, supplemented by general studies in Zuñi ethnology. The author is indebted to R. Benedict's *Patterns of Culture*, pp. 57 ff., for the description of the Zuñi configuration.
54. Based on personal information and the reports of Franz Boas, especially *The Social Organization and the Secret Societies of the Kwakiutl Indians; The Kwakiutl of Vancouver Island*, Jesup Expedition, vol. 5, Part II (1909); *Ethnology of the Kwakiutl*, Annual Report of the Bureau of American Ethnology, vol. 35, Parts I and II (1921); *Kwakiutl Ethnology*, Columbia University Contributions to Anthropology, vol. 3 (1925).
55. Based on Malinowski's various accounts, especially *Argonauts of the Western Pacific, The Sexual Life of Savages* (London, 1929), *Coral Gardens*, and a short paper, "Primitive Economics of the Trobriand Islanders," *Economic Journal*, vol. 31 (1921), pp. 1–16.
56. Malinowski, B., "Primitive Economics of the Trobriand Islanders," p. 8.
57. Fortune, R. F., *Sorcerers of Dobu*, pp. 200 ff.
58. Malinowski, B., *Argonauts of the Western Pacific*, p. 89.
59. Fortune, R. F., *Sorcerers of Dobu*.
60. Malinowski, B., *Argonauts of the Western Pacific*, p. 64.
61. *Ibid.*, pp. 510, 511.
62. Landes, R., *The Ojibwa Woman*, Columbia University Contributions to Anthropology, vol. 31 (1938).
63. Bogoras, W., *op. cit.*
64. Bunzel, R., *A Guatemalan Village* (Ms.).
65. See Sumner, Keller, and Davie, *op. cit.*, vol. 4, pp. 995, 1106.
66. Firth, R., *op. cit.*
67. Diaz del Castillo, B., *A True History of the Conquest of New Spain*, translated by A. P. Maudslay, vol. 5, p. 334.

68. Roscoe, J., *The Bakitara.*
69. Grinnell, G. B., *The Cheyenne Indians* (1923); Mishkin, B., *Kiowa Economics* (field notes, 1935).
70. Driberg, J. H., *op. cit.*
71. Mead, M., *Cooperation and Competition among Primitive Peoples* (1937).
72. Radcliffe-Brown, A. R., *The Andaman Islanders* (Cambridge, 1933).
73. Seligmann, C. G. and B. Z., *op. cit.*
74. Boas, F., *The Central Eskimo.*
75. Fortune, R. F., *Sorcerers of Dobu*, p. 71.
76. Barton, R. F., *op. cit.*, p. 425.
77. Bunzel, R., *Zuñi Texts*, p. 53.
78. Bunzel, R., field notes.
79. Malinowski, B., *Sexual Life of Savages*, pp. 104–107.
80. Benedict, R., "Marital Property Rights in a Bilateral Society," *American Anthropologist*, vol. 38 (1936).
81. Radcliffe-Brown, A. R., "Matrilineal and Patrilineal Succession," *Iowa Law Review*, vol. 20 (1935), pp. 286–303.
82. Stayt, H. A., *The Bavenda* (Oxford, 1931), p. 143.
83. Radcliffe-Brown, A. R., "Matrilineal and Patrilineal Succession."
84. Junod, H. A., *op. cit.*
85. Keysser, C., "Aus dem Leben der Kai-leute," in R. Neuhauss, *Deutsch-Neuguinea* (Berlin, 1911), p. 26; Thurnwald, R. C., "Status of Women in Buin," *Oceania*, vol. 5 (1934), pp. 142 ff.
86. Reichard, G. A., *Social Life of the Navajo Indians*, p. 140, amplified in personal conversation; Grinnell, G. B., *op. cit.*, vol. 1, p. 140; Lowie, R. H., *The Crow Indians* (1935), p. 51.
87. Driberg, J. H., *op. cit.*
88. Bunzel, R., *Quiché Village* (Ms.).
89. Bogoras, W., *op. cit.*
90. Bunzel, R., *Zuñi Economics* (Ms.).
91. Armstrong, W. E., *Rossel Island* (Cambridge, 1928).
92. Mead, M., *Social Organization of Manua.*
93. Mead, M., *Kinship in the Admiralty Islands*, Anthropological Papers, American Museum of Natural History, vol. 34, Part II (1934).
94. Firth, R., *op. cit.*
95. Boas, F., *Social Organization and Secret Societies of the Kwakiutl.*
96. Roscoe, J., *The Bakitara.*
97. Williams F. E., *Orokaiva Society* (Oxford, 1930), pp. 316–317.
98. Seligmann, C. G. and B. Z., *op. cit.*, p. 6.
99. Tüting, L. T., *Native Trade in Southeast New Guinea*, Papers of the Bernice P. Bishop Museum, vol. 11, no. 15 (1935).
100. Armstrong, W. E., *op. cit.*
101. Bunzel, R., *Zuñi Texts*, pp. 31 ff.
102. Lowie, R. H., *The Crow Indians*, p. 219.
103. Mishkin, B., *Rank and Warfare in Plains Indian Culture* (Ms.).
104. Meek, C. K., *The Northern Tribes of Nigeria* (London, 1925), vol. 1, pp. 287 ff.

GENERAL REFERENCES

Beaglehole, E., *Property* (London, 1931).

Ford, D. C., *Habitat, Economy and Society. A Geographical Introduction to Ethnology* (London, 1934).

Hobhouse, Wheeler, Guinsberg, *The Material Culture and Social Institutions of the Simpler People* (London, 1930).

Mead, M., *Competition and Cooperation among Primitive Societies* (1937).

Thurnwald, R., *Economics in Primitive Communities* (Oxford, 1932).

CHAPTER IX

SOCIAL LIFE

GLADYS A. REICHARD

There are solitary ants, bees, and wasps, but nowhere and at no time has normal man lived alone. In discussing man's social organization, it is necessary to differentiate that which is "natural" and that which is cultural. A glance at forms of social organization among animals lower than man shows that forms may be found which suggest certain analogies to our own social organization. In the animal world more or less permanent polygynous, polyandrous, or monogamous matings are found. Family organization occurs among certain insects and fishes and is familiar to all as existing among birds and the higher mammals. Of paramount interest are the complex ant colonies with a definite division of labor, where social classes, as workers, agriculturists, slaves, warriors, and even guests, each have a peculiar function in the state. A number of groups intermediate between the small family group and the large, highly organized state, such as the local group, herd, open and closed band with their proper leaders and sentinels, may be differentiated. Peculiar too are the ceremonies of bowerbirds, one of which (*Amblyornis*) chooses for the dance a place which has a background of foliage, and decorates it with berries and flowers. Most remarkable is the fact that, as soon as the decorations wilt, they are replaced with fresh ones. Certain cranes perform dances which seem to be an expression of pleasure and are not made primarily for the sake of pairing. There are even certain rudiments of property. Insects, fishes, birds, and mammals choose particular areas for their homes and defend them against all comers. In fewer cases animals (usually mammals) appropriate articles for their individual use and feel ownership.

It is still a moot question whether these developments are to be accounted for entirely by instinct, or whether in some cases there is actual proof of learning, or whether instinct and intelligence have combined to create a result which may be called tradition or culture.

Birds change their songs by changing their environment. Examples of mammals learning complicated processes are common. The amount of evidence showing that animals can learn is constantly accumulating. There are cases, too, where animals make original discoveries. Chimpanzees work out solutions for themselves. Knowledge may be cumulative. If birds build nests through sheer instinct, it can hardly be said that instinct alone accounts for the finish with which the nests of older birds are made. The nests of the younger inexperienced birds are adequate but untidy. The same is true of the little mouse (*Mus minutus*). Examples like this show that these animals have by experience acquired skill. Whether virtuosity has been gained by imitation or practice is not important here. Accumulation of knowledge, however obtained, is pertinent. At the best, however, animals have amassed culture only in the weakest sense of the term. Man, on the other hand, has culture; that is, a high development of material and spiritual life which is not the result of his biological inheritance or determined by his geographical environment.

So as not to press the analogy of animal and human organization too far, several important facts should be stressed. The elaborate states of ants, bees, and wasps are not comparable to human states in that they are primarily assemblages of females, whereas all human groups are about equally (theoretically) divided as to sex. Another differentiation is the fact that most animals, except anthropoids, in a state of nature have restricted periods of sexual activity. In this respect man more closely resembles the domesticated animals. A third fundamental difference is that man, with few exceptions, has the same social groupings the year round, whereas animal groups may change according to seasons. Birds may live in family groups during the brooding season, and solitary or in unisexual flocks the rest of the year. Where seasonal changes occur in human groupings they are social, economic, or religious rather than biological. The clan groupings on the Northwest Coast of America are less important in the winter than new units centering in the winter ceremony. In South Africa men of fighting age are segregated for years to form military units.

Various attempts have been made to classify social phenomena with the idea of establishing correlations between them and the geographical environment where they occur. Dr. Lowie, in his discussion of subsistence (Chapter VII), has pointed out the fallacy of economic determinism as an adequate cause for existing forms.

A more detailed study of animal sociology shows that classification even in this realm is not absolute. It shows too that social development does not necessarily parallel biological progress. The articulates have the most highly organized colonies of large populations. Monogamy, a form of marriage considered by many the peak of social achievement in the evolution of marriage types, is found among birds (penguins, herons, guineas, gulls, parrots, ravens, many pigeons, ducks, cormorants, and others), among rhinoceri, and among the higher apes. Monogamy among these animals is sometimes temporary, although there is good evidence that it is permanent for some ostriches, cranes, swans, and geese. Some of these animals may not live in pairs the entire year. The male lives alone for a part of it and returns to the same female in the mating season. Surely this array does not establish any kind of systematic sequence. The birds for which monogamy is most surely established are not by any means the highest biological forms, nor do they by any means belong to the same genera. Only a twisted evolutionary scheme would account for the rhinoceri between the birds and the apes.

The case of animal polygyny is no clearer. Bark-beetles, semi-domesticated pheasants (wild forms are monogamous), the Indian buffalo, deer, antelope, wild sheep and goats, elephants, and certain apes have organized groups of one male and many females which are intolerant of intrusion by other males. Within the same families (bees, ants, and wasps) solitary species are found as well as highly social varieties.[1]

In the case of man many conditions other than the biological are important. He alone of all the animals possesses a complex culture. There is no evidence that emotional and moral elements enter into the social adjustments of ants. Certain emotions, such as jealousy, from which arises combativeness, are evident among higher animals — elephants for example — but only in human relations is there the complexity due to economic, social, political, and religious factors. To these the influence of geographical environment should be added in order to gain some notion of the probable diversities which may arise. It is in the infinity of possibilities resulting from a combination of such elements, most of which are uncontrollable, that the unpredictability of social phenomena lies.

Family organization on different economic levels. The family consisting at least of parents and children is a universal social unit. All reasons which have been advanced for its necessity have their vulnerable points. Some theorists consider the father's care indispensable for the protection and upbringing of the children. Yet there are cases, in a society with matrilineal descent, where a woman with an independent income which she can keep up by her own efforts can and does raise a family without any assistance from the father or fathers of her children.

If Malinowski's summary [2] is correct, the Australian family could have existed on the labor of the woman. Even if animal food must be procured by men, some system of provision other than by family regulation is quite conceivable, as in all cases in which game is communally distributed. Protection also can be arranged by organization of men in military groups as it is in parts of South Africa. Hunting and war are male group activities, but family organization is not necessary to carry them on.

The theory that marriage is necessary for sexual gratification is as weak as the theory that children must be helped and protected by their fathers. We have too many examples of satisfaction for the sexual impulse outside of marriage to consider this a sole reason for the establishment of the family. The reasons are probably deeply rooted. Since many of the animals have a family organization of some kind and since all men have it, it is perhaps the one social phenomenon which we are justified in calling "natural."

The form of the family does not depend primarily on economic conditions, for on various economic levels we find highly diversified forms of families. The Eskimo, Bushmen, and Australians are frequently referred to as tribes in the "lowest" stage of cultural development. No two of these lower hunters and food-gatherers show similar types of social organization. The Eskimo have a small family unit but are generally considered examples of social anarchism. The Bushmen of South Africa have a definite system of child ownership. The child, in case of the father's death, must be raised by the mother until adolescence. At that time he leaves his mother and goes to live with his father's family. In this tribe there is a maternal obligation to bring a child safely to adulthood, and a privilege on the part of the father's family to enjoy the benefit of the woman's efforts.[3] Such a combination of right and privilege does not result in a custom as simple as one would expect from the primitive Bushmen.

It is difficult to find a more unfavorable geographical environment than that of the Australian. His economic condition is consequently exceedingly low, but his social organization is so complex as to be the despair of observers. Not only are there moieties subdivided into classes, phratries, and smaller units, but the principle of generation enters into all relationships and marriage restrictions and, as if that were not enough, there is a close relationship between economic life, social organization, and religion which manifests itself in the totem.

A consideration of the "highest" stage of economic development, the sedentary agricultural level, reveals no closer correlation. The horticultural Thonga of East Africa are strictly patrilineal; the Pueblo gardeners of North America are as markedly matrilineal. It seems more profitable, then, in the face of the negative results of such attempts at classification, to analyze in a detailed manner the phenomena with which we are concerned, in order thus better to determine trends in development which, though they may not be absolute as are physical laws, may nevertheless give a truer picture of any particular culture and finally may result in more accurate generalizations.

We are concerned in this analysis not only with form but also with the psychological attitude toward form as it occurs in a particular culture. A man's attitude toward his mother-in-law and hers toward him is not the same in every tribe in which mother-in-law avoidance is found. This has an important bearing on our final conclusions. Present-day attitudes cannot be expected to give us ultimate origins, the search for which is at best speculative, but they are certain to cause our speculations to run in a groove approaching truth.

This discussion will proceed from a consideration of the smallest and most fundamental unit of social structure, the family, to the larger and less obvious groups, sib, association, phratry, moiety, etc. A series of groupings, gradually increasing in size, culminates in the state, which is occasionally found among the peoples we call primitive, but the most constantly used term is *tribe*. By a tribe we usually mean an economically independent group of people speaking the same language and uniting to defend themselves against outsiders. This is a definition which requires, as do all ethnological definitions, flexibility of meaning according to the part of the world where it is found. The Todas of India are referred to as a tribe, but they are not economically independent. The Dobuans of New Guinea as a tribe comprise many hostile village groups which act as a unit only on rare and specific occasions. In general, however, this is a working definition.

A characteristic feature of the tribe is that it is a closed society. By this we mean that laws and morals apply only to its members. Strangers may not enter it on the same terms. The individuals composing it are "my" people and all others are "not mine." There are specific rules of behavior for "my people." Many of these are highly ethical. Killing a tribesman is murder; butchering a neighbor of a different tribe may be of the highest religious importance to all my people. In Oceania many illustrations of this attitude may be found. Strangers may be sacrificed in dedicating a canoe or a house. None of our own moral ideas necessarily apply in our relation to other tribes. We, as a tribe, only twenty years ago slaughtered by thousands our enemies, the Germans, and they retaliated. Both "tribes" have as one of the articles of their moral code the commandment, "Thou shalt not kill."

The sib. The universal social unit is the family. In its narrowest sense the family consists of parents and children. Our own family is of this simplest type, but a family is not defined merely by membership at a given moment. In delimiting the confines of the family, descent must be known. Without it one could not determine to what family he belonged, as each of his parents belongs to a different one. We are accustomed to a bilateral organization, but many tribes consider a child as belonging only to one side, the father's or the mother's. Our family system reckons descent through the mother *and* father but with strong emphasis on patriliny. The man is still the head of the family. Inheritance is in the paternal line, although not exclusively, and there is always regret if, through lack of male heirs, the family name dies out.

Patrilineal descent is by no means necessary. In many parts of the world a man belongs to his mother's family and cannot become a member of his father's family. This type of descent is called matrilineal. There are also tribes which have strictly patrilineal descent so rigidly defined that a man may not be a member of his mother's family. One-sided inheritance of position as a member of either the male or female line is what constitutes the unilateral family. Such family groups are designated as clans or gentes. Neither term has, however, been used with consistency although some writers denote by the term "clan" a matrilineal unilateral family and by "gens" a patrilineal one. Since there is only confusion in the use of these terms it is perhaps better to call the unilateral family a sib.

A sib has many more members than the restricted family. We shall take as example a maternal sib since it differs more radically from our system than the paternal. The individuals belonging to a sib are a woman, her children, her daughter's children, her daughter's daughter's children, and so on *ad infinitum*. A marked difference between such a unit and ours is that a man gets his sib name, if the sib has a name, from his mother. Since his children also take theirs from their mother, it usually differs from their father's because often members of the same sib are not allowed to intermarry.

It is not at all unusual to find three, four, or even five generations of a family living in the same house, or at least in the same general locality. The reason is that primitives often marry young. For example, a girl, A, married at sixteen has a child, B, at seventeen. This child may in turn marry and have a child when her mother is only thirty-two, still bearing children. At the age, of forty-eight, not yet past the age of child-bearing herself, A may be a great-grandmother. A simple illustration like this not only gives a conception of the increasing number of family members in generations — vertically, we may say — but it also shows how a child of B may have as his contemporaries and playmates in his own family his uncles and aunts, or great-uncles and great-aunts, thus extending the family horizontally.

Grouping by residence gives a certain view of sib membership, although not a complete one. The individuals who live together or in close proximity will differ according to the type of residence customary with the tribe. Sometimes newlyweds establish an independent home; sometimes the woman goes to live at the man's home, in which case residence is said to be patrilocal. In other cases the man comes to live with the bride's people, and residence is termed matrilocal.

If we consider sib membership within a residence group in which residence is matrilocal, we may find conditions approximately like the following. A woman, X, of the sib Lone Tree, lives at a certain place. She has married a man of Folded Arms sib who lives with her. They have children, all Lone Trees. The girls, when grown, marry men of still other sibs and their husbands live with them. The members of one such household may therefore represent a number of sibs. On the other hand, the sons of X have married women who also belong to other sibs and have gone to live with the families of their wives. All the women of this particular house consequently are Lone Trees, as are also the children, but all the men have other sib names. Thus grandparents, parents, children, and perhaps uncles, aunts, and cousins may all be living in one house and acting as a family unit; yet not all are members of the same sib. Within our own experience the intimacy between relatives more remote than parents and children is more variable because our family group is more restricted.

There may be a further extension of this already large family. Among the group of playfellows there may be adopted children — adopted because the mother has died, or because the adopting family lacks an heir. In many parts of the world, it is considered unlucky not to have children. This is true, for instance, in many parts of Melanesia, on the Northwest Coast of America, and in other places where stress is laid on rank or property and where the lack of an heir is looked upon as the direst tragedy; or in Africa where children are an economic asset. Children adopted under such circumstances are treated as own children, and it may even be considered an insult to refer to the fact that a particular child was not born into the sib whose name it bears.

Although the extension of the family may be illustrated along the lines of the residence group, such a unit is not exactly or completely a sib. Only some of the members of a sib live in such a group; others are to be found elsewhere, for the sib may be large and, in a sense, an abstract conception. Except under circumstances depending on other factors, such as moiety organization, endogamy, and the like, which must be considered in their turn, there may be other families who use the same sib name. The members of such a group may feel such a close relationship that they use the same kinship terms in addressing one another as we do members of the same family: sister, brother, uncle, grandfather, and the like, whether actual blood relationship is traceable or not.

The terms "matriarchate" and "patriarchate" are sometimes used for maternal and paternal sibs. They are misleading because, throughout all our history, the term "patriarchate" has a special significance. It has been used not only for tribes having patrilineal descent but for that group of people over which some old and powerful leader or sib head, the patriarch, has final control, even to the power of life and death. The Hebrew patriarchs come instantly to mind. Patriarchate is not only a social order; it is also a system of government. If then, we use the term "matriarchate," we think by analogy of a society ruled over by a woman, a matriarch, who has equal power over the individuals of the group she heads. I know of no case where this condition prevails. Cases where women are "the power behind the throne" are not rare, but it is not easy to find tribes where they are absolute rulers, even though matriliny is found extensively in all the major land divisions. I shall be content, then, with the more accurate term "maternal sib."

In some cases the sib may be composed of lineages — that is, unilateral families believing they are descendants of a common ancestor. This is the case among some Californian tribes[4] and among the Hopi,[5] for example. More commonly, however, especially in large tribes, the conditions are as if all Smiths in the United States should consider themselves relatives of all other Smiths whether they have common ancestry or not. Concomitant with this attitude is usually the belief that it would not be "good" for a Smith to marry a Smith. It would be "better" for him to marry a Jones or a MacCarthy. When marriage within a group is not approved, the group is said to be exogamous. Exogamous sibs are found in all the important world quarters. Some sibs are endogamous; that is, they require marriage within the group. The rightness of sib endogamy was expressed by the scorn of the Bella Bella of the Northwest Coast of America who said, "Who ever heard of a Raven marrying an Eagle?" in contrasting their own custom with that of their exogamous northern neighbors, the Tsimshian.

The Navajo like to create friendliness between sibs by marrying many members of one sib to individuals of another. This seems to come about quite naturally. Some time after a Lone Tree man has married a Folded Arms girl, her brother may look for a wife. If her husband's sister is available the problem is nicely settled, and the sibs become doubly friendly. If the husband has no sister, his mother's sister may have a daughter whom she is willing to let the Folded Arms man have as a wife, and the affiliation between the two sibs is strengthened.

The friendliness which is fostered by the Navajo is further emphasized by the regard in which all members of the father's sib are held. A Navajo, meeting an entire stranger for the first time, may give up a choice possession upon learning that he is a member of his father's sib. Although the Navajo are always hospitable, hospitality is exaggerated in the case of individuals having relationship reckoned through the father.[6]

Instead of friendship there may be conflict between sibs. In parts of Melanesia, where the pattern is one of suspicion and distrust, there may be antagonism between the wife's sib and the husband's.[7] This may be the case even if the wife and husband live together in perfect accord.

Sibs may own property of all kinds. On the Northwest Coast of America sibs own rights to use certain crests and myths which explain their relationship to supernatural beings.[8] Zuñi households which are subdivisions of the sibs own the house which the members call home.[9] Privilege to use land among the Hidatsa was owned by the sib, as was the produce.[10]

A man may take part in a ritual because of his membership in a sib. All Hopi ceremonies are held in trusteeship within a sib.[11] The Todas of India have, to an exaggerated degree, combined religious functions with the sib. Some of the buffalo herds are sacred; others are common or profane. Each of the Toda sibs has specific duties and privileges in connection with the elaborate rites of the buffalo dairy, and each is entitled to respect according to the degree of sacredness of these duties.[12]

In parts of Australia the sib has economic as well as religious functions. It is the duty of the sib to increase by the performance of magic that part of the food supply over which it has control, for the benefit of the rest of the community. The Kangaroos are not allowed to eat kangaroo, but they perform elaborate ceremonies to provide kangaroos for the Witchetty Grubs and the Emus. The Witchetty Grubs and Emus reciprocate by magically increasing the witchetty grub and emu supply for the other sibs.[13]

One of the most important activities of the Plains region of North America was the buffalo hunt. The pursuit of buffalo entailed the moving of the tribal population, for the buffalo grounds were far from the more permanent villages. In a region where war and horse-stealing were esteemed there was a strong need for protection. Sibs in some tribes had the honor and the duty of policing. The tribe set up tipis in the form of a camp circle with the entrance usually (theoretically at least) toward the east. The tipis at either side of the opening to the camp circle belonged to the police sibs. Their prime duty was to watch the camp and, if danger threatened, to call a council of wise men to plan a defense or an attack. These sibs not only had temporal power but were of special importance because of supernatural power which they possessed from their names and tradition.[14]

The functions controlled by the sib vary greatly the world over. They may be social, religious, economic, or political.

Up to this time we have been concerned with the sib as a group. We shall now illustrate sib relationships from the viewpoint of a few of the members belonging to it. The first to be considered are the father and the mother's brother. In a maternal sib the father does not leave his wealth to his own children, but is rather the guardian of his sister's children, who may expect to inherit from him. He may have the final say as to whom his sister's children shall marry. Since a payment is commonly made to the bride's family, the amount and settlement are made by the bride's maternal uncle.

The importance of the mother's brother in the economic and social life of the maternal sib should not lead us to think that children living in this sort of society do not love their fathers, or that the fathers do not love them. There is no necessary correlation between father-love and inheritance. Fathers in these societies may fondle and teach their children; indeed, the men of the Trobriand Islands of Melanesia take pride in attending to the physical care of their very young children.[15]

That type of organization which exaggerates the importance of the maternal uncle in family affairs is called the avunculate. Where it is found, children may be particularly fortunate in that they have two fathers: their actual father, who plays with them, teaches them his techniques and lore, takes them hunting or visiting and is, in general, a fine adult companion; and the uncle who, because of his social and economic obligations to his sister's children, sees to it that they learn the lessons of the tribe and grow up to be responsible men and women. There is a degree of overlapping of social contacts and teachings of father and maternal uncle, especially if the latter lives near his sister's children.

The social machinery does not always run smoothly. In the Trobriand Islands there is sometimes a conflict between father-love and avuncular duties. A man may become so fond of his son that he wishes to give him his most cherished possessions, which, according to tribal custom, he should give to his sister's son. Among these people magic is the most important of a man's possessions. There is a belief that just a certain amount of each kind of magic exists. Consequently it must be used as a whole; it cannot be divided. Therefore, if a man knows magic, he cannot teach some to his sister's son, to fulfil legal requirements, and some to his own son, to satisfy his parental emotions. If he chooses his son for his favors, his sister's son may disgrace him by publicly accusing him of running counter to custom.[16]

The avunculate is by no means restricted to matrilineally organized tribes. Among the Thonga of Southeast Africa there is pronounced patriliny. Wives go to live in the husband's village, and children are thought of as the property of the father's village. However, the mother's village is a secondary haven for a man. He may be sent there as a young child and be practically raised by his mother's people. Later he may stay for long visits, but it would never be "good" for him to settle there upon marrying. For among the Thonga, as in many parts of Africa, all individuals are looked upon as village acquisitions, and a man's male relatives would ridicule or even censure him for choosing to "increase" his mother's village. Together with the strongest kind of patriliny and patrilocal residence there is, nevertheless, a strongly developed avunculate. The maternal uncle of a Thonga child should prepare the first soft skin in which it is wrapped. He claims a right to a part of the betrothal payment made for his sister's daughter. As the head of the child's maternal family, he provides also certain bridal equipment; he may be required to make sacrifices for his sister's child. He has special duties at the time of mourning, and he has the right to "renew his village." That means that if he has no children he may, instead of negotiating a marriage for his sister, refuse the betrothal gift. He will then take the responsibility for her burial (ordinarily the duty of a husband) by a promise, and the sister will have lovers. Any children which are the fruit of her relationships will belong to his village because he has refused the bride price. Thus is the continuance of the line made secure.[17]

If the uncle under the avunculate has duties, correspondingly the nephew has privileges. In many of the South Sea islands there are no restrictions whatever in the treatment by a nephew of his maternal uncle's possessions. Such freedom of behavior may amount to destruction of property or abuse of privilege without calling down upon the abuser any punishment whatsoever. Junod cites the example from Africa of an uncle's anger at finding food upon which he had depended all eaten. However, just as soon as someone explained that his sister's son had eaten it he smiled and made no more to-do.[18] This is an example of what has been called the joking relationship, of which we shall have more to say later. It obtains

between maternal uncle and nephew in many parts of the world
but is not by any means restricted to this relationship.

In the larger family groups the relationship of a child to his
mother's sister may be as close as that to his mother. One reason
for this may be matrilocal residence, and another may be the sororate. This term defines the custom of a man marrying more than
one sister of a family. If he has more than one wife at a time, it
often happens that the wives are sisters. The sororate may also
prevail in monogamous tribes. In such case a widower marries his
deceased wife's sister and she may bring up her sister's children as
if they were her own.

An expression of this relation is found in many kinship systems
in which "my mother" and all her sisters are addressed by the
same kin term, so that any one of them is really "a member of the
group of sisters to which my mother belongs" (see page 454).

If, from earliest childhood, I live in close contact with four or five
women and address them by the same term and they treat me with
equal affection and care, it is unlikely that I shall regard one quite
differently from the others. If I do, it is not necessary that my
favorite be my actual blood mother. The idea of absolute mother-
love is an exaggeration of our own culture. There are many cases
where a mother's sister, a foster mother, or even a neighbor is regarded more fondly by a child than his real mother. Primitive society
gives no proof of the stepmother idea as a natural human characteristic. On the contrary, it shows by attitudes of different relatives
toward children and toward adoption that ours and other similar
attitudes are based on particular prejudices not founded on biological instincts that unite parents and children.

In our own society the relationship between cousins depends
almost entirely upon *rapport* between families and upon where they
live. Among primitives residence is of even greater importance when
it is matrilocal or patrilocal — that is, markedly one-sided, as opposed to the setting up of an independent home by a newly married
couple. If residence is matrilocal, mothers' sisters' children are constantly thrown together, and under ordinary circumstances mothers'
brothers' children and the children of fathers' sisters and brothers
do not see one another so frequently. If residence is patrilocal, the
children of brothers have more intimate contact than the others.

In dealing with the relationships and attitudes of primitive
peoples it is necessary to distinguish two kinds of cousins. Since

English has no general word to indicate sisters and brothers, we shall use the term "siblings." The children of my mother's sisters, and those of my father's brothers, are my parallel cousins, so-called because the parents through whom we are related are siblings of the same sex. If we were related through parent siblings of opposite sex we should be cross cousins. In other words, my parallel cousins are children of my mother's sisters and of my father's brothers; my cross cousins are the children of my mother's brothers and of my father's sisters.

Parallel cousins are often treated as brothers and sisters. They address one another as such, and marriage rules apply to them exactly as if they were blood siblings. Cross cousins are considered a different kind of relative. Whereas the behavior of parallel cousins of opposite sex toward one another may savor of avoidance, especially as they grow up, it is not unusual to find a joking relationship between cross cousins. This behavior will be further discussed under the titles of avoidance and joking (see page 446).

We may recall that the extended family includes individuals of two, three, or even four generations. Grandparents are often useful and productive members of the primitive family. Perhaps this is true because they are nearer the age of their descendants than grandparents in our own society. Old people may, however, be respected merely because old age is honorable. Because he is old a man has wisdom and judgment which can come only through long experience; hence his counsels should be regarded. The same argument may apply to old women. Treatment of the aged is by no means uniform in different parts of the world, and there are areas where old age is despised and becomes a burden.

There are tribes, too, in which neither extreme is the case, but grandmothers have their duties just as do the younger individuals. Mohave grandmothers * conduct "nursery schools" while their daughters pursue their "careers." One sees an old woman tending a row of babies, her charges, while their mothers are at work in the fields or away from home. One Mohave woman, upon being asked why she had no children, replied, as if the answer were self-evident, "But how could I? The child has no grandmother to bring it up!"

Primitive family organization is not by any means always unilateral. Since we are more familiar with the bilateral family, it will be sufficient to emphasize by a few examples the fact that even bi-

* Personal information from Dr. Ruth F. Benedict.

lateral inheritance need not be like ours. Among the Ashanti of the west coast of Africa there is a peculiar and interesting type of descent.[19] It can be explained only by dividing heritable property into material and spiritual. A man inherits material things, as sib name, blood (blood particularly is important), property, and succession from his mother. From his father he inherits spiritual wealth, *ntoro*, which includes soul, health, power, and success.

There are few societies in which inheritance is not important (see below). Wealth is passed down through one line or through both, and the privileges which it may provide differ greatly. Where a sense of high nobility is developed, good birth gives a man a running start in life which nothing else can equal. The inheritance a man or woman can pass on to their children depends upon the rules of the society in which they live. Certain tribes of the Northwest Coast of America, for example, have sib exogamy. They reason, almost certainly *ex posteriori*, that a man can give his children a better heritage if he marries a woman of another unilateral family who is as wealthy or nearly as wealthy as he. Another tribe in the same region has sib endogamy, and reasons that marriage within the sib will concentrate wealth for its members and children. So exaggerated has the latter reasoning become in special cases that members of very noble families can find no other family of sufficiently high nobility, and occasionally men are urged to marry their half-sisters. The ancient Peruvians and Egyptians sometimes sanctioned marriages between full siblings to retain inherited nobility in the line.

Among the Loango of the Congo region nobility is developed, but it is not hereditary. There is alternation of class with matrilineal descent. A king must take a commoner for a wife, and their children are commoners. If the power ever comes back into the king's family it is a matter of accident. On the other hand a princess takes a commoner for a husband, and their children will be nobles. The explanation given for this state of affairs is that all princesses are considered sisters of the king, and for that reason could not marry him.[20] This case illustrates nicely the extension of exogamic rules to include all members of the noble sibs, whether actual blood relatives or not, and demonstrates an attitude which is the exact opposite of that held by the ancient Egyptians and Peruvians.

The custom of destroying a man's property at his death is widespread. Where it exists there is no need for inheritance rules applied to material possessions. At the same time, however, rights to fishing grounds, fields — in short, the use of nature's gifts — may be passed down according to formal requirements.

During the course of this discussion we have seen that many types of family organizations are possible, from the highly extended unilateral family to the small, loose, simple family group like that of the Eskimo or our own, and that they have no necessary connection with cultural level. It cannot be shown that one form is necessarily derived from one of the others. The data do not justify the assumption so often made that the family developed from early promiscuity to matriliny until finally the pinnacle, patriliny, *our* type of organization, was reached.

An examination of the facts shows that there are no tribes, however rude economically, without family life. There is no positive evidence to show that man ever existed without the family. The argument freely advanced, that the matrilineal family was the first orderly arrangement, is based on the assumption that everyone knows who his mother is, but may never be certain of his father. An answer to this is the example of certain Australian tribes who, without any interest in the function of the father in procreation, nevertheless have a strongly developed family with paternal descent.[21] Even among them the father is considered necessary, as it is put, "to open the woman." The Eskimo [22] believe that the child crawls up the bootlace and into the womb of a woman, but the semen is necessary to "feed the child."

The proof for unilinear evolution from promiscuity to patriliny through definite stages would require evidence showing that, wherever change in historical times is found, the development was in this direction. Such a development would be "natural." Cases where there has been a change from matriliny to patriliny are few. They are, however, illuminating where they occur, since reasons for the change may be detected.

The Trobriand Islanders show several weak signs of transition from matriliny to patriliny. Inheritance of land, privilege, and material goods is in the mother line, and some of these may be enjoyed by a man during the lifetime of his mother's brother, provided he pays for them. Nevertheless a man occasionally bestows such right of use and enjoyment upon his own son gratis. Upon the death of the father the son must return the property to his maternal cross cousins, so that the change from favoritism of the female line to that of the male line is so far only an emotional one obtaining in certain families, and not one which enjoys tribal sanction.[23] It is not difficult to imagine that this tendency might be emphasized and tolerated so frequently as to change a social structure. If that should happen certain rationalizations of incompatibility between the two basic ideas would have to be made, some of which might seem to fall into ready-made categories of an evolutionary scheme. The natives themselves explain the present-day tendency as an outgrowth of father-love, and this in face of the fact that they deny the part played by the father in procreation.

Malinowski's presentation of this material suggests that the situation may be viewed as an outgrowth of a pose protesting ignorance of the father's function in procreation. If it is that, it is not difficult to understand the exaggerations and affirmations of the natives about fatherhood, or the social instead of the biological importance of the father in the tribe. Formal protestations of the same kind are common indeed in native explanations of social usage.

The other example of a possible change being made between matriliny and patriliny, although it has taken place in the direction opposite that posited by the evolutionists, is more convincing because it is further advanced than the Trobriand condition and the details of its cause are more positive. The Kwakiutl Indians of the Northwest Coast of America have, within historical times, taken over certain aspects of matriliny which show themselves to be adjustments to a patrilineal system.[24] The Kwakiutl rightly fit into the pattern of the Northwest Coast culture south of their area and in so doing have bilateral descent with favor on the paternal side. They have, however, been thrown into intimate contact with their neighbors to the north, who are markedly matrilineal. Accordingly, among the Kwakiutl a nice adjustment has been made whereby a man acquires certain types of rank and wealth from his wife's father. They are given to him in trust and he transmits them in his turn to his daughter's husband. In the north a man inherits from his mother's side directly. Altogether the Kwakiutl case shows a meeting of two principles due to geographical contiguity and an adjustment to make both fit in.

A view of the prevailing types of family structure, including many more examples than we are able to cite here, shows that there is no 'natural" basis for unilinear development; that when it prevails, some kind of conflict, economic, sociological, or psychological, also exists, making it necessary for the group to rationalize their behavior or modify the structure in some way or other. After all, the family is a two-sided group which must adjust itself somehow to the demands of mother's and father's relatives.

The Trobrianders give the father social compensation for the assumed deprivation of biological function, although they would certainly never put it this way, and are not conscious of the fact. The Kwakiutl have made formal adjustments between the mother's and father's lines based, as is to be expected here, on the transference of wealth from one generation to another; and with all the social machinery, there are constant quarrels about individual cases. The Navajo, who have retained their unilateral view of inheritance, have made the compromise of friendliness with the father's relatives so that they almost bend over backward in compensating the paternal line socially for what it may seem to lose economically; and because of this compromise, as well as because of the tolerance of individualism in this tribe, the type of social conflict here discussed is absent.

Totemism. A unilateral kin group often has the name of some animal, plant, or natural phenomenon. Raven, Wolf, Corn, Sunflower, Turquoise, Water, Sun, Cloud, are a few examples. Associated with the name is often the feeling on the part of the sib members that there is some special relationship between them and the animal whose name they bear. This relationship is sometimes a belief in direct descent from the totem animal. Tribes of the Solomon Islands and others of Australia hold such beliefs. In other cases, as on the Northwest Coast of America, there is a myth or tradition accounting for a supernatural experience which a remote ancestor had with an animal or some natural phenomenon. In the northern part of this region there is no belief in actual descent, and it may even be that the name and the supernatural with whom the ancestor was concerned are not the same. The Raven sib of the Haida, for example, has the killer whale as a crest animal, and among the Eagles of the same tribe the beaver is as important as the eagle.[25]

Closely connected with belief in totemic experience is the possession of a crest or coat-of-arms. Crests may be of many kinds. On the Northwest Coast they are patterns which some members of particular sibs are allowed to use. These designs of a symbolic and artistic nature may be painted or carved on totem poles, houses, posts and doors, or ceremonial paraphernalia, or they may be tattooed on the body.[26] No one would think of using a crest which does not belong to him. Usually he inherits it, but there are other ways of obtaining the privilege of use, as by marriage or by gift. The possession of a coat-of-arms by a kinship group is not confined to America. In Melanesia a very elaborate type of openwork carving has developed. Certain carvings are erected in honor of the dead. Many of the designs are artistic or religious, but all the memorial carvings must include the totem animal, which is often a bird.[27]

The Omaha of the Plains area had a most unusual type of crest. It consisted of the right to cut the hair of a child in a peculiar fashion. One sib, for instance, cut off all the hair except a ridge which stood up from the forehead to the nape of the neck. This was said to symbolize a buffalo's back as it stood up against the sky. Another sib shaved the head but left four square tufts, one at the forehead, one at the nape, and one at each side above the ears. This cut had reference to the eagle with which the sib felt itself connected. These peculiar crests were unusual in that they were exhibited only by the young children; adults wore the hair long and in the more usual hairdressings found among Indians.[28]

The name, crest, and supernatural relationship of men to the non-human world may characterize a kin group. Closely connected with all these elements may be also the presence of a taboo. Most frequently it forbids members of the group to kill or eat the animal whose name they bear. Members of a certain Australian Emu totem, although performing ceremonies for the purpose of increasing the emu supply, must never eat it, but they may hand it to individuals of other totems and watch them eat it.[29]

Frequently taboos concern activities other than eating. In the Santa Cruz group there is a Grass sib which may not walk on grass, and a Bowl sib which may not eat out of a bowl.[30] A taboo against touching certain objects characterizes the Omaha sibs, although there are also restrictions against killing and eating. One sib is not allowed to touch the horn of a buffalo, another is prohibited from touching the unborn young of an animal, and to a third it is forbidden to touch charcoal or verdigris. Still another would avoid contact with creeping insects, bugs, worms, and similar creatures.[31]

Exogamy may be connected with a totemic sib as well as with any other kind, but there is no special necessity for it to be so. The Bella Coola sibs were endogamous although they have many totemic features.

Almost any of the features and functions of the unilateral kin group may characterize the totem. When they are the same, sib and totem are identical, as on the Northwest Coast of America, but the sib need not have totemistic features, even though it be exogamous. On the other hand, groups whose members do not consider themselves kin may show many of the manifestations which have been assigned to totemism.

Certain Australian totems, for example, consist of individuals who reckon their totem from the place where their mothers believe them to have been conceived. Totem spirits, which may also be called ancestor spirits, are believed to inhabit particular localities. When a woman passes one of these the spirit may impregnate her, and her child will belong to the totem named for that spirit. Such a social group is consequently composed of fortuitously selected individuals. It may be considered as a horizontal rather than a vertical section as is the sib. Except for its composition it has the characteristics of the sib, such as an animal name and belief in descent from the animal. Sometimes it has also its functions — such as the obligation to perform a ritual to increase the supply of the name-animal, with an attendant taboo against eating it. In this particular case exogamy exists not as a totem manifestation, but rather as a factor belonging to a larger group.

Another type of non-kinship horizontal grouping is the society association, or lodge. Groups of this sort are determined in a variety of ways. There are societies composed of men (or women) of approximately the same age. Payment of a large amount of valued goods may be the membership requirement. Where this is the case as in Melanesia, the higher degrees are enjoyed by older men, as they are more likely to be wealthy, even as in our own society.

In other regions, such as the North American Plains and South Africa, associations are composed of men of military prowess and they may or may not have military duties.

Whatever the method of selection, most of the factors mentioned for the totem may be present. Associations almost always have names; frequently they are animal names. They likewise may consider their relationship to animals close. The Leopard societies of West Africa and the medicine societies of the Pawnee have animal names. Their members believe also that they are in close *rapport* with these animals. Practically all associations have some symbol of membership which may be called a crest, be it a headdress, possession of a mask, or a scar received at initiation. Taboos are also common. They may be killing or eating taboos and may or may not involve the animal believed to be related.

The African secret societies, as well as the Melanesian and Pawnee, to mention only a few, all have the performance of ritual as one of their chief functions; still the purpose of that ritual differs in every case.

Although in primitive society women's societies are not entirely lacking, they are nevertheless fewer than the men's, as well as much less powerful. They are often imitations of men's associations, for in each community where they occur their functions are of the same pattern, the essential difference between societies and totem groups being that the former are divided along sex lines, thus ruling out any question of exogamy. Nevertheless, sexual privileges may enter into association membership as is the case among the Crow Indians.

In this tribe the Foxes and Lumpwoods are rival military societies. There is a certain time every spring during which a member of either society may kidnap the wife of one of his rivals provided she was once been his mistress. There are social features of this kidnapping which may be regarded as rules of a game, one being that a man thus deprived of his wife must exhibit the greatest indifference. If he takes her back he not only disgraces himself but he may cause the entire society to become prey to its rival.[32] This peculiar situation shows that, even though association groupings along sex lines rule out the possibility of exogamy, they are not necessarily barred from making marital or sexual stipulations.

The so-called totemic characteristics do not attach themselves to associations and kinship groups alone, but even to individuals. They often have names similar to totem names. Many individuals have crests, symbols which they regard as peculiarly theirs and effective in one way or another. Not infrequently they believe in descent from, or relationship to, an animal. The pursuit of the vision or the attainment of the guardian spirit in North America is a religious custom which might give rise to any of these peculiarities.[33] Individuals, likewise, often have taboos and set up rituals for themselves which have a purely personal significance.

These brief facts, chosen from a large body of similar ones, show that the manifestations which are often called totemic do not belong to a kinship group any more than to a group constructed on other lines, or to an individual.

It is quite conceivable that a personal idiosyncrasy, like the avoidance of a certain kind of food, may in a given family become habitual and acquire some kind of additional significance. A strong individual may well communicate his peculiarities and beliefs regarding them to his fellows, his kin, or associates in a closely knit association of some other type.

I have used this simple example to show how any one of the phenomena called totemic may attach itself to any kind of group either in combination with all the other characteristics here mentioned, in combination with some of them, or quite independently.

Too much has been written of totemism in its different aspects, and the catchwords "totem," "totemic," "totemism," have been used too often to permit leaving it entirely out of the discussion. Frazer,[34] Durkheim,[35] Lowie,[36] Goldenweiser,[37] and Boas[38] have discussed the matter exhaustively from a religious and social point of view.

In my opinion the discussion must be taken finally to conclude that, since the manifestations are so varied in different parts of the world, since their resemblances are only apparent, and since they are phenomena which may occur in many settings not related to real or supposed consanguinity, they can by no means be fitted into a single category.

Marriage. Every individual secures a definite status by reason of his birth. He is a slave or a noble according to the standing of his mother or father in the community; a Lone Tree or Bitter Water according to the name of his mother or father. After birth, perhaps the most determining event of his life is marriage.

In primitive society the individual concerned has not much influence over his or her marriage. It is rare to find a tribe where romantic love is appreciated, and still rarer to find one where absolute freedom of choice is allowed. Even where love is valued and theoretic freedom of choice prevails, that freedom is not often actual. In our own society, where we boast of such freedom, the percentage of cases where a man or, even more so, a girl marries the mate he or she *really* wants is low. Family desires, position, success, social stratification, relative wealth, and other considerations weigh more heavily than free choice.

In primitive societies it is common to find an attitude toward love or passion that is very different from, and often unrelated to, the marriage state. Motives other than that of sexual gratification lie behind marriage, and of these motives the most common is economic

Two families unite by the intermarriage of one or more sons and daughters. The affiliation may be marked by payment or a ceremony, but such ceremony does not by any means complete the manifold obligations assumed by both sides.

Exogamy and endogamy. Before we can discuss the various points related to this matter it is necessary to have a clear understanding of the terms "exogamy" and "endogamy." These two terms may be defined most simply as meaning "marrying out" and "marrying in," respectively. We have family exogamy, for there is no general approval of marriage between close relatives; in other words, individuals must marry "out of the family." There is a strong feeling of preferential endogamy among orthodox Jews and Catholics; in these cases it is felt that one should marry "in the religion." Certain families are opposed to their children marrying any but Americans; this is "national endogamy." The terms may be applied to groups of various kinds: kin groups, religious groups, political groups. There is as much variety among primitive peoples, but the convention of marrying in or out is almost always present.

It is quite possible, in fact common, to have exogamy and endogamy in the same tribe. Many peoples discourage marriage with outside tribes and are therefore tribally endogamic. At the same time, however, they may have class, phratry, or sib exogamy. The Todas of India illustrate this condition. The tribe is divided socially into two parts. When there is a twofold division of a tribe we refer to each division as a "moiety." The number of individuals belonging to each is not necessarily equal. One of the Toda moieties considers itself superior to the other and has definite and important religious functions. The moieties are endogamic; therefore, each member must marry *within* his own moiety; but the moieties are composed of a number of paternal sibs, and these sibs are strictly exogamic. If I, for instance, am a member of moiety 1 and of sib A, I must marry a member of moiety 1 who is not of sib A. I could choose an individual whom we may call 1B, 1C, 1D, or 1E, according to his sib.

Forms of marriage. The particular form of marriage permitted or demanded is not always the same. There are only a few possible forms, and this undoubtedly accounts for similarities in many parts of the world. Our discussion does not concern itself with unrestricted intercourse between the sexes before marriage, which is permitted among some tribes, or with breaches of sanctioned forms of marriage, which occur everywhere. There is a great difference between

sanctioned form and actual practice. Our own society with a pre
tense at absolute monogamy but with its attendant promiscuity i
a good example.

In one form of marriage a group of men may marry a group o
women, sexual relations being restricted to the members of the two
groups. This form is called group marriage. When a man or woman
has more than one mate, the marriage is said to be polygamous
Polygamy exists in one of two forms: when a woman has more than
one husband it is called polyandry; when a man has more than one
wife, polygyny. The final possibility is that one man has only one wife
at a time, the form of marriage familiar to us and called monogamy

Of all these types of marriage the rarest is group marriage. The
best example exists side by side with polyandry and polygyny and
is, in fact, an extension of these forms. The Todas of India formerly
practiced polyandry to a great extent. When a woman married a
man it was understood that she should be the wife of all his brothers
Any children born to the woman considered as their father the man
who performed the so-called "bow" ceremony with the woman
This man was ordinarily the eldest brother. It was customary for
the second eldest brother to perform the ceremony after two or
three children had been acknowledged by the eldest, but the man
was the "father" of all the children born to a woman until she went
through the ceremony with another man. So highly formal has the
system finally become that a male born years after a ceremonial
father has died considers him, nevertheless, his father if his mother
failed to change his social father by means of the ceremony. This
is another example where form has overcome all interest in actual
fatherhood, the fixing of fatherhood for *social* purposes being the
significant feature.

A change in the Toda form of marriage has occurred within
historical times for a sociological reason. In former times female in
fanticide was practiced. Since the British occupation of Toda ter
ritory, it has decreased to a great extent. The result has been an
increase in the number of women in proportion to men and the de
velopment of a kind of group marriage. A group of brothers now
marries a group of sisters. When a man takes a wife she is considered
the wife of his brothers also, and the group of brothers have marital
rights to her sisters as well. Rivers prefers to call the system one
of combined polyandry and polygyny.[39]

There is some indication of group marriage in Australia, but the

evidence is so highly problematical that we can merely refer to the
possibility of its existence there.

Polyandry is a more definite form of marriage and is found spo-
adically on the several continents, in Africa, Madagascar, in southern
ndia — Toda polyandry is probably to be explained as a part of this
rea — in Tibet, among the Eskimo of North America, and among
he Pawnee and some other tribes of the Plains of North America.
Altogether, however, polyandry is not a common form of marriage.

Polygyny, the marriage of a man to more than one woman, is
common in many parts of the world. It is not restricted to any
particular economic stage. There is every reason to believe that the
Navajo and Apache of the Southwest were as polygynous when they
were food-gatherers as they are at the present time when the Navajo,
at least, are primarily pastoral. The Eskimo hunters are polygynous,
as are pastoral tribes in Asia and agricultural tribes in Asia, Africa,
and America.

It is difficult for us, with our ideals of fidelity and our belief in
jealousy as an "innate" or "natural" trait, to realize how groups
of women can live peaceably with one man, or groups of men with
one woman. The example of the Todas shows that it is not only possible but quite satisfactory if the mental twist is different from that
o which we are accustomed.

The Navajo have an extended notion of fidelity. In earlier times,
woman expected her husband to desire another woman, especially
* she herself were sexually inactive because of illness, pregnancy,
r old age. Instead of behaving jealously she sought for him a younger
woman — if possible, from her own sib; if not, from an affiliated or
friendly sib. Fidelity was not absolutely lacking. There were cases
here a man remained faithful to one wife for many years, some-
imes for life, but the idea of faithfulness could be extended to in-
lude two or three wives.

The reasons for the development of the different types of family
re obscure. Polygamy, although common, seems to be due to dif-
erent causes. The theory that it is due to differences in sex ratio is
ifficult, if not impossible, to substantiate. We have no exact statistics
n the ratio of the sexes. The Todas, who practice polyandry, have
roduced a lack of women through female infanticide. It is gratuitous
) claim that this custom was introduced to support polyandry or
hat polyandry is its consequence.

The prevalence of polygyny among the Eskimo is neatly explained by the theorists who proclaim the dangers of Eskimo life as the cause for high male mortality. It is easy then to argue that since more women survived, a man must care for more than one. If this is accepted, polyandry of the Eskimo should be explained on the same grounds. Since life is so rigorous a woman must have more than one husband to care for her and her children. One argument cancels the other. Infanticide, too, has been attributed to economic causes, and it is supposed that the Todas may have killed female babies because of food shortage. Rivers, however, can see no evidence for this.[40] I venture to predict that if statistics were available for different tribes the ratios of males and females of marriageable age would differ greatly, and that the excess percentage of one sex or the other would not for a large number of tribes show close correlation with the forms of marriage.

In primitive tribes most individuals are married. If this is the case and there is a surplus of males or females, other balancing factors must be at work. Among the Navajo, for example, where extreme polygyny is the rule, it is likely that there are more marriageable females than males. But even if the sex ratio is not equal, other factors may even up the marriages. The Navajo themselves suggest that balance is maintained through instability of the marriages. Suppose, for example, there are three men and three women. If one man has three wives, then two must be without wives; but if one woman leaves her husband after a time, another man gets her for a while. It is extremely difficult, if not impossible, to get data on the length of time each individual lives with his spouses, especially since marriages may be very unstable.

Another explanation of universal marriage with a disproportionate sex ratio is the relative number of years the men are sexually active as compared with the women. The women are adolescent, let us say, at fifteen and the menopause occurs at fifty or later where many children are the rule. Thirty-five or forty years of sexual activity among the women compare with fifty among the men, some of whom beget children at sixty-five or over. This is merely a suggestion that in a statistical survey the numbers of individuals sexually active should be compared. It has particular significance in view of the fact that many primitives do not consider it necessary that mates should be nearly of the same age. It is not at all unusual to see a man of seventy-five with a wife of twenty, or a woman of fifty with a husband of twenty-five.

The evidence is too conflicting to give an absolute reason for the existence of polyandry in one tribe and monogamy in another. As is the case with all social phenomena, it is quite likely that one cause, which can be determined, operated in one case; another, which cannot be determined, in another; and that in still another various causes combined to yield the results we find today.

Extramarital relations. There is probably no tribe in which formal marriage alone is sexually satisfactory. Perhaps it would be more correct to say that sex is not the most significant fact of marriage. We have previously noted that sex relations in our own society are anything but monogamous even though monogamy is our established form. There is, however, one great difference between our attitude in this matter and that of most primitives. That is, in our society extramarital relations are not *sanctioned;* in primitive societies certain such relations not only are sanctioned but may even be obligatory. In this connection primitive conditions are more nearly comparable to conditions in Europe, where prostitution is considered a necessity, rather than to those in America, where it is said not to exist even though it is a thriving business. Even this comparison is remote in its accuracy because primitive sexual relations outside the family after marriage are more frequently of a ceremonial — and therefore of a religious — than of a business nature, although actual prostitution is not unknown.

We have referred to the form of Toda marriage in which a number of men have a right to a number of women in a marriage bond. The only individuals who may live together in this way must be members of the same moiety. The Todas also sanction intercourse outside the moiety. The system in its entirety is complicated. A man of moiety 1 may get permission to live with a woman of moiety 2 from her husband or husbands. He makes a small payment to the husband, gives a larger gift to the woman's parents than the husband has given at marriage, and goes through a ceremony similar to the marriage ceremony with her. He may then live with the woman as if she were his wife or visit her at intervals as he desires. The chief difference between this and the regulation marriage is that the man of the moiety not the same as that of the woman can never be the social father of her children. Besides acknowledged lovers of this sort, certain dairymen, who have particular ceremonial offices in the community, may be the ceremonial lovers of the girls belonging to their own moiety. I know of no case in primitive society

where marriage and sanctioned sexual relations are as complicated
as among the Todas.[41] There is apparently no conception of sexual
immorality, or any attitude of sex jealousy.

Among the Eskimo the idea of hospitality as a moral obligation
is so highly developed that a man is willing to lend his wife to a lone
stranger visiting his village for any length of time. A refusal to do
so attaches to him a moral stigma. In connection with a particular
ceremony held to drive off evil spirits the same tribe require extramarital relations for a day and a night.[42] The Ba-Ila of Northern
Rhodesia have the courtesy to lend a wife to a visitor, but consider
it an offense if the visitor takes the privilege without an invitation
Sexual license is indulged in at mourning feasts.[43]

In Australia minutely defined restrictions are placed on formal
marriages, but during the period of the tribal assemblies or cor
roborees all these restrictions break down — men, regardless of their
class, totem, or kinship, provided they are not father, brother, or
sons of the women, may have access to them. Not only are mating
taboos broken on these occasions but other customs also break down
Ordinarily a man must avoid his mother-in-law most carefully, but
at such times he may even have intercourse with her should she be
assigned to him by the council of old men.[44] In fact, ceremonial
license commonly exists side by side with formal marriage and may
be not only sanctioned but even demanded.

The question of sexual relations may not be dismissed with mere
marital relationships and ceremonial license between married adults
There are parts of the world where premarital intercourse is not
only allowed but expected, it being a part of the cultural fabric
In parts of Melanesia, young people have great freedom in their
social activities. The Trobriand Islanders put no curb whatever on
young children who imitate their elders in sex matters. In these
islands there are clubhouses for unmarried men and women. Children
as they approach adolescence spend more and more time in the
house delegated to their sex. The boys visit the girls in their club
houses at night and there is considerable experimentation in love
making. Gradually, however, a boy and girl become more perma
nently attached to each other and there is a period of sexual life
in common which leads up to marriage and enables their families
to make economic preparations for it. During this preliminary period
public display of the relationship of the two individuals is proper
it corresponds to the period of engagement.

The Trobriand case is interesting because it marks the direct opposite of our own customs in affairs of love and marriage. As soon
as a girl and youth are married the strongest kind of prudery is observed. A man may not touch his wife in public, even if she is ill
and needs physical support. No matter how attached to each other
they may be, they must never give evidence of tenderness when
others are present. They may, however, joke and gossip as long as
no allusion to sex, however remote, is made.[45]

The Trobriand type of trial marriage is not unique. It is found
throughout the South Sea area. Among the Bontoc of the Philippines,
the custom is pushed so far that a man will not marry a girl until
she is pregnant, for he wants proof that she is not sterile. In this tribe,
if a girl is deserted by the father of her child, her chances for a good
marriage are better than if she had no child.[46]

Restrictions and preferences. Customs such as those just described
are likely to give the impression that the tribes among which they
prevail are loose as regards their morals. The fact is that morality
among them is set in an entirely different direction. There are few
primitive tribes which have no rules regulating the persons who may
mate. The most general of these rules applies to incest, which is
abhorred. The term "incest" may mean not only the mating of
parent with child, or of brother with sister, but mating between
any two individuals who are by tribal law forbidden to marry. Marriage between two members of the same clan is a greater "sin" to
the Navajo than sexual immorality is in our society. Such incest
has no biological significance.

Our large, hybrid population from which to choose mates, our
simple social organization based on the most elementary unit, the
family, with practical absence of exogamy, incest laws applied only
to members of the immediate family, and our theoretic (if not always
practical) admiration for romantic love, combine to limit restrictions in the choice of a mate. Such restrictions as we have are not
inherent in our tribal law, but are rather personal and individual.

A number of people still cherish the superstition that cousin
marriage is unfortunate, and some in their ignorance create such
a suggestive atmosphere as to make it so. It is of course true that
marriage between cousins of families affected by heritable diseases
increases the chance of offspring developing the same disease. However, the belief that the marriage is bad is not founded on this sort
of scientific evidence, and it does not distinguish between weak and

strong family lines. Some states have laws against cousin marriage. A few people still believe that to marry a person of the same name will bring bad luck. And we even hear the old saw, "Change the name and not the letter, change for worse and not for better." But we cannot say that any of these superstitions, held only by the more ignorant and unreasonable of our population, has a great influence on our type of marriage. Much less may they be said to be marriage laws, rules, or even customs in the sense in which we find regulations in primitive tribes.

No primitive tribes countenance parent-child alliances, and very few sanction sister-brother connections. In a few sanctioned instances of sister-brother marriage they were (or are) not the regulation type of marriage for the group, but rather particular sanctions extended to nobles with the underlying idea that no individuals have sufficient prestige to perpetuate the line except the members of the ruling family. Brother-sister marriage was known in ancient Egypt and Peru, in Hawaii, and for half-brother and half-sister on the Northwest Coast of America, all societies in which hereditary nobility was important.

The extension of the incest idea is well illustrated by attitudes toward "cousins." Parallel cousins are frequently regarded as sisters and brothers and the incest laws apply to them. This may be true whether they belong to the same sib or not. Cross cousins, on the other hand, not only may marry but in many cases *should* marry.

The incest group includes many individuals who are not blood relatives. It may be extended to members of the sib or to individuals belonging to a larger unit including several, even many, sibs. Such a unit may be called a phratry. Indeed, there are tribes which consider marriage within their own tribe "not so good" as marriage outside it.

The punishment for incest differs greatly from tribe to tribe. In parts of Australia it is death. Among many peoples it is believed to come through supernatural means. Where that is the case any ill luck incurred by the participants for years after will be ascribed to the breaking of the taboo. Bad luck to the society in general may be the result of breaking a taboo. Some tribes merely use ridicule, some have a form of ostracism.

Although there are many marriage restrictions, there are also certain preferences of which cross cousin marriage is perhaps the most common. There are several explanations for the preference. It is a way of keeping property in a family. In a matrilineal exogamic society, a man's sister's son is his legitimate heir. His property may be enjoyed by his own daughter, a blood relative, but not a sib relative, if she marries her cousin (her father's sister's son), and at the same time the marriage regulations will be followed.

Among the Miwok [47] a man (1) in former times had marital rights to the daughter (4) of his wife's (2) brother (3). If a man made use

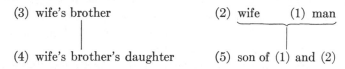

 (3) wife's brother   (2) wife   (1) man

 (4) wife's brother's daughter   (5) son of (1) and (2)

of these rights he had this woman (4) as one of his wives. Inheritance was patrilineal and wives, except one's own mother, were inherited. The man's son (5) then inherited from his father his own cross cousin; that is, his mother's (2) brother's (3) daughter (4). These two examples show clearly how different the origin of a given custom may be in different sociological settings.

The cross cousin preference is only one of many specified for so-called "good" marriages. Second cousins are sometimes the first preference. The Navajo consider marriage between grandchildren (through sons or daughters) of two blood brothers an excellent match.

There are types of prescribed marriage other than those obtaining between blood relatives. One of the greatest favorites is the type called the sororate. By sororate is meant, in polygynous tribes, the marriage of a man to two or more sisters. In monogamous tribes the term signifies that a man takes the sister of the deceased wife as his second wife. Where polygyny is the rule, a common explanation of the sororate is that two sisters are likely to get along better together as the wives of one man than would two strangers. From our own viewpoint such a result seems unlikely, but from the point of view of the natives, who rarely romanticize marriage, who feel family or sib solidarity as more important than love, and who do not necessarily have the "sole possession" idea of sex, one can well understand that the sororate may be an admirable institution. A Navajo woman may of her own accord suggest that her husband marry her younger sister. If he does, the chances are that all will be happy in the subsequent relationship. In Africa there does not seem to be the same harmony. The Thonga man has a preferential right to his wife's younger sister and to the daughters of his wife's brother, but there is constant jealousy and wrangling among the wives.[48]

A reason often given by natives for a man marrying his deceased wife's sister is doubtless a rationalization. They say she will take care of her sister's children better than a strange woman would. This may be true, but orphans are frequently cared for by some woman other than their mother's sister. Sometimes property laws give a man rights to his sister-in-law. Marriage is almost always accompanied by some business transaction in the form of a gift, payment, or service. If one person is lost or destroyed, another must be supplied by the same social group.

The levirate is a custom corresponding to sororate, and means that a man takes over the wife or wives of his deceased brother. He may have the duty of providing for them, or he may have rights to them as a part of his inheritance. The brother or other male members of a deceased husband's sib had a prerogative to the Navajo widow, and she could not marry another unless they gave her up. She could pay his family and be free to marry a member of another sib. This circumstance leads to the supposition that, if the husband's sib did not consider the woman herself a form of property, at least her person represented rights and status. Customs as widely distributed as sororate and levirate do not admit of explanations as to singleness of origin; yet they emphasize the solidarity of the family or sib and the powerlessness of the individual to escape his status.

Betrothal, engagement, wedding. The interrelationship between betrothal, engagement, and the time when marriage is considered achieved is so close that often the three periods are not exactly defined. Many tribes have some form of betrothal which is practically as binding as marriage. In parts of Melanesia, where marriage is largely an economic matter, the betrothal is marked by a settlement demanded of the man by the girl's family. Usually the period of engagement is the time allowed for the families of the contracting parties to accumulate the necessary property. In the Trobriands this period is preceded by a kind of trial marriage. Where the man pays the woman's family, as among the Pentecost Islanders, his family must contribute a certain amount, and the girl's family must furnish the feast, a ceremonial matter which frequently demands considerable coöperation and generous contributions on the part of the family members. Conditions in the island of Pentecost are so peculiar that one can hardly differentiate betrothal and mar riage. What may be called the wedding ceremony is .carried out; the girl goes to live at the home of her husband's mother; and if she is very young she does not speak to her husband for some time, even for a number of years. He spends his time at the clubhouse and tries, after the girl is old enough, to tempt her to speak to him. There are no sexual relations until she does so, and there are said to be cases where a woman has died without her husband ever having really lived with her.[49]

There are a number of methods of obtaining a wife, of which purchase, gift, trade, and service have common elements. When one family presents a gift to another it does not always mean that the person of the betrothed or the bride is considered alienable property, although that idea is possible. The northern Californians, of whom the Yurok are typical, considered social status to depend upon the amount of wealth paid by a man for his wife. It seems as if a girl's father demanded much, not because he was mercenary but rather to assure the daughter's position as well as that of her children. A child was legitimate or illegitimate according to the amount paid for his mother. In this case there was no sexual immorality in premarital experiences, but for social and economic reasons a girl was prudent or protected. The fact that a bride of a well-bred, rich Yurok brought with her a large amount of property when she joined her husband shows that she was not considered "sold" by her father. The sum required of the groom was exact and bargained for; the wealth brought by the bride was turned over without agreement and was indefinite in amount, but only rarely equivalent to that paid by the groom. The man's family paid according to tribal law; the woman's, according to good taste.

It is not at all unusual for the two families concerned with a marriage to exchange gifts, rather than for one side to make all the demands. I believe this custom to be more directly related in some respects to native attitudes regarding generosity than to those of property and property rights. That the concept of person as property may also enter in is shown by the fact that events subsequent to marriage are of moment as related to payment. The Yurok, for example, consider the bearing of children as a condition of retaining the bride price. If a woman leaves her husband, her family is expected to return the bride price. If, however, the couple have children and the wife allows her husband to keep one of them, only part of the bride price is returned. If two or more children are

given him, the entire payment is canceled. Betrothal of very young
children was sometimes agreed upon as a payment of debts if a man
was in pressing circumstances. The responsibility of securing a good
price for a girl was incumbent upon her brothers in case her father
died, and they were entitled to the payment.[50]

It may happen that a man is not able, with the help of his family,
to furnish the entire price demanded for the purchase of his bride,
and he may make part of the payment in service. Indeed, there are
tribes where nothing but service is expected. The Yukaghir of Siberia serve the father-in-law for the bride, but Jochelson considers
such service more as a test of ability than as the equivalent of a
bride price. The period of service is indefinite and may be shortened
if the man has good qualities or shows that he would not leave the
house of his father-in-law, or if the woman becomes pregnant. Such
service as is performed takes place before the families have agreed
upon the marriage. The approval of both families legalizes the marriage. To all intents and purposes the behavior of the bride and
groom differs in only the smallest details during the time of courtship and after marriage. In the case of the Yukaghir the girl's
father seems to demand a guarantee of faith that the son-in-law
will stay with him. If he does not have that, he prefers a prolonged
period of courtship rather than a sanctioned marriage. The young
man is subservient to the elder man of his wife's family at least until
a child is born, when he may leave.[51]

Another method of securing a wife is by means of exchange. A
brother and sister of one family may marry a sister and brother of
another, thus squaring the indebtedness. In northern California
although the payment by one side of the family canceled that of
the other, nevertheless two single payments were made. This example shows how important was the public formality of payment.
Even in tribes where it is not considered necessary to go through
two transactions, ordinarily some minor formality is observed to
show the agreement between the two families, and therefore the
legitimacy of the marriage.

Examples of payment of a bride price are numerous. Payment of
a dowry, if it occurs at all, is exceedingly rare. In most cases gifts
are exchanged by the members of the husband's and wife's families.

These particular ways of acquiring a mate determine the duties
of an individual for a long period, depending on the customs prevailing in the tribe to which he belongs. If there is infant betrothal

or marriage his fate may be decided when he is born or even before. The fact of purchase, gift, service, or exchange follows the persons concerned through life, may attach the children to the mother's or father's family in case of divorce, and may even determine the fate of an individual in case the mate dies.

There are several other ways of getting a spouse, the importance of which was previously much exaggerated. One of those is marriage by capture and the other is elopement. It is questionable whether there are any tribes in which marriage by capture was ever the sole recognized formality, it being found most often side by side with other conventions, among which capture figures less importantly. The same is true of elopement. There are tribes in which elopement is decried and a few in which it is countenanced, even formalized. Among the Kurnai of South Australia elopement was the more usual way of securing permission to marry.[52]

Free choice is exceedingly rare. Among the Trobriand Islanders, for instance, a girl may choose her husband but he will not be approved by her family unless he is of another totem and of practically equal rank. Romantic love is known in this area, but cannot be defined exactly as among ourselves. In former times there was regard for romantic love in Hawaii and, if all the "ifs" regarding class, rank, etc., were met, lovers might marry.

On the whole, there are three general features which differentiate primitive marriage from our own. (1) The individuals contracting the marriage have comparatively little choice in the matter. (2) The fact of marriage with its attendant preliminaries and subsequent obligations is a group affair, involving most particularly the families or sibs of the contracting parties. (3) The religious and particularly the moralistic ideas related to marriage differ so widely from ours as to be practically noncomparable. Marriages, instead of being made by "God," are definitely and realistically made by the families of the incumbents and obtain sanction by frank, definite, often public, demonstrations of some economic arrangement. The moralistic phase is attended to before sanctions of any kind are given, which means usually before betrothal. The most widespread conception of "sin" in reference to marriage is that of incest. Whatever may be the definition of the incest group — and the definitions are legion — marriage within it is "bad," not because it is an offense against the supernatural punishable in another life, but because it brings harm to the group to which the offenders belong.

A discussion of weddings would lead into descriptions too involved in detail to be taken up here. Suffice it to say that we meet the same amount of variability as to wedding formalities as we move from tribe to tribe that we do in other social phenomena. We find in some cases entire absence of formality. The tribes of California east of the Sierra and those on the Colorado River have none. A man and a woman go to live together, and marriage consists in that fact. They are as simply divorced. No economic or religious elements enter into these cases. From this simplest type of marriage there are all gradations up to the elaborate ceremony of the Manus of Melanesia and the wedding potlatch of the Indians of the North-west Coast. In general, however, the negotiations leading up to marriage, and the fulfillment of the duties and enjoyment of privileges after marriage, function more strongly than anything having to do with the wedding itself.

The fact of marriage, either potential or actual, may set in motion a whole series of adjustments, not only between the individuals concerned but also between various members of their families. It may cause an entire change in their behavior.

When a Manus girl is engaged, as early as the age of seven or eight, she must begin to hide her face from certain men in the village because of their relationship to her fiancé. Even if she herself is not engaged, her sisters or cousins may be, and she will have to avoid the boys to whom they are betrothed. The number of taboo relatives is so great and the requirements of avoidance so exacting that many childish pleasures must gradually be given up. A little girl's father ceases to take her with him because he does not need to avoid the men she does. The men do not retreat; if the taboo is to be kept — and kept it must be — the girl must retire in their presence. Consequently it happens that her activities are much restricted and her pleasures curtailed until at ten or twelve there is little freedom left, and that little ceases absolutely as soon as menstruation begins.[53]

This description is only one of many which might be given to illustrate the prevalence of "avoidance." The tribes which have it are numerous, but the forms in which it exists differ greatly from one area to another. One of the most usual forms is that a mother-in-law avoids her son-in-law completely. This may mean that a woman may never even see her son-in-law, much less speak to him. If, by accident, she happens to meet him on the trail she must turn aside and cover her face. One can easily imagine how inconvenient such a custom may become, especially in small communities where the people live close together. There is no better example of the fact that efficiency and convenience are not felt to be important than the cases where matrilocal residence and mother-in-law taboo prevail.

The Navajo have both. A man lives with his wife's people in a house built near that of his mother-in-law. Habits of avoidance are developed by both parties and they are aided by other members of the family. For example, a daughter will tell her husband where her mother is before he attempts to enter her house. So exaggerated is the taboo that a woman may not even attend her daughter's wedding. Death alone removes it.

Among the Apache, neighbors and relatives of the Navajo, the taboo is kept by all the sisters of the mother-in-law as well as by all those called "sister" by her. Consequently, if a man has married more than one woman, either through the practice of polygyny or because his wife or wives have died, there is a large group of women which he will have to avoid.

Avoidance is by no means restricted to the mother-in-law relationship. It may be found between father-in-law and son-in-law, as in certain Siberian tribes, and between other relatives by marriage. All individuals addressing others as siblings of the opposite sex may completely avoid one another. This form of the custom is common in Melanesia. Altogether the differences in avoidance are great as to the individuals who observe them as well as in the degree to which avoidance is carried. The Navajo mother-in-law is an example of complete avoidance, as is the Melanesian type in which a brother may never enter the house in which his sister is. Not being allowed to hand an object directly to a person to be avoided is a milder degree of this custom. A sister and brother may eat together, but if the girl wants something near her brother, either she gets it for herself or the brother picks it up and places it on the floor or table near enough for her to reach it. Another mild form is name avoidance, in which case one of the individuals concerned is not allowed to mention the name of the other; still another is the custom of addressing the avoided person in the third person, as "he" or "she," instead of as "you."

In many tribes — and often they are the same as those which have some type of avoidance — there is a custom quite as peculiar but diametrically opposite. Certain relatives, frequently those of opposite sex, have the privilege of saying anything they wish to each other. Whereas avoidance frequently takes the form that matters pertaining to sex must be particularly avoided, privileged familiarity especially emphasizes the fact that sex may be joked about. A typical example is joking between cross cousins. They may tease each other about shortcomings. The teasing may go to great lengths of criticism or censorship. The joking relatives may make public exhibitions of fondness for each other — such exhibitions are usually denied other individuals in the community — and may joke about sex matters. For instance, the thought of marrying into one's own clan should properly be put out of mind; nevertheless cousins may accuse each other of doing so, or of having sexual relations with members of their own clan. In its most exaggerated form joking is obscene, not only in our sense, but even in the native sense of the word. The most important rule of the game — it may well be called a game — is that the persons standing in joking relationship may not become angry no matter what one may say to another. One of my Navajo informants told me he would never get angry if one of his cousins teased him, no matter what he said, but three or four of them could sometimes "tease him down."

The freedom of joking relationship entitles one of those concerned to free use of the other's property. In parts of Melanesia a man and his mother's brother observe a joking relationship. The nephew may appropriate any of his uncle's property for use or for abuse. He may even destroy a favorite canoe and his uncle will not object. In an Hawaiian tale a hero begged to be taken on an expedition his ten brothers were undertaking to get rid of him. The brothers all refused him, but when he begged his brother's son the latter could not refuse, and they had to take him although their undertaking then lost its purpose.[54]

The very fact that so many reasonable theories have been propounded to explain the peculiar customs of avoidance and joking is perhaps as good proof as any that neither is subject to a blanket explanation. There is not space here to go into a detailed examination of the theories which have been advanced. We may briefly summarize some of them, however, in order to give some idea of the theoretical importance of customs such as these.

Frazer has assumed that avoidance between members of the opposite sex is due to an extension of the incest group from the small and purely biological to the larger social ones. He further advances the opinion that taboos between members of the same sex may have grown out of those observed toward members of the opposite sex.[55]

Freud applies the findings of psychoanalytic methods in a western European culture to primitive tribes and concludes that avoidance is motivated by a desire to prevent incest. The reasoning whereby he evolves his conclusions differs greatly from Frazer's, which is based on sociological factors entirely ignored by Freud.[56]

Tylor, in a statistical study, correlates the various sociological phenomena of avoidance, joking relationship, residence and teknonymy (the custom of naming a parent father or mother of so and so — that is, the name of the child) and argues that each must be explained in terms of the others. That is, customs of this kind certainly have a reciprocal effect on one another. He concludes, on this basis, that avoidance is due to residence; that in a society where residence is matrilocal one might reasonably expect mother-in-law and son-in-law avoidance; and where patrilocal residence is the rule, daughter-in-law and father-in-law avoidance. He further argues that individuals marrying into a family and coming to live with it are "cut" because as strangers they arouse suspicion and irritation.[57]

Tylor's theory is a part of the theory of "group hostility" which was more specifically developed in another way by Rivers.[58] In his study of Melanesian society he finds brother-sister avoidance only in those tribes which were influenced by the intrusion of outsiders. He accepts avoidance, therefore, as a means of preventing the sexual laxity which accompanies the advent of new peoples — in this particular case, the Polynesians. He suggests that brother avoidance is a survival from a time when brothers had wives in common, the change to a condition when only one brother had rights to a woman giving rise to a restraint now continued as avoidance. Rivers's explanation of avoidance between relatives-in-law is that it was established to prevent even the semblance of approach between individuals when one was in a disadvantageous position, thus premising an attitude of hostility between two moieties. He realizes that particular details seem to refute rather than support his explanation, but in general subscribes to the theory that "hostility is a function of the social grouping" whereas "helpfulness between relatives by marriage is a late development based upon the development of individual marriage." Rivers's arguments depend upon faith in the survivals of a prehistoric past.

Parsons summarizes the various theories previously propounded and advances one, in my opinion, more humanly probable. She differentiates between hostility and embarrassment and insists that avoidance, at least between relatives-in-law, may be explained by the fact that strangers coming into a family cause a feeling of restraint whether residence is common or not. This reserve may be expressed by requiring the newcomer to observe conditions of respect — that is, to recognize the family status. In other words, each individual must be kept in his place.[59]

Lowie assumes that the horror of incest between brothers and sisters is instinctive and that social avoidance is not a biological necessity. He further emphasizes the principle, advanced by Goldenweiser and Rivers for specific areas, that "social and sexual restrictions go hand in hand," and supplements it with another, "that licensed familiarity generally obtains between potential mates." In order to substantiate these principles, he quite rightly finds it necessary to differentiate between parent-in-law avoidance and similar taboos observed by members of the opposite sex of the same generation. To explain the Crow restriction between father-in-law and son-in-law, and between two brothers-in-law, he falls back on Dr. Parsons's solution of the necessity of preserving status.[60]

No matter what the causes — no one cause can be proved for the many types — of avoidance, certain it is that at the present time it is a matter of respect. A woman does not demand that her son-in-law observe the taboo because she is hostile to him, but because she wants him to respect her. This is the case in many parts of America and there is reason to believe it to be the case in Melanesia and Africa as well. In my opinion, Dr. Parsons's insistence on preserving status explains more of the manifestations of avoidance than any of the other theories and it might even include the reason for privileged license, for that is recognition of status which allows disrespect.

Lowie's theory that privileged familiarity obtains between potential mates does not hold in such cases as that of the Navajo, where it obtains between cross cousins of the same and of opposite sex. Cross cousin marriage is even strongly disapproved and is rarely found in actual practice. The joking relationship is indulged in also by a man and his maternal or paternal uncles and aunts.

As regards the cross cousin joking occurring with absence of cross cousin marriage Rivers would undoubtedly have argued that the fact of joking pointed to a survival of cross cousin marriage which was common in some earlier period of Navajo history. Westermarck pointed out quite reasonably that by the theory of survivals one might prove anything, and that since it is based on speculation it takes unfair advantage of positive evidence. The survival theory, which can as easily assume one form as another, cannot be accepted, because cultural elements may be found widely scattered in space with constantly changing interpretations, and even in a given tribe the interpretation of a custom may change through a period of time.

The other part of Rivers's theory — namely, that avoidance was a defense calculated to ward off the influence of foreigners — must likewise be repudiated. To begin with, the amount of intermarriage between hostile tribes is so small in comparison with the total number of marriages within a given group as to be negligible. Even if it were a powerful factor in that part of Melanesia discussed by Rivers, it is nevertheless a tiny portion of the world in comparison with the other areas where avoidance is practiced.

Of all the theories Freud's seems to me the weakest, because it shows no comprehension of the hold culture has on individual or group thinking. It assumes that all the world must think as a Viennese thinks.

Parsons belongs to that school of anthropologists which contends that the complexity and close interrelation of various social phenomena forbid giving a general cause for each as it is found the world over. Lowie also belongs to this school and emphasizes the fact that each time the custom is found it should be studied with close attention to the entire social setting. If a society is studied as a whole, it is quite likely that in one region a given cause is plausible, and that in another region the cause is entirely different.

Divorce. Ideas regarding divorce among primitives are as varied as those regulating marriage. Within a given group, however, there is likely to be a more uniform attitude than among ourselves. In many cases adultery is one of the least important causes for divorce. Where it is considered a cause, it is often tied up with the fact that marriage represents a business transaction. A woman's person is, in some of these cases, subject to her husband's control. Violation is the same as theft. Such is the case, for example, in parts of Africa where adultery is considered a crime. It is far more likely, however, to be punished by a fine than by divorce, unless the woman remains with her lover, in which case her family must return the bride price to the husband.

Among the Ila more common grounds for divorce, which means

the return of the bride price, are virulent or contagious disease, laziness, neglect to provide food for the husband, and sterility.[61] The last is a cause for divorce among the Thonga, as are also incompatibility and witchcraft.[62]

Barrenness is perhaps the most common ground for divorce. This fact shows how important offspring are for the family as a social and economic unit. It is also a part of the attitude regarding the price paid for a woman at marriage as we have previously seen in the case of the Yurok.

There are only two reasons for a Toda to divorce his wife. One is that she is a fool; the other, that she will not work. Barrenness is no reason, for in case no children are born, a man takes a second wife. When, for either of the reasons given, a man wants a divorce he pays one buffalo to his wife's people and receives in return any buffalo he may have paid for the bride price.[63]

In the Southwest of North America, among the Zuñi, who are monogamous, and among the polygynous Navajo, divorce is declared by the woman. She simply places her husband's belongings outside the door — he lives in her house — to indicate that he is *persona non grata*. The man, who accepts his wife's decision, goes back to his mother's house, which is his permanent home. He may also leave on his own initiative.

In most cases where property is involved divorce consists in the property being returned. Divorce then, as well as marriage, is a family affair. In Africa it happens frequently that this arrangement is a curb on easy divorce, for often the amount paid for a wife has been used by her family to secure a wife for her brother, or for other purposes. It may consequently be very inconvenient to allow the divorce, and the members of the family try to tide over the differences between the spouses by arbitration.

Kinship terms. In many primitive societies the personal name is not used as a term of designation. Often it has religious significance. The Eskimo believe that a name strengthens a child's soul, and if the child is sickly its name may be changed to one which will make it stronger.[64] The Navajo use the name as a charm to drive off evil, for they believe it has strong magic power which will help its owner out of difficulties. Consequently it should not be used except in emergencies, for its power may wear out.[65] Among the Ila in Africa the birthname of any person may be used only by his closest relatives — that is, by parents and siblings — because, since a person is thought to be the reincarnation of an ancestor, the name is sacred and is to be treated with the greatest respect; that means it should be avoided.[66] On the Northwest Coast of America names are property, in the sense that they may be applied only to those who are entitled to them through inheritance, marriage, gift, or purchase.

The function of the name is so varied in different tribes that the ethnologist tries to learn what it is before asking, "What is your name?" The question may give rise to keen embarrassment, or it may even be considered a grave insult. Usually there are complicated rules of etiquette on the use of the name based on prevailing beliefs and, in addition, on the relationship between individuals bearing the name and those using it. If there is an avoidance relationship it is likely to affect the use of the name. A common way of getting around such difficulties is to avoid the "real" name — that is, the one bestowed ceremonially or for reasons of belief — and to use instead nicknames which may have reference to an occasion, a locality, a personal idiosyncrasy, or a form of behavior.

More commonly kinship terms are used, not only for members of the family, but even for strangers. Almost every tribe has a title of respect for old persons which may be the same as the kin term for "grandmother" or "grandfather." Since the organization so often differs greatly from ours, it is reasonable to expect that the kinship systems will also differ greatly. Differences depend upon linguistic and social factors, the factor of language determining to some extent and limiting the terms. Besides this, social requirements may change the original meaning of a kin term so as to make it vary greatly among the different tribes using it. Widely separated tribes having closely related languages may have the same kin terms with different meanings; neighboring tribes speaking languages entirely unrelated may use certain kin terms in common. Sometimes a word is borrowed, together with the meaning; and again the word may be taken over in an entirely different context. Furthermore, the interpretation of the word may be borrowed without the word itself.[67]

The most essential features of language are classification and generalization. When I say "flower" I do not think of all the characteristics of a flower, but I may mean columbine, wild geranium, house lily, or orchid, none of which have the same description. In the same way I may say "uncle" or "cousin" and the listener will understand well enough what I mean, but he will not know whether I speak of my mother's brother or of my father's, nor will he know a first from a second or more remote cousin. It may not be necessary for him to know how we are related; if it is, I explain by circumlocutions, my father's brother's or my mother's sister's son.

All words in a class have some features in common, and of these we are rarely conscious because we do not stop to analyze them. We use our kinship terms just as thoughtlessly. If, however, it be- comes necessary to learn another system, the differences between it and ours can be understood only through analysis. "Cousin" is to us a term having no sex differentiation, but there is a difference between German "Cousine" and "Vetter," the former being a fe- male, and the latter a male. All languages have similar peculiarities. However, when we consider systems belonging to social organiza- tions of unusual types such as have been described in the preceding sections, greater and more fundamental adjustments must be made than any which may be applied to European kinship systems, be- cause they are based on entirely different principles.

In all systems the relatives by consanguinity, that is, blood rela- tives, must be distinguished from affinals, relatives by marriage, even if these should be at the same time blood relatives.

In our own system only three principles apply, not all of which function for every single term belonging to it. They are descent in direct or collateral line, generation, and sex of the person spoken about. This is shown in the following table.

	Generation	Line	Sex	Affinity
Father........	ascending	direct	male	——
Mother	ascending	direct	female	——
Uncle.........	ascending	collateral	male	——
Aunt	ascending	collateral	female	——
Brother	own	——	male	——
Sister.........	own	——	female	——
Cousin........	own	collateral	male and female	——
Wife..........	——	——	——	female
Husband......	——	——	——	male
Son...........	descending	direct	male	——
Daughter......	descending	direct	female	——
Nephew.......	descending	collateral	male	——
Niece.........	descending	collateral	female	——

For terms of affinity the same terms are used in address — *cousin*, *nephew*, *niece* sparingly; in description with the addition of *-in-law*.

The preceding and succeeding generations are set off by the addition of the qualifying *grand-*; the next one by *great-grand-*, and so on.

The combinations of these principles, although simple enough, may not seem adequate for a social system in which the avunculate makes it important to know whether I refer to my mother's brother or my father's, nor would they suffice for a system which emphasizes cross cousin marriage, or a taboo against the marriage of parallel cousins. The relationship between such sociological phenomena and a given kinship system may be very close. On the other hand, a kinship system may be based on linguistic principles which do not reasonably or consistently meet the present social requirements.

Primitive kinship systems may use all the principles we find in our own, but there are others which must be understood, and even those which we use are sometimes omitted or take on new distinctions. Many systems differentiate relatives according to sex, but it is not necessarily the sex of the person spoken of. The distinction may be made according to the sex of the speaker. A man, for instance, in addressing his son may use a term quite different from that which his wife uses. A complete set of these terms is given in the following table.

| Sex of person spoken of .... | Male | Male | Female | Female |
Sex of speaker	Male	Female	Male	Female
Generation 1	Boy's father	Girl's father	Boy's mother	Girl's mother
Generation 2	Boy's brother	Girl's brother	Boy's sister	Girl's sister
Generation 3	Man's son	Woman's son	Man's daughter	Woman's daughter

Still another variation of the sex principle distinguishes between sex the "same as" or "opposite from" that of the speaker. For instance, a boy speaking to his brother, and a girl speaking to her sister, would use one term; but a boy speaking to his sister, or a girl speaking to her brother, would use another term. This principle applies most often to siblings and cousins.

The kin term used may depend upon the sex of an intermediate relative. My father's sister and my mother's sister, my father's brother and my mother's brother, my son's child and my daughter's child, may be designated by separate terms; and the reciprocal terms would follow the same categories: man speaking, my sister's child, my brother's child; woman speaking, my sister's child, my brother's child; my father's parents, my mother's parents. These terms may again be differentiated according to the sex of the person spoken of.

In the case of cousins the sex of two intermediate relatives is relevant. If the fathers of the cousins are brothers, or if their mothers are sisters, they are parellel cousins. If the father of the one is the mother's brother of the other one, they are cross cousins.

Still another possibility is that to address a grandparent one may use exactly the same word which the grandparent uses in addressing the grandchild. For instance, the grandparent may say *nali* meaning "son's child," and the child also may say *nali* meaning "father's parent." When the same terms are used in both directions they are called reciprocal terms. In our system "cousin" is a reciprocal term; I call my cousin "cousin" and he or she calls me the same. Our sibling terms are partially reciprocal. I, a female, call my sister by the same term she uses for me, and my brother does the same for his brother. But when sisters address brothers, or the reverse, the reciprocity vanishes and the sex principle enters in to require distinction. There are systems which disregard the sex principle in fraternity, in which case all siblings use the same terms to and for one another, regardless of sex. Quite commonly, too, kin systems of primitive groups use reciprocal terms across generations, especially across two generations — that is, for grandparental terms.

Many systems, like our own, distinguish only three generations; others have special terms for relatives as many as three, four, or even five generations apart; still others disregard generation entirely. For instance, in a matrilineal sib organization all the males of my father's sib may be designated by the same term regardless of generation.

Many systems distinguish between direct and collateral descent; others do not. It is not unusual to find systems in which the mother and all her sisters, or the father and all his brothers, are addressed by the same terms, which are to be defined as "one woman of the group of sisters to which my mother belongs," "one man of the group of brothers to which my father belongs."

When a number of persons are included in a single term, the terms are often said to be "classificatory" kin terms. Understanding as to which individual of the whole group is meant may depend on situation or context, or he may be defined by circumlocution. If I speak of my aunt, the listener cannot tell whether I mean father's or mother's sister, or the wife of my father's or mother's brother. If he does not know me or my family it may make no difference to him; if it does, he asks me and I name her or describe the relationship of the person in question — "my mother's brother's wife," or whatever it may be. In the same way natives indicate which person of the classificatory group they mean. A common way of describing mother's sister is by using the word "little mother."

Just as our kinship system lacks the distinction between maternal and paternal lines, so also it lacks age groupings. None of our terms indicates the relative age of the persons concerned. Although our own system never makes this distinction, it is nevertheless common. There may be no general term for brother or sister, but rather specific terms such as "elder brother," "younger brother," "elder sister," "younger sister." A similar differentiation may be made for cousins, and it may even be carried beyond the contemporary generation so that a distinction must be made between an uncle or aunt older or younger. An uncle or aunt may also be distinguished as older or younger than parent. Psychologically we make the age distinction between uncle and nephew, but there is nothing in either word to signify it. We consider it a bit peculiar nowadays to have an uncle younger than a nephew, although the circumstance occurs. With primitive peoples marrying as young as they do, and with little feeling against discrepancy in age between the individuals of a pair, cases are frequent where a person of a genealogically older generation is younger than some of his relatives of a younger generation. Often this makes no difference in the kinship term, but there are other cases where the term we must translate as "uncle" really means "male, one ascending generation removed, younger (or older) than I, related in collateral line."

The preceding examples show that the principles underlying systems of relationship terms vary greatly. We mentioned generation, sex of person spoken of, sex of speaker, direct or collateral descent, relative age, relations to some intermediate common relative or relatives (as in cross and parallel cousins).

The terms so far discussed are terms of consanguinity; that is, terms applied to blood relatives or relatives reckoned as blood kin for social reasons, such as sib organization and the like. Kinship terms of affinity constitute another important class. They are terms used for relatives through marriage and apply most often to the contemporary generation and one generation removed. Whenever the laws of intermarriage allow consanguineous marriages, like those between cross cousins, a choice of terms results. The maternal uncle becomes at the same time father-in-law. Where the custom of the sororate prevails, it may happen that a male calls not only his actual wife but her sisters and even her parallel cousins by the same term, "a group of sisters and cousins one of whom is my wife." This may be due to the fact that they are his potential mates. It may happen, on the other hand, that such terms represent categories which have purely linguistic and no social significance. It happens that two or even three terms may be possible for a particular relative, according to which principle determines each definition. Since that is the case, choices must be made, and such choice may give a clue to the dominant principle of the system or perhaps to the emphasis read into the term according to the social organization of the group. The Navajo, for instance, often have a choice of relationship as reckoned through the mother or father because of the close interrelationship between sibs which is constantly encouraged (see p. 417). The choice of terminology invariably selected by the individuals concerned is that based upon relationship through the mother. It is, they say, "closer." This is certainly due to the emphasis in the whole culture on matrilineal sibs and their accompanying functions.

Although it is possible to establish the fundamental principles of a system of relationship terms, it is seldom totally consistent. In our own simple system the classificatory principle of sex is disregarded in the term "cousin." In the affinity terms the qualifying element -in-law is omitted in the term of mate's uncle and aunt, who are also simply designated as uncle and aunt.

In Dakota and Coeur d'Alêne the terms for brother and sister are differentiated according to the sex of the speaker, sex of the person addressed, and relative age; but for younger brother both sexes use the same term in Dakota while in Coeur d'Alêne both sexes use the same term for elder sister. The principle of generation which prevails in the Dakota system also breaks down in the term used by a person for his or her father-in-law and mother-in-law and the reciprocal term for child-in-law, which are closely related derivatives of those used for one's own grandparents — namely, grandchildren.[68]

It should be noted that in many systems the point of view is established for certain close relatives such as father, mother, sibling, etc., and then all relationships are based upon this fixed point of view. Thus, if I call many men "father" I reckon my relationship to his relatives on the basis of this fact. My father's brother is my "father"; then his children must be my "siblings," and all persons whom he calls "brothers" must be "fathers" to me.

Systems which differentiate between cross and parallel cousins in the contemporary generation often dispose of the distinction in the next generation. That is to say, although my parents distinguish between *their* parallel (siblings) and cross cousins and I distinguish between *mine*, I do not differentiate the cross cousins of my *parents* from their parallel cousins (siblings).

In order to understand any social system basically, it is necessary to know the relationship between the kinship system and the social customs. But a descriptive knowledge of these is not enough; it is important also to know the attitudes behind them both. It is possible, though not necessary, that a child may have a different attitude toward his mother's sister, whom he calls "mother," from that which he has toward his father's sister, whom he addresses by another term. This attitude may be different because of the term, or the term may be different because of the attitude; or it may be that neither has at present a determinable connection with the other. The Hupa Indians of northern California, for instance, have the same attitude as the Navajo of Arizona regarding the relationship of a woman to her sister's children. She should treat them as her own children; if her sister dies, she should marry the widower and become a mother to his children. In both groups the sororate is the rule; the attitudes are the same and correspond to those which the sororate should require. In spite of all this, Hupa children use different terms to address "mother" and "mother's sister"; the Navajo use the same terms for both. The Hupa word for "stepmother" is, however, the same as the word for "mother's sister."

Among the Teton there is a rule which regulates behavior to all individuals, behavior which is determined not primarily by relationship of the persons speaking, but by the attitude held by intermediate relatives. Thus a Teton woman has a joking relationship toward her father's brother and an avoidance relationship toward her mother's brother because her father jokes with his brother and her mother is avoided by her brother. Their kinship terms are the result of classifications that arose at one time in the history of the people, but there is no way of telling whether the present attitudes grew up because of the kinship terms. Certain it is that at present the two are so closely interrelated that the attitude of an individual toward a stranger will depend upon the kin term the two will determine upon after considering relationships which may be very remote.

It is to be expected that kin systems, customs, and attitudes will not generally maintain a consistent relationship as they occur repeatedly from tribe to tribe. The reasons for lack of uniformity and for inconsistency are diverse; not only do they depend upon social organization itself, but organization, in its turn, influences and is influenced by all the other phases of the life of a tribe, economic, artistic, and religious. A kinship system, although in itself complicated and composite, is nevertheless only an elaborated detail of the larger pattern of each culture.

Prestige. Our discussion up to this point has laid emphasis on status due to "natural" causes, birth and marriage. The latter, though it may be called "natural" in its universality, has been shown to vary greatly in the machinery which brings it about and in its interrelations with other phases of social, economic, or religious life. Questions inevitably asked are: To what family does a man belong by birth? With what family has he become affiliated by marriage? Where does he live? To what association does he belong?

In this respect primitives are no different from us. The answers establish a man's place in the world, and the consequent behavior of his fellows is regulated by them. It is likely, however, that the attitude is not formulated or defined; it is merely taken for granted. On the other hand, an individual whose antecedents are modest and whose marital affiliations are not exciting has certain means by which he may bring himself before the public eye, means by which he may increase his prestige. In modern America the chief of these means is wealth. Among a small portion of the population, the title of "doctor" or of "professor" is impressive. Sudden and perhaps temporary prestige may be secured by some sensational achievement, no matter how trivial. There are communities where just getting a name in a headline, even for crime, causes a rise in personal stock.

If we keep in mind such customs of our own we can better understand the examples of primitives who secure prestige by what at first thought would seem to be peculiar methods. One great difference between them and us is that in a given tribe or area a certain way of attaining rank is stylized, whereas among us the methods are varied, and new ways of coming into the public eye are constantly being originated. This is due to the complexity of our civilization, which emphasizes rapid communication, and to the speed at which we live.

Dr. Bunzel has described (see pp. 357 ff.) the system of gaining prestige on the Northwest Coast of America. Although the status of a person as firstborn of a noble lineage is important, the maintenance of the status is intimately related to the economic system. Furthermore, she has pointed out that the purpose of the potlatch, the end to which all participants devote their energies, often the struggles of a lifetime, is to secure prestige, perhaps for self, but often for children. The acquisition of prestige is not manifested in a subtle way, but it is blatant. It is recited in pompous speeches; it is counted and recounted publicly to large audiences; it may even furnish sanction for taking a life. Many features of the potlatch are striking, but the desire for prestige in the abstract is the end to which a rival bends his efforts. Property is important, but not its possession so much as its use and even its destruction. The grease feast, which is actually "burning money"; ostentatious squandering of food through gift; throwing the copper into the sea — all these show that something higher than the mere possession of wealth is valued.

A man may exist in an impoverished condition as the key individual of the system because of previous dispersal and destruction of valued goods. His children (sons, daughters, or sons-in-law) may bask in the warmth of the glory reflected by their father's "generous" (and always public) exploits for at least a generation. However, if son or son-in-law should allow the source of the power to dim by failing to add to it, his own children might suffer from weakening of the prestige, but it will take more than two generations for the community to forget or to discount completely the extreme potlatching of the most noble ancestor. A child of the family will always have tradition to bolster up his own weakness in the system or its failure through circumstances such as exist at present because of the breakdown of the economic structure due to the laws and exploitation of the Whites.

There is one fundamental difference between this system and our own, the difference due to use and destruction. A noble of the Northwest Coast "is" because he "has not"; he has traded his goods for something more abstract, the respect of the community. If he piled up his wealth *ad infinitum* with stress on "having," he would not attain his goal. Instead of attaining honor in his group, he would simply be despised as one who had not followed the course to its inevitable conclusion.

The rewards of the potlatch system and of ours are quite similar. All activities are regulated by the acknowledged position of the individual who has himself attained the prestige and the consequent power inherited from his forebears. In all gatherings the honor of each is known to all; the guest with highest names has the place of honor, the second highest sits next, and so it goes.

An important feature of Northwest Coast culture is the winter ceremonial, during which potlatches are given and boys are initiated into secret societies in order to secure guardian spirits. Duties and offices in the winter ceremonial are performed or held according to rank. A man is often proud of holding an office which entails great personal sacrifice because of taboos and restrictions.

The pantheon of one of the Northwest Coast tribes, the Bella Coola, is organized in a manner which parallels the notions of rank in actual life, certain gods being of great importance with only the slightest duties whereas others not nearly so important have many more or more greatly extended activities. One god sits in the back of the house, a position of no significance, because he has given up his position near the fire to his nephew.[69]

A person with high prestige has, moreover, the privilege of treating his inferiors with the greatest arrogance. For, although a noble or chief is expected to see to it that his people are never in physical need, he nevertheless looks down upon them, derides his inferiors, and exalts himself in his speeches. He teaches his son to behave in the same way to the children of lesser nobles and of commoners.

Although the kula trading expedition of New Guinea (see pp. 361 ff.) is organized on a different basis from the potlatch of the Northwest Coast, and there is no provable relationship between the two, there are, nevertheless, certain fundamental attitudes which are similar. The trading of armbands or necklaces is the culminating stage of a long series of preparations and trading which gives the participant the most desirable ranking in his community. There is rivalry. The armbands and necklaces are not valuable in themselves but because they have history, trade, names, magic, behind them. In virtue of the tradition adhering to the trade objects, a man gains status in his group not by *possessing* an object but because he *has* once possessed it. Only by contributing to the tradition which the object carries with it — that is, by passing it on — may he add to his own honor. Keeping a treasure for a time longer than the rules specify gives rise first to mild criticism tinged with wonder, then to censure and suspicion. If the possessor of an object keeps it unduly long he may even lose his place altogether.

Destruction of property is not as pronounced in the kula as in the potlatch, but artistic exhibits of choice garden products are allowed to rot to show the owner's position in the course of kula preparations. Place in insignificant as well as in more important regulations of daily life is quite as important as it is on the Northwest Coast. Priority of right and privilege depends likewise upon a man's place in the series. The element of magic, of the greatest importance in the kula, gives it a tinge somewhat different from that of the potlatch, into which magic hardly enters. Another of the most apparent differences is the attitude which a Trobriand chief, high in the kula, shows toward his inferiors. The arrogant disdainful manner of the Northwest Coast noble toward those beneath him in rank is absent. "The fact that he [the chief] is accorded marks of great deference, and approached in the manner as if he were a supreme despot, does not mean that perfect good fellowship and sociability do not reign in his personal relations with his companions and vassals." [70]

Prestige accredited by "divine right" — that is, by right of inheritance only — was known among the Polynesians, the ancient Mexicans, and the Peruvians. An idea of this sort may be expected to work out differently in different groups, but it is a prestige pattern well understood by any student of European history. In Polynesia the right to nobility was inherited by the oldest male in direct line, and so exaggerated did the right of primogeniture sometimes become that the youngest brother of a large fraternity might rank no higher than a commoner. [71]

Emphasis on order of birth was closely related to belief that impersonal supernatural power (mana, see p. 630) was inherited — in large measure by the eldest male scion of a line, to a lesser degree by his younger siblings. Because of birth and possession of mana a high noble was "taboo" — that is, doubly dangerous. He had superhuman power for good, but that very power made things touched or used by him dangerous to his inferiors. It is sufficient to point out the existence of these relationships between social and religious concepts without entering into specific details of their operation.

South and West Africa are other large territories in which right and order of birth attach prestige, usually political and economic, to particular individuals, and once more the pattern is a familiar one with changes, of course, in operating details.

In contrast to the Old World prestige patterns, the potlatch of the Northwest Coast of North America is a unique development. Even more unusual is the basis upon which prestige was developed in the Plains region. Before the coming of the Whites the most important activity of this area was warfare. Fighting was exploited not for territorial or tribal expansion — the tribes roamed over a large region in their pursuit of bison — but for the honor it could bring to individuals. Within this system, common to many tribes, it was not the fact of killing an enemy which counted, but rather being the first to touch him after he had fallen. Suppose, for example, there were a number of men in a war party — only the most foolhardy charged alone — and an enemy was slain. All rode as fast as possible, not for the purpose of finding out whose arrow struck the fatal blow, but to be the first to touch the prostrate body. This custom is referred to as "counting coup." The one who first touched counted first coup; the second, second coup; and the third, third. Even fourth and fifth coups were counted by some tribes. For this purpose each warrior carried a coupstick, a short, highly polished, clublike stick made of yew or mulberry.

There were definite times in the tribal ceremonies when each man of rank recited his coups. They were counted almost like blue, red, and yellow ribbons at a county fair. The man whose total was highest was ranked the highest, noblest of the tribe, and had the privilege of displaying symbols of his prowess on his robe or tipi, as well as many other honors.[72] In this area there were no classes. One reckoned status in prowess recited, but all lived in the same way. Those having the highest prestige might be the richest because they had accumulated the property of their enemies. Coups were also counted for horse-stealing, which vied in honor with killing. The premium was put upon bravery. Horses were kept close to the camps of buffalo-hunting or sedentary Indians. A man was therefore exposed to great danger in stealing horses, and the greater the danger he survived, the greater the subsequent prestige.

Among the Dakota prestige may also be obtained by the liberality of parents who give away freely on behalf of their child, who is thus raised in respect and who is expected for that reason in later life to measure up to the highest standards of conduct.

Behavior of persons of rank — that is, chiefs — is in direct contrast to that on the Northwest Coast. Hospitality, beneficence, and kindliness were virtues inculcated in all the tribesmen of the Plains, and required of chiefs or of men counting high war honors. The arrogance expected of the Northwest Coast noblemen might be a cause for the withdrawal of collective respect from a Plains chief. The kindly relations demanded of a man with high prestige toward his fellows who counted lower totals, or even none at all, are doubtless related to the Plains attitude toward property. For although it might be "good" upon occasion to secure much, it was "better" to distribute it periodically in the "give-away" (see p. 338). Such distribution — after a death, for example — might well leave the incumbent completely devoid of possessions; and besides, it did not entail the necessary gain in prestige which took the place of possession on the Northwest Coast. An individual did not remain bitterly impoverished for too long a period because of the generosity of his fellows, but neither did he expect a return in kind and count as did the potlatch participant. In the long run, it is likely that many were at times wealthy, some were always poor, but all were sometimes without any possessions whatsoever, for death came to all families and always someone survived. On the other hand, no one suffered actual want except as he continued in a state of indigence to express his emotions — sorrow for instance — but all were taken care of.[73]

The means of establishing or sustaining status are impressive because they are unique or, at least, because they are manifested in a positive manner. There are, however, many regions in which one individual is not set off against another by artificial means or even by the accident of birth. In some cases, modesty may be encouraged. The Navajo chanter, in whose hands the spiritual well-being of the tribe is entrusted, is a modest soul, highly respected, but with none of the blatancy which trumpets prestige on the Northwest Coast or in the Plains. There are today men who have made their practice of religion a source of wealth, but the ideal chanter is a man who has given up everything, sometimes even family, to devote himself to the cause of religion. Some chanters have greater power than others, but that is because they "know more," not because they "have more."

Arrogance, boastfulness, impatience — all these are antithetical to the spirit of the religion which seeks to adjust the minds of the tribesmen "in beauty" to the requirements of the supernaturals. This means that extreme boastfulness must be avoided. Demonstration of power in the Navajo region as well as in the vast northern region of North America, including the Mackenzie and Eskimo areas, is a matter of learning and technique. Success will do the boasting; there is no tribal machinery for it. This is likewise true of the vast region of Siberia, where respect is accorded individually to him who shows close affiliations with the supernaturals. There is no class distinction regarding the man to whom a supernatural may appear.

Although there may be no specific social stratification according to which all individuals of a tribe are classed, most — perhaps all — tribes have stages of respect in which certain men are classified. Many of these respect-categories define certain ethical ideals. The Eskimo accord high respect to a good hunter, but not to a stingy, mean one no matter how skillful or lucky he may be. The Coeur d'Alêne of northern Idaho are only one of many tribes who value ability to express opinion, setting great store not only on the gift of oratory but also on soundness of judgment behind the sometimes florid diction.

The Wiyot Indians of northern California have a short verb stem which means "a person is most highly respected in his (or her) community." This word is rarely used, but the feeling it expresses rests on solidarity of opinion, not necessarily orally expressed, and certainly not on any kind of tribal systematization designed to establish it.

All the attitudes which have been noted have parallels in our own society. The man of wealth has political, social, and even religious privilege; the clergyman, although he may not be wealthy, has economic and social privilege because of his calling. "Place" is also recognized although it may change with changing circumstances. Every position at Washington carries with it a theoretical social placing, even though a question often arises about seating at table, for instance, when there is doubt as to the rank of one office whose position has not been numbered with respect to another. The whole question of place in Washington is quite comparable to that of the Kwakiutl or the Marquesans, and to some it is quite as amusing.

The zest for gain has the same rationalization among American business men as among the Kwakiutl or Trobrianders. They may even say that their gains are not for themselves, and that they are working solely for the welfare of their children. Rarely, however, does an American turn over his place in life to an heir to occupy the humblest position himself.

There are elements of our own society as intangible as the names of the Northwest Coast and the tradition belonging to a Trobriand arm shell. Title is one of these symbols. A man may be a successful banker, copper king, or an oil magnate who covets that magic symbol, a college or university degree. If he asserts his position openly, as does the Kwakiutl or the Plains chief, he may buy a degree outright. If he is a little more subtle he presents a gift to a college or university. The institution shows its gratitude by conferring an honorary degree upon him, or by naming a building for him.

A matron with social aspirations may devote a lifetime and even that of her children, if they allow her, to securing an invitation from a woman whose position is more sure. She may even show her own superiority by nonchalantly refusing the invitation once she has succeeded in getting it. This behavior seems quite comparable with that of the Trobriand Islander who exerts all his physical, artistic, and magical powers to produce a fine crop of yams and leaves them to rot on the seashore!

If we could stand apart and view ourselves and our own behavior with due perspective, we should not be more surprised at the customs of primitive people than at our own. We should find such as these based primarily on human conceits, pleasant if we are used to them, "funny" if we are not.

Woman in primitive society. Inheritance determines to a degree the place of an individual in his group; marriage fixes or raises that position; and he may even elevate it through his own ˙efforts, such as trading, as on the Northwest Coast or in Melanesia, or by prowess made possible and strengthened by supernatural help, as in the Plains. Birth into a particular family or society is an accident as far as a particular individual is concerned. Another accident, that of being a woman, may greatly extend or limit the position of half the population of a tribe, for woman's place is definitely fixed in each society although there are only a few common bases upon which this placing is adjusted. In only a few cases is there a "woman question," and in no case can we determine why woman has the high or low position she occupies.

There are certain general limitations to woman's activities created by the function of child-bearing which has made her also home-maker. These activities restrict her mobility, and for this reason generally, hers are the duties which require prolonged and careful attention, those which are tedious and enduring but not of them-selves arduous. In contrast to this general limitation men may at any time cut loose the shackles of home and home cares and venture afield — far afield, if need be, on hunting, trading, or warring ex-peditions. When, in rare cases, women become Amazons, some special arrangements have to be made for home-making. Female warriors may be set apart as a class and are not expected or allowed to have children.

In general, however, there are not many activities in most cultures in which women are unable to participate. Although an Eskimo woman can hardly exist without a man, or a man without a woman, there are emergencies in which women may be obliged to perform duties which are usually considered the province of the men. The reason Eskimo women occasionally save the lives of White explorers is that the Eskimo women have mastered the technique of combating the environment, whereas the White men have not; it has nothing to do with biological superiority.

Hearne in his journal [74] notes that men in the Arctic would not start out without women in the party because they were necessary to the success of the expedition. In this case they had to look after the clothing of the party and were used as pack animals. We have few examples where the "position" of women is so "low."

A deal of anthropological literature implies that women who work hard must necessarily have a low position in the tribe. If this were true, it would mean that woman's position in our own country is lower than it was before "women's rights" with so-called sex equal-ity. Women who now pursue careers, if they are not economically independent, have twice the responsibilities they had previously, for the career has not permitted them to give over their former cares.

Judged by the amount of labor she performs, one might on the other hand be forced to conclude that the woman of a luxurious harem, or of Victorian Europe, had a high position. As a matter of fact, stress on a useful function in a group might far outweigh the pleasure in idleness and beauty if women in certain groups could express their opinion.

All this really means that there is no such thing as the "high" or "low" position of women, but that it is relatively high or low within particular domains. Although woman in America has a high position socially, economically, and politically, in one important realm, that of religion, she has no status whatsoever, and this in spite of the fact that religious forms are practiced among us more commonly by women than by men. Female ministers and leaders are rare. Such as there are are sneered at and condemned no less by the women themselves than by the men. It is unthinkable that a woman could attain to the position of bishop, cardinal, or pope.

Conditions in our own society point to a need for a different approach to the study of woman's position among primitives. Some tribes like the Navajo and Zuñi have almost complete equality between the sexes; in others, like some of northern California, women excel in religious activities,[75] for there are more female than male shamans. Some tribes, like the Ashanti [76] of West Africa and the Iroquois [77] of eastern North America, gave women so much political power that they dictated to the "throne," but in only a few cases did they become the "throne."

When a Navajo child is born, he or she is given a lamb or a kid; gifts and increase are added from time to time so that the woman, just as the man of an enterprising family, has a good flock when she comes of age. She is therefore economically independent whether she marries or remains single, whether her husband is rich or poor, and even if her husband leaves her with a family of children. Besides her flocks, she may bring cash to the family by the sale of her hand-woven rugs. Her husband has his own resources, and although the two may see fit to pool them temporarily, it is by no means necessary that they should. Labor is allocated according to family personnel and size of flocks or amount of land under cultivation. It is often the woman who dictates the duties of the day, the direction of pasture and the herder.

Socially the matter is about the same. The woman is hostess and manager, cook and counselor, and if her judgment is good she may have not only voice in family matters, but even the decisive vote. A medicine man may be important, but he respects the opinion of his wife, especially if she is old and therefore experienced. The artificial respect imposed by the mother-in-law taboo increases woman's disguised power, for her wish must be obeyed blindly; there can be no talking back.

It seems that the Navajo of early days had an institution corresponding to coup-counting by which people gained prestige. Prowess in war entitled one to be considered as a War Chief, of which there were twelve. By some means not clear now, but at least signifying honor, twelve Peace Chiefs were also chosen. Women could occupy these positions as well as men. Women were permitted to go to war, although it does not seem that a large percentage did so.

They were, and are today, allowed to participate on equal terms with men in the most important tribal activity, that of religion. There are several women who can sing major chants, the Night and the Mountain Chant; and the ultimate authority for another, the Shooting Chant, is vested in a woman. These women do not practice much now for various reasons, one being that some are too old. It seems also that the men singers show jealousy when they do perform, but this seems to be due to notions secured from Whites, and those same men singers do not hesitate to go to the women to check up on old details and to learn new ones. There is a more potent reason for the small number of women chanters than any of those given, namely, that women are generally not interested in the details of the chant. According to Bunzel,[78] Zuñi women may belong to medicine societies but they have little interest in doing so. I know of no reason why this should be, or why conditions of this sort should differ now from those of the past as they do among the Navajo.

I know of no other region outside the Southwest where the position of women is as equally divided among the various cultural activities. One-sided emphasis is, however, quite frequently found. Among the Papago of the Mexican border the men secured through vision the "crystals" which gave power for curing. Chona, who was not only intelligent but powerful, refused the gift of revelation because she was a woman; indeed, she even had the power driven out of her by ritual. Her autobiography, recorded when she was over eighty, indicates that she, as well as some of her family and tribesmen, considers that she may possibly have erred in not accepting the power of curing, even though the women of her tribe did not generally have it.[79]

Women of California, on the other hand, were more likely than men to receive and accept a "call" or "dream" which gave them power although both sexes practiced shamanism.[80] The mystery of woman's menstrual period and of her ability to bear children may be interpreted either for or against her in religious practice. In northern California, as in many regions of North America, a menstruating woman is "dangerous," but the mystery which makes her so may, if properly treated, also enable her to use that power for good; hence she becomes the personal exponent of the notion that "what kills also cures," and she controls the power as it affects others.

Political status was possessed by the Iroquois women of the woodland region of North America. The five tribes were united in a confederacy for defense and it was governed by representatives from the several tribes. The tribes were divided in their turn into phratries which were composed of matrilineal sibs. If a vacancy occurred in the confederation council it was filled by the vote of the women of the sibs. They selected the candidate on the basis of merit; their suggestion must be approved by each successively larger unit in order that the vacancy be filled. And yet there was a stricture against a woman being one of the representatives or even a tribal chief. Only once, and then temporarily, did a woman ever occupy such a position.[81]

In numerous African tribes the situation was similar though the governmental structure was entirely different. Africa was the land of kingdoms; a man who was king or chief had considerable judicial and executive power. He had, moreover, an elaborate court with followers and insignia fundamentally no different from those of the European courts of the past. At the same time, the Queen Mother or Sister had her own court, which was almost an exact replica of the King's except that it was composed of women. In some cases, the Queen seems to have been a mere figurehead; in others, as among the Ashanti, all executive orders must be approved by her before they could be carried through, and the King consulted her and conceded to her decision in all matters, large and small. However, she was seldom the actual executive officer, hardly more than the "power behind the throne," [82] although in some other tribes the Queen had even executive power.

These examples, like those illustrating modes of attaining prestige, are positive ones. They refute a point which is often only implied, but nevertheless tenaciously held; that is, that if the position of one sex is high, that of the other must necessarily be low. The Navajo man does not consider himself downtrodden because he respects the judgment of his intelligent womenfolk. He has his place and they have theirs, and that is all there is to it. Because the North Californian woman happens to be a shaman does not mean that she treats her family and friends differently from the woman who has not accepted a dream, nor does it mean that she can domineer over her husband or the other men any more than the other women.

A good deal has been written of people who treat their women badly, but the viewpoint is generally that of a White person who interprets a situation on the basis of his own emotions and bias. If he sees an African with many wives, they must have low position because no husband could be equally attentive to several wives. The writer may not record, because he may not know, the fact that the more wives there are, the happier all may be because it means that they have a rich husband who can afford to get help for them in their work. Some American women consider European women slaves to their husbands and despise the husbands for allowing their wives to perform certain tasks for them which to us seem menial. The European woman, on the other hand, has the deepest sympathy for American men. She actually pities them because they have no woman whose sole duty and pleasure it is to care for matters which a bootblack or tailor can do better. And so it may often be among primitives. On the surface it may appear that one or the other sex is discriminated against, but the inner spirit and attitude of the tribe may show that it is not; or more likely, neither men nor women ever think of the matter at all.

Education. With all the complicated conventions primitives have been shown to observe, and many more, it is obvious that there must be means of passing them from one generation to another. Our information about the education of the primitive child is scanty enough, but it is sufficient to be highly suggestive. Besides, it shows that educational methods are by no means uniform as we view them from tribe to tribe. One respect in which primitives differ from us is that they are sure of what they want to teach. The young child of the Northwest Coast starts life in the atmosphere of the potlatch, and his training continues to include more and more of it as he grows older. The Plains child starts as early to practice counting coup,[83] and neither would ever have to face the choice as to whether he should be a coup-counter or a potlatch-giver. This follows for every tribe whether it be one with a definite cultural stress or one with less emphasis on any particular side of the culture; consequently limitations are set at once.

One kind of learning general among primitives sets them distinctly off from our own — particularly our city-bred — children, not only in the *kind* of thing learned but also in the *manner* of learning it. This is that primitive children early learn the inevitable facts of nature, which means also the physical properties of materials and things, matters about which our students may remain blissfully unconscious for life. I cannot imagine, for instance, that any primitive child who had ever seen a coconut *could* possibly ask, as did a college student, "Is a coconut a root?" or even that he could be as unaware of his surroundings as to be completely surprised, as was another, when told that electricity had to be paid for. She had never thought of such a thing. She had supposed that lights just "were," like the sun.

Most tribes know a great deal about various crafts. But even if no definite stress is laid upon making things, the most elaborate sort of knowledge, skill, patience, and resourcefulness may be necessary to carry on an existence by hunting and food-gathering. All crafts require materials. Collecting materials requires knowledge of plants, their times and rates of growth, the age and relative strength of their parts, methods of preparation and preservation, to mention only a few items. To achieve success in hunting, a man must know the habits of the animals he pursues; he must know the dodges used by the animal for its own protection; he must work out some device for catching it which is a shade cleverer than the animal — the point at which curiosity or greed overwhelms caution, for example, or the time necessary to wear out or confuse the animal in the chase. He makes snares and cages to catch it. Some of these are simple, but they will work only if they take due account of the senses of the animal. Does it see well at day or night or does it depend more upon scent or hearing for its protection? Does dependence on speed force the animal inadvertently into an impound or a spiked pit? Will the confusion which causes stampeding be useful or detrimental to man's attack on the herd? Can it be controlled once it is set in motion?

There is no limit to this kind of knowledge possessed by primitive man, and a child acquires it along with his mother's milk. One reason why it is difficult to study primitive education is that one method used to teach these things is intangible. It is a method as old as the life of man but one which our self-conscious analysts often forget: simply that children do not do what adults *tell* them to do, but rather what they see adults *do*. Primitive people do not lay stress on telling. In many languages the word for "teach" is the same as the word for "show," and the synonymity is literal. One of the things which amuses natives, at the same time making them lose respect, is the habit White people have of asking questions: "What are you going to do next?" "What are you doing that for?" The craftsman or hunter always knows what he is going to do next, but he may not be able to give orally the reason for doing it. In most cases, it will be apparent at the very next operation and there will be no need to ask. It will be apparent, however, only to him who knows the properties of the materials being used, the steps in the process already finished, and the end result sought.

All these things the primitive child picks up by constant observation and by imitation. Our children have little chance to do this because their elders make few things, and have very little interest in, or knowledge of, the world of nature or materials. This fact makes them capable of considering a coconut a root, and forms an exact parallel to the Indian who rubbed a small stick along his pants until he wore them through trying to get a spark, for he had seen a White man perform this wonder. The White man knew how to use the match, and he knew it was a specially prepared stick, but he almost certainly did not know how it was prepared. The Indian, though observant, did not notice the fact of this particular preparation. On the other hand, he would have been able to interpret the entire story of a visitor to his house in his absence, that story being written only in tracks, sometimes almost invisible, and in signs which only the detective of a mystery story could read for us.

Knowledge of physical properties as applied to crafts or economic techniques includes also a determination of standards. As the child watches its mother weave, it sees her skillful hands move between warps, setting an even line with the weft, neither warp nor weft tearing, but when she sees her unskilled sister at work the warp tears, the weft lies unevenly, the edge of the blanket pulls in. The mother shows the sister what to do about all these things, and the little girl, watching, notes that mistakes, though tolerated, are not passed over. In addition to all the patience exhibited in mastering complicated processes, she will hear the unbiased criticism her mother gives not only of her own blankets but also of those of her friends, and they in their turn will criticize hers. All this is done in an impersonal way, and no stigma attaches to the worker, but she derives stimulation and even encouragement from the criticism of her errors, for the good points are appreciated and remarked as well.

The output of primitive industry at the peak of its development is sometimes astounding in quantity and quality as our museum collections constantly attest. Two characteristics of handmade objects are strength and durability. A Navajo child learns strength and control very young. I saw a child less than two years of age, and small for her age, pour water from a full two-quart coffee pot into a bowl which held about half of it when filled to the brim. She then picked up the bowl and drank from it without spilling a drop. Strength, firmness, control, all depend upon fine accommodation of muscles to the materials or objects handled. Generally speaking, this adjustment which we call skill may be acquired in two ways, for observation alone is not enough; there must be extensive experience in handling and in judging the materials and in pursuing the ideal.

The first and the commonest of these methods is the patient "showing," criticism, and help given by the adults who want their children to learn. The large majority want to learn, and craft instruction is individual. There is some evidence that an indifferent attitude on the part of the elders may stimulate a child to achievement.

Atlnaba, a little Navajo girl, was patiently taught to weave by an older sister and was expert at the age of five. Her younger sister did not even start to learn until she was over eight, although she had always cherished secret desires to emulate her sisters. By this time the eldest sister had died and the mother had not the patience to help her small daughter. This, however, did not quench her fervor, but she learned in spite of lack of instruction rather than because of it. Secretly she made her own loom from crude sticks; she stole bits of yarn from her mother; she used ruse to discover her mother's manipulation of warps in making design. Her adult skill, of which her mother was duly proud, was attained by stubborn perseverance accompanied at times by tears and anger.

A somewhat similar example is that of the Tami who inhabit a small island southeast of New Guinea and who are skillful woodcarvers. These people never tell the boys to carve. If one wants to do so, he is allowed to try his hand at making a bowl. No help is given him. If he shows aptitude at his first trial he is encouraged and advised, but if his first try is a failure no one takes the trouble to comfort him, and the chances are he is never again allowed to try. The Tami believe that one should not work unless he feels like it. If a person were forced to work when the mood was not on him, something dire was bound to happen and no one could expect success.[84] Since the population of the Tami area is small and the output in wood-carving large, it is to be concluded that many individuals showed aptitude and that there were many times when they "felt like" working.

Learning a craft imposes its own discipline as anyone who pursues one can attest. A badly spun string will tear, a granny knot will slip, a cut in wood deeper than necessary cannot be uncut, a fish weir loosely fastened will be washed downstream. Consequently art and industry need no human coercion, for nature, by her laws, takes its place. Many of the older writers make general statements to the effect that primitive children are not disciplined, but that they are always indulged. The whole question, like so many others, depends upon the side of culture to be stressed and particularly upon the motive behind it. Although discipline does not necessarily include corporal punishment, it may be even more severe than that meted out by the puritanical paterfamilias who demanded unthinking obedience above all things.

The Manus of New Guinea have no interest in craftsmanship but they idolize property. They are a water people and consequently have to meet the demands made by the sea. They do not hesitate to slap the tiniest baby in teaching it to grasp its mother's neck, and a child who breaks one of the large pots valuable in trade is shamed almost out of countenance. It is just as important for the child to swim as it is to clasp its mother's neck strongly, but it is not thrown into the water to "sink or swim." On the contrary, it is taught gently and patiently to *like* the water. Every new effort is applauded; no retrogression in learning is tolerated. Discipline along other lines is practically nonexistent. Adults are almost slaves to a child's minor fits of temperament and they do nothing to free themselves.[85]

A Fox Indian mother taught her child by moral suasion but did not hesitate to use force when it became necessary, for it was better that her child should become a worthy woman than that she should have an easy life. She says, "If you happen to know how to make everything when you no longer see me, you will not have a hard time in any way. That is why I constrain you to make anything, not to treat you meanly." The daughter learned by example, by watching her mother, by practicing. In her tribe there was a great deal of explaining, of oral moralizing. Not many children were whipped, but if they were very naughty they were made to fast. Their cheeks were painted with charcoal so that the village would know they were being punished, and no lodge would offer them food.[86]

Training in social and religious customs is perhaps more subtle, but as efficacious as training in practical matters. In a tribe which observes mother- and son-in-law avoidance children may be sent by one to locate the other in cases of doubt. Or if one approaches the place in which the other is, the children may give warning.

Indians who seem in certain respects exaggeratedly indulgent of their children may be as exaggeratedly strict in matters relating to fundamental beliefs. Djiba, a Navajo child of about four, was accustomed to go into a fit of screaming whenever she wanted something or something did not suit her. No one did anything at all to break this habit, and it got so bad that her cousin, a boy of eight, would use the same technique. Both had excellent endurance and each eventually won his point. Djiba was at this time my favorite and I was hers, so that she took advantage of every possible occasion to be with me, at which times she sat on my lap or, if I was busy, crawled over and around me in a clinging, petting way.

By undergoing the ceremonial order of the Shooting Chant I became "dangerous" for four days. That is, the chant having been sung for me would give me "power," but only if I took care to let it get into me (which would mean control of it) for four days after the last rite by not working and not touching fire or water. Only those for whom the same chant had been sung were "safe" in coming close to me or in doing anything for me. They too had the power under control. During this period Djiba and I were left together for about half an hour. Instructions must have been issued to her in no uncertain terms, for during this time she remained at a respectable but short distance from me, constantly tempted to come but always resisting. Her sister was once made to desist from disobedience by being told that she was "sitting on an ant." The bugaboo is often used and because of the character of religious beliefs and the strength with which they are held they are more numerous and more potent than any we generally use with our children. However, it was no different from, and certainly not as difficult as, the burden a White mother placed upon her daughter when she taught her always to consider first her responsibility to God.

There is no exact point at which informal education ends and formal education begins. Many, perhaps most, tribes have no form of formal or group education. Others again carry this form to the extreme. They are the tribes in which all individuals belong to one of two categories: the initiate or adult, and the uninitiate or immature, members of the tribe. The Africans and Australians are examples of these. "Initiation," "maturity," "adulthood," with them means likewise "maleness," for women, particularly in Australia, continue always in the class of uninitiated.

Among the Thonga [87] of East Africa boys are not considered adult members of the tribe until they have gone through the circumcision school. This school is held every four or five years and boys of from ten to sixteen years of age attend. For three months they are isolated from the rest of the community. During that time they are subjected to a number of tests which purport to make them brave and to teach them endurance. Suffering is one of the important features of the instruction. The boys are subjected to blows from the attendants; they must suffer not only the cold of the long nights, but while the top part of the body may be very cold the feet close to the fire may be nearly burning. During the entire initiation period they are not allowed to drink a drop of water. They are made to eat unsavory food which at first repels them. After a few trials, however, they become accustomed to it and thrive on it. One of the greatest hardships is being forced to eat much more food than is welcome or required. The large quantities of food must be eaten fast, too. Any infringement of the rules or any disobedience is a cause for severe punishment. Formerly those who divulged the secrets to the uninitiated or who tried to escape were hanged, but not until they had completed the term of the school. Thus, by the most severe, even cruel, measures were the tests of manhood made among the Thonga.

Besides the endurance tests the boys had instruction in formulas and songs, learning them by rote. Many hours were devoted to formal learning, the object of which seems to have been to praise the school. There were a number of proverbs which taught acquaintance with sex matters. The only practical art taught was hunting. Other features of the retirement period were masked dancing, ceremonial bathing, and the choosing of a new name. Much of this training has the same relation to tribal life as our teaching of Latin has had to our everyday, practical, or even intellectual world; it was done purely for the sake of discipline.

In Australia there is also group teaching of youths. The initiation

rites are concerned likewise with teaching the boys the secrets of
adulthood, but the rites center around the operations of circumcision
and subincision and are more unified than among the Thonga. The
trials and tests are quite similar; there is beating, starving, hard
manual labor, not to speak of the suffering involved in the operation
of subincision. All of the tests, however, seem to have a closer relation to the future life of the boys than they have among the Thonga.
In Australia one of the most secret and sacred things is the bull-
roarer. No one may see it but initiates. It represents an ancestral
spirit, and its noise is the voice of the spirit. The penalty for an
uninitiate seeing it may be death. Other things taught along with
the knowledge of the bull-roarer are totem secrets and the history
of the ancestors. One part of the instruction takes place during the
totem ceremony.[88]

In this case the training has definite reference to the tribal life.
It may be, however, that the Thonga training was also more closely
related to daily life if the interpretations were known. On the other
hand, there are numerous places where the occupation or pursuit
of the novice is related to his probable later needs only indirectly,
or to beliefs in imitative magic. An adolescent girl, for instance, may
spend hours picking fir leaves from the branches.[89] She may never
have to do this afterward, but it is a way of keeping her busy. The
fact that she does it will cause her henceforth to be industrious instead of lazy.

In the section on etiquette and ethics I shall mention cases of morals
as exacting as ours, but carried out for reasons the direct opposite of
ours. The moral ideas of a given group are taught, as are industries
and social customs, in various ways, but the most outstanding method
of impressing them is by example. Industrious women with high
standards of virtuosity will, in the long run, have skillful daughters
with high standards. The upstanding, independent good traders of
Manus have sons (either their own or adopted) who ape their behavior. Adults with lazy slipshod habits are likely to see those habits
reflected in their children. Primitives are almost uniformly aware
of these facts. Indeed, among the Oto Indians, parents are respected
according to the behavior of their children.[90]

There are perhaps few fallacies as firmly believed in as the one
that posits for the origin of folk tales the purpose of instructing
children. Even among the Africans, where the moralizing element is
ever-present in fables, the stories are tales for adults and are enjoyed

by them as much as by the children. Among the American Indians myths and tales may be said to be primarily for the grown-ups. This does not mean that the children do not know them or that they do not appreciate moral or ethical allusions. Children from the earliest infancy hear them; they learn automatically from the intonation of the voices of the elders, and from the discussions and analogies drawn, what their parents consider good and what bad. However, the myth-body is not primarily for the children, but is rather an aesthetic adult outlet and may be told to put adults as well as children to sleep. Almost every tribe has stories which they consider children's tales, or moralizing stories for the main purpose of inculcating virtue; but an outsider, without knowing the philosophy of the particular tribe, would not be able to pick out these stories from the others.

I would emphasize, nevertheless, the fact that the very rehearsal of tales by adults with the children present, as well as frequent reference to the tales in various situations of daily life, exerts a potent influence in the teaching and learning process. Children learn the right and wrong of a matter by implication and inference and by repetition, and it would be difficult, if not impossible, for them to tell how they know many things. Know them they do, and without analyzing or thinking about them they react automatically as do their elders to a given situation.

In Africa and other parts of the Old World the proverb is a well-developed literary form. Proverbs have an important place in all phases of daily life and are constantly being quoted. One class of such proverbs refers especially to the training of children, but another quite as extensive stresses the ideal behavior of parents to children.[91]

Ethics and etiquette. Ethical behavior means conformity with the standards of the community. According to the importance of an action in the life of the community, nonconformity may be merely a breach of etiquette, an irritating misconduct, a crime, or, when accompanied by a religious connotation, a sin. The rules of conduct are different for behavior toward members of the community and outsiders. They may not be the same for every tribal member, for ethical conduct among members of the family, sib, or society of which a person is a member may differ from that toward outsiders.

Since the customary standards of a community are very different the question must be asked whether there are any generally valid standards that are binding in the narrow community of which an individual is a member. There is no doubt that the distinction be-

tween good and bad conduct is universal, but it is not easy to find
an absolute criterion of what is good and what is bad, for in many
cultures murder, theft, and lying are sanctioned under certain conditions. It is only when we confine our consideration to the smallest
groups which have social solidarity that we find these acts considered as crimes. When there is no group of firm solidarity, when
individual is pitched against individual, the concept of crime is weak.
Such extreme cases are rarely found. Ordinarily the ethical standard
within the group demands mutual helpfulness and respect for the
welfare of all members. Murder, rape, theft, and lying within the
group are condemned. Altruism and even self-sacrifice for individuals,
but first of all for the group, are demanded.

There is no tribe, be it ever so primitive, which does not have an
ethical code. This code refers, however, to the relations of a man to
his fellow-men and does not need to be related to rewards or punishments in after life.

A sharp distinction must be made between the behavior of man
to members of his own group and to outsiders. In most primitive
societies the alien is always an enemy. The custom of many people
to designate themselves as "men" and to give to foreign tribes
names as to animals shows the difference of attitude. The foreigner
is dangerous, and the duty to one's own tribe is to destroy him. In
the following chapter these external relations and their weakening
in more complex societies will be described. We are here interested in
the moral code which is binding for members of a society in their
mutual relations.

We often hear in our own society the formulation of an individual
code, "I believe I can do anything so long as I do not cause others
to suffer from my action."

I shall not go into the complicated matter as to how we know
whether others are affected or not, but I may point out by this attitude the great difference between primitive man and ourselves. To
the mind of primitive man there are few acts which affect the individual alone. Practically everything he does, be it to us ever so
trivial, affects his group. By obeying the moral code he may bring
good fortune to himself and to his people; by neglecting it, not only
will he himself suffer, but all his fellows with him. Punishment is
real and immediate; it is not reserved for a later time and world.

I have headed this section *Ethics and Etiquette* advisedly, for it
is impossible even in our own society to make an absolute division

between these categories. Physical cleanliness is often a more potent reason for accepting or rejecting a stranger than is honesty or some other sterling moral quality. A person who eats with his knife is rarely accepted at all; if he is, it is only by the most tolerant of our population.

These two illustrations show that for practical purposes the domain of ethics may overlap that of etiquette, and also that there is a great discrepancy between ideals and practice, a truism we need not discuss for our own society. There may be as great a difference between teaching and practice in primitive society. With respect to ideas concerning morals and manners there is a great abundance of material. I shall be able to cite only a few examples which show even better than our previous discussion that all depends upon a "state of mind."

In East Africa, for example, a child who does not pay attention to an elder when addressed is severely punished. This is a matter of morals, for if the child is not respectful to his living ancestors, how can he ever properly observe the respect due to those who are dead, but who nevertheless exert great power over the living? [92]

At the present time we have no practical definition of modesty, although it is not so long ago that the exposure of an ankle was almost a "sin." Missionaries have "made it a sin," in the South Sea islands and other places to which they have gone, for women to appear with uncovered breasts. An example from primitive life matches the attitude in ridiculousness. In a certain area of northern New Guinea where women wear not a stitch of clothes it is customary to wear a particular kind of earring. No woman would be so immodest as to appear in public without these earrings. To do so would bring down violent criticism upon her head.

Cultures are composed of small elements, and it is no novelty to find a major catastrophe growing out of the most trivial cause, but let us consider some of the greater "sins." There is among primitives behavior which is equivalent to crime, but which may not be defined just as we define it, nor is it handled in exactly the same way.

Perhaps the most general "sin" is incest. In more simply organized tribes incest would be defined in its narrower sense as it is with us: sexual relations between siblings or between parents and children. In more complexly organized societies where the sib, totem, or phratry prevails, it may be considered as great an offense to marry a member of a sib or phratry as to mate with a parent. Punishment for such an offense varies greatly, from mild criticism to severe supernatural vengeance wreaked upon the offenders, their progeny, even on their group.

In contrast to this emphasis on incest is the almost utter lack, in our sense at least, of ideas like our own regarding sex relations. Polyandry and polygyny have been discussed as recognized patterns of marriage. Trial marriage is approved in certain areas and is even successful. The Todas of India are perhaps as loose as any regarding sex matters; nevertheless a man may not acknowledge his own child if it is born to a woman not a member of his own moiety.[93]

The Eskimo are only one of a number of tribes who consider lack of hospitality a social vice. This idea goes so far that a man is considered stingy and asocial if he refuses to lend his wife to a stranger who has not brought his own with him.

The Chukchee place several other moral ideas in different order from ourselves. Just as hospitality is a virtue and wife-lending no sin, so filial piety is so important that a man may have to lay aside all paternal sentiment in favor of obedience. Old people who begin to lose their faculties and who think they are becoming a burden to their families may request their sons to kill them. A faithful son should obey his parents in such a case, no matter how opposed the action may be to his emotions. When the deeper significance of such an obligation is known it is not difficult to understand. The Chukchee believe that in the future world everyone continues to live just as he left this world.[94] Naturally no one wants to be for eternity old, feeble, blind, or helpless.

The value set on human life is exceedingly varied. There is perhaps no tribe which has no definition of murder. If an Eskimo kills another a feud between the families is precipitated. It is a murder and must be atoned, but if a man proves to be a menace to the community through greed or other antisocial behavior, the men of the community, after giving him a chance to improve his behavior, may agree to do away with him if he does not, and the murdered man's family will seek no redress.[95]

In many places, where human life is taken, it is in the belief of a higher good. In West Africa the power of the fetish of a secret society may be renewed by the spilling of human blood. The renewal of this power is for the good of the whole community. Even cannibalism may have a lofty ideal. In parts of Melanesia where it is prevalent, it may give power to warriors, houses, canoes. In the Trobriands the tasting of the flesh of a deceased father, though abhorred, is nevertheless considered a duty of love because that parent nursed and cared for the child who now accords him this honor.[96]

The origins and purpose of infanticide are difficult — usually impossible — to determine. In Africa, however, abnormal children, such as twins and those born with teeth or with a harelip, may be killed in order to preserve the rest of the tribe from abnormality. This, too, in spite of the fact that mothers may love these children and destroy them only because of social pressure.[97]

These are a few of the prevailing attitudes regarding offenses and crimes in specific communities. Not only do ethical ideas overlap into the domain of etiquette, but they may also overlap such formulation of law as may exist. Duties to an African chief may be obligatory because of his high birth, which may give him political power, but they may be enhanced by the fact that his ancestors are tribal gods. In the same tribe a man may be required by that chief, exerting the power of the law, to pay a fine to another man for an offense, and in lieu of the fine may pawn himself or his child for service to work it out. This is an example which shows how social, religious, political, and legal notions interlock, no behavior being easily classified in any one of these categories.

Breaches of etiquette, ethics, or law are punished in many different ways varying from a slight feeling of insult for what we might consider a major crime to punishment by death or isolation for something we should classify merely as an "act of God." The murder of a stingy Eskimo by his fellows is not felt to require retaliation; it is "capital punishment." The birth of twins to a woman of West Africa, an "accident" many in our society would welcome, stamps her as an outcast for the rest of her life. She is punished in a pitiable manner for having been "abnormal" according to Yoruba definition. Many offenses are social, as may be seen by the punishments they entail, but they overlap into the realm of the religious when punishment is meted out by the supernatural, as is frequently the case.

The material we have on primitive ethics is largely implicit in other writings. Collections of African proverbs, for example, are most instructive in pointing ideals; fables and folk tales may show the discrepancy between ideals and practice. In studying primitive ethics one must be hypercautious in interpretation of motives, because one thing we may assuredly depend upon: namely, that the cultural background, religious belief, social practice, oral tradition, even economic and industrial habits, may determine the attitudes of the

natives to any one ideal, and that hardly any one will agree with
ours. Consequently the question must be viewed, as should all questions of a similar nature, from the point of view of the culture in
which it is found and not from our own.

FOOTNOTES

1. The details are summarized from Alverdes, F., *Tiersoziologie* (Leipzig, 1925).
   The English edition, *The Psychology of Animals* (1932), does not include
   all the examples cited in the German edition. See also Wheeler, W. M.,
   Ants (1926).
2. Malinowski, B., *The Family among the Australian Aborigines* (London, 1913),
   p. 288.
3. Trenk, Oberleutnant, *Buschleute der Namib*, Mitteilungen aus den deutschen
   Schutzgebieten, vol. 23 (1910), p. 169.
4. Gifford, E. W., "Miwok Lineages and the Political Unit in Aboriginal California," *American Anthropologist*, vol. 28 (1926), pp. 389–401.
5. Lowie, R. H., *Notes on Hopi Clans*, Anthropological Papers, American
   Museum of Natural History, vol. 30 (1928), p. 330.
6. Reichard, G. A., *Social Life of the Navajo Indians*, Columbia University
   Contributions to Anthropology, vol. 7 (1928), pp. 30, 34, 60 ff.
7. Fortune, R. F., *Sorcerers of Dobu* (1932), p. 8.
8. Boas, F., *Tsimshian Mythology*, Annual Report of the Bureau of American
   Ethnology, vol. 31 (1916), p. 481.
9. Bunzel, R., *Introduction to Zuñi Ceremonialism*, Annual Report of the Bureau
   of American Ethnology, vol. 47 (1932), p. 477.
10. Wilson, G. L., *Agriculture of the Hidatsa Indians: An Indian Interpretation*,
    University of Minnesota, Studies in the Social Sciences, no. 9 (1917),
    pp. 9, 10.
11. Lowie, R. H., *op. cit.*, p. 338.
12. Rivers, W. H. R., *The Todas* (1906), pp. 542 ff., 643 ff., 679 ff.
13. Spencer, B., and Gillen, F. J., *Northern Tribes of Central Australia* (London,
    1904), p. 149.
14. Fletcher, A. C., and La Flesche, F., *The Omaha Tribe*, Annual Report of
    the Bureau of American Ethnology, vol. 27 (1911), pp. 137, 155, 162,
    188.
15. Malinowski, B., *The Sexual Life of Savages in North-Western Melanesia* (Lon-
    don, 1929), p. 20.
16. Malinowski, B., *Crime and Custom in Savage Society* (1932), pp. 78 ff.
17. Junod, H., *The Life of a South African Tribe* (London, 1927), vol. 1, pp. 46,
    267 ff.
18. *Ibid.*, pp. 232–233.
19. Rattray, R. S., *Ashanti* (Oxford, 1923), p. 82.
20. Bastian, A., *Die deutsche Expedition an der Loango-Küste* (Jena, 1874–75),
    p. 197.
21. Malinowski, B., *The Family among the Australian Aborigines*, p. 179; Spencer,
    B., and Gillen, F. J., *op. cit.*, pp. 606, 616.

22. Boas, F., *Eskimo of Baffin Land and Hudson Bay*, Bulletin of the American Museum of Natural History, vol. 15, Part I (1901), p. 483.
23. Malinowski, B., *The Sexual Life of Savages*, pp. 209–210.
24. Boas, F., "The Social Organization of the Tribes of the North Pacific Coast," *American Anthropologist*, vol. 26, no. 3 (1924), pp. 323–332.
25. Boas, F., *Tsimshian Mythology*, Annual Report of the Bureau of American Ethnology, vol. 31 (1916), p. 481.
26. Boas, F., *Primitive Art* (Oslo, 1927), pp. 250–251.
27. Seligmann, C. G., *The Melanesians of British New Guinea* (Cambridge, 1910), p. 74.
28. Fletcher, A. C., and La Flesche, F., *op. cit.*, p. 162.
29. Spencer, B., and Gillen, F. J., *op. cit.*, p. 149.
30. Rivers, W. H. R., *The History of Melanesian Society* (Cambridge, 1914), vol. 2, p. 76.
31. Fletcher, A. C., and La Flesche, F., *op. cit.*, p. 188.
32. Lowie, R. H., *Primitive Society* (1920), p. 290.
33. Benedict, R., *The Concept of the Guardian Spirit in America*, Memoirs of the American Anthropological Association, no. 29 (1923).
34. Frazer, J. G., *Totemism and Exogamy* (London, 1910).
35. Durkheim, E., *The Elementary Forms of the Religious Life* (English translation, London, 1915).
36. Lowie, R. H., *Primitive Society*, pp. 137 ff.
37. Goldenweiser, A. A., "Totemism: An Analytical Study," *Journal of American Folk-Lore*, vol. 23 (1910), pp. 179–293.
38. Boas, F., *Tsimshian Mythology*, Annual Report of the Bureau of American Ethnology, vol. 31 (1916), pp. 515 ff., and "The Origin of Totemism," *American Anthropologist*, vol. 18 (1916), pp. 319–326.
39. Rivers, W. H. R., *The Todas*, pp. 518, 519.
40. *Ibid.*, p. 521.
41. *Ibid.*, pp. 526, 529.
42. Boas, F., *The Central Eskimo*, Annual Report of the Bureau of American Ethnology, vol. 6 (1888), p. 579.
43. Smith, E. W., and Dale, A. M., *The Ila-Speaking Peoples of Northern Rhodesia* (London, 1920), vol. 2, pp. 69, 114.
44. Spencer, B., and Gillen, F. J., *op. cit.*, pp. 96, 97.
45. Malinowski, B., *The Sexual Life of Savages*, pp. 51–75, 109–141.
46. Jenks, A. E., *The Bontoc-Igorot*, Ethnological Survey Publications, vol. 1, (Manila, 1905), pp. 66–67.
47. Gifford, E. W., "Miwok Moieties," *University of California Publications in American Archaeology and Ethnology*, vol. 12 (1916), p. 190.
48. Junod, H., *op. cit.*, vol. 1, p. 286.
49. Rivers, W. H. R., *The History of Melanesian Society*, vol. 1, p. 209.
50. Kroeber, A. L., *Handbook of the Indians of California*, Bulletin of the Bureau of American Ethnology, no. 78 (1925), pp. 27 ff.
51. Jochelson, W., *The Yukaghir and Yukaghirized Tungus*, Jesup Expedition, vol. 10 (1926), pp. 86 ff.
52. Malinowski, B., *The Family among Australian Aborigines*, pp. 55, 56.
53. Mead, M., *Growing Up in New Guinea* (1930), pp. 155, 157.

54. Thrum, T. G., *Fornander Collection of Hawaiian Antiquities*, Memoirs of the Bernice P. Bishop Museum, vol. 4 (1916), p. 48.
55. Frazer, J. G., *op. cit.*, vol. 4, pp. 105 ff.
56. Freud, S., "Über einige Übereinstimmungen im Seelenleben der Wilden und der Neurotiker," *Imago* (1912), pp. 30–33.
57. Tylor, E. B., "On a Method of Investigating the Development of Institutions," *Journal of the Royal Anthropological Institute*, vol. 18 (1888–89), pp. 245–272.
58. Rivers, W. H. R., *The History of Melanesian Society*, vol. 2, pp. 153 ff.
59. Parsons, E. C., "Avoidance in Melanesia," *Journal of American Folk-Lore*, vol. 29 (1916), pp. 282–292.
60. Lowie, R. H., *Primitive Society*, pp. 84–110.
61. Smith, E. W., and Dale, A. M., *op. cit.*, vol. 2, p. 51.
62. Junod, H., *op. cit.*, vol. 1, pp. 190, 199.
63. Rivers, W. H. R., *The Todas*, p. 525.
64. Boas, F., *The Central Eskimo*, p. 612.
65. Reichard, G. A., *op. cit.*, p. 96.
66. Smith, E. W., and Dale, A. M., *op. cit.*, vol. 1, pp. 365 ff.
67. Radcliffe-Brown, A. R., "The Social Organization of Australian Tribes," *Oceania*, vol. 1 (1930), pp. 58–59. Illustrates similar varieties of combination between kinship and social systems.
68. Riggs, S. R., *Dakota Grammar, Texts and Ethnography*, Contributions to North American Ethnology, vol. 9 (1893), pp. xviii ff.
69. Boas, F., *Mythology of the Bella Coola Indians*, Jesup Expedition, vol. 1, Part II (1898).
70. Malinowski, B., *Argonauts of the Western Pacific* (1922), p. 65.
71. Lowie, R. H., *Primitive Religion* (1924), p. 77.
72. Lowie, R. H., *Primitive Society*, p. 340.
73. Deloria, Ella, unpublished MS.
74. Hearne, S., *Journey from Prince of Wales Fort in Hudson's Bay to the Northern Ocean 1769–1772* (London, 1795), p. 313.
75. Kroeber, A. L., *op. cit.*, p. 4.
76. Rattray, R. S., *op. cit.*
77. Goldenweiser, A. A., *Early Civilization* (1921), chap. 3.
78. Bunzel, R., *Introduction to Zuñi Ceremonialism*, pp. 518, 528, and personal information.
79. Underhill, R. M., *The Autobiography of a Papago Woman*, Memoirs of the American Anthropological Association, no. 46 (1936).
80. Kroeber, A. L., *op. cit.*, pp. 45, 46, 63.
81. Goldenweiser, A. A., *Early Civilization*, chap. 3.
82. Rattray, R. S., *op. cit.*
83. Linderman, F. B., *American: The Life Story of a Great Indian* (1930), pp. 8, 19.
84. Bamler, G., "Pädagogik der Tami," *Beilage zu den Abhandlungen der Naturhistorischen Gesellschaft zu Nürnberg*, vol. 20 (1913), pp. 1–24.
85. Mead, M., *op. cit.*
86. Michelson, T., *The Autobiography of a Fox Woman*, Annual Report of the Bureau of American Ethnology, vol. 40 (1925), pp. 295–349.

87. Junod, H., *op. cit.*, vol. 1, pp. 71–93.
88. Spencer, B., and Gillen, F. J., *op. cit.*
89. Teit, J., *The Thompson Indians of British Columbia*, Jesup Expedition, vol. 1, Part IV (1900), p. 315.
90. Whitman, W., *The Oto*, Columbia University Contributions to Anthropology, vol. 28 (1937), p. 43.
91. Doke, C. M., *Lamba Folk-Lore*, Memoirs of the American Folk-Lore Society, vol. 20 (1927), p. 310.
92. Junod, H., *op. cit.*, vol. 1, p. 360; vol. 2, p. 590.
93. Rivers, W. H. R., *The Todas*, p. 505.
94. Bogoras, W., *The Chukchee*, Jesup Expedition, vol. 7 (1904–09), p. 563.
95. The informal article by Boas, F., "An Eskimo Winter," summarizes and emphasizes many moral ideas of the Eskimo. *American Indian Life*, edited by Elsie Clews Parsons (1922), pp. 363 ff.
96. Malinowski, B., *The Sexual Life of Savages*, pp. 155–156.
97. Talbot, P. A., *The Peoples of Southern Nigeria* (London, 1926), vol. 3, p. 720.

GENERAL REFERENCES

Benedict, R., *Patterns of Culture* (1934).
Goldenweiser, A. A., *Early Civilization* (1921).
Lowie, R. H., *Primitive Society* (1920).
Rivers, W. H. R., *The Todas* (1906).
Thurnwald, R., *Die menschliche Gesellschaft* (Berlin and Leipzig, 1932).

CHAPTER X

GOVERNMENT

JULIUS E. LIPS

In the study of government among primitive tribes, we encounter the same difficulties of terminology that we find in almost all questions of primitive law. This may be due to our persistent inclination to substitute our modern conception of law for legal conditions of an entirely different character. Even a simple description of *facts* pertaining to law in a primitive tribe may, if we use our legal terminology, cause a distortion of the legal content of primitive institutions.[1]

The study of primitive law is further complicated by the fact that neither in our present state of civilization nor in that of primitive people can law be regarded apart from the ramifications of the whole culture. Law is intimately interwoven with other correlative component factors of human civilization, particularly with economy.[2] The question as to the priority of law or of other social phenomena is misleading. We may, however, state that functional interrelations exist between economic, social, and legal institutions. This does not mean that in the case of a people with a certain economic pattern we must necessarily meet with corresponding legal institutions, for it is entirely possible that in the course of history legal institutions were taken over from others without adoption of the corresponding economic pattern, and vice versa. Attempts to establish the origins of human social development and the primeval forms of law have not been lacking. The endeavors made by modern economists and students of law to define this primeval state by pure abstraction have not taken into account the fact that legal terms as well as the content of legal patterns have developed historically and are an expression of cultural structure.

In contrast to this tendency other students, instead of trying to establish a line of development of law among primitive tribes, question the very existence of such development, and direct their efforts first of all to monographic descriptions. On this basis it is gradually becoming possible, through comparison of the legal institutions of several peoples, to find what differentiates them and what they have in common. This aim has been expressed by John Wigmore in these words: "There is almost nothing [available in literature] by way of comparing and contrasting the ideas in different systems and of elucidating their correspondence or divergence — in short, of the evolution of legal ideas." [3] And a similar note is sounded by the resolution of the International Congress for Comparative Law held in the Hague (1932): "That the next Congress put on its agenda for study and reports . . . written and customary laws of the peoples of Africa, Asia, and Oceania in order to bring the study of exotic law into the field of consideration in comparative law, and give opportunity for the ethnology of law and the archaeology of law to be of greater mutual aid . . . that there be assigned a special section to consider legal history, legal ethnology, and folklore in future meetings of the Congress." [4]

Although the demand for a general historical study of law has been so clearly expressed, the majority of students still follow the historical school of law founded by Savigny. The attempt is made to discover through deduction the primitive conditions of law; to seek for a mathematical congruence between the differentiated legal concepts of modern law and the laws of earlier cultural stages. Thus Post, one of the founders of the modern study of comparative law, accepts the views of Hobbes, and states that a legal community in which the prerogatives of the individual are given up can arise only through the collective alliances of individuals. In the world of primitive man no such thing as an individual in our legal sense exists. As in other respects, so also in legal concepts the individual in these cultures is merged in the society in which he lives, and his individual acts have repercussions in the whole social structure. The individualistic conception of law as a matter concerning the isolated individual and not the individual as a member of society [5] has been established in extreme form by the private law of modern civilization.

The technique of comparative law up to the most recent time suffers therefore from three assumptions which cannot be accepted: first, that the primitive forms of law may be traced back by means of pure deduction; second, that a similarity exists in the concepts of legal forms and norms in all cultures; and third, that the individual as a legal unit and legal subject exists from the beginning. These concepts are valid to a great extent among highly civilized peoples and

tribes with advanced agriculture; they fail, however, when applied
to simpler agricultural tribes, and are entirely inapplicable to food-
gatherers and hunters.

The failure to ʻappreciate the connection between the problems
of law and the cultural structure as a whole has been an obstacle in
the way of studies of the historical development of law. Thus Radcliffe-Brown, supported by Roscoe Pound, with the help of interpretations taken from modern law, expressed the opinion that no
law whatsoever exists unless a legal norm is enforced by compelling
legal statutes and by "the systematical application of the force of
politically organized society. . . . In this sense some simple societies
have no law." [6] If this method were generally applied we should
have to deny also the existence of religion, art, and other fields of
culture in primitive civilizations. However, there is no people without
fire, without language, without religion, or without law. Our social,
religious, and legal concepts do not coincide with those of the
primitives; what we must do is to find the correct equivalent for
our modern institutions in primitive societies. This consideration
should correct the impression of those students of primitive law who
cling to the idea that the existence of sanctions is necessary as a
definition of law.[7]

Boas has already pointed out that in the study of primitive cultures the rigid definitions of our modern institutions cannot be used,
and he has especially emphasized the relativity of cultural factors.
Malinowski makes a fundamentally similar demand — with special
reference to the field of primitive law [8] — for the establishment of
the primitive equivalents as shown in the functions of institutions.
However, knowledge of the function of a legal institution does not
imply a knowledge of the primitive law of the tribe in question;
it is concerned neither with the pure nor with the preventive legal
norm,[9] but merely with the dynamic factor of a legal process. The
functional study of primitive law especially neglects the problem of
the development of law and of single legal norms while stressing their
present status. Some historians of law are disinclined to regard the
function as the essential characteristic of law, but even in primitive
cultures there exist definite legal norms and legal "statutes," so that
law by no means has a purely functional existence.

When we look about in the world of primitive man for an institution which we moderns could describe as government, we should,
strictly speaking, first discuss the terminology of our concepts of

"government" and "state." That cannot be done here. It should be remarked, however, that among modern ethnologists Schmidt and Koppers [10] as well as Graebner [11] apply the modern term "state" even to the earliest cultures of the food-gatherers and hunters. Lowie is much more cautious. Leaning to a great extent on Morgan, he would prefer to avoid even the term "political organization" in reference to early cultural stages.[12] Oppenheimer,[13] basing his ethnological data on Schmidt and Koppers, whom he sometimes misunderstands, rejects the term "state" for early cultures and uses this term only for the "class state resulting from conquest and subjugation." Menghin [14] uses the term "state" in Oppenheimer's sense. In a definition of "state," as in that of "government," the deciding factor is whether the viewpoint we adopt is that of twentieth century man or of primitive man within his respective society.

The aims of such institutions among primitives are much more amenable to modern analogues than are the devices and institutions used for their realization. For here too — and this holds true of all primitives — their principal service is to secure "life, liberty, and the pursuit of happiness," whatever that happiness may be,[15] for members of the community, the local group, the tribe, or the people. The purposes and aim of government in a primitive society are legally and socially the same as in modern society. They serve to regulate life within and without. However, the devices for the attainment of this goal are different. It has frequently been emphasized that the tribes of food-gatherers and hunters are completely without government. Stow [16] remarks with reason that authors who believe this "can have been in contact only with degenerated and almost completely destroyed tribal relics, with a miserable fugitive group." We might use instead of "government" the terms "governmentlike institutions" or "pre-government" for the simpler cultures,[17] in order to indicate that the aims coincide relatively with similar ones in our political life, but that their specific forms are distinct, although they may seem to be similar. We may define government among primitives as the institutions which serve the purpose of holding the community together, safeguarding its food supply, and guaranteeing peace within and without its borders.

Among simpler primitives there are above all two principles which form the foundation of government: first, the territorial principle — that is, the geographically limited area belonging to a number of people; second, the community which exceeds the single family, be it local group, clan, tribe, or people. On these two pillars repose the governmentlike institutions of primitive cultures. The territorial principle has often been neglected in literature. Whenever we hear of communities not tied to the soil, as in the case of certain Central African pygmies or tribes of South American fishermen, we are dealing with secondary conditions, and our sources happen to contain no reference to territory. The objection that conquering tribes, such as the Hyksos, during their great migration and their occupation of Egypt, had a government without territorial principle is not valid either. They had a territorial principle in their homeland, and after the conquests they created a similar one. The objection holds true only for the era of migrations and expeditions of conquest.

Food-gatherers and hunters. In such tribes as the Australian aborigines and the Tasmanians, the Bushmen, the Veddas, Botocudos, and Fuegians, the territorial legal unit is the local group, not the single family or the single individual. The territory of such a local group varies among the Australians from 4000 to 10,000 square miles, and there are from twenty to one hundred members in the legal community. The boundaries of the country claimed by the group are well known, not only to the members of the group but also to those of the neighboring groups. They are mainly natural, rarely artificial. If the hunting territory of a local group is subdivided into family hunting grounds, as is the case among the Bushmen and some Australian tribes, the boundary of another family's hunting ground is not violated under any conditions.[18] Among certain tribes of the northern part of southern Australia, boundaries are marked by stone heaps or (among the Veddas) the forest paths are closed off.[19]

The group in its entirety reacts against a violation of its territory — not the single individual or the single family. Even among the Tasmanians a violation of the boundary was equivalent to a declaration of war.[20] The same applies to the Australian food-gatherers and hunters, for whom the atonement for boundary violations always was a war between the groups. Excepting boundary violations, the local group resorted to war only in cases of revenge for murder or abduction of a woman. It was the group's task to take vengeance on the group, not the individual's or the family's task to revenge itself on a family. The strength of feeling of solidarity of the local group is shown in a report from Northwest-Central Queensland.[21] "When about to swim across any big stream or river that he suspects or fears, the aboriginal will speak to this Being [that is, the Kammare, a supernatural water-snake] . . . about as follows: 'Do not touch me. I belong to this country.' But were he to cross even his own country's river with a stranger he might be engulfed.''

Wars waged on account of the violation of hunting grounds are not continued until one of the local groups is destroyed. Often it is decided that an equal number of men from each side shall fight. In most cases the quarrel is settled by means of a duel ordered by the group.[22] Indeed, even then there is no intention to continue the fight until one of the combatants is killed. It is sufficient that one shall be incapacitated. The Botocudos, in such a duel, leave their bows and arrows at home and use sticks only. Prince zu Wied [23] describes in detail such a duel which resulted from the violation of a hunting ground, the women taking part by general hair-pulling.

Sometimes a local group was forced, because of the increase of its members and the consequent necessity of extending its economic basis, to make an active invasion into the territory of another group. J. Frazer [24] reports such a case in connection with a local group of the Walarai. "They sent their public messenger to one of the adjoining subtribes, asking for a part of the latter's land. This was refused, as being against tribal law, and also because the 'taurai' in question was not big enough to admit of the proposal. The former subtribe then sent to say they would come and take what they wanted. The latter answered that in that case they would appeal for justice and help to the neighboring subtribes. Thereupon both sides prepared for war, met, and, as usual, much talking and angry speech-making followed. It was at last agreed that next day an equal number from each side should fight it out, but when the time came the dispute was settled by single combat. This is the common cause and issue of a tribal quarrel."

Though in general death was the punishment for any transgression of the boundary, there were certain preferred persons, messengers who bore some distinguishing mark, who were permitted to enter foreign territory at the order of a neighboring clan for the purpose of buying, exchanging, or conferring with others of their kind. This happened especially when the region belonging to a clan contained needed natural products, such as stones for axes, ochre or the much desired narcotic *pitcheri* in large quantities. If such goods were wanted in exchange, the local group concerned had to be officially notified. In most cases an invasion of foreign territory without permission meant death.

Howitt [25] reports from Southeast Australia that a Wudthaurung man had broken stones from a quarry of the Wurunjerri without their permission. The two groups met at the boundary line between their hunting ground to discuss the case. "At the meeting the Wudthaurung sat in one place, and the Wurunjerri in another, but within speaking distance. The old men of each side sat together with the younger men behind them. Billi-billeri had behind him Bungerim, to whom he 'gave his word.' The latter then standing up said, 'Did some of you send this young man to take tomahawk stone?' The headman of the Wudthaurung replied: 'No, we sent no one.' Then Billi-billeri said to Bungerim, 'Say to the old men that they must tell that young man not to do so any more. When the people speak of wanting stone, the old men must send us notice.' Bungerim repeated this in a loud tone, and the old men of the Wudthaurung replied: 'That is all right, and we will do so.' Then they spoke strongly to the young man who had stolen the stone and both parties were again friendly with each other."

These few examples give us a picture of the local group's reaction to outsiders in regard to land ownership. The solidarity of the community expressed in their reactions to conflicts with outside communities binds it with strong ties and holds it together. This is natural, when we consider that a person cannot leave the territory of his local group without the fear of being killed.[26] One of the great goals is to secure outward peace. Within the community too, the preservation of peace and mutual assistance in the securing of food is the supreme task.

The facts just described, referring to the relationship of the local group to its territory and the group's reaction to the outside, show that in the legal consciousness of the food-gatherers and the hunters the complex quality of legal norms predominates. That is to say, when there is no legal differentiation between the soil and the plants growing on it and the animals which are hunted we may conclude from the local group's outward reaction that the problem of providing food is not an individual one, as Buecher believes, but a collective one, for the animals and the plants belong to the community as a whole; neither has the woman an *exclusive* right to the plants gathered by her for food, nor has the man any such right to the animal he has killed. At the most he has a right to use it, a right of usufruct which can be nullified at any time by the community.

In fact, our sources are quite explicit on this point. The provision of food is, as we should put it today, determined by a reciprocal insurance, sanctioned by public opinion. Every individual knows the norms which bind the legal community.[27] The distribution of the kill is definitely regulated, and the part of the animal given to the less fortunate hunter is not a gift but merely the fulfilment of a legal obligation. When a hunter has killed a kangaroo,[28] one hind leg belongs to the hunter's father, the other to his paternal uncle, the tail to his sister, the shoulder to his brother and the liver to himself. Among the Ngarigo only the head of the killed wombat belongs to the hunter; all other parts are distributed within *and outside of* his immediate family.[29] Regulated distribution has been reported of a great number of other Australian tribes of food-gatherers and hunters.[30] The providing of food is an obligation not only within the family, but it extends to the local group. The same applies to other tribes of food-gatherers and hunters, such as the Bushmen, Botocudos,[31] and Veddas. Concerning the last named the Sarasins report that the honeycombs of the rock bees (*Bambara*) are equally divided among all families.[32]

Since we see that the disposition of land and the regulation of food supply are problems of the community as a whole, we are justified in asking whether there is any private property at all in our sense, and if so, how it is regulated. The answer to this question is not easy. But we may say that if the term "property" is used in our modern sense, "the absolute domination of one person over one thing," then there is no private property here.

When our sources give reports of private property, such as self-made weapons, tools, ornaments and articles of dress, or even quarries of ochre deposits, we must realize that such private property is often burdened with so many rights of third parties that we can probably speak only of a right similar to proprietorship, a sort of representative right which is a commission or usufruct but not a dominium.[33] At any rate movables which are valuable and necessary to the clan can never be private property. "The individual is not recognized. He has no independent rights," write Fison and Howitt.[34] The consciousness of personal property in our sense is altogether lacking, and presents from White people, for instance, which were given to certain persons will in a short time appear in the possession of other persons who received them from their "owner." This is by no means contradicted by the fact that investigators, when they want to obtain some object from a child, have their attention called to the point that this object is the child's "property." Certainly children too may have these rights of disposition among food-gatherers and hunters. Weapons, ornaments, dress, and household utensils made by the individual may be things to which this individual has a right. The community will not interfere so long as its interests are not threatened. Another factor enters into the situation. Especially among food-gatherers and hunters we find the idea that an individual's weapons, clothing, and ornaments are indissolubly connected with his person and are given him to take along into his grave, so that in this case these objects are legal objects of a special type.*

No doubt we might arrive at greater clarity on the question as to the concept of private ownership of things which are important for the community if the language of the tribes in question were studied with this point in mind. I have repeatedly made the point that a study of the possessive pronoun would probably show that in a great number of languages the terms "me" and "my" in connection with certain nouns are lacking and are replaced by "our." This would be a great help and would give greater clarity to the problems discussed. Boas, for instance, recently showed that among the Dakota certain objects like food, water, etc., could never be used with the possessive pronoun.[35] A study of legal terms may cast new light upon many legal institutions of primitive tribes. The occurrence and significance of expressions of gratitude in language and behavior may also be significant. When is a term for thanking used, if it occurs at all in a language? The Montagnais-Naskapi have no word for it, not even a circumlocution, while the Eskimo have the term constantly at the tip of the tongue. Even after borrowing a boat, the Montagnais borrower does not express his gratitude. The Dakota gives thanks for help rendered in work, but not for gifts which honor the giver and not the recipient. In the reciprocal aid in providing food the use of a term for thanking might be regarded as superfluous, since the giving of help and the dividing up of the booty are legal obligations, but in regard to private law valuable conclusions re-

* It might be objected that these rights which I describe as similar to proprietorship do signify property even in our modern sense, especially when we consider the present legal situation in Germany, where the legal norm of private ownership can be and is broken at any time. From this viewpoint the food-gatherers and hunters certainly do have property in our sense, or, I should say, modern German law has embraced the legal concepts of the hunters and food-gatherers.

garding individual prerogatives might be drawn from the occurrence
and the type of thanking.

Thus the entire daily life of the individual is embedded in the
social and legal care of society, whose strongest weapon for the enforcement of internal peace is public opinion. Preventively it forces
the individual to obey the law; actively it brings about punishment
of transgressions. The individual cannot escape unfavorable public
opinion, for he cannot leave the local group and join another community. This would be certain death. For this reason alone public
opinion is the strongest regulating agency among food-gatherers and
hunters. The agencies of execution do not need to be well developed,
and exist only in rudimentary form. Whole sections of our modern
law are lacking. Only a few specified transgressions in "private and
criminal law" are possible; but here too the community acts only
in a secondary manner, when a settlement of the quarrel between
the two parties concerned cannot be reached. The fundamental rule
that peace within the community must be upheld does not always
permit the law of equivalent retribution, a *lex talionis* — often not
even in the most serious of all crimes, murder within the group.
The Kaingang of southern Brazil form one of the exceptions.[36] For
most transgressions of the law definite punishment has been designated. Among the Tasmanians, for instance, adultery was punished
by beating and driving a spear through the offender's leg.[37] Among
the Botocudos the woman who has committed adultery is beaten
or branded by her deceived husband.[38] In Australia the same crime
is atoned for by a duel of the conflicting parties, which, however,
never ends in death.[39]

In Australia and among some other food-gathering tribes the executive agencies of public opinion were the old men who, seasoned in
life and in the tribal laws, not only informed the younger ones concerning the boundaries of the clan territory but also instructed them
in the laws of marriage, the rites of initiation, the distribution of
food — all those norms existing from time immemorial. In the hands
of these elders also rested that judicial power which had to do with
the community or was called upon when a settlement between the
parties was impossible. Aside from boundary violations, the settlement of which I have already described, these old men had to mete
out judgment in the case of a murder committed on a clan member
by a person from outside the clan — which always meant war.
Within the clan, the cases brought before the council of the elders

were those connected with murder, sorcery, infringement of marriage regulations, or betrayal of the secret ceremonies at the boys'
initiation. The punishment usually consisted of the wounding of the
culprit with spears, but without killing him.[40] We know very little
about the method of taking evidence in such criminal processes.
Trenk reports that the Bushmen of the Namib desert arrange a
smoke trial as soon as anyone is suspected of a crime. The column
of smoke points to the guilty one. If it divides, there are several
accomplices; if the smoke rises straight up, the suspected persons
are innocent.[41]

Our sources report unanimously that chieftainship was slightly
developed or absent. The person with greater physical or mental
agility was able to exert considerable influence over his group, but
he too was dependent upon public opinion. Whenever chiefs and
their functions are described in this stage of culture, they have
usually been given such positions by the White people to facilitate
dealing with the group.[42] A revealing example is given by Dawson,[43]
in the facsimile of the treaty which some of the first White settlers
in Australia concluded with some so-called chiefs about the cession
of 100,000 acres of land.

These, roughly speaking, are the regulations in the legal life of
the food-gatherers and hunters. The facts show that it is altogether
erroneous to describe the legal status of these tribes as anarchic, as
Grosse,[44] Knabenhans,[45] and others have done. On the contrary, the
legal concepts and norms, their structure and their applications, are
shown with amazing clarity in the reported facts. For these societies
of food-gatherers and hunters the definite formulation of the territorial principle is significant, a principle which, contrary to Oppenheimer's [46] opinion, makes it impossible "for families to easily
dissolve their ties with others." Added to the territorial principle is a
complexity of legal norms. Solidarity of the community against outsiders in the case of a boundary transgression or of war, and inter-
nally in respect to the provision of food, is a characteristic feature.
There are only slight beginnings of private ownership, though it
cannot be denied that certain individual rights similar to ownership
exist, but not in reference to the soil or objects valuable to the entire group or necessary for its sustenance. The pressure from without,
the wall formed by the limits of the tribal area, is one of the strongest
supports of public opinion and of its executive agencies for the enforcement of legal norms within the group.

Arctic hunters and related tribes. Among Arctic hunters and tribes influenced by them, the institutions which serve the purpose of holding the community together, safeguarding its food supply, and guaranteeing internal and external peace present a picture somewhat different from that of the societies just discussed. Almost all observers emphasize their strong communistic tendency. For example, we find reports that among the Eskimo the borrower of a boat does not have to return it if the person from whom he borrowed it had two boats,[47] and that the great whale hunt was an affair of the entire community.[48] The "communistic traits," if we want to call them so, of the Arctic people are no more strongly developed than those of the tribes of other food-gatherers and hunters, among whom we have already found the community established as legal unit and legal subject. The distinguishing mark of the Arctic culture is a stronger tendency toward individualism within a definitely democratic pattern. Although I do not go as far as Bogoras,[49] who says, referring to the Chukchee, "It may be said that a lone man living by himself forms the real unit of Chukchee society," I believe that this individualistic trait is quite easily recognizable in the Arctic world.

The boundaries of the local group fluctuate, and transgression of the hunting boundaries is not punished by death, either within the group or in the case of a member of a strange tribe. Often it is not punished at all.[50] Thus Schrenck reports that the Tungus of the lower Amur River did not usually keep within their territory but would hunt on the land of others, especially on that of the Gilyak, without any quarrels ensuing.[51] The hunting ground, which at first probably belonged to the local group, is sometimes divided among several family groups. These two principles may exist side by side or even alternate at times. An excellent example of this was related to me by Speck in reference to the Northeast Algonquians of the St. Augustin band. Their land consists partly of forest and partly of tundra, and hunting is organized either in family groups or as a joint affair of the entire local group, according to the number of animals to be hunted. A similar arrangement exists among the Central Eskimo, the families scattering during the summer over a wide territory and hunting by themselves, while in winter they live in larger villages and hunt in the neighborhood.[52]

The political unit depends upon the territorial principle and not upon the kinship system. Among the maritime Chukchee, for instance, the village does not consist of families related to one another, but of those privileged to hunt.[53] Generally the economic unit is a smaller group than the political society. Among the maritime Chukchee, for instance, the fishing unit is the crew of a boat and their families, whose leader also divides the catch.[54] Among the people of Arctic Asia and the Alaskan Eskimo, the economic unit, be it the crew of a fishing boat, a hunting family, or a group of families, often uses property marks for safeguarding its catch.[55] However, there is no proof that these are individual property marks. They are few in number and refer to a number of people — that is, the economic unit.

The safeguarding of the food supply is first of all an affair of the respective economic group and beyond that, of the whole community. The economic security of each member of the community forms the focal point of the legal aspect among Arctic tribes to such an extent that all individual rights are secondary to it, but this is true only when the life of an individual is threatened by lack of food. From the great mass of examples I shall select only two of the most typical ones. Among the reindeer-breeding European Lapps extensive use of individual property marks exists, together with an obvious inclination toward strong individual definition of property rights in connection with movables. These individual rights, however, may be broken through at any time, under certain circumstances. This goes so far that even the theft of reindeer can be legal, if the thief required the stolen animals for his own use, as, for instance, to obtain meat for eating. From the Lapp's point of view this is not considered a theft, even though the sharply defined right of personal ownership has been violated.[56] This example is not typical of the herdsmen, but only of the Arctic hunters. This part of Lapp law is a hunter's and not a herdsman's law. Another example, taken from the Montagnais-Naskapi, is on the same legal level. The hunting privilege referring to a particular hunting ground can be violated at any time and by anyone who finds himself in need of food. The stranger may hunt and may set traps, but only for his own personal benefit — that is, to satisfy his hunger and sustain his life. Indeed, he may even prey upon a beaver house marked as someone's property when he is in need, but only then.[57] This mutual assistance is concerned only with the maintenance of life and goes no further — especially not in the law referring to debts. Obligations are not fulfilled by a father in his son's behalf, nor by a widow in her dead husband's behalf. There is no such thing as solidarity in regard to obligations among members of a family. What mutual assistance there is, is not necessitated by pressure from the outside, as is the case among other food-gatherers and hunters, but is compelled by public opinion, which, in a single-class society, is much more powerful than in ours and has a totalitarian meaning.

Public opinion is effective among the Northeast Algonquians not only within the local group but beyond it, and can prevent an ill-reputed member of a local group from finding refuge in another group. In many cases this means death in the forest. Political authority is not held by the chief — if there is any chief at all; at times it is held only by the elders. In last analysis it rests with the public opinion of the local group as a whole. The question of the executive agency for the enforcement of this opinion and the type of enforcement are problems which will be dealt with later. The chief's lack of power among the Central Eskimo has been described by Boas [58] in these words: "His authority is virtually limited to the right of deciding on the proper time to shift the huts from one place to the other, but the families are not obliged to follow him. He may ask some men to go deer-hunting, others to go sealing, but there is not the slightest obligation to obey his orders." The same powerless position of the chief — if there was any such office to begin with, and not one just created artificially by the Russians — is reported by Bogoras [59] of the Chukchee; and from my own experience I can say the same of the Naskapi, among whom the Mistassini band has had no chief for years and up to now has not elected one, in spite of the Indian agent's demand that they do so.* In certain Eskimo tribes of Alaska we find exceptions to this rule; these are the tribes which have perhaps been influenced by the social stratification of the Northwest Americans and who had not only a tribal organization with a chieftainship but also a vertical classification of society, including a class of slaves. Beginnings of slavery are further found among the inhabitants of the Aleutian Islands, and also among the Chukchee (probably influenced by the herdsmen tribes which were advancing from the south), who in their battles with the Western Eskimo made slaves of their prisoners of war. Social stratification, however, was very little influenced by this.

Expert trappers and hunters enjoy special authority, dependent

---

* The last Mistassini chief's name was Ntáhoota (traveler). He died of influenza in 1928.

upon their personalities, and therefore they often occupy the rôles of mediators and peace-makers in the community, but they too have no unconditional authority. If a quarrel cannot be settled, or if one party does not want to listen to reason, the elders are powerless.[60] To keep peace as long as possible and as long as the community as a whole is not disturbed is the fundamental motive in the attitude of these tribes. In this respect public opinion has a twofold task: first, that of a preventative which, by virtue of its existence, compels a positive and lawful behavior of the individual; second, that of intervening actively in connection with any violation of law. However, here too it is required that an interested group call for action and that the case be such as actually to threaten the peace of the community. Thus the occasional trap-thief or trespasser or quarreler is not taken to task by the community, but his punishment is left to the injured party or to the group concerned. The community take part more or less as neutral spectators, as for instance in the song contests of the Eskimo. Indeed, even in the case of a murder, blood vengeance is left to the parties concerned. But the community takes a part whenever its economic security is threatened by the behavior of one of its members. This is the case with incorrigible thieves, persons who habitually hunt on the land of others, chronic quarrelers, and fighters; in brief, with those whom today we should call habitual criminals. The punishment may be tying to a tree, as among the Montagnais-Naskapi; beatings, as among the Eskimo of Bering Strait [61]; exile; * or a sentence of death which is carried out according to circumstances by shooting,[62] knifing,[63] drowning,† harpooning, or in some other way.[64]

The procedure and the executive agencies of public opinion were not uniform. Among the Montagnais-Naskapi it was the chief, together with the council of elders, who had the culprit brought before them, convicted him with the aid of witnesses, but without sworn testimony, and then punished him. Among the Chukchee action was taken by a group of especially notable men selected by the community. Finally, even a single person, without any legal procedure, could receive the command or the tacit consent of the community to kill the criminal. As proof for the conviction of the criminal, use

---

* A Tête-de-boule man, Amechichi ("a man who strolls about"), was exiled about 1870 because he kept hunting on the hunting grounds of others, although he had his own.

† Formerly the practice among the Montagnais-Naskapi.

was often made of an oath of the accused, never of an oath by witnesses. Thus the accused Chukchee called upon the Sun as helper, or he swore by the Bear.[65] *

Harvesters and related tribes. I shall describe as harvesters a group of tribes whose "food supply is derived from the harvesting of one or a few wild-growing food plants which provide the chief sustenance for the entire year." [66] The harvesters are neither pastoral nor agricultural, but are tribes which possess an economic form based upon the harvesting, not just the gathering, of wild plants. The regions where they occur predominantly are Australia and Melanesia, especially on the southern and western coasts of New Guinea, and in the most eastern, southern, and northerly districts of Australia. In these districts the basis of the food supply is: in New Guinea, the sago palm tree; in Australia, the wild yam, the nardoo seed (*Marsilea quadrifolia*), which is ground and made into cakes,[67] lily root,[68] the bunya-bunya, and others. It is significant that these fruits are kept in their natural state or worked over into forms more easily preserved, and thus provide the main sustenance for the entire year. This is the case everywhere except in the bunya-bunya tribes, who form a link between the food-gatherers and hunters and the harvesters. In some instances treatment of food by fermentation is known, as among the tribes of the Carpentaria Gulf,[69] a process which is further developed in Polynesia and among certain Arctic tribes.

In Asia the ancient reindeer-breeders were probably originally fishermen and harvesters before the rise of reindeer-breeding. Even today large sections of the Arctic region are inhabited by the Chukchee, the Yakut, and Tungus in whose life harvested wild roots, onions, and garlic play an important rôle. The Chukchee especially gather roots and the center portion of *Claytonia acutifolia Willd.* in great quantities. This plant is pickled and eaten all year long up to the next harvest time. The Polynesians, no matter whether they had agriculture or not before their migrations, could not have settled on coral atolls without the existence of the wild breadfruit tree and the wild coco palm. The structure of their law is related in many respects to that of the harvesters and herd men.

In Africa we find scarcely any real harvesters. In the middle Sudan and in East Africa the wild rice, and in ancient Egypt the lily root, played a certain rôle without, however, forming the eco

* The author recommends that the discussion of the Plains Indians be read in connection with the preceding part. See footnote on p. 512.

nomic basis of life. In South America, in the Chaco region, the *algaroba* and the *tusca* were harvested,[70] and among the Araucanians and ancient Peruvians the wild potato. In the region of the Canadian lakes the Algonquian tribes and some of the Siouan tribes based their economic pattern in part on the harvesting of the wild water-rice. Some of the Californian Indians must also be numbered among the harvesters, and the legal structure of some tribes of the North-west who are primarily fishermen, secondarily harvesters, corresponds somewhat to that of the harvesters.

The economic basis of these tribes has been the cause of various special forms of legal structure and government, different from those found among the food-gatherers and hunters.

Since the Australian tribes furnish particularly good material, and since through a study of their law I arrived at the concept of the class of harvesters, they may be dealt with particularly. Furthermore, in Australia there was no admixture of harvesters with agriculturists, as is the case in North and South America, so that a description of the special forms of the legal structure among Australian harvesters will offer a clearer picture.

The territorial principle and the legal norms of the group are different in these tribes from those of the food-gatherers and hunters. Though here, too, the local group holds the ownership of a limited territory, the inviolability of the land is infringed upon. Using modern terms, we might say that the absolute value of real estate shifts to the harvesting ground, the part essential for the food supply of the community. This part of the territory of the community increases in value. Being the main source of support of the local group, it now occupies the focal position in the economic and legal situation. The size of this harvesting area is sometimes immense. Hodgson [71] reports that the bunya-bunya tree district extends over seventy miles. Our source material gives us similar statistics in regard to the lily-root territory among the Gnanji, on the Roper River, and for the nardoo among the Arunta. The harvesting ground is usually the place where the local group takes up its residence,[72] for the economic structure demands a certain settled mode of living, at least it demands secure storage space.[73] Thus the harvesting ground becomes the chief factor in the accumulation of people. The number of members of a local group is far greater in these tribes than it is among the food-gatherers and hunters. Among the Obota and Waka-imi tribes of New Guinea,[74] tribes which live in the sago swamps, such a camp comprises about 1000 people; among the Winnebago, about 300.[75] Australian sources estimate that in exceptional cases as many as 2500 persons are present on a harvesting ground.[76] Such a number is attained, however, only temporarily, during the great invitation ceremonies when many tribes assemble.

This leads us again to the reaction of the local group to outsiders and to the special legal concepts which have developed in reference to their behavior toward the neighboring groups. While among food-gatherers and hunters a transgression of the boundaries of the tribal territory meant certain death, this is not the case among the harvesters. There is no punishment for any transgression of the boundaries. Indeed, the elasticity of the boundary conditions can go so far that the boundaries are in a way nullified. Curr [77] reports that the Bangerang and related tribes could take refuge in one another's territory. At times two groups could even possess a common harvesting ground.[78] When the fruit of the harvesting ground matures, the neighboring tribes are invited to partake of the superabundance. Among the bunya-bunya tribes this happens only every third year. Ridley suggests that this might perhaps be a right obtained through war.[79] But neither among the bunya-bunya tribes nor among the other harvesters is there any support for this assumption. We are only able to state that at the time when the fruit matures, the surrounding tribes arrive, sometimes from as far as 100 miles away,[80] but only to harvest the bunya-bunya. The guests are forbidden to hunt any animal and to gather any plant except the bunya-bunya. This taboo is so effective that there is probably some truth in the reports of occasional cannibalism among the guest tribes, on account of the lack of meat.[81] The invitation to the bunya-bunya harvest was usually for a period of six weeks. Dawson [82] reports that over twenty tribes speaking different languages took part in one of the great harvesting meetings.

These meetings exercised an important cultural influence. They affected, so to say, external politics and were the source of many new legal institutions in the field of primitive "international law, trade law and 'copyright' law." The tribe which gave the harvesting feast sent out invitations through envoys who from three weeks to three months before [83] were sent out with message-sticks,[84] to carry the invitations to the several local groups.[85] These diplomats not only were not interfered with in their travels through the territory of hostile tribes but were even received with hospitality.[86] At times instead of these messengers, smoke signals were used to notify the prospective guests.

Trade, the mutual exchange of local products, was important at these meetings. Thus, for instance, the Warramunga and their northern neighbors, the Pjingilli, in central Australia are famous for their stone knives.[87] Stones for axes, and also the selong gum, which was especially valuable for attaching stones to handles,[88] spears, boomerangs, narcotics,[89] and red ochre were exchanged for other goods. The elders decided who was to take part in the meetings, and participation of those so designated was obligatory.[90]

Furthermore these meetings served for common initiation ceremonies which signified the acceptance of young men as full-fledged members of their tribes. This ceremony was usually deferred until an initiation could take place in several tribes on the occasion of a harvesting feast. Either the elders or the respective chiefs set the time when a number of young men were to be received into the class of adults.[91]

These meetings are extremely significant for the dissemination of cultural elements. They are not only occasions for trade, for common initiations, for corroborees and games; they also bring about cultural exchange between these tribes. In speaking of the Kabi, Curr reports the following concerning the traveling about of corroboree plays: "The poet having introduced his work to the neighboring tribes, these in turn invited their allies to witness it and aid in the performance. In this manner a corroboree traveled, and was sung with great enthusiasm where not a word of it was intelligible. The dramatic part in these performances was sometimes very considerable." [92] The idea of a "copyright" law is by no means unfamiliar to these harvester tribes, and they provide for an effective protection of this law.[92a] We already find here the beginnings of an international "copyright" protection.

Many of our sources tell of so-called neutral territories which are not to be regarded as boundary sections abandoned out of the fear of hostile neighbors, as is sometimes the case among the food-gatherers and hunters, but which are closed by what we would call today an international treaty of neighboring tribes.[93] Curr [94] reports that the tribes on the banks of the Gregory through mutual agreement created a neutral territory fifty by one hundred miles in extent, in order to hold their meetings there. The reason for the creation of such a territory is economically as well as legally conditioned. Economically, through the mutual agreement prohibiting the use of this land, the supply of plants and wild animals which form the economic basis for the meetings of these tribes is preserved. Legally this institution indicates that only among tribes whose economic foundation is secure within the tribal territory is the creation of neutral regions possible.

Our Australian sources leave no doubt that the harvesting ground, like the land in general, belongs to the local group as a whole. Temporarily, at the time of the harvest, individual families may receive an assignment of certain parts of the harvesting ground, but there is no doubt that the land as a whole is the property of the community. The situation in this respect is not quite so clear among some of the American harvesters. Of the Chaco tribes and the tribes which harvest the wild potato, also of the Hyanyam in the Matto Grosso, the reports are unanimous to the effect that the ownership of a harvesting ground is in the hands of a local group. In regard to the North American Ojibwa, the Menomini, and the Winnebago, early sources such as Catlin and Schoolcraft make it clear that the harvesting ground belongs to the entire local group, which distributes the field anew before each harvest to the single families, though the interpretation of the custom of tying the fruits in bundles as a protection against birds is probably incorrect. This ancient custom seems to be referred to also in Densmore's statement: "In the old days each family *or small group of families* had a portion of a rice field as it had a 'sugar bush' for making its maple sugar." [95]

The original ownership of the rice fields by a local group is even more clearly shown in the report, likewise given by Densmore, that the rice which had not been tied into bunches was common property for only through the work of preparation done for about ten days before the harvest and consisting of the twisting up of the bunches was the claim of a family or of several families to a certain part of the harvesting ground secured. This fact appears very clearly in a remark by Ellis: "This gives the party twisting the bunches a kind of preëmption to so much of the rice, which before was all common." [96] Ruth Landes, however, reports that she found among the Ojibwa individual ownership of rice fields, berry bushes, and maple trees — a sign of the speedy adoption on the part of the Indian of the White man's conception of law, which seems quite foreign to the general attitude of the Indian to land tenure. Originally the harvesting ground was not divided so that each lot belonged to a family consisting of parents and children, but rather to the large recognized social units constituting the tribe. In Australia as well as in America these were economic but not political units.[97] Thus the property marks erected in the fields of the Winnebago bear the sign of the totem clan.

However, aside from the harvesting products, the plants gathered and the animals hunted are not always the exclusive property of the gatherer or the hunter, but are handled according to rules similar to those prevailing among the food-gatherers and hunters. The right to this kind of food is regulated by rules affecting a number of people. As Strehlow has described in detail,[98] the Arunta and Loritja have exact prescriptions for the assignment and distribution of the kill.[99] At times the hunter has no right at all to his prey and others dispose of it.[100] The right of disposal, however, does not rest here with the political local group but with a smaller unit, the totem clan, which exists in general as an economic unit, united also by supernatural bonds. The relation between economics and totemism is also indicated in North America. Thus a legend of the Menomini, whose name means rice men,[101] says: "They visited the Bear phratry, offering maize and fire in exchange for wild rice, which is the property of the Bear. . . . The bargain was concluded and since that time the Bear and the Big Thunder phratries have lived together." [102] In cases of need the economic unit was responsible for the food supply of the individual. "It must not be lost sight of, however, that if the food of any worthy family fails, the entire food supply of the social group is available to make up the deficiency"; [103] and Chief Pokagon writes of the harvesters of the Potawatomi: "Our people always divide everything when want comes to the door." [104]

While the totem group is also the economic group in regard to food supply, the local group as a political unit takes on this function immediately whenever things not absolutely necessary for sustenance are to be acquired by trade expeditions. It is necessary to emphasize this, because W. Schmidt attempts to support his conception of Australian totemism with the claim that only members of a certain totem would take part in trade expeditions.[105] These expeditions have no relation to the totemic division of the local group. The selection of their numbers is made from the local group as a whole, as Howitt and Siebert unanimously report of the ochre and pitcheri expeditions of the Dieri.[106]

Just how such an expedition takes place is described by Curr, Howitt, and Gason,[107] who give a vivid picture of the Dieri, among whom every winter, in July or August, following a decision by all the old men, an expedition is sent out to obtain red ochre — a dangerous enterprise, extending over a road of several hundred miles. Older and younger people are selected for this expedition, and the council of the elders appoints a leader. The preparations are kept secret, especially from the women, because, owing to the dangers of the journey, their influence over their husbands is feared. The journey takes about six to eight weeks, and the booty brought back amounts to about seventy pounds of ochre for every member of the expedition. On the way out and back they travel only at night, so as to avoid hostilities, as far as possible. The narcotic *Duboisia Hopwoodii*, which occurs only in isolated spots, is an extraordinarily important trade article which is exchanged over an area of hundreds of miles, for spears, boomerangs, and other goods.[108] The harvester tribe of the Yantruwunta, on its dangerous expeditions, provided itself not only with red ochre but also with sandstone slabs from a quarry 300 miles away. These stones were used for grinding their harvested grain. All these local products, such as stone, ochre quarries, and narcotics, were common property of the tribe in whose territory they occurred.[109]

Besides the collective responsibility of the totem group in respect to supplying food, and of the local group in respect to political reactions, there also exists among the harvesters a development of more detailed legal rules regarding private ownership, which is protected by the tribe. Anyone who breaks these rules is punished; however, a violation of property rarely occurs.[110] For example, private ownership of fruit trees exists and is always respected. Among the Arunta,[111] the ownership of such a tree is indicated by placing a bunch of grass on the branches. When, in spite of this, someone steals its fruits, the injured party has the right to "spear the thief to death." Or, when a man finds a nest of bees, he marks the tree by pulling up the grass around the roots and placing sticks against the tree.[112] The punishment of spearing is also meted out to anyone who takes a killed animal without the hunter's permission. The same punishment also applies when an animal, merely wounded, is caught without the consent of the hunter by someone not entitled to it. If, however, the person asks the hunter, he has the right to demand part of the prey. The thief who steals things not essential for the support of life does not fare quite so badly. If he returns the stolen objects, the matter is regarded as settled.[113] But if he refuses to relinquish the stolen goods, the owner has the right to spear the culprit's leg or throw a boomerang at him.

Private property is usually inherited by the eldest son, and if there are no sons, by the near relatives.[114]

The adulterer is occasionally punished by a temporary exile from the local group, lasting for about two to three months.[115] Among the food-gatherers and hunters such a sentence would mean death. Here it is a mild punishment, and the temporal limitation can be understood in a harvester tribe only.

Among the tribes of the harvesting peoples there has also developed what might be called a clearly defined copyright law. The right to perform certain rituals, cults, mimic performances, songs, and dances, or to tell certain stories, belongs to individuals (as among the Arunta), and sometimes to a group (as among the Warramunga), represented by the chief of the respective totem.[116] The right to performances or even the exclusive right to use them may be obtained by payment.[117]

The organization of public power and its executive agencies among these tribes show a fairly uniform picture: there is no specifically developed chieftainship, though its beginnings are present more clearly than among the food-gatherers and hunters. Even hereditary chieftainship occurs. Two ways to chieftainship are open: the one through membership in a totem group, in so far as sometimes the head of a numerous and powerful clan could become chief of the local group [118]; the other through individual qualities. The deciding power always lies in the public opinion of the political community; that is, in the members of the local group,[119] sometimes represented by a council of elders or a council of the chiefs of clans. It has often been pointed out that especially among totemic tribes the legal rules are strongly religious in character and have their roots in the totem myths. I have not found any support for this theory; on the contrary. Strehlow states expressly [120] that among the Arunta the fundamental legal concepts are not derived from the tribal ancestor, but apparently have been developed by the council of elders, who impart their knowledge to the young men at the initiation ceremonies.

Of the Narrinjerri, Taplin tells us that every local group has its chief, whose title signifies "owner of land," and who is war chief as well as spokesman in intertribal affairs.[121] Even within the clan he seems to have great power, together with the council of elders which consists of the heads of families: "They actually have an institution which is extremely like trial by jury, and they have had it from time immemorial. This they call the Tendi. It is the judgment council of the elders of the clan. Every clan has its tendi. The number of tendi is not fixed; it appears to be regulated by the size of the clan; but it always consists of experienced elderly men. When any member of the tendi dies, the surviving members select a suitable man from the clan to succeed him. This council is presided over by the chief or rupulle of the clan. He is generally chosen for his ready speech, temper, and capacity for authority. The office is not hereditary but elective in the council itself. A seat in the tendi is called 'tendi lewurmi,' the judgment seat. All offenders are brought to this tribunal for trial."

Curr reports of the Kabi that in this tribe two or three men who are equally powerful administer the affairs of the community, control the relations with neighboring tribes, and see to it that the laws are not broken; and he adds that these men had raised themselves to this position by their personal courage.[122]

Another especially interesting legal institution found among these tribes is the right of asylum and the law of taboo, the two being closely connected. We have already seen that the harvesting ground was taboo until harvesting time, and that this taboo was lifted on a certain day by a person privileged to do so. After this, harvesting was allowed. Taboos similar in effect, though not in cause, are connected with certain localities which are regarded as the domicile of the totem spirits or as hiding places for the sacred totem utensils of the tribe. Spencer and Gillen[123] report an institution found among the Arunta which is clearly a right of asylum for members of the tribe as well as for strangers. The criminal and the stranger are safe and cannot be seized when they flee to this tabooed place. Animals and plants, too, are taboo there.[124] The right of asylum was probably religious in origin but had predominantly economic consequences. It is an example of the reorientation of purpose in primitive law.

Let us once more clarify the differences between the legal institutions of harvesters and those of food-gatherers and hunters. The legal norms are no longer subordinated to the principle of tribal territory; a transgression of the tribal or sib territory is not punished, and only particular parts, such as the harvesting ground or the place of refuge, are protected by taboos. However, here too the political unit is represented by the local group, while the economic unit is smaller. The differences in economic form and the resulting relaxation of enmity against outside groups have two obvious results. One is the accumulation of a greater number of people, not only of those belonging to a single tribe, but sometimes even of those belonging to distinct tribes. The legal result in reference to outsiders is the creation of institutions intertribal in character (neutral territories, intertribal festivals); in reference to internal institutions, the creation of forces making for a great differentiation of law and norms. How much the external political picture has shifted is shown by the fact that in the North American rice fields villages are peacefully inhabited by members of four different tribes.[125] According to Oppenheimer's [126] theory of the state and his law of "Bodensperre" (soil limitation), harvesters might be expected to develop "conquest and class states" when the harvesting ground is conquered by a foreign tribe. Our sources do not report any such development, unless we interpret the structures of the Inca and Aztec empires as developed by agricultural groups conquering harvesters. We do know about the fights between the Ojibwa and the Dakota over the rice fields,[127] but no state formation in Oppenheimer's sense has occurred. This may have something to do, so far as America is concerned, with the strong democratic trait which distinguishes all organizations of the North American Indians, to which I shall return later.

In the realm of internal politics the organization is stricter than among the food-gatherers and hunters; above all, however, perhaps as a reaction, a stronger emphasis upon individual rights has developed in such matters as do not relate to the safeguarding of the communal food supply. I have in mind here the development of the "copyright" law particularly. These tribes, too, do not recognize individual ownership rights in respect to land. Larger unions beyond the sib exist.

A number of similarities and further developments in the legal institution of government discussed above may be found among the fishermen of the American Northwest Coast. Here too, among the Kwakiutl for instance, the territory of the sib * is common property,[128] and this probably applies also to the strictly defined fishing grounds,[129] though information obtained on this point is contradictory. In these tribes the social demarcation is unusually elaborate. We find chiefs,

* The term "sib" is used here for a tribal subdivision although its form does not strictly conform to the usual definition.

nobility, middle class, bondsmen, and slaves, and there is even another class of preferred people who rate above the chief, but only in the potlatch — those "who are first to receive." [130] This class division seems to operate not so much politically as socially, for the chief's position is politically quite limited and depends upon the public opinion of the sib. "I depend on it that you will stand behind me in everything." [131] Even in regard to the gifts to the chief the latter is not omnipotent: "Generally the chief and the fisherman quarrel and often fight until one of them is killed, when the chief thinks that he has not been given enough." [132] Even at the giving of a potlatch he is dependent upon the good will of the members of the sib, who cannot be forced to put their property at his disposal. Therefore, the great potlatches are not really the affair of a single individual but rather of the entire sib, the individual members of which give their property for the *do ut des* game. The economic bond which holds the members of the sib together affects the outsiders, inasmuch as quarrels with the members of another sib who fish or gather fruit without permission lead to fighting and killing.[133] Whether we can speak here of any stronger development of individual property right, aside perhaps from the protection of the "copyright," seems doubtful to me, because of the ever-recurring leveling institution of the potlatch. It does not permit any lasting accumulation of riches, and serves in the end only for the attainment of abstract honors which have no resulting political influence upon the community.

*Indians of the Plains.** Let us sketch in brief the government of the Plains Indians who belong economically to the hunting tribes. Before the extermination of the buffalo it provided them with their chief food all the year around. We know, however, that the Plains tribes adopted a pure hunting life in historic times, and that the introduction of the horse caused them to extend their hunting grounds westward and to settle on the Plains. Their legal institutions have many similarities with the Arctic and sub-Arctic hunters previously described, especially with the Montagnais-Naskapi; but we find also influences from the eastern agricultural tribes. Taken as a whole, it seems that two principles which we find among the Arctic hunters are further developed here: the individualistic and the democratic principle, the latter bound and regu-

* The author had placed the discussion of the Plains Indians following that of the Arctic hunters (p. 502). The editor is responsible for its insertion at the present place.

lated by a very powerful public opinion, as Lowie has excellently described.[134] The political unit — and to a certain extent the economic unit too, especially during the great buffalo hunts — was the tribe and not the local group. It also seems that the tribe and not the band had the right of ownership in regard to land. Land ownership in our sense was entirely foreign to the thinking of these Indians. Land and water were to them merely the conditions for that which they regarded as their common property — the buffalo. The active element of the political organization of these tribes appears clearly during the great buffalo hunt. It was not the local group but the entire tribe which went forth to the common hunt "in an organized militarylike manner." [135] Among the Dakota, Mandan, Hidatsa, Crow, Blackfoot, and Cheyenne the surveillance and direction of the hunt, the order of marching, etc., were entrusted to a special group which was drawn from all the men who had been divided into age classes. The members of this special group were appointed by the council and installed by the chief. When the tribe met at the meeting place agreed upon, every local group had its traditional place in the camp circle, which was open toward the east and in the center of which stood the ceremonial tents. During these hunts there was no room for individual freedom of action which was otherwise so conspicuous. The police even had the right to kill an individual who, to the detriment of the community, did not obey their instructions. Aside from these annual buffalo hunts and war expeditions, the unity of the tribe was very lax, and a division into politically independent local groups and even smaller units was the rule.[136]

Chieftainship showed very little elaboration. Usually the chief or chiefs were elected; only rarely was this office hereditary as among the Omaha, but even the Omaha changed from hereditary succession to elective procedure.[137] The number of elected chiefs, who were chosen from among the bravest warriors and the men with the best reputation in the community, varied. The Cheyenne, for instance, had a chiefs' council of four high chiefs and forty chiefs. The Omaha had seven chiefs who were elected for life, but in this case there were also, in an advisory capacity, five members of the tribe *ex officio:* "The keeper of the Sacred Pole; the keeper of the Sacred Buffalo Hide; the keeper of the two Sacred Tribal Pipes; the keeper of the ritual used when filling them; and the keeper of the Sacred Tent of War." [138] The responsibility for a decision of the council devolved upon the seven chiefs. The majority principle in voting was unknown;

the chiefs' council conferred until unanimity was established. "All must accept it and then carry it through as one man. . . . The seven must have but one heart and speak as with one mouth."

For the execution of its resolutions, the council appointed respected members of the tribe who watched over the war expeditions undertaken by individuals and who at times would return the booty brought back from such expeditions to its original owners, so as to avoid warlike complications with neighbors. The officials who organized the buffalo hunt were also, as said before, appointed by this council. The work of these officials was over after the hunt, but even then they or others played a certain rôle in the execution of the tribal laws. Among the Cheyenne they had a sort of umpire position during quarrels within the community,[139] and Fletcher and La Flesche report that among the Omaha the members of the buffalo hunt police were entrusted also after the hunt with the preservation of law and order within the community. "Men who had once filled the office of 'soldier' were apt to be called on to assist the council in the preservation of order within the tribe." [140]

Since the provision of food was regulated collectively and since there was therefore little room for the development of private ownership, there were hardly ever any cases of theft. When such a case occurred, the thief was not punished; he merely had to return the stolen articles. Even insults, bodily attacks, and murder were subjected to adjustment by the parties concerned, who, however, were forced into action by the tribe, as in the case of the Comanche.[141] If they did not respond, the "tort" became a crime; that is to say, the community and not the party concerned avenged the wrongdoing. The solidarity of consanguineous groups was common among the Plains Indians, in contrast to the Naskapi. Anyone could be held responsible for the acts of his blood relative. Adultery was punished severely, but even here the settlement was left to the parties concerned. The guilty person was sometimes even knifed or beaten to death. In regard to "copyright" law there was a distinction between the property of the religious societies, that of the clans, and that of an individual. However, among the Omaha we also find songs which were free to be used by anyone, especially during the $wa'wa^n$ ceremony.[142] The immediate property of a dead person accompanied him into the grave. Other property was inherited by the adult children or the brothers of the deceased.

Crimes which aroused an immediate reaction in the community, as represented by the chiefs, were above all those that were directed against the authority of the elected leaders, such as the attempt to deride their authority or to go through with the plans for a war party, though this had been forbidden. Today we should say that only purely political crimes brought about an immediate action in the community. Sometimes the culprit was warned by having his horses poisoned or beaten to death. If he did not heed this warning, he himself was killed. Among the Omaha this was done by wounding him with a poisoned ironwood stick.

Larger associations, extending beyond the tribe, existed only in weak forms, such as the "seven council fires" of the Dakota, and were entirely different from the intertribal leagues of the eastern farming tribes.

I have described in some detail the tribes characterized by acquisitive economy, first, because our source material is scanty and fragmentary, and also because the existence of legal institutions with these tribes has often been denied altogether.

I cannot here undertake to give descriptions of each of the countless agricultural and pastoral tribes and of those of mixed economy. Space permits me to give only a very cursory and brief sketch of the government of some of these societies.

Simpler farming societies. The central territorial unit of these farming societies, which are found especially in eastern Melanesia, western Africa, the central portion of South America, and eastern North America is the village; that is, the limited area of the village, with the numerous huts of single families, or those of family groups, or a single sib house in the center. The tribes seem to be divided everywhere into such independent villages, headed by a chief who sometimes is loosely dependent upon a high chief. However, his importance is very slight. Keysser [143] tells of the Kai in New Guinea that the chief's position was indicated only by the fact that he possessed the largest field, but that his greater wealth had to be utilized in obligatory hospitality toward the chief's own village and toward strange guests. His power was extremely meager and lay in representation exclusively. He had no right over life and death at all — except among a few South American tribes in case of war. This purely representative position of the chief in the farming societies of the central and northern part of South America is likewise reported by other investigators. Aside from representation, it was the chief's duty to arrange for new clearings for himself or for others. The details of the preparation of a new field for planting are vividly described in Karl von den Steinen's study of the Xingú tribes.

Authority is vested in the council of elders. Among the horticultural tribes matriliny was probably originally prevalent in regard to laws of descent and inheritance, although owing to an intricate conglomeration of factors, we have not everywhere a very clear picture of this development. Today, in the woodland tribes of Cameroon the family is patriarchally organized, but this order is obviously of recent origin, for even women could be chiefs [144]; and among the Cross River tribes, the Bakwiri,[144a] the Duala,[144b] and the Batanga tribes the originally matrilineal organization may still be clearly recognized. Land was originally common property, and it is doubtful whether its cultivation created property in our sense or merely a right of usufruct. The limitations imposed upon the sale of land are a criterion. The Iroquois said: "Land cannot be bought and sold, any more than water and fire can." In Melanesia and West Africa, too, land is not an object of trade. As a rule, land was common property of the village, but in regard to cultivated land we find the beginnings of sib, family, or individual ownership. In West Africa, Melanesia, and South America women had no political rights or enjoyed such rights only as members of a secret society. Thus in West Africa certain women, members of the Bundu secret society of women, sometimes had political influence, even the power over life and death. In contrast to this the Iroquois woman stepped into the political foreground. Women apportioned the arable land every second year and they elected the chiefs; they had a veto right in the council of men, even when war expeditions were planned. They also had the right to take strangers into the tribe through adoption and could decide on the fate of prisoners of war.

The mutual help rendered in clearing fields which frequently occurs in Melanesia and South America, and more rarely in Africa, indicates that the provision of food is not individual but that in last analysis the community bears the responsibility for it. However, this is noticeable only in times of need, and prevents a pronounced plutocratic development. In general, movables are privately owned, but not land. In West Africa we find a stronger development of such private ownership. This is well illustrated by the exaction of dues for membership in the secret societies.

Especially in Melanesia and Africa secret societies which probably grew out of the age groups had more important juridical powers than the chief and the council of elders.[145] In the Bismarck Archipelago and on the Gazelle Peninsula notably the *dukduk* and the *ingiet* societies, in South America the *jurupari* society, in Cameroon, especially among the Ekoi of the northwest, the *ewi-ngbe* secret society [146] (*ewi-* law, *ngbe-* leopard society), in the south among the Pangwe the *bokung-elong*,[147] among the Bakosi [148] and Basa the *Losango* secret societies,[149] play a dominant rôle in the legal and social life of these tribes. Among the Ekoi the legislative and executive power is vested in the *ewi-ngbe* secret society, which can decide even on the adoption or rejection of public laws. It is also the highest court of appeal in all legal actions. Admission to the secret society and advancement into its higher degrees usually depend on the payment of an entry fee. Anyone is free to leave the society, but the advantages of membership are such that this is of rare occurrence. The societies exert an authoritative jurisdiction within the small, self-centered, democratic legal community. In groups of more recent origin such jurisdiction is taken by the village community, which in these tribes is represented by the chief and the palaver of the elders. The entire legal structure, its elaboration of the system of composition, the free arbitration between parties, the often only subsidiary jurisdiction by chief and elders, to mention only a few elements, rest on the secret societies. These must be regarded as the strongest factor in the formation and development of laws, and they stand out especially as the agencies of executive power in legal procedure. They play a great rôle in both criminal and civil law.

How a legal process takes place may be demonstrated by the following example. When among the Bakosi a creditor demands a goat which the debtor refuses to pay, the creditor goes to the members of the Losango society and asks them to help him to obtain justice. They put their insignia in front of the debtor's hut. This usually works at once. For this service the society receives from the debtor a goat. If the debt is not paid at once and if the society's insignia have to remain on the hut until the next morning, the price is one ox, which is eaten by the members of the society. For this reason every debtor tries to satisfy his creditor and the society as quickly as possible. The secret society also intervenes when a man has seduced another man's wife and refuses to pay. Among the Basa the *mungi* and *um* secret societies in secret nocturnal meetings decide on orders, judgments, and punishments and also have them executed secretly — the punishment almost always being death. It was then said: "The Mungi has judged us."[150] Anyone, even a person who is not a member, has the right to seek legal aid from the society, just as is the case in the *egbo* society of the coast tribes.[151]

Political societies extending beyond the village are on the whole unknown among these tribes of the Old World. The intertribal instrument is the secret society, which is not limited to the village, not even to the tribe, but extends, especially in West Africa and Melanesia, over large areas, without, however, leading to an organization of larger political units — a significant phenomenon. Yet the absence of political organization into larger groups is typical only of the Old World; in the New World we find just the opposite to be the case among the corresponding tribes. The best instance of this is found in the league of the Iroquois.[152] The league comprised five — later six — tribes represented by a central council which made decisions unanimously, not by the majority principle. This central power was quite loose, in spite of a hereditary chieftainship. Any tribe could go to war independently or conclude peace as long as the interests of the league were not interfered with. Unlike the conquering societies of the Old World, especially in Africa and Asia, the trend toward intertribal alliances was strong in some parts of America, even among the tribes of pre-state structure — indeed, especially among the latter. Some of the later developments of this type may be connected with the invasion of the Whites and their influence, as was the case when the Cherokee created for themselves a governmental organization after the pattern of the United States of America. The conquest of a tribe by another and the resulting formation of classes and of an autocratic state, which was the rule in the Old World, especially in Africa, is entirely absent in the American statelike structures in the regions of the present United States.[153] Another dissimilarity between the North American and West African societies of similar economic status is to be found chiefly in legal procedure. Among the West African forest tribes there exists, besides the right to self-help and the appeal to the secret society, a well-developed procedure before a palaver court, composed of the chief and the elders.[154] The defendant is summoned in various ways, directly through the parties or through the chief. The methods of proof are torture, oath, ordeal of drinking poison, testimony by witnesses, visual and documentary evidence. The judgment is preceded by a secret conference of the court, and the decision is reached through a majority of the votes. The composition system dominates the procedure. Vengeance and punishment are usually averted by the payment of a fine. This clearly regulated legal procedure is lacking among the American tribes. Except for certain formulas of solemn declaration by the parties, other methods of proof, especially the many forms of the ordeal, are unknown.

Herdsmen and related societies. The foundation of the life of the herdsmen, for whom we have no corresponding societies in America (in Peru we find only a *tending* of the llama and the alpaca), is as a rule combined with harvesting or farming, or so strongly influenced by higher civilizations that there are probably no pure societies of herdsmen left today. Yet this economic form is the principal foundation for a number of cultures which in the Old World occupy a strip extending from northeastern Siberia through Central Asia, Arabia, North and East Africa, down to the southernmost point of Africa and the Bushman region. Siberian and European tribes such as the Lapp, Samoyede, Chukchee, and Tungus raise reindeer. Central Asiatic tribes, Mongol and Turki tribes raise cattle, sheep, horses, and camels. The Africans, especially the East and South African herdsmen, raise chiefly cattle. In the north there have been influences from the Arctic and sub-Arctic regions, in Central Asia from the adjacent high civilizations, in East Africa and in part also in North Africa and Arabia from the farming societies which had come into contact with the herdsmen.

Thus we find that most of the societies of herdsmen today are recognizable clearly as mixed cultures. In Djagga law [155] the law of grant and lieu can be explained only as the result of a mixture with the laws of farming tribes, and among the Ovambo the law of inheritance shows completely matrilineal characteristics.[156] Even among herdsmen as definite and ancient as the Chalcha-Mongol, Chinese, and Tibetan high cultures have shown their influence and have changed the marital law of the princes and noble families.[157] Yet we can establish common traits of government, conditioned by the economic pattern, among the Central Asiatic and the African herdsmen. The pastures are always the property of the entire tribe. But as among the harvesters, they are not clearly defined, and driving the herd to pasture on a strange territory without permission is not punished. The tribe as such has hardly any legal function. The individual and the patriarchal family group are the outstanding feature. The older collectivistic element is replaced by individualism. The social unit is the patriarchal family group (brothers, nephews, sons, grandsons), which also lays claim to political independence. The tribe is headed by a chief who has been elected or whose office is hereditary.[158] His influence, however, depends mostly upon his personality and upon his liberality, which means that it depends ultimately upon the public opinion of his tribe. Besides the chief there is a council of elders (among the Kirghiz the so-called white-beards, among the Herero the *umakarere*) without whose consent the chief cannot decide anything, especially in regard to land. The fact that the chief cannot dispose of land was demonstrated to the German government on the occasion of the Herero war. The Germans had concluded agreements with the chiefs concerning the cession of land, but the chiefs did not have the right to dispose of the land, and the war resulted from ignorance of tribal law.[159] Larger political associations beyond the tribe did not originally exist among the individualized societies of herdsmen, especially not among the camel and horse breeders. Jurisdiction, especially in cases calling for blood vengeance, was an affair of the parties involved. A composition and payment of wergild is originally not customary, but is due to influences of a secondary nature. Typical among the herdsmen is, above all, the development of private ownership and the accumulation of wealth in the form of stock. This at the same time presented the opportunity of developing class distinctions and of a vertical stratification of society, a differentiation of rich and poor. These beginnings of a hierarchic system among the herdsmen did not flourish until they came in contact with the agricultural societies. The law of inheritance in most of these tribes is marked by primogeniture; only under Mohammedan influence do we find a certain degree of equal age-right of inheritance.

The societies of herdsmen of the Old World brought about a political revolution by the creation of large empires in Asia as well as in Africa. Their centrifugal, warlike demeanor, which contrasts with the centripetal, democratic one of the older farming societies, has so intrigued modern sociology that it seems justifiable to describe briefly a few examples of the influence of the penetration of herdsmen upon the development of law in a conquered farming tribe.

The conquest of Adamaua by the Fulbe early in the nineteenth century illustrates all the phases of the intrusion of herdsmen into the land belonging to settled farming societies. The reason for their migration was economic. They sought new pastures for their zebus. At first they lived among Negro tribes, merely tolerated by them, often even oppressed by them. For a long time the Fulbe even granted to the chiefs of the settled farming societies the *jus primae noctis*.[160] This peaceful penetration turned into a warlike expedition of conquest at the beginning of the nineteenth century, when Scheu-Usmanu called his people to a sacred war against the heathen. The result was the founding of the large Sokoto empire between the Niger and the Shari. The war lord Modibo Adama added to this the territory called after him Adamaua. During his forty-two-year reign he subjugated the heathen tribes or pushed them back into the mountains. After his death in 1847 the conquests were extended southward, especially by his son Laual; and Tikar, Wute, and Baja were subjugated and made tributary. These expeditions of conquest were made possible by one factor only: the armored cavalry of the Fulbe. This shows that not only in Asia, but also in Africa, breeders of riding animals (camels and horses) and not necessarily the cattle-breeders were the conquerors.

It seems extremely important to emphasize this point. As far as I know, the Fulbe offer the only instance in recent times which permits us to study the process of a meeting of farming societies and herdsmen in all its phases and without European influence. They conquered Adamaua not as cattle herdsmen but by their tactical superiority, through their armored cavalry, to which the farming tribes had nothing similar to oppose. The Fulbe subjugated the heathen tribes, made them their subjects and bondsmen, and divided the whole of Adamaua into a number of despotically governed states which merit the designation of state even in the modern sociological definition of the conquest-state and in its vertical classification. The people are divided into slaves (prisoners of war and persons born in slavery), bondsmen (the subjugated tribes), freemen (native members of the tribe), and the nobility, which is composed of the officials selected from among the slaves, and the class of *lamidos*. Aside from this classification we find one according to occupation. The state is headed by the emir or sultan, supported by a large hierarchy of officials, mostly recruited from his slaves. There is a prime minister, a chief general, a master of ceremonies. In addition to these there are numerous lesser officials.

The entire structure of a Fulbe state has much in common with the feudal states of medieval Germany.[161] The country is divided into a number of provinces and districts which are governed by a vassal, a *lamido* of the sultan. This official must furnish support in case of war and is obliged to pay a yearly tribute. At the court the representatives of the "minorities" and of the strangers were the *galadima*, who functioned as mediators and councilors between their people and the sultan. The land originally belonged to the sultan, who could augment his income through the sale of land. His income also comprised several kinds of taxes, of which the market toll collected by the *ssărika n kasúa* (market master) was very lucrative. Jurisdiction was meted out by the *alkali*, the professional judge appointed by the king. Among the Mohammedan Fulbe the Koran was usually the code of law.[162] Mutilations and punishment by degradation or imprisonment play a large rôle in criminal law. For murder, theft of slaves or of horses, a second offense was punishable by death [163]; simple theft was punishable by chopping off the offender's right hand. In the law referring to debts the development of debt slavery is worthy of notice. In place of blood vengeance we find the payment of fines, part of which go to the sultan — that is, to the state.

This sketch of the Fulbe government is a fairly typical example for the Sudan tribes, from the Ewe in the west to the Kafficho in the east; indeed, even beyond this sphere, for the government structures of the Mongols and Huns in historical times. In the Sudan we find a gradual intensification from west to east of centralized structures of high culture. The government of the Kafficho, who were conquered in 1897 by the Habeshi, showed ancient Egyptian traits. The emperor-god, who remained ever invisible to the people, was the owner of the land, the source of law (for law and king the same word, *tā'tō*, was used), the supreme war lord, the empire itself, the master over life and death of all Kafficho.[164] Actually the ruler depended on the seven *mikire'čō*, the members of the supreme council who had the power to depose him. In other regions of Ethiopia and North Africa this council could even pronounce a death sentence over the emperor after a certain number of years of reign or for certain reasons.[165] The land was divided into crown land and hereditary fiefs, the latter given only to free Kafficho. Among the crimes which were punished by public law we do not find murder, which was avenged by the family through blood vengeance; but mutiny, treason, sorcery, robbery, cowardice in battle, rape, and bodily injury. In the process of obtaining evidence the testimony of children, women, liars, thieves, robbers, and strangers was not counted. Punishment was meted out immediately after judgment, and consisted of fines, flogging, outlawing, mutilation, hanging, decapitation, throwing off a cliff, starvation, and abandonment.

An American equivalent of these more highly developed structures which arose in Africa through the contact between herdsmen and farming tribes may be given. In the region of the United States the Natchez, an agricultural tribe, offers such a basis for comparison.[166] The organization of the Natchez was theocratic; that is, the king, the "Great Sun," was at the same time high priest. The vertical principle of organization shows a strictly defined class structure with slaves as the lowest class. Next came the common people, called Stinkards. These were ruled by the nobility, which itself was divided into three ranks: the Suns, the Nobles, and the Honored Men. The marriage laws permitted no marriage within the same rank, but only from one rank into another. Thus the Suns, even the king and his sister, were allowed to marry only into the class of the people. In general, the children among the Natchez belonged to their mother's class, but the children of the union of a Noble with a woman from the people belonged to the nobility. Advancement into a higher class was also possible through bravery in war or through specially prescribed, often cruel, religious services for the king or, let us say, the state. Thus the Stinkards could advance into the class of the Honored Men and the latter into the class of the Nobles. But only a personal nobility could be acquired, as the children did not inherit it. The rôle of war chief was open only to Nobles and Suns. Here, too, the dislike of any absolutism embodied in one person, that of the king — a feature which we find in all Indian tribes — seems to have created the rule that in most important affairs such as war and foreign politics a council of old chiefs and warriors was called. The decision rested with them, not with the king. The classes had to pay tribute to the king, who also had the say over life and death. The territorial principle was embodied in the king, though in a weaker form.

Polynesia. The tribes of Polynesia are harvesters and farmers at the same time. A Polynesian civilization is unthinkable — nor would a settlement of the islands, except New Zealand, have been possible — without the wild breadfruit tree and the coco palm. The question as to whether the Polynesians were originally pure harvesters, as I am inclined to believe,[167] or whether they have always been agricultural, as Heine-Geldern thinks, may remain unanswered here. In spite of the fairly uniform type of Polynesian culture the insular isolation has brought about special formations of legal institutions. The differences are expressed in details and do not detract from the uniformity of the general characteristics. There are obvious similarities with the harvester and herdsman societies. In general, a definite caste system (slaves, freemen, landowners, nobles) with godlike kings is peculiar to Polynesian society. Class distinctions find expression in the use of special language and in external insignia (fan, tattooing, the chief's axe, special ornaments). We are best acquainted with the legal institutions of Samoa through a number of excellent works by Krämer, Stair, Schultz-Ewerth, Mead, and Hogbin, and consequently the following description of government refers mainly to Samoa.

The territorial principle in Samoa was embodied in the sib, which extended over several villages and in which the ownership of land was vested. The land was subdivided among the several families of the village, which, however, had only the right of possession and usufruct, which was awarded by the matai, the talking chief, to the single families for cultivation.[168] The village is the smallest political unit within the regions headed by a high chief or king. In Samoa, however, the village constitutes the political and legal unit. Large political associations are rare in Polynesia anyway. As Lowie [169] has pointed out, the reason for this does not lie in the insular character of the country, for in New Zealand this reason did not exist. Samoa may have been an exception, for after the wars with Tonga the king had four titles which were acquired through conquest. In external politics it was not the village but the district which was the active political unit, especially in case of war. Through diplomatic messengers it even kept in touch with the enemy and avenged any injury or insults inflicted upon these envoys, who were protected by a taboo. The government and administration of the village is not despotic but parliamentary, and is in the hands of the village assembly, which meets on the village place. Decisions are not made by majority vote; the deciding factor is the authority of one or several participating matai, who can, however, be influenced by a third party before the assembly meets. Such preparatory conferences were quite customary. The chief or the talking chief tries "to discover in advance what the general temper is, and to direct public opinion into the desired channels." The village assembly also decided on criminal processes, but only in so far as they were of a public nature and concerned the village community as such. Among such public crimes Mead mentions the ridiculing of a chief or a *taupou*, theft as a second offense, incest, and instigation or denunciations between two matai.[170] Other quarrels were settled by the matai or the head of the family, who acted as arbiter.[171] For punishment the village community decreed either fines or sentences of work in bondage, destruction of property,[172] outlawing, exposure to the sun, hanging, and the like.[173] The condemned man, in order to escape punishment, could ask any matai for an asylum. Whether the matai could give him this protection depended upon his authority within the village. However, there existed commonly respected places of refuge in Samoa — for instance "the house of the chief Tofaeono in Vaimaunga" — and Krämer[174] tells of two public places of refuge in Hawaii.

In spite of the collective ownership of the sib in respect to land and of the family in respect to food there exists private ownership of movables. Closely connected with the law of ownership and property, but also with public law, is the institution of the legal taboo in Polynesia. Polack[175] tells of public taboos among the Maori for the safeguarding of a conquered territory or of the interests of the community. The violation of such a taboo meant death if the culprit was a member of the tribe, and war if he belonged to a strange tribe. The property and food taboos in Polynesia, regarded from an economic angle, seem to have contributed a good deal to the accumulation of individual property and to the increase of class distinctions. In Manga Reva the sturdiest breadfruit trees and coco palms were tabooed for the chief, and in New Zealand anything that the chief desired would become his property because of the power of his taboo.[176] The sign of the taboo varied considerably. It might consist of banana leaves tied around the trunk of a coco palm, a string or a thread tied around an object, a post painted with red ochre, articles of clothing, bunches of grass, or other objects.[177]

Conclusion. We have tried to elucidate the various forms of government on the basis of the close connection between economic patterns and legal institutions.

I do not claim that this method of approach is the only proper one. Our investigation has shown that we are justified in speaking of law and of legal norms even in reference to the most ancient primitive tribes in the earliest stages of human civilization. These

laws rule the life of the community, though to a great extent the
norms are not expressed in statutes, but present negative rules of
behavior rather than positive commandment. Even in the history
of logic the rule of antithesis preceded that of identity. Characteristic of the earlier cultures is the complexity of legal norms and the
low degree of differentiation in legal concepts. The pressure from
outside and public opinion within the society are the strongest
regulating factors. The ownership of land is originally collective, in
the hands of the local group; only the usufruct is sometimes allotted
to a group of families or to a single family. The cultivation of land
does not in itself create ownership. Even in the empires of the
Sudan and of Ethiopia, where the land belonged to the king, land
was not private property in our sense, for the king-priest was a
demigod, and as an individual he was killed if the welfare of the
people demanded it. The land belonged to him only as personification of the state. Food was also originally collective property. Connected with this is the collective responsibility of the group for a
sufficient food supply for the individual. The development of private
property shows definite beginnings among the harvesters, who also
are characterized by their stronger development of a "copyright"
law and of intertribal law. The right of asylum is found among the
harvesters, herdsmen, and Polynesians, and its further development
may be traced to the Greek and Mexican temples. The differentiation of classes has been most strongly developed among the
herdsmen and the Polynesians. In legal procedure we can clearly
distinguish between various tendencies which are described in the
several chapters. However, we have also seen that structures of the
Old World do not *per se* apply to tribes of the New World, and
that the individualistic and at the same time democratic traits of
the Indians stand out in strong contrast against the structures of
African societies. The state, in Oppenheimer's sense, has developed
in Asia and Africa through the conquest of societies of agriculturists
by herdsmen. For the Old World, Oppenheimer's theory is justified.
Not so for the New World, where before the advent of the Whites
there have never been any tribes of herdsmen. Yet high civilizations
such as the empires of the Incas, Chibcha, Maya, and Aztec developed in the New World, and structurally they are entirely comparable to the ancient high civilizations of the Old World. In interstate
attitudes, as in the various associations of the Iroquois, the Algonquians, and the Hurons, the resulting formations cannot be com-

pared with similar ones of the Old World, but only, at best, with the very modern institution of the League of Nations. They form a sharp contrast to the despotic empires of Africa. Finally, the political organizations of Polynesia also admit doubt as to the validity of Oppenheimer's arguments. This much, however, should be clear: that among aborigines very close relations exist between government and land; that the land belongs to the clan, the tribe, or the people, but not to the individual; and that also in regard to the provision of food the community occupies the center of attention. For the primitive it is not the individual who is eternal, but the people, land, and law.

FOOTNOTES

1. Lips, J. E., "Die Anfänge des Rechts an Grund und Boden bei den Naturvölkern und der Begriff der Erntevölker," *Festschrift für P. W. Schmidt* (Vienna, 1928), and "Kamerun," in *Das Eingeborenenrecht. Sitten und Gewohnheitsrechte der Eingeborenen der ehemaligen deutschen Kolonien in Afrika und in der Südsee,* edited by E. Schultz-Ewerth and L. Adam, 2 vols. (Stuttgart, 1930), vol. 2, p. 153.
2. This has been pointed out especially by E. Grosse, *Die Formen der Familie und die Formen der Wirtschaft* (Freiburg, Leipzig, 1896).
3. Wigmore, J., "Jottings on Comparative Legal Ideas and Institutions," *Tulane Law Review,* vol. 6 (1931), p. 50.
4. *Tulane Law Review,* vol. 7 (1932), p. 58.
5. Wundt, W., in his *Völkerpsychologie,* vol. 9, "Das Recht," (Leipzig, 1918), pp. 460 ff., supposes just the opposite course of development of law; that is, from individualism to collectivism.
6. Radcliffe-Brown, A. R., "Primitive Law," *Encyclopaedia of the Social Sciences,* (1933), vol. 9, p. 202.
7. Hogbin, H. I., *Law and Order in Polynesia: A Study of Primitive Legal Institutions.* With an introduction by B. Malinowski (London, 1934).
8. *Ibid.,* Introduction.
9. I use the phrase "legal norm" in the sense of K. Binding, *Die Normen und ihre Übertretung* (Leipzig, 1890).
10. Schmidt, W., and Koppers, W., *Völker und Kulturen* (Regensburg, 1924), pp. 174 ff.
11. Graebner, F., *Das Weltbild der Primitiven* (Munich, 1924), p. 16.
12. Lowie, R. H., *Primitive Society* (1920), pp. 358 ff.
13. Oppenheimer, F., *System der Soziologie* (Jena, 1929), vol. 4, Part 1, pp. 1 ff.
14. Menghin, O., "Die weltgeschichtliche Rolle der uralaltaischen Völker," *Archaeologiai Értesitö,* vol. 42 (1928), pp. 289 ff.
15. Lips, J. E., "Public Opinion and Mutual Assistance Among the Montagnais-Naskapi," *American Anthropologist,* vol. 39, no. 2 (1937).
16. Stow, G. W., *The Native Races of South Africa* (London, 1905), p. 33.
17. The term "pre-government" was suggested to me by K. N. Llewellyn.

18. Passarge, S., *Die Buschmänner der Kalahari* (Berlin, 1907), p. 52.
19. Seligmann, C. G. and B. Z., *The Veddas* (Cambridge, 1911), p. 113.
20. West, J., *The History of Tasmania*. Quoted from Ling Roth, H., *The Aboriginals of Tasmania* (Halifax, 1899), pp. 59, 76.
21. Roth, W. E., *Ethnological Studies among Northwest-Central Queensland Aborigines* (Brisbane and London, 1897), vol. 1, p. 160; and Ridley, W., *Kamilaroi and Other Australian Languages* (Sydney, 1875), p. 159.
22. See Howitt, A. W., *The Native Tribes of Southeast Australia* (London, 1904), p. 332.
23. Wied, M., Prinz zu, *Reise nach Brasilien* (Frankfurt, 1821), vol. 1, pp. 370 ff., Pl. II.
24. Fraser, J., *The Aborigines of New South Wales* (Sydney, 1892), vol. 1, p. 37.
25. Howitt, A. W., *op. cit.*, pp. 340 ff.
26. Radcliffe-Brown, A. R., "Three Tribes of Western Australia," *Journal of the Royal Anthropological Institute*, vol. 43 (1913), pp. 143–194.
27. Wundt, W., *op. cit.*, vol. 9, "Das Recht," p. 14.
28. Palmer, E., "Notes on some Australian Tribes," *Journal of the Royal Anthropological Institute*, vol. 13 (1883), p. 285.
29. Howitt, A. W., *op. cit.*, p. 759.
30. See for instance, Dawson, J., *Australian Aborigines* (Melbourne, 1881), pp. 22 ff., and Mathews, R. H., "Ethnological Notes on the Aboriginal Tribes of New South Wales and Victoria," *Journal of the Royal Society of New South Wales*, vol. 38 (1904), pp. 56 ff.
31. Wied, M., Prinz zu, *op. cit.*, vol. 2, pp. 27 ff.
32. Sarasin, P. and F., *Die Weddas von Ceylon*, in *Ergebnisse naturwissenschaftlicher Forschungen auf Ceylon*, vol. 3 (Wiesbaden, 1893).
33. Taplin, G., *The Folklore, Manners, Customs and Languages of the South Australian Aborigines* (Adelaide, 1898), vol. 1, p. 11, expresses it clearly when he says: "In the clan there can be no personal property . . . all implements, weapons, etc., belong to the members collectively. . . . If he [the native] has a weapon, or net, or canoe, which is in some sense his own, he knows that his property in it is subject to the superior rights of his clan."
34. Fison and Howitt, *Kamilaroi and Kurnai* (Melbourne, 1880), p. 128.
35. Boas, F., in "Reine und Angewandte Soziologie," *Eine Festgabe für Ferdinand Tönnies* (Leipzig, 1936), p. 264.
36. Henry, J., unpublished material.
37. Bonwick, J., *Daily Life and Origin of the Tasmanians* (London, 1870), pp. 60 ff.
38. Wied, M., Prinz zu, *op. cit.*, vol. 2, p. 38.
39. Roth, W. E., *op. cit.*, vol. 1, p. 139.
40. Howitt, A. W., *op. cit.*, pp. 295 ff.; Knabenhans, A., *Die politische Organisation bei den australischen Eingeborenen* (Berlin, 1919), pp. 129 ff.
41. Trenk, "Die Buschleute der Namib," *Mitteilungen aus den deutschen Schutzgebieten*, vol. 23 (1910), p. 169.
42. For example, Wied, M., Prinz zu, *op. cit.*, vol. 2, p. 3.
43. Dawson, J., *op. cit.*
44. Grosse, E., *op. cit.*

45. Knabenhans, A., *op. cit.*
46. Oppenheimer, F., *op. cit.*, vol. 4, Part 1, p. 3; Schmidt, W., and Koppers, W., *op. cit.*, p. 179.
47. Byhan, A., *Die Polarvölker* (Leipzig, 1909), p. 104.
48. Kohler, J., "Zur Urgeschichte der Ehe," *Zeitschrift für vergleichende Rechtswissenschaft*, vol. 12 (Stuttgart, 1897), pp. 186–353; Rink, *Tales and Traditions of the Eskimo* (Edinburgh, 1875), p. 27.
49. Bogoras, W., *The Chukchee*, Jesup Expedition, vol. 7 (1904–09), p. 537.
50. Amundsen, R., *The Northwest Passage* (1908), vol. 2, p. 45.
51. Schrenck, L. von, "Reisen und Forschungen im Amur-Lande," *Die Völker des Amur-Landes* (St. Petersburg, 1891), vol. 3, p. 580.
52 Boas, F., *The Central Eskimo*, Annual Report of the Bureau of Ethnology, vol. 6 (1888), p. 461.
53. Bogoras, W., *op. cit.*, p. 628.
54. Czaplicka, M. A., *Aboriginal Siberia: A Study in Social Anthropology* (Oxford, 1914), pp. 24 ff.
55. Boas, F., "Property Marks of Alaskan Eskimo," *American Anthropologist*, vol. 1 (1899), p. 601.
56. Solem, E., *Lappiske Rettstudier* (Oslo, 1933).
57. Lips, J. E., "Public Opinion and Mutual Assistance among the Montagnais-Naskapi."
58. Boas, F., *The Central Eskimo*, p. 580.
59. Bogoras, W., *op. cit.*, pp. 543 ff.
60. See for instance, *ibid.*, p. 662.
61. Nelson, N. C., *The Eskimo about Bering Strait*, Annual Report of the Bureau of Ethnology, vol. 18 (1899), p. 293.
62. Boas, F., *The Eskimo of Baffin Land and Hudson Bay*, Bulletin of the American Museum of Natural History, vol. 15 (1901, 1907), p. 668.
63. Jenness, D., "The Life of the Copper Eskimos," *Report of the Canadian Arctic Expedition, 1913–1918* (Ottawa, 1922), vol. 12, p. 197; Boas, F., *The Eskimo of Baffin Land and Hudson Bay*, p. 118.
64. Kane, E. K., *Arctic Explorations: The Second Grinnell Expedition in Search of Sir John Franklin, 1853, '54, '55* (1857), vol. 2, p. 127.
65. Byhan, A., *op. cit.*, p. 106.
66. Lips, J., "Die Anfänge des Rechts an Grund und Boden," pp. 490 ff., and *Einleitung in die vergleichende Völkerkunde* (Leipzig, 1928), pp. 24 ff.
67. Worsnop, T., *The Prehistoric Arts, Manufactures, Works, Weapons, etc., of the Aborigines of Australia* (Adelaide, 1897). Concerning the nardoo seed Worsnop (p. 582) tells us a not very plausible story: "Some years ago there was a story current in the colonies that a White captive was held by an interior tribe, whose influence on them was very great. He had taught them (so the story runs) to cultivate the nardoo plant and store the seed for future use."
68. *Melumbium speciosum* and *Nymphea gigantica*. Eylmann, E., *Die Eingeborenen der Kolonie Südaustralien* (Berlin, 1908), p. 289.
69. Westgarth, W., *Australia Felix* (Edinburgh, 1848), p. 72.
70. H. Trimborn has successfully demonstrated the correctness of my idea in regard to Peru: "Die kulturhistorische Stellung der Lamazucht in der

Wirtschaft der peruanischen Erntevölker," *Anthropos*, vol. 23 (1928), pp. 656–664.

71. Hodgson, C. P., *Reminiscences of Australia* (London, 1846), p. 147.
72. Spencer, B., and Gillen, F. J., *Across Australia* (London, 1912), vol. 2, p. 469.
73. Lips, J., "Die Anfänge des Rechts an Grund und Boden," p. 492.
74. Wollaston, A. F. R., *Pygmies and Papuans* (London, 1912), pp. 83 ff.
75. Bancroft, G., *History of the United States* (London, 1840), vol. 3, p. 242.
76. Dawson, J., *op. cit.*, p. 2.
77. Curr, E., *Recollections of Squatting in Victoria* (Melbourne, 1883), p. 247.
78. Perron d'Arc, H., *Aventures d'un voyageur en Australie* (Paris, 1870), p. 276.
79. Ridley, W., *op. cit.*, p. 159.
80. Mathew, J., *Two Representative Tribes of Queensland* (London, 1910), p. 94.
81. Anonymous in Curr, E., *The Australian Race* (Melbourne and London, 1886), vol. 3, p. 121.
82. Dawson, J., *op. cit.*, p. 2.
83. Ridley, W., "Australian Languages and Traditions," *Journal of the Royal Anthropological Institute*, vol. 2 (1872), p. 271.
84. Howitt, F. G. S., "Notes on Australian Message Sticks and Messengers," *Journal of the Royal Anthropological Institute*, vol. 18 (1888), Pl. XIV, figs. 1, 14.
85. Dawson, J., *op. cit.*, p. 79.
86. Fraser, J., *op. cit.*, p. 37; Wheeler, G. C., *The Tribe and Intertribal Relations in Australia* (London, 1910), p. 29.
87. Spencer, B., and Gillen, F. J., *op. cit.*, vol. 2, p. 373.
88. Dawson, J., *op. cit.*, p. 78.
89. Spencer, B., and Gillen, F. J., *op. cit.*, vol. 1, p. 106.
90. Dawson, J., *op. cit.*, p. 78.
91. Cameron, A. L. P., "Notes on Some Tribes of New South Wales," *Journal of the Royal Anthropological Institute*, vol. 14 (1884), pp. 344–370. See also Mathews, R. H., "The Bora of the Kamilaroi Tribes," *Journal of the Royal Anthropological Institute*, vol. 24 (1895), pp. 411 ff.
92. Curr, E., *The Australian Race*, vol. 3, p. 167; also Palmer, E. V., *The Australian Corroboree*, *Nineteenth Century* (1906), p. 317.
92a. Roheim, G., "Die Urformen und der Ursprung des Eigentums," *Internationales Archiv für Ethnographie*, vol. 28 (Leiden, 1927), pp. 1–30.
93. Bischofs, P. J., "Die Niol-Niol, ein Eingeborenenstamm Nordwest-Australiens," *Anthropos*, vol. 3 (Vienna, 1908), pp. 32–40.
94. Curr, E., *The Australian Race*, vol. 2, p. 293.
95. Densmore, F., *Uses of Plants by the Chippewa Indians*, Annual Report of the Bureau of American Ethnology, vol. 44 (1928), p. 313.
96. Ellis, *Fifty-four Years' Recollections of Men and Events in Wisconsin*, Wisconsin Historical Collections, vol. 12 (1873–76), p. 265.
97. Radin, P., *The Winnebago Tribe*, Annual Report of the Bureau of American Ethnology, vol. 37 (1923), pp. 79, 203.
98. Strehlow, C., *Die Aranda- und Loritjastämme in Zentralaustralien*, Veröffentlichungen aus dem städtischen Völkermuseum (Frankfurt, 1907, 1915), 4 Parts, § 2, p. 4.

99. See also Curr, E., *The Australian Race*, vol. 1, p. 81.
100. Dawson, J., *op. cit.*, p. 22.
101. Hoffman, W. J., *The Menomini Indians*, Annual Report of the Bureau of Ethnology, vol. 14 (1896), Part I, pp. 12 ff.
102. Jenks, A. E., *The Wild-Rice Gatherers of the Upper Lakes: A Study in American Primitive Economics*, Annual Report of the Bureau of American Ethnology, vol. 19 (1900), Part II, p. 1091. Also *Handbook of the American Indians North of Mexico*, Bulletin of the Bureau of American Ethnology, no. 30 (1910), Part II, p. 787.
103. Jenks, A. E., *op. cit.*, p. 1072.
104. *Ibid.*
105. Schmidt, P. W., "Die soziologische und religiös-ethische Gruppierung der australischen Stämme," *Zeitschrift für Ethnologie*, vol. 41 (1909), p. 352.
106. Howitt, A. W., *op. cit.*, pp. 710 ff.; Siebert, "Sagen und Sitten der Dieri und Nachbarstämme in Zentralaustralien," *Globus*, vol. 97 (Braunschweig, 1910), p. 54.
107. Curr, E., *The Australian Race*, vol. 2, p. 70; Howitt, A. W., "The Dieri and Other Kindred Tribes of Central Australia," *Journal of the Royal Anthropological Institute*, vol. 20 (1891), pp. 76 ff.; Gason, S., *The Native Tribes of South Australia* (Adelaide, 1879), p. 280. See also *Journal of the Royal Anthropological Institute*, vol. 24 (1895), p. 167.
108. Thomas, N. W., *Natives of Australia* (London, 1906), p. 117; Spencer, B., and Gillen, F. J., *Across Australia*, vol. 1, p. 106; Eylmann, E., *Südaustralien*, p. 306.
109. Spencer, B., and Gillen, F. J., *Native Tribes*, p. 590.
110. Eylmann, E., *op. cit.*, p. 48.
111. Strehlow, C., *op. cit.*, p. 10.
112. Curr, E., *The Australian Race*, vol. 3, p. 162.
113. Strehlow, C., *op. cit.*, p. 10.
114. Curr, E., *The Australian Race*, vol. 2, p. 249.
115. Strehlow, C., *op. cit.*, p. 10.
116. Grey, G., *Journal of Two Expeditions to Northwest and Western Australia* (London, 1841), vol. 2, p. 304.
117. Lips, J., "Die Anfänge des Theaters bei den Naturvölkern," *Tagungsberichte der deutschen anthropologischen Gesellschaft* (Leipzig, 1928); Roheim, G., "Die Urformen und der Ursprung des Eigentums," *Internationales Archiv für Ethnographie* (Leiden, 1927), vol. 28, pp. 1–30.
118. Mathews, R. H., "Australian Tribes, Their Formation and Government," *Zeitschrift für Ethnologie* (Berlin, 1906), pp. 943 ff.
119. Nordenskiöld, E., *Indianerleben, El Gran Chaco* (Leipzig, 1913), p. 34.
120. Strehlow, C., *op. cit.*, p. 10.
121. Taplin, G., *op. cit.*, vol. 1, pp. 32 ff.
122. Curr, E., *The Australian Race*, vol. 3, p. 162.
123. Spencer, B., and Gillen, F. J., *Native Tribes*, pp. 133 ff.; Hellwig, A., "Nachträge zum Asylrecht in Ozeanien," *Zeitschrift für vergleichende Rechtswissenschaft*, vol. 19 (Stuttgart, 1906), pp. 41–102.
124. Spencer, B., and Gillen, F. J., *op. cit.*, p. 134.
125. Jenks, A. E., *op. cit.*, p. 1112.

126. See Oppenheimer, F., "Die Wanderung, vorwiegend vom universalhistorischen und ökonomischen Gesichtspunkte," *Verhandlungen des 6. Deutschen Soziologentages vom 17. bis 19. September 1928 in Zürich* (Tübingen, 1929), pp. 147–172.

127. Schoolcraft, H. B., *Summary Narrative of an Exploring Expedition to the Sources of the Mississippi River in 1820; Resumed and Completed by the Discovery of its Origin in Itasca Lake 1832* (1855), p. 544.

128. Boas, F., *Ethnology of the Kwakiutl,* Annual Report of the Bureau of American Ethnology, vol. 35 (1921), Part II, p. 1346.

129. Boas, F., *Geographical Names of the Kwakiutl Indians,* Columbia University Contributions to Anthropology, vol. 20 (1934), p. 37, Pls. 19–22.

130. Boas, F., "The Social Organization of the Tribes of the North Pacific Coast," *American Anthropologist,* vol. 26 (1924), p. 331.

131. Boas, F., *Ethnology of the Kwakiutl,* p. 1341.

132. *Ibid.,* p. 1335.

133. *Ibid.,* p. 1347.

134. Lowie, R. H., *Primitive Society* (1920), p. 385.

135. Wissler, C., *North American Indians of the Plains* (1912), p. 21.

136. Lowie, R. H., *Primitive Society,* p. 387; Fletcher, A. C., and La Flesche, F., *The Omaha Tribe,* Annual Report of the Bureau of American Ethnology, vol. 27 (1911), p. 199.

137. Fletcher, A. C., and La Flesche, F., *op. cit.,* p. 202.

138. *Ibid.,* p. 208.

139. Letter from K. N. Llewellyn, July 27, 1935.

140. Fletcher, A. C., and La Flesche, F., *op. cit.,* p. 210.

141. Oral report by E. A. Hoebel.

142. Fletcher, A. C., and La Flesche, F., *op. cit.,* p. 376.

143. Keysser, C., "Aus dem Leben der Kai-Leute," in Neuhauss, R., *Deutsch-Neuguinea* (Berlin, 1911), pp. 1–242.

144. Lips, J. E., "Kamerun," p. 160.

144a. Leuschner, S., and Steinmetz, R., *Rechtsverhältnisse von eingeborenen Völkern in Afrika und Ozeanien* (Berlin, 1903), p. 16.

144b. Buchholz, R., *Land und Leute in Westafrika* (Berlin, 1876), p. 42.

145. Bastian, A., *Die Reehtsverhältnisse bei verschiedenen Völkern der Erde* (Berlin, 1872), p. 402; Lips, J. E., "Kamerun," p. 160. Cf. *ibid.* for further literature.

146. Mansfeld, A., *Urwalddokumente* (Berlin, 1908), pp. 159 ff.

147. Tessmann, G., *Die Pangwe* (Berlin and Leipzig, 1913), vol. 2, p. 65.

148. Frobenius, L., "Die Masken und Geheimbünde Afrikas," *Nova acta. Abh. der kaiserlich Leopoldinisch-Carolinisch Deutschen Akademie der Naturforscher,* vol. 74, no. 1 (Halle, 1898), p. 77; Lips, J. E., "Kamerun," p. 169.

149. Buchner, M., *Kamerun* (Leipzig, 1887), pp. 26 ff.; Bastian, A., *Der Fetisch an der Küste Guineas* (Berlin, 1884), p. 91.

150. See also Plehn, A., "Beobachtungen in Kamerun, über die Anschauungen und Gebräuche einiger Negerstämme," *Zeitschrift für Ethnologie,* vol. 36 (Berlin, 1904), pp. 715 ff.

151. Bastian, A., *Der Fetisch an der Küste Guineas,* pp. 9 ff.

152. Morgan, L., *League of the Iroquois* (1904); MacLeod, W. C., *The Origin*

of the State, Reconsidered in the Light of the Data from Aboriginal North America (1924). References in this to further literature on the subject.

153. According to early descriptions the empire of Powhatan formed an exception. At the time of its greatest extent, this empire, which was founded mainly by conquest, comprised more than 8000 square miles and more than 150 towns. See Beverly, R., *History of Virginia* (1855), p. 135; Strachey, W., *The Historie and Travaile into Virginia Britannia*, Hakluyt Society Publications (London, 1849), p. 63.

154. See Lips, J. E., "Kamerun," which also contains reference to further literature on this subject.

155. Gutmann, B., *Das Recht der Dschagga* (Munich, 1926), p. 462.

156. Krafft, M., "Die Rechtsverhältnisse der Ovakuanjama und der Ovandonga," *Mitteilungen aus den deutschen Schutzgebieten*, vol. 27 (1914), pp. 17–35.

157. Consten, H., *Weideplätze der Mongolen* (Berlin, 1920), vol. 2, p. 108.

158. See Paulitschke, P., *Ethnographie Nordostafrikas*, 2 vols. (Berlin, 1893, 1896); Nigmann, E., *Die Wahehe* (Berlin, 1908); Karutz, R., *Unter Kirgisen und Turkmenen* (Leipzig, 1911).

159. Lips, J. E., "Ethnopolitics and the Indians," *Commonweal*, March 15, 1935.

160. Struempell, K., "Die Geschichte Adamauas nach mündlichen Überlieferungen," *Mitteilungen der Geographischen Gesellschaft in Hamburg*, vol. 26, Book I (Hamburg, 1912), pp. 52 ff.

161. Passarge, S., *Adamaua, Bericht über die Expedition des Deutschen Kamerun-Komitees in den Jahren 1893–94* (Berlin, 1895), p. 490.

162. See also the procedure in the finding of a thief. Passarge, S., *op. cit.*, p. 96; Nachtigal, G., *Sahara und Sudan* (Berlin, 1879–89), vol. 2, p. 748.

163. The hangman's position is quite exalted. At the court and among the people he often occupies a position similar to that of the court jester. See also Passarge, S., *op. cit.*, p. 278.

164. Bieber, F. J., *Kaffa*, vol. 2 (1923), pp. 1144 ff.

165. Lips, J. E., *Thomas Hobbes*. Appendix, *Behemoth oder das Lange Parlament* (Leipzig, 1927), pp. 186 ff.; also Frobenius, L., *Und Afrika Sprach* (Berlin, 1914), vol. 3, pp. 146 ff.

166. Swanton, J. R., *The Indian Tribes of the Lower Mississippi and Adjacent Coasts of the Gulf of Mexico*, Bulletin of the Bureau of American Ethnology, no. 43 (1911).

167. Lips, J. E., *Einleitung in die vergleichende Völkerkunde*, pp. 32 ff.

168. Schultz-Ewerth, E., "Samoa," *Das Eingeborenenrecht* (Stuttgart, 1930), vol. 2, p. 704.

169. Lowie, R. H., *Primitive Society*, pp. 362 ff.

170. Mead, M., *Social Organization of Manu'a* (Honolulu, 1930), p. 169.

171. Brown, G., *Melanesians and Polynesians* (London, 1910), p. 290; Stair, J. B., *Old Samoa* (London, 1897), p. 96.

172. Schultz-Ewerth, E., *op. cit.*, p. 710.

173. Hogbin, H. I., *op. cit.*, pp. 274 ff.

174. Krämer, A., *Hawaii, Ostmikronesien und Samoa* (Stuttgart, 1906), p. 106.

175. Polack, J. S., *New Zealand* (London, 1838), vol. 2, pp. 70, 252 ff.

176. Lehmann, R., *Die polynesischen Tabusitten* (Leipzig, 1930), pp. 192 ff.
177. Best, E., *The Maori* (Wellington, 1924), vol. 1, p. 390; Firth, R., *Primitive Economics of the New Zealand Maori* (London, 1929), p. 248.

GENERAL REFERENCES

Bastian, A., *Die Rechtsverhältnisse bei verschiedenen Völkern der Erde* (Berlin, 1872).

Gutmann, B., *Das Recht der Dschagga* (Munich, 1926).

Hogbin, H. J., *Law and Order in Polynesia: A Study of Primitive Legal Institutions* (London, 1934).

Lowie, R. H., *The Origin of the State* (1924).

Lowie, R. H., *Primitive Society* (1920).

Malinowski, B., *Crime and Custom in Savage Society* (1926).

Oppenheimer, F., *Der Staat* (Frankfurt, 1907).

Oppenheimer, F., *System der Soziologie* (Jena, 1929).

Radcliffe-Brown, A. R., "Primitive Law," *Encyclopaedia of the Social Sciences* (1933), vol. 9.

Vinogradoff, P., *Outlines of Historical Jurisprudence* (1920).

Vollenhoven, C. van, *Hed Adatrecht van Nederlandsch-Indië*, 3 vols. (Leiden, 1931–33).

Das Eingeborenenrecht. Sitten und Gewohnheitsrechte der Eingeborenen der ehemaligen deutschen Kolonien in Afrika und in der Südsee, edited by E. Schultz-Ewerth and L. Adam, 2 vols. (Stuttgart, 1929–30).

Zeitschrift für vergleichende Rechtswissenschaft (Berlin).

CHAPTER XI

ART

RUTH BUNZEL

Antiquity and universality of art. In the caves of the Aurignacian period of the Old Stone Age, associated with the bones of animals long extinct and with human remains and tools of primitive types, are found bits of shell and stone worked into beads and pendants with which early man adorned himself. At about the same period we find the beginnings of the extraordinary school of realistic painting of animals which is so eloquent a witness of early man's esthetic sense. Before man learned to ensure his food supply by the cultivation of plants, or to lighten his labors by domesticating animals to his use, long before he had stumbled upon simple inventions like the wheel, or primitive industries like pottery, he had developed a pictorial art so perfect in style that the modern painter stands in wonder before his creations. Here is the pageant of the ancient forest, teeming with game, from which man drew his sustenance, and to which he reacted emotionally with great vigor. Concerning the "purpose" of these paintings, placed in the deep recesses of caves where daylight never penetrated, there have been many theories. We may speculate endlessly concerning their possible religious or magical significance, and nothing can be proved or disproved. But whatever may have been the connection of these paintings with religious cults or private magic, they still display stylistic features in the treatment of animal figures that mark them as belonging to a highly sophisticated art form. We know nothing about our earliest ancestors' conceptions of the supernatural, but of their sense of form and ideas of perspective we know a great deal.

Just as the antiquity of art proves it to be a basic form of human behavior, so also does its universality among the living races of man. Among all existing groups there is none, however rude its culture, that does not have some characteristic form of art. The Andamanese, who have been described as not knowing the art of kindling fire, decorate their bodies with elaborate painted designs and wear ornamental headbands, girdles, necklaces, bracelets, and anklets on their otherwise naked bodies. And no people, however harassed by economic need, is without some form of literary art. All peoples tell tales, presumably for the pleasure of telling them; all peoples sing songs and dance; and all peoples have more or less elaborate patterns of behavior for public performances. All these activities, besides serving their purpose in the economic or social life of the group, give pleasure by their intrinsic qualities. Wherever these inherent values have been enhanced by formal elaboration we may speak of art.

Esthetic emotion. Most definitions of art presuppose the existence in man of an esthetic emotion which can be evoked by qualities inherent in objects or activities. Esthetic emotion differs from other forms of pleasure in being a direct response to the object, unrelated in any way that we can see to biological satisfactions. Therefore, the kind of pleasure which may be evoked by a song differs from such pleasures as those of satisfied hunger or thirst or appeased sexual desire or repose after exertion. These things restore the normal equilibrium of the body after a state of tension. A song, by giving pleasure, may serve to mitigate fatigue or provide a channel of release for the pangs of unappeased hunger. But its ability so to compensate depends entirely on its ability to evoke esthetic emotion.

There are two distinct aspects to esthetic emotion: the pleasure of creating and the pleasure of contemplating beautiful forms. These may be quite independent of each other. The Thompson Indians decorate the sides of their leggings with fringes strung with colored beads (Fig. 83). The beads are strung in regular patterns, showing complex rhythmical arrangements. But the design is completely lost when the garment is worn and the fringes fall together. Even more striking is the case of the hide boxes and cases of the Sauk and Fox (Fig. 71A). The piece of hide from which the box is to be made is covered with painted patterns, carefully balanced and symmetrically arranged. But the lines of the pattern have no relation to the structure of the box, with the result that when the box is cut and folded, the original cohesion of the pattern is completely lost (Fig. 71B). Part of the original pattern is cut away, and the rest broken up by the folding, so that on certain faces only fragments irregularly joined appear. In these cases the artist was certainly more concerned with the creative process than with the visual effect of the finished article.

The same tendency may be illustrated in the field of primitive literature. An important feature of the rituals of the Zuñi Indians is the recitation of prayers in elaborate poetic form. The rhythm, the grammatical structure, the use of metaphor, and the general form into which ideas are cast are all highly characteristic. In a few

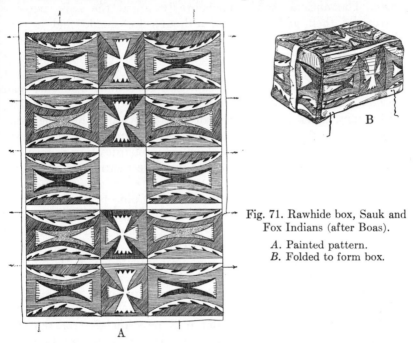

Fig. 71. Rawhide box, Sauk and Fox Indians (after Boas).

A. Painted pattern.
B. Folded to form box.

cases these chants are loudly declaimed, but the usual method of delivery is to speak them very rapidly and in a low voice so that bystanders may not hear them. The elaborate literary pattern is preserved for the pleasure of the performer alone.

The quality that is able to evoke this feeling of esthetic pleasure is variously called "the beautiful," "significant form," etc. A term like "the beautiful" has the disadvantage of implying the existence of absolute standards of beauty and evaluation in terms of such standards. A glance at the varying canons of beauty in different ages and among different peoples shows the impossibility of assuming the existence of any such absolutes. The mutilations of the human body in the name of beauty have always been striking. The Cretans cultivated wasp waists for men and women thousands of years ago, and the ancient Egyptians shaved their heads and wore wigs. The Kwakiutl Indians deform the heads of babies; the Chinese women bind their feet. Australian aborigines cover their bodies with raised scars; certain African tribes file their teeth to points. So also with the objects on which men lavish their skill and taste. The ancient Aztecs undoubtedly found the most massive statues of their gods beautiful, although we should find it very difficult to agree. It seems quite unnecessary to multiply instances of standards of beauty which differ from our own; the absence of absolute criteria in the realm of art has so long been recognized that it is almost banal to point out again that concerning taste there can be no argument. But, although not all peoples like the same thing, within any given group practically all individuals like the same thing in art just as they do in morals. This standardization of taste is a cultural phenomenon as striking as standardization in forms of marriage, and presents a problem for investigation to which we shall return later.

Among primitive peoples the production of objects solely to gratify esthetic impulse is rare, although not wholly lacking. The Eskimo and the Koryak of Siberia make many "useless" carvings in bone and ivory. Much of the wood-carving of Africa also is without other purpose than its own beauty,[1] and probably much of the ancient Peruvian pottery. The manufacture of various small articles misleadingly called "toys," but which are not intended for children's amusement, is one of the most important folk arts of Mexico. One might quote other examples. But it is nevertheless true that the greater part of the art of primitive man is applied to useful objects. And usually the maker or user evaluates the object in terms of its two functions, giving greater weight to usefulness. "Pretty but not strong," was the criticism of a famous Hopi potter in discarding a very handsome pot which a collector had selected for purchase. However, ornamentation sometimes runs away with utility, and produces utensils that are more ornamental than useful — pots like those beautiful black ones of the pueblo of San Ildefonso which will not hold water, axes like those of the Cook archipelago that were never intended to hew wood, and the diminutive baskets of the Californian and Mexican Indians. These objects correspond to the bric-a-brac of the age just past.

Usefulness may rule in other arts besides decoration. Song is frequently, but not always, incantation or is otherwise useful.

Ritual is almost always directed toward some practical end. Literature seems to be the art that, among primitive peoples, is most completely independent of practical purposes. The proportion of primitive tales that are neither informative nor edifying, even from the point of view of the tellers, is indeed striking.

The decorative arts. Among all peoples are found some examples of plastic art, some objects which have been subjected to elaboration of form in response to the esthetic impulse. Almost any object of daily use may be singled out for artistic elaboration. Utensils of wood, stone, clay, or fibers; habitations; clothing; objects intended for religious use, such as fetishes, masks, altars; and the human body itself have all, each in its time and place, been selected as suitable for artistic embellishment. The different groups of mankind chose one or another field for exploitation. One tribe makes highly decorative pottery and only the simplest of baskets, while their neighbors decorate their baskets and leave their pots plain and crude, while still another group lavishes all its skill on the ornamentation of the body. In the artistic products of the Indians of Middle and North America, for example, great diversity of expression may be noted. The tribes of the highlands of Guatemala restrict their artistic interest to clothing, in which they exhibit skill and taste. Each village has its distinctive costume, hand woven in elaborate and tasteful patterns, and great importance is attached to the making and wearing of these beautiful garments. Houses and house furnishings and utensils, on the other hand, are simple serviceable objects. The earthenware vessels used for food are factory-made in one or two villages and traded over the region. They are adequate in technique and attractive in design but, although hand-made, possess no more individuality than modern American aluminum kitchenware. Both have forms which happen to be pleasing, but neither has any esthetic value to the persons who make or use them. A few miles further north, in Mexico, the aborigines, with a few notable exceptions, especially in southern Mexico, have no esthetic interest in clothing, accepting the factory-made uniforms that meet the requirements of decency imposed by the ruling classes. Here also architecture is neglected, in spite of the splendid architectural tradition. But imagination and taste are given scope in household utensils and toys. Here, too, villages are specialized; from one village come lacquered gourd bowls and boxes; from another fine, brightly colored baskets; from another, decorated earthenware;

and from others the so-called toys that were never meant for children's play. Due to active trade, these find their way about the country and are treasured possessions in many huts far from their place of origin. Among the Pueblo Indians further to the north, architecture, religious appurtenances, and, until recently, clothing were highly artistic while household utensils, with the exception of earthen water jars, remained plain and crude and strictly practical. Their nomadic neighbors have no artistic architecture but find adequate expression in clothing and ornaments, and in religious paintings of colored earths. The Indians of the Plains had a highly characteristic architectural form, the painted tipi, and elaborate clothing. California was artistically the most highly specialized area, having no art works other than baskets. The Indians of the Northwest Coast displayed little artistic interest in clothing but constructed houses, boats, utensils, and religious paraphernalia of the highest artistic excellence. We might multiply indefinitely the list of the artistic products of primitive man to demonstrate that not only do techniques vary from place to place, which is obvious to anyone who has visited a museum, but that different fields of esthetic interest are developed in different cultural groups. Not only do some people make pots and others baskets to solve the same problem, but among two tribes, both making pots, one may have a ceramic art and the other may not. Like the Navajo, they may make pots when necessary, but use basketry in preference as a medium for plastic expression. However, when we say that one group has a ceramic art and the other has none, we are not presuming to evaluate the respective products in terms of fixed standards, but are merely pointing out the varying fields of esthetic interest.

Problems of form. The character of any work of art depends upon many factors: the nature of the material from which it is made, the technical processes involved in the handling of the material and the skill achieved in these processes, the use — if any — for which the article is designed, the traditional standards of taste, and the personality and vision of the maker. An artistic conception must be expressed through a medium, and in all art, whether sophisticated easel painting or the most primitive mat plaiting, there exists a more or less close interaction between the material and the conceptual factors which determine the character of the product. Even in those cases where the artistic conception precedes the search for a suitable medium, the artist, in the realization of his conception, starts with the unformed material, and the nature of this material will exert its influence on the conception.

Consideration of materials cannot be divorced from a consideration of the various technical processes to which substances lend themselves. In order to produce a beautiful object, the artist must know his material and the process of working it. Regularity of form is prized everywhere, and regularity always depends upon complete control of the technique. Wherever an industry develops until great technical skill is attained, artisans delight in their skill and use it to produce unnecessary refinements. The development of stone-chipping in prehistoric times, for which we have incontestable historic sequences, illustrates this process (see page 158). Beginning with the crudest forms, the skill of the craftsman improved in the course of time, until finally he was playing with his technique, exhibiting his skill for its own sake. Many of the refinements in wood-carving, weaving, and other crafts of later ages were developed, in all probability, by similar processes. The expert weaver experiments with fancy weaves; the expert potter with various

Fig. 72. Coiled clay water jar, Prehistoric Pueblo (after Holmes).

technical possibilities. Among the Pueblo Indians pottery is built up by adding coils of clay to a cuplike base. Ordinarily these coils are an inch or more in diameter, and after having been added to the base they are smoothed over with a scraper and the walls of the vessel are gradually shaped and thinned. At one period in prehistoric times the virtuoso potters, instead of using thick coils of clay, worked the clay into thin ribbons, less than half an inch broad, and built up their vessels by winding these ribbons in continuous spirals, leaving the overlapping edges unsmoothed (Fig. 72). Considering the plastic nature of the material and the fact that no shaping tool could touch those delicately fluted surfaces, these vessels must be acknowledged as unsurpassed achievements in ceramic technique. The characteristic forms and texture of this type of pottery could be developed only by potters of great skill who understood thoroughly the nature of the material with which they were working and could exploit to the full its plastic quality.

As we go on to consider in somewhat greater detail various materials and techniques employed by primitive peoples, it will become increasingly apparent that each material has its own character and presents its own problems of form. Stone must be handled differently from clay; therefore, although clay after firing bears a superficial resemblance to stone, the forms developed in clay must necessarily be essentially different from those developed in stone.

Considered from the point of view of the technical problems which they present, there are three types of materials: solid materials such as stone, wood, bone, shell, ivory; plastic materials such as clay and metals; and flexible fibers, such as sinews and vegetable fibers.

Stone can be handled in three ways: by chipping or flaking; by battering and grinding; and by hewing. Flaking utilizes the property of certain classes of rocks to fracture in smooth surfaces when struck; battering and grinding wears away the material; hewing breaks it away by means of a cutting tool. In all, the essential technical problem is the same: the development of the desired form by reduction from the original mass of raw material. Stone architecture, which is a construction of separate parts, is in reality no exception to this, since the separate parts have been carved out of larger blocks and retain the massiveness of the material in its original state. This is one of the factors which contribute to make a stone building differ esthetically as well as technically from a building of steel construction.

The Japanese have an art of arranging stones in lacquer trays as household ornaments. In these arrangements stones are selected for their natural form and texture, which must be preserved unaltered because there is an esthetic appreciation of the essential qualities of stone, its ruggedness and permanence. The general tendency in stone sculpture is to retain some suggestion of the form of the original block.

Of the three ways of handling stone, flaking was the first to be used, and the very earliest works of art preserved for modern eyes, as well as the earliest artifacts, are chipped flints. The earliest of these were crude and clumsy; but as skill slowly developed, forms became more delicate and varied. Presumably the early tool-makers discovered that regular chipping gave a pleasing texture to the surface, so that with the advance of skill more attention was given to the surface as well as to the cutting edge of the implement. By the middle of the Old Stone Age in Europe stone-chipping had become an art as well as a useful industry. The material was carefully selected for color, translucence, and luster, and the distinctively colored product of famous French mines was traded far and wide over Europe. The stone was then worked with infinite care into delicate and symmetrical forms. The minute jewellike points and thin lustrous blades of Solutrean and later deposits answer to more than a practical need. They should be examined with respect as the earliest works of art that have been preserved to us.

In Neolithic times, with the development of new techniques such as pottery and weaving, stone began to decline in importance as an artistic medium, and in the Old World did not again become important until the development of metal tools facilitated stone architecture and sculpture.

Among contemporary primitive peoples stone work is not one of the more important artistic techniques. There are isolated examples of stone used decoratively — the slate dishes of the Indians of the North Pacific coast carved out of soft stone by the technique of wood-carving; figures of animals made by flaking out of obsidian by the Alaskan Eskimo; dishes and mortars pecked out of rough stone; ornamental stone axes from Polynesia; occasional stone figures from many places; monumental figures from Easter Island; Pueblo Indian stone architecture. However, highly developed art in stone belongs to the past of the human race. And in the past the greatest artists in stone of any primitive people (the Egyptians and Oriental peoples were not, according to our arbitrary definition, "primitive") were the Indians of Middle America. The temples and sculptures of the Mayas are among the greatest works in stone of any age. The Aztecs, although they produced some great architecture and sculptures, never equaled their neighbors and predecessors. The abandoned cities of the Mayas, of which the most famous are Chichen Itzá and Uxmal in Yucatan, and Copan, Palenque, Tikal, and Quirigua in the lowlands of Guatemala, comprise many-chambered palaces and temples, some of them placed on lofty pyramids. The buildings of white limestone are all of noble proportions, massively built with thick walls and characteristic "vaulting," and are elaborately decorated inside and out with relief sculpture and painting. There are also sculptured monuments covered with hieroglyphic

Pl. IV. *Top.* Casa de las Monjas Chichen Itzá, Maya (after Totten). *Bottom.* Maya Relief Carving (after Totten).

PL. V. HEAD OF A MAIZE GODDESS, COPAN, HONDURAS
Courtesy of the Peabody Museum, Cambridge.

inscriptions[2] (Pl. IV). The Chac-Mul, a votive figure from Chichen Itzá, is the most famous of their sculptures in the round, and compares favorably with the best sculpture of the Old World. Both the Mayas and the Aztecs made many exquisite small sculptures in crystal, jade, obsidian, and alabaster.

The general problem in working wood is similar to that of stone: the reduction of the raw block to the required form. Wood is always carved with a cutting tool, except for the inside of large hollow vessels, where the labor of hollowing out may be facilitated by burning. The finished surface may be polished by friction. Wood is at the same time a more limited and a more elastic material than stone. Blocks of stone may be had in any conceivable size and shape; the form and size of pieces of wood are necessarily limited to the dimensions of the trees from which the blocks come. However, wood, being softer and easier to handle than stone, is susceptible of greater variety of treatment. Wood is durable and has certain intrinsic qualities as material which can be developed in the process of working it. The natural grain of the wood may be brought out by stains or polishes; the tooling may be developed decoratively as in the chipping of stone. And the formal possibilities of wood are almost unlimited. As we shall see, it is the most versatile of all the materials used by primitive man.

Since wood is more perishable than stone, we have no wooden implements of an antiquity equal to that of the earliest artifacts of stone. On the other hand, in contrast to stone work, wood-carving is one of the most highly developed and widespread of primitive arts today. Almost everywhere, wherever wood is found, it is utilized for artistic purposes. Even the Eskimo, inhabiting a treeless region, occasionally make ornamental carvings of driftwood. The highest development of wood-carving is found in equatorial Africa, especially in the Congo and the west coast regions; in Oceania, in particular New Zealand, and on the North Pacific coast of America.

In Africa, carving in the round is the favorite way of handling wood. Even musical instruments, drums or stringed instruments, are carved in the semblance of human or animal forms. From the Congo come the famous masks and human figures, magnificently carved of hard, fine-textured wood, and highly polished (Pl. VI and Fig. 73).[3] Relief carving is of secondary importance here and, except for certain masks, there is almost no use of applied color. On the western coast of North America, however, carving in the round is used on masks,

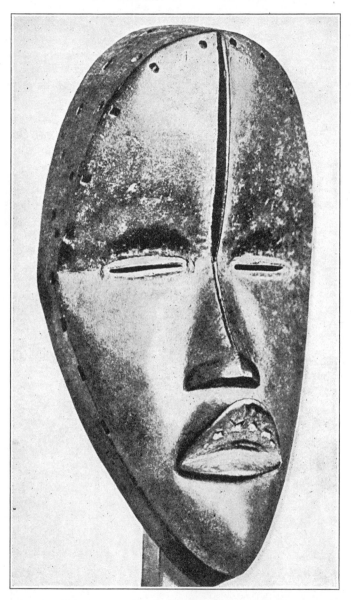

PL. VI. African Negro Mask, Dan Ivory Coast
(after Kjersmeier).

house posts, vessels, and implements (Fig. 74). Besides this the technique of low relief on flat surfaces, with applied colors, is much used.[4] In Oceania the characteristic types of carving are relief and open work in delicate patterns. These three areas illustrate the enormous range of technical possibilities in wood. We have yet to consider the even greater range of possibilities in design.

Ivory, bone, and shell appear sporadically as artistic material. Bone ornaments and decorated tools are found in early prehistoric deposits. The use of bone for body ornaments has shown a remarkable tenacity. The use of animal teeth and claws for the same purpose is widespread. Necklaces of claws and teeth are the most common ornaments. The carved

Fig. 73. Wooden mask, Urua, Congo
(after Boas).

Fig. 74. Carved house post,
Haida (after Swanton).

elephant tusks of Benin show elaborate relief carving on ivory; the
Eskimo sculptures in walrus ivory show similar material differently
handled. Shell is used for bodily adornment. Strings of shell disks

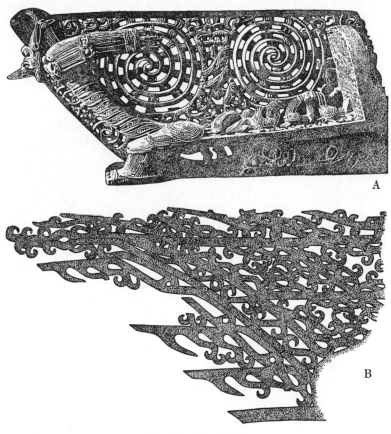

Fig. 75. (after Boas).

A. Canoe prow, New Zealand
B. Canoe prow, Dutch New Guinea

are used as ornaments and, in widely separated parts of the globe,
as a medium of exchange. Its use in this capacity is probably due
to the fact that it is valuable as an ornament, practically indestructible, and easily transported. Carved shell gorgets were extensively
used in America.

Clay is the most important plastic material. Pottery is a very ancient industry, although not so ancient as work in stone and wood. Plastic earths abound in all parts of the world, but the development of ceramic industry depended upon the discovery of two properties of clay: its plasticity when moist, and its hardness and resistance to water and fire after exposure to intense heat. Clay in its plastic state is an amorphous mass which invites the artist to experiment in variety and subtlety of form (Fig. 76). The smooth surfaces which may be developed lend themselves readily to decoration in applied color. Since the essential quality of clay is its plasticity, characteristic ceramic forms are light and graceful, with delicate curves that suggest the mobility of the material which has been arrested in flux. Clay vessels will therefore always have a character which is entirely different from the

Fig. 76. Prehistoric clay bowl, Arkansas (after Holmes).

Fig. 77. Terra cotta head, Yoruba, Africa (after Boas).

massive heaviness that is appropriate in hard stone. In some places primitive people have developed sculpture in clay; an example of clay sculpture from Africa is shown in Figure 77. But, for the most part, clay is used for household utensils, principally cooking pots and containers for food and water. In Europe, northern Africa, and Asia the invention of the potter's wheel introduced new and more adaptable methods.

Clay is one of the most versatile of materials, but since most clay objects are designed for use, considerations of strength, lightness, and appropriateness have resulted in a remarkable conservatism in formal treatment. In general, simple forms predominate.

The decoration of pottery may be either plastic or pictorial. Plastic ornament consists of flutings, indentations, corrugations, and incision of the material, the addition of pellets or threads of clay, and modeling in the round of handles, rims, and sometimes whole vessels (Fig. 78). But the most common ornamental device in ceramics is painting. Painting is often used in connection with one or more of the plastic techniques. Glazing by

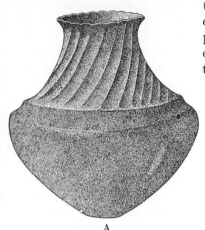

A   B

Fig. 78. Modeled clay vessels.
A. Santa Clara Pueblo, New Mexico (after Holmes).
B. Costa Rica (after MacCurdy).

covering the product with a vitreous coating, sometimes of contrasting color, is a late invention. It gives added interest to the surface texture.

Aside from the purely technical problems of selection and handling of materials, ceramic industry presents special artistic problems. When the material has once lost its original plasticity no changes or corrections are possible; therefore, where pottery is built up by hand, the form must be clearly visualized from the start. Also the types of vessels usually made present certain problems of decoration, such as that of a decorative field which is continuous, but which does not all lie within the field of vision at one time. This factor, in addition to demanding a high degree of skill in modeling and painting, has influenced the choice of decorative material and the style of arrangement. The easiest solution to the problem of the continuous surface, that of decoration in horizontal bands repeating small units, has developed wherever painted pottery is found.

According to the archaeological record, pottery first appeared in Europe in the Neolithic period and has developed continuously since that time. At the present time there are large areas of the globe where pottery was never developed; others where it has been displaced by basketry, wood work, or other techniques; and others where it has remained in crude stages of development. None of the primitive pottery of the present day equals the best products of the past, either in technical resourcefulness or formal development. The pottery of ancient Peru, which is unsurpassed among the primitive pottery of the world, exhibits the highest degree of technical excellence coupled with lively perception and imaginative sense of form. The portrait jars, possibly mortuary pottery, are among the choicest portrait sculpture of any period or in any technique (Pl. VII). The painted beakers and bowls are also of outstanding excellence.[5]

Metals made their appearance as part of man's equipment late in human history, and their use among primitive people of the present is confined to very few groups. The working of metals requires considerable scientific knowledge, skill, and the development of delicate tools. An early use of metals was for ornaments. After the art of melting metals had been invented and their plasticity in heated state had been discovered, they were found to possess the plastic quality of clay in a still greater degree, combined with greater tensile strength. Metal is therefore a suitable medium for the most delicate and intricate designs, such as could never be worked out in clay.

The metal work of Europe in the Bronze Age reached a high excellence. Outside of Europe the most striking use of metal by a primitive people was the bronze-casting of Benin in West Africa. Gold, silver, copper, and bronze were used with skill and excellent esthetic effect in Peru, and gold and copper were used in Central America, but most of this art was destroyed by the Conquerors.

Since textiles are highly destructible, we have no idea at what period in human history they were first developed, but the almost universal distribution of basketry leads to the inference of great antiquity. Baskets are made almost everywhere where suitable materials can be found, and there are almost no regions completely devoid of suitable vegetation.

The textile arts are various, the most important being matting or plaiting, basketry, and weaving of spun fibers. In all these types of technique the artist has to work with little strips or fibers out of which he must gradually build the finished form of which the raw material contains no suggestion. But whereas the form is not suggested in the material, both form and ornament are largely deter-

Pl. VII. Clay Effigy Vessel, Chicama, Peru (after Lehmann).

mined by the process of construction. Plaiting and weaving result in flat flexible forms. The same materials that may be plaited into mats may produce firm baskets of varying forms when tightly twined or coiled. In all textile arts, with the exception of embroidery, which is rare among primitive peoples, ornament is an integral part of structure and is built into the material instead of being applied to it later as in pottery. This has certain far-reaching effects on the character of all textile design. In the first place textile art, more than any other, is dependent on a high degree of technical skill. All the checkerboard, diapered, diagonal, and zigzag patterns are texture patterns in which one error or a slight unevenness in texture muddles the whole design. Children can paint pleasing designs; wood-carvers with inadequate technical equipment can produce carving which, despite its crudity, shows a vigorous and esthetically valuable conception; but an inept weaver who makes errors in counting gets no pattern at all. Moreover, since the decorative pattern is built into the object as it is constructed, the whole decorative scheme must be visualized in relation to a form which does not yet exist, and must be planned to fit it. To do this without a pattern, as is done by most primitive weavers, requires great clarity of conception as well as skill in composition and analysis. The intimate relation between design and structure in the textile arts has influenced the types of ornament developed. There is a great development of all kinds of patterns that arise out of the weaving process, such as stripes, simple and broken checks, diamonds, diagonals, herringbone and diaper patterns, all types of simple angular ornament, and the use of color contrast. Since curves cannot be rendered but only approximated in the finest woven cloths, all designs must be angular and representations must be conventionalized to conform to this technical requirement. Hence textile ornament is much less free than that of pottery or sculpture. The primitive people who went furthest in overcoming these obstacles were the ancient Peruvians, whose tapestries display a wealth of representative ornament. And in this region the same type of conventionalization which was developed in tapestries, where it was made necessary by the requirements of weaving, appears also in pottery. Its use here was probably a result of the transfer of patterns developed in weaving to pottery.

Matting, though by no means confined to the tropics, seems to flourish best in warm climates where suitable materials abound. Owing to the relative coarseness of the materials, only simple geo-

Fig. 79. Primitive basketry.
1. Philippine, 2. Tlingit, 3. Hupa, 4. Barotsi, 5. Maidu, 6. San Carlos Apache,
7. Barotsi. (Collections, American Museum of Natural History)

metric patterns are available. Matting depends for beauty on even-
ness and fineness of texture. Occasionally color is introduced in
simple stripes and diagonals. Fine mats are made in certain parts of
Mexico and throughout Polynesia, where they are highly valued.

The materials out of which baskets are made are as varied as the
geography of the regions from which they come, and the forms of
baskets are almost as varied as the materials. Always the primary
considerations in basket-making are strength and regularity of construction. Ornament is always secondary. Basketry has reached its
highest development in California,[6] where it is the only well-developed art practiced. Here baskets are used alike for storage, cooking,
carrying water, for soup bowls, and for hats. For curiosities and as
a proof of skill expert basket-makers make little round baskets,
smaller than peas and ornamented with beads or feathers. Diminutive
baskets are made in Mexico also. The cooking baskets of the Hupa,
which are woven closely enough to be water-tight and are sufficiently
heat-resistant to permit the boiling of water by red-hot stones, are
among the most remarkable baskets made anywhere. The more
ornamental baskets of the same tribe show the same technical excellence coupled with tasteful decoration. The shallow baskets of

Fig. 80. Poncho, Titicaca, Peru (after Lehmann).

the more southerly tribes of the same region (the Pomo and others), although coarser in texture, show great smoothness and regularity and great skill and originality in the handling of the radiating designs.

The weaving of cloth involves more technical knowledge and more elaborate tools than matting or basketry. The fibers must first be spun and then placed in some kind of frame. However, fine

A

B

C

PLATE VIII (after Boas).
A, B. African pile cloths, Congo.
C. Carved wooden bowl, Bambala, Congo.

cloths can be woven on very crude looms, as is proved by the ancient Peruvian tapestries and the modern figured cloths from Guatemala, all of which were woven on simple portable looms, and the Chilkat blankets woven on a loom consisting of a single horizontal bar between two uprights [7] (Fig. 80).

Although the technical problems in weaving are enormous, the esthetic problem is a relatively simple one: that of the treatment of a flat surface. The problem of ornamentation of a piece of cloth is much simpler than that of the design of a basket. But cloth, being made of finer materials than baskets, affords greater scope for the development of elaborate ornamentation.

These are some of the more important materials and techniques of primitive art. In discussing them we have not tried to give an account of primitive industry, but merely to suggest the lines of interrelationship between technique and form. Given a similar practical problem, say the creation of a receptacle for food, the form and esthetic character of the vessel will be different according to whether it is made of stone, wood, clay, basketry, or other material. Furthermore, certain technical processes give rise to ornamental forms, of which we have already mentioned outstanding examples. But ornamental forms that arise almost spontaneously in one medium frequently migrate to another, where they take on a new interest in the unusual setting. The carving of the Bambala, a Congo tribe, is a striking example of textile patterns applied to wood-carving (Pl. VIII). The Chilkat blanket of the Tlingit Indians is one of the rarer cases where designs developed in wood-carving and painting have been transferred to weaving. This latter is no hypothetical case, since the history of the Chilkat blanket clearly demonstrates the origin of the patterns (Fig. 81).

One further caution is necessary. It is not to be inferred that, because material influences form, there is such a thing as a "ceramic style" or a "textile style" of ornament. Certain materials lend themselves more readily to certain types of treatment than others. But the most striking and successful art is frequently that which handles the material in a completely unconventional way, even denying its nature.

General formal principles. So far we have been concerned principally with the rôle of technical factors in decorative expression. There are also certain purely formal principles that dominate all works of art, whether they be music, poetry, dance, or decoration:

namely, unity, rhythm, symmetry, and balance. The first principle
in art in any medium is delimitation. The work of art must be an
entity clearly separable from, although not unrelated to, the rest

Fig. 81. Blanket of mountain goat wool, Tlingit, Alaska (after Emmons).

of the universe. In the decorative arts the limits of forms are usually
clearly defined and set by considerations of practicality or technique.
There is no difficulty for the artist or observer in distinguishing
what is pot from what is not pot. But the problem of delimitation
of form is not always so simple. An easel painting is complete in
itself wherever placed. The same picture painted directly on a wall

Fig. 82. Zuñi medicine altar (after Stevenson).

cannot be considered an absolute unit. The artist may frame his picture to preserve its unity, but, being fixed in space, it is brought into permanent relations with other things, and these relationships must be considered. An interesting case of artistic unity is seen in the arrangement of altars among Pueblo Indians (Fig. 82). Various sacred objects are set out for veneration in an ordinary dwelling room. Sometimes the limits of the altar are indicated by a dry painting in meal or colored earths on the floor, more often not. But the arrangement is so closely integrated that even if one did not recognize sacredness in the character of the objects themselves the arrangement alone would suffice to mark off the limits of the altar from the rest of the world.[8]

The principle of delimitation holds for literary arts as well. In songs it is obvious; a song has a definite beginning and end in time. One is never in doubt as to what is song and what is not. A song may be fixed in a cycle or embedded in ritual, and in that case its form must be considered in relation to its antecedents and sequels. Tales, which utilize the language and intonations of everyday speech, present a special problem in delimitation; it is solved by many primitive peoples by the use of formal opening and closing phrases. Sometimes, as in Zuñi folk tales, these phrases are meaningless syllables whose only purpose is to mark the boundaries of the literary form. Everything inclosed within these brackets is an artistic unit.

Rhythm is the regular repetition of similar units. The pleasure derived from rhythm probably has a physiological basis. Regular motion is in harmony with physiological processes. The fundamental decorative rhythm, the repetition of a single unit, corresponding to the regular pulsation in music, is frequently based upon regularity of bodily movements. Examples of simple rhythms that arise directly from bodily movements are the regular series of chippings in stone or adzing in wood, the even stitches in basketry, regular flutings and indentations in pottery. The simple banded designs that predominate in the pottery of all ages and places are but one step removed from the basic rhythms of the craft. Holding the brush in one hand, the potter makes simple marks at regular intervals as the pot is slowly revolved with the other hand. Alternating rhythms are also basic and even more closely related to physiological processes. The contraction and expansion of the lungs and the left-right alternation in walking are some of the more apparent physiological manifestations of alternating rhythm. It is the alternation of stressed and unstressed beats that underlies all rhythmic development in music, poetry, and dancing. Indeed, even the simple repetition of a single unit is really an alternation since there is always something, if only a point of rest, between the two units. In weaving, alternation is inherent in the technique; the simplest finished web always displays double rhythms, up and down stitches alternating horizontally and vertically. There is also a regular diagonal rhythm, which may be emphasized in twilling. In painting and carving, the fret and the serpentine line constitute the simplest alternating designs. More complex arrangements of three or more units, especially the type in which one unit alternates successively with several others, the $a\,b\,a\,c\,a\,d\,\ldots$ type, is probably based on the pleasure experienced in encountering the familiar after variety. The great popularity of songs with burdens and all developments of the rondo form in music is perhaps due to this. Highly complex rhythms in decoration are usually restricted to techniques employing many different colors, such as weaving, bead work, and embroidery, the colors being used to ring changes on one or two forms. Complexity of rhythm in a relatively simple art, that of bead-stringing, is illustrated in the fringed leggings of the Thompson Indians (Fig. 83), already referred to.[9] There is a primary alternation of plain and beaded strands in groups of five $a\,b\,a'\,b\,a\,/\,a\,b\,a'\,b\,a\,/$, a and a' being the two beaded strands which differ from each other in the arrangement of the beads. The fringes fall together when the garment is worn, and the rhythm is lost, only the balance in the distribution of color being evident. The enormously complex rhythms of Peruvian tapestries have been analyzed by

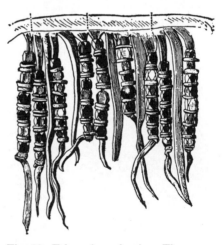

Fig. 83. Fringe from legging, Thompson Indians (after Boas).

Boas.[10] The Peruvians used up to nine colors in their weaving, and since the technique was tapestry-weaving, they were able to combine the colors at will, ringing all the changes in design and background. A most fascinating example is a cloak of nine colors from Ica, covered all over with human figures. These are alike in form but of six types in regard to color arrangement. The figures are arranged in groups of four, two different series alternating on the horizontal lines, but so placed that simple alternating rhythms emerge in the diagonals. This cloak can be read from left to right, from top to bottom, or from corner to corner, and each way new and interesting rhythms of color emerge.

In some cases great rhythmic complexity may be due to a desire to distribute colors evenly over the surface with a pleasing balance of light and dark, while yet avoiding the appearance of rigid patterning. For instance, a string of kindergarten beads of six colors and five forms is to be assembled that will utilize all varieties in a balanced distribution while still retaining the appearance of having been accidentally assembled. The only way in which one can be sure of giving equal weight to each variety is by a complex system of permutations regularly repeated. The same problem of studied casualness is familiar in flower arrangements.

Symmetry is the balanced arrangement with reference to one another of the elements within a unit. The most familiar type of symmetry is that represented by the outward form of the human body in which the parts on both sides of a vertical axis mirror each other. The two hands are the same in structure, but inverted with reference to one another. Radial symmetry appears in lower animals, for instance in the starfish.

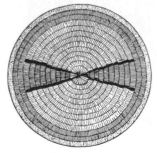

Fig. 84. Coiled basketry tray, Hopi Indians (after Holmes).

Perfectly balanced form is the goal of all craftsmen. The exacting craftsman considers beautiful only the pot that shows no bulges and that exhibits perfect symmetry of line when viewed from any angle, the basket that does not tip over, the robe that has straight edges and true right angles.

All types of symmetry in ornament have been utilized by primitive peoples, the type very largely depending upon the form of the object. Radial symmetry is common on round objects, particularly on round basketry (Fig. 84) and on pottery vessels. In these bilateral symmetry is rarely found, perhaps because of the preponderance of

Fig. 85. Designs from ancient pottery bowls, Mimbres Valley, New Mexico (after Boas).

circular forms and continuous surfaces. In certain circular forms inverted symmetry may be developed. In these designs the paired figures are completely inverted with reference to each other; not only is what is right in one figure left in the other, but what is up in one is down in the other. The swastika is an excellent example of inverted symmetry. In a round field inverted symmetry always suggests circular motion, and the patterns are probably developed in motion, being derived either from border patterns that move in to occupy the central field, or from radiating patterns that revolve (Fig. 85). Such patterns always have a dynamic quality that marks them off sharply from the immobility of the bilaterally or radially symmetrical design. Inverted symmetry is rarely applied in the decoration of objects that are not round. One of the most striking examples is found on Dayak shields (Fig. 86). Similar forms of inverted symmetry occur in New Guinea. There is a considerable amount of pottery design which is completely unsymmetrical, as, for instance, the circular bowls of the Hopi.[11] The single asymmetrical decorative motive is

Fig. 86. Wooden shield, Dyak, Dutch East Indies (after Hein).

placed in one sector of the circular field. But the heavy band that surrounds the field anchors the design firmly and with it forms a perfectly balanced composition (Fig. 87).

In weaving, the decorative problem is the handling of large surfaces, and balance of color or texture is more important than symmetry of line. However, inverted symmetry of the kinds already spoken of is fairly frequent. In such cases the rectangular field is divided into four quarters, the sections being paired diagonally and inverted.

Fig. 87. Ancient Pueblo bowl, Hopi (after Fewkes).

Rhythm and symmetry are complementary principles, and symmetry is the essentially plastic quality. A Peruvian textile is highly symmetrical. It has a perfect balance of light and dark masses and a regular but subtle distribution of color. On analysis this is seen to be the result of a complex structure of small units. These units, when viewed successively, present regularly recurring sequences. Hopi water jars illustrate even more clearly the relation of rhythm and symmetry in plastic forms. The decoration is applied to the sloping upper portion. When seen from the side only half of the decorative field lies within the field of vision (Pl. IX). As the pot is revolved, the designs appear in regular order in fairly complex sequences. However, when viewed from above the whole field is in sight and the design is seen to be completely integrated and radially symmetrical, like patterns appearing in opposite sectors (Fig. 88). The potters themselves always consider the designs from this angle. Rhythm is an analytical concept and always implies a time element. It is a derived quality, not strictly plastic. It emerges in

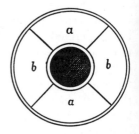

Fig. 88. Diagram of Hopi water jar (after Bunzel).

the construction and breaking down of complex forms; symmetry is a quality inherent in the forms themselves.

Style. We have already referred to the traditional concepts which mould artistic products. Among all people artistic expression tends

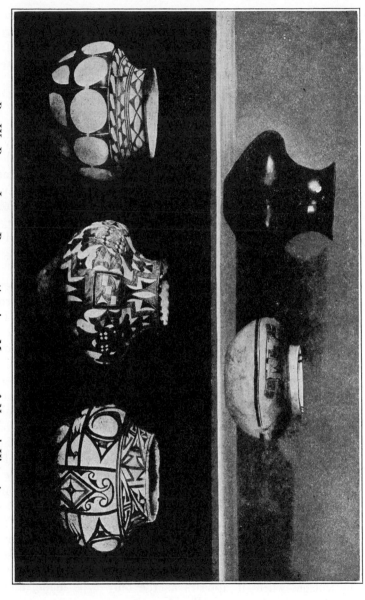

PL. IX. PUEBLO INDIAN POTTERY (American Museum of Natural History).
Above, Santa Clara, Hopi. *Below*, Santo Domingo, Acoma, Zuñi.

to become set in fixed forms characteristic of particular groups and special periods. Just as the phonetic system of a language is an elaboration of a few sounds seemingly arbitrarily chosen from an infinite number of possible sounds, so decorative style is a development of apparently arbitrarily chosen formal characteristics. Just as speech in order to be intelligible as symbols of thought must operate with recognized sounds, so also a work of art in order to possess formal significance must be stylistically oriented. It seems safe to assume from the conformity revealed by an objective study of the art of any primitive group that canons of art have much the same traditional sanction in the minds of the makers as, say, marriage regulations or grammar. Wherever it has been possible to study the primitive artist at work, the binding force of tradition is felt. But whereas adherence to traditional forms in language has always been taken for granted, and conformity in social behavior is rarely questioned, the dominance of traditional style in art has always been rather grudgingly admitted even by the artists themselves. For even primitive societies have artistic rebels bent on achieving originality.

When examining a collection of contemporary pottery from the pueblos of New Mexico and Arizona anyone who is at all familiar with the pottery of the region can immediately identify each piece with reference to provenience and age. There are certain minor distinguishing technical characters, such as color and texture of the paste; but without handling the pots or examining them closely one can identify them by their form and, with even greater certainty, by their decorative treatment. With the exception of special treatment in firing at Santa Clara and San Ildefonso, the process of manufacture is uniform throughout the region, involving the same materials, tools, and motor habits. Nevertheless a number of highly differentiated styles have grown up. Historically these can be shown to have developed by a process of local differentiation from older types of wider distribution. This variety, therefore, represents a purely artistic development. Let us examine the outstanding features of some of these types. The six types chosen to illustrate contrasting styles of ceramic art are all contemporary; they are made in six villages within a radius of fifty miles, and each type is restricted to one village, where it appears as the only type made, and shows considerable uniformity [12] (Pl. IX).

The pottery of the pueblo of Santa Clara is jet black and highly polished. The forms of the vessels are varied. The most common is the water jar with a small base, a gradually swelling body, and fairly long neck, with slightly flaring rim. Whatever ornamentation these jars bear is purely plastic, consisting of vertical or spiral flutings, indentations, crimping of edges, modeled handles. Besides the water jar there are many other forms, including hemispherical bowls, similarly ornamented, and double-spouted jugs.

At San Ildefonso, also, the contemporary type of pottery, which is of very recent appearance here, is a highly polished black ware. The forms are simple, shallow bowls predominating. These are decorated with very simple designs in dull black paint. The patterns are applied in narrow bands to the rims of the vessels. Simple continuous borders consisting of parallel lines, rows of dots, scallops, or triangles predominate. The motives are derived for the most part from the more complex patterns of the antecedent polychrome pottery. Some of the designs are of Hopi origin and are now used by Hopi potters, but with entirely different effect. The potters consider the greatest beauty of the pot is its lustrous black surface, and the dull designs are therefore made inconspicuous and serve chiefly to bring out by contrast the polished surface. The principal artistic problem is the handling of surfaces for balance and contrast.

The form of the water jar of Santo Domingo is similar to that of Santa Clara, the high neck and flaring rim being its most characteristic features in contrast to other types from the pueblo region. The jar is slipped with red below, white above. On the neck and upper part of the body is a series of narrow horizontal bands decorated with very simple geometric patterns. The distinguishing feature of these bands is an effect of negative painting. The background is painted black; the simple triangular or hexagonal designs remain white. The designs are small and very simple, both as regards elements and composition, and they are very regularly applied. The resulting effect is a black and white patterned surface, almost like that of a textile. Large bowls are similarly decorated on their outer rims.

The Hopi water jar is low and widespreading, curving in sharply above to a small mouth. The polished surface is creamy yellow tinged with rose. On the almost flat top the designs are painted in brown and red. The most common arrangement is four panels alternately paired. Seen from above the patterns are symmetrically arranged and frequently show duplicating symmetry within each unit. Open bowls are decorated within with a single unit placed off the center, touching the rim at one point. The majority of design elements are highly conventionalized bird forms. Sometimes the head and tail of the bird are developed, more often the tail only. All the designs show a great feeling for line, and no interest whatever in the balancing of masses. Potters always speak of "getting the line of the design."

At Zuñi are made large painted water jars of characteristic form elaborately ornamented. They are narrow at the base, wider in the upper portions, sloping in somewhat at the top, to a large mouth. The lower portion is left unpainted and is reddish brown in color. The middle and upper portions are painted white. The whole of the white portion is decorated with designs in black with touches of red. A heavy black line drawn on the curve above the largest portion divides the jar into two zones, the narrow neck and the broad body. The neck is decorated with a paneled band of alternating units, usually two pairs. The body may be further subdivided into rectangular fields of different proportions. There may be as many as eight such fields, two upright fields separated on each side by three horizontal fields of different widths. A design is placed in each field so created, the same pattern being used consistently throughout the jar in analogous positions. The designs are named and their usage is restricted. Most of the patterns themselves are developed from spirals and a characteristic stepped figure. There are a few representative forms, notably the deer, birds, and flowers, all somewhat conventionalized. The designs are all executed in outline against a white background with an avoidance of large masses of color. The decorative problem is seen as a synthesis, a fitting together of distinct units in accordance with fixed rules to form a balanced arrangement.

Acoma water jars are similar in form to those of Zuñi, but very different in decorative treatment. The decoration covers without break the whole whitened surface from its lower border to the rim of the vessel. The prevailing lines of the design are diagonal. The patterns are, with one exception, geometrical and prevailingly angular. The composition is very complex and the surface is broken up into small units. There is no background, white, black, red and fine line hatching constituting a four-color palette. The decorative problem is conceived to be to cover completely a fairly large surface, meanwhile keeping the composition light and graceful with a symmetrical color distribution. In the general relation of form and ornament this style partakes of some of the characteristics of Moorish arabesque.

We have here characterized briefly six pottery types historically and technically closely related, yet sharply differentiated stylistically in form, color, and ornamentation. In each case the local style represents a selection and development of certain decorative ideas. Santa Clara pottery shows the development of the plastic idea in the manipulation of clay, with great attention to surface texture. In San Ildefonso, the surface theme is still more fully developed by the use of painted ornament for contrast. The ornamental patterns, drawn from several earlier polychrome wares, have been greatly simplified to meet the demands of this new interest. At Santo Domingo also the chief interest is in surface effects, here attained by regular patterning with small motives which are in themselves extremely uninteresting. The three polychrome wares from Zuñi, Hopi, and Acoma all show pictorial but not necessarily representative quality. Here interest is focused on the ornamentation, with manipulation of line and color in complex composition, along with increased interest in decorative content. Of all the pottery that of San Ildefonso is the most complex and subtle in conception.

These six contrasting ceramic products show that style is more than a choice of decorative material; in Hopi and San Ildefonso pots we have the same decorative material derived from ancient Hopi pottery, but applied to different problems. Style is more than the arrangement or patterning of this material; it involves the whole approach to and conception of the esthetic problem in the chosen medium. From the point of view of the artist the only important fact is that we find six such distinct types developed; but from the anthropological point of view the most significant fact is that each of these types is localized in one group where it so controls the imagination of the artists that no other type is made, although all are known.

The hold which these traditional concepts of form have upon the imagination of the artist is evidenced in the stylistic cohesiveness of any group. Boas [13] quotes a number of examples of fixity of form in primitive products. In some of these cases, notably Zuñi water jars and Haussa embroideries, the same decorative elements appear over and over again in the same combinations. In both of these cases the characteristic feature is the breaking up of the field into a number of clearly defined smaller fields, a procedure which readily lends itself to rigidity and sterility. Much more striking and provocative, however, are those cases such as modern Hopi pottery or Northwest Coast

wood-carving, where duplication never occurs, but where, nevertheless, each object bears the unmistakable impress of its source. In
such cases it is not always easy to isolate the characteristic features.
It is of course impossible to define any style of art since it is of its
nature without fixed limits or precision. It is equally unrewarding
to attempt to describe individual works of art, the essence of which
is untranslatable. One can analyze in terms of underlying principles,
but never describe. The characteristic of a style of art is a tendency,
a set of principles. It is a grasp of these principles rather than an
analysis of the content of designs that is essential to an understanding of any work of art. And primitive artists are by no means so
naïve concerning these matters as is commonly supposed. It is not
accidental that Hopi potters always speak of line, Zuñi potters of
the number and distribution of designs, and San Ildefonso potters
of surface texture and luster, adding "It doesn't matter what you
paint so long as you put it on straight." Each woman is here speaking of the fundamental tendency of the style in which she operates.

What, then, is it that makes a Hopi bowl absolutely unmistakable?
Its form and color, although characteristic within the pueblo area,
are not definitive; they are shared by pottery from other parts of
the world. The ornament, however, is quite distinctive. Its special
characteristic is the handling of line in relation to the circular surface of the bowl, or, more accurately, the line that bounds the surface. Hopi artists in analyzing their designs always refer to this feature of their painting. "I study the line of the design," or "I always
use a one-line design; it must start at the rim and returns to the rim
again." The particular decorative units that are used in any pot
are of secondary importance. These patterns are varied and highly
characteristic. They represent in symbolic form animals, but informants are never quite sure whether any particular design represents a bird, serpent, squirrel, or an anthropomorphic rainbow. Bird
forms predominate. The designs are curvilinear and, in general, form
a crescent along one side of the bowl. Usually only wing and tail
feathers are represented; rarely heads. The bodies are further em-
bellished with geometrical ornament. Obviously the interest of the
potters is in the formal rather than in the representational character
of their designs. It has been noted that many of the same elements
are used at San Ildefonso, but with what a difference! The Hopi
water jar presents a different problem; the designs used are usually
simpler and more abstract, although employing some of the same

Fig. 89. Painted house front representing Thunderbird catching a whale,
Kwakiutl Indians (after Boas).

elements. But even in jars there is a tendency for the pattern to hug
the clearly marked line around the rim, with the balance of the jar
undecorated and the lower margin of the design frequently not
defined.

For contrast let us now turn to another highly differentiated art
of North America, and one that also uses conventionalized animal
representation: that of the Indians of the North Pacific coast.[14] The
principal material is wood, with horn, soapstone, copper, and slate
occupying positions of minor importance. All the possessions of these
people, from house posts to fishhooks and dance hats, are elaborately
decorated. Carving in relief and in the round and painting are used,
but the same style and the same artistic problems rule in all techniques. Even the rare textiles have in recent years been incorporated
into the same style. In all this art the problem is definitely one of
representation. The Hopi use certain animal forms, but their primary
purpose, as we have seen, is not to depict the animals; the artist is
more concerned with the formal than with the symbolic content of
his painting. From a purely objective point of view Kwakiutl paint-

ing is no more realistic in its treatment of animal forms than the Hopi, but in the mind of the artist the compositions are strictly representational (Fig. 89). The difference is fundamental. The Northwest Coast artist chooses to represent animals by a highly systematized symbolism selecting certain characteristic features of the animal for emphasis and treating the rest of the body formally. Thus the beaver is symbolized by large incisors and a broad scaly tail (Fig. 90), the killer whale by the high dorsal fin and blowhole, the sculpin by two spines over the eyes and a joined dorsal fin, the hawk by a sharply curved beak, the bear by its claws and large teeth. In addition to this there is a complex symbolism for the treatment of eyes, ears, tails, viscera of various animals. The hawk has one type of tail, the eagle another. However, this second system is largely theoretical. For the most part, except for the two or three definitive features of each animal, the figures are treated in accordance with certain

Fig. 90. Carved spoon handles representing beaver, Tlingit Indians (after Boas).

general conventions and the formal requirements of the decorative field. As we have seen, the decorative field may be anything from the side of a house to a spoon handle. An underlying formal principle is that the decoration must completely fill the field. With the exception of dishes, which are given a general resemblance to animal forms and carved, the surface to be decorated is quite unrelated to the form of the object to be represented. All attempt at realism is sacrificed to formal requirements; the significant parts and as much besides as can conveniently be included are represented. Relative size is not considered important, nor the relation of the parts in life. The ideal is to represent the object completely, both sides of an animal in profile, or the unforeshortened body seen in full view and the internal as well as the external anatomy. This results in further distortion of the form. A wolf pictured on a house front may be shown with his head over the door, his tail under the ridgepole, his right and left sides spread

Fig. 91. Painted wooden box, Tlingit Indians (after Boas).

on either side of the door, as if he had been split down the belly and
pinned out. Or the body may be dismembered and its various external and internal organs distributed in arbitrary arrangement (Fig.
91). Nor do the parts themselves bear any resemblance to living
forms. There are many other characteristic features in Northwest
Coast art. On the purely formal side there are characteristic treat-
ments of light and shade, of excentric circles, avoidance of exactly
equidistant lines, and motives within motives which cannot be described here, but which are apparent in the illustrations. In this place
we cannot concern ourselves with details, but merely point out the
general principles. However, the hold of these stylistic features on the
imagination of artists is such that they creep into supposedly realistic drawings, such as the illustrations of folk tales drawn for Boas
(Fig. 92).

Those who seek to enjoy and evaluate new and unorthodox movements in modern art have learned to judge works of art in terms
of the esthetic problems which the artists are attempting to solve.
Painting is not of necessity representational, certainly not realistic.
Nor, on the other hand, is content *a priori* irrelevant. Some artists

Fig. 92. Haida drawing illustrating a myth (after Boas).

are absorbed by the problem of representation — it may be the outward aspect or the inner reality of objects, or
the content of the mind which they wish
to express, but their concern is with the
intrinsic character of things. To others
content is irrelevant; they have set for
themselves a formal problem and are interested in objects only in terms of their
formal values. Pictures must therefore
be approached from the point of view of
the artist's intention. This applies no less
to the art of primitive peoples. But the
problem is rarely explicit and can hardly
ever be revealed by a purely objective
study of one or two objects. One must

Fig. 93. Tlingit mask representing dying warrior (after
Boas).

know the makers or, failing that, study with sympathy a great
many objects of the same tradition for their underlying principles,
the problems, and the materials for their solution. It is the consistency with which the basic problem is posed and solved
that gives cohesiveness to any style. In certain styles, such as
Zuñi pottery or Kwakiutl carving, the rules may be strict;

other styles are freer. In any vital style there will be many answers to the problem. If we choose to consider art a form of play, as many do, we might suggest an analogy from some game of skill, say from chess. For the lover of chess the object is not only to win, but to win in as many ways and in as original ways as possible, without breaking any of the rules. There is plenty of evidence to show that the good artist, whether in Paris or Walpi, will solve his problem in many ways without breaking the rules. The very great artist anywhere will set his own problem and make his own rules. But great artists are rare. Most craftsmen are content to keep to well-trodden paths and to achieve variety of detail within the fixed patterns.

It seems impossible to give an empirical explanation of the psychological basis for the development of traditional styles and their hold upon the creative imagination of artists. Obviously one art style is no better intrinsically than another, nor better adapted to the physical or social milieu than another. One would like to see some social or religious implications in the fact that Zuñi pottery contains representative forms, while Acoma and Santo Domingo pottery do not. But it seems improbable that even the most confirmed functionalist could make a case for it. Nor are universal sequences any more valid for art than for other forms of culture. We shall have to consider the question of the origin of art styles, like all questions of origins, unanswerable.

If our first question is unanswerable, the second question, that of conformity, is hardly less difficult. Artists certainly do not wish to be conservative; it is often directly contrary to their expressed intention. Pueblo potters reiterate the claim that each pot is a creation new-forged in the imagination. Nevertheless, with nothing to guide her except an inner perception of form, the potter reproduces without hesitation the characteristic vessel of her tribe. The technical limitations are such that the finished form must be clearly visualized at an early stage, for after the first coils are laid no corrections are possible. The application of ornament is also largely controlled by nonrational mental processes. Although artists' comments are frequently illuminating — as, for instance, the Hopi potter's comment about line, quoted above — the perception of relations is largely intuitive. Conscious preoccupations are largely with matters of technical perfection. Conformity to traditional forms is due in a large measure to the dependence of artists upon the visual image. Visual images, whether consciously called up, dreamed, or otherwise involuntarily evoked, are, for most people, of things once directly perceived. The usual dream is a composite of different experiences, familiar elements appearing in new combinations. Primitive artists dream just such designs.

Is art for this reason stable? Obviously it is not. In fact, it is one of the most unstable forms of human behavior, and therefore provides an excellent field for the study of cultural change. Modified reproduction of the kind just described results in gradual but continuous change, frequently in a definite direction, which eventually ends in a style very different from the one from which it sprang.

In ceramic art, where we can unravel some of the history because of the imperishability of the material, a number of historically verified sequences illustrating this kind of development can be found. On the other hand, we must not overlook the part played by the creative genius who appears every once in so often. The whole art style of a group can be changed within a few years by a single gifted individual. One of the characteristics of creative imagination is the ability to experience mentally what has not been experienced sensually, and to embody this experience in tangible form. In the pueblos of San Ildefonso and Hano (Hopi) ceramic art has been revolutionized in recent years, in each case through the discriminating imagination of a single individual. In each case the change was the result of outside influences and general cultural instability working upon the mind of a sensitive individual endowed with imagination, taste, and technical equipment. Art, the purpose of which is to bring beauty into life, is, perhaps more than any other aspect of culture, continually in a state of tension, an exciting condition of unstable equilibrium between the exuberance of individual imagination and the weight of tradition as expressed in formal patterns.[15]

Symbolism. Thus far we have touched only incidentally upon the content and meaning of specific art forms. We have been dealing with art as form, but plastic art anywhere may become a medium for the expression of specific impressions and ideas of the outer and inner worlds. In decorative arts we may find represented human, animal, and plant forms, the features of earth and sky, and even abstract religious and philosophical concepts.

It is a truism to say that all art is either abstract or representative. It is not, however, so obvious, and is as a matter of fact frequently overlooked, that this classification is not an objective one; it is a classification on the basis of intention, not on the basis of accomplishment. The same pattern may be representative or symbolic in one place and quite without meaning in another. Furthermore, by "representative" we do not mean "realistic." Realism and symbolism are two opposite tendencies in the art of representation.

Absolute realism is something which is impossible of attainment in any plastic art. All art, therefore, is in a sense symbolic, no less so when the attempt is in the direction of realism. In painting, a relatively free medium, for example, it is impossible to represent a three-dimensional object on a two-dimensional surface without eliminating certain aspects and adopting certain conventional ways of representing the balance. A photograph, claimed to be the closest approximation to reality, reproduces mechanically not the object itself but the image which it forms on the retina of the eye. Aside from the obvious impossibility of reproducing color and texture in this medium, and from distortion due to the selective limitations in various types of lenses, a photograph is unsatisfactory as representation for a number of reasons. It does not reproduce the sense of depth attained through binocular vision; in showing objects in motion it shows them at one instant and in order to suggest motion a time sequence must be indicated in different parts; it represents but one aspect of the object; it is unselective, or whatever selection exists is mechanically determined by the speed and depth of the lens, rather than intelligently determined on the basis of significance. Systems of perspective drawing do not have all these defects, with the result that a good perspective drawing is a more suggestive approximation of nature than a photograph. This type of drawing is confined to sophisticated societies. However, all drawings must make some compromise with the fact that only one aspect of the object can be shown. The Egyptians managed this by representing the head of the human figure in profile, the torso *en face*, the legs in profile. In substituting conventional for directly realistic reproduction the artist has taken another step in the direction of symbolism. Sculpture, which, aside from the color and texture of the material, can approximate the form of nature, suffers most from the second limitation of the photographic approach: namely, that in a representation of motion, time sequence must be suggested. Successive stages must be combined, as they are in any sculpture of a man walking. The suggestion of reality can be gained only by distortion. In sculpture also, the tendency must be away from naturalism and in the direction of symbolism.

Most art styles, especially those of primitive peoples, while retaining the representative intent, definitely abandon realism. Nonrealistic representation may be handled in several ways: by simplification, by distortion, by arbitrary substitution — symbolism in the narrowest meaning of the word. Of course, these are not mutually exclusive processes or tendencies. A very simple form may be derived from a more complex form or be arbitrarily chosen. Frequently the part is used to represent the whole, as in Hopi bird designs where only the feathers are depicted, but the design is nevertheless thought of as a bird.

Simplification of forms — what is commonly called conventionalization — is especially marked in textile arts, where it is made necessary by a technique which can handle only simple angular forms. Usually these forms are not only simplified but have been made more regular and symmetrical than their prototypes in nature. Basketry designs from all parts of the world and European peasant embroideries are outstanding examples of this type of art. To this the peasant embroideries of central Spain, with their grotesque animals and fantastic flowers, are a notable exception. When life forms are used on pottery they are usually of this simplified type — the animal forms, deer and birds, on Zuñi pottery, for instance, belong to this simplified type of symbolic representation; those on Hopi pottery, which have already been discussed, do not.

Haddon, in *Evolution in Art*, and other writers have claimed that geometric art has originated in the simplification of representative forms due to inadequate technique. This theory is based on the fallacy inherent in all evolutionary arguments: namely, the assumption that universal sequences of cultural forms can be established, and that contemporaneous variants represent points in such a sequence. The theory as it applies to art has been disposed of many times but still finds supporters. Boas in his study of Alaskan needle cases establishes a sequence reversing that of Haddon's. An ancient widely distributed geometrical form gradually took on resemblance to various animal forms. It is especially significant that the form did not always suggest the same animal to different artists.

Simplification is not the only method for treating the difficult problem of symbolical representation. Much more characteristic of primitive art is the tendency to representation by distortion. Distor-

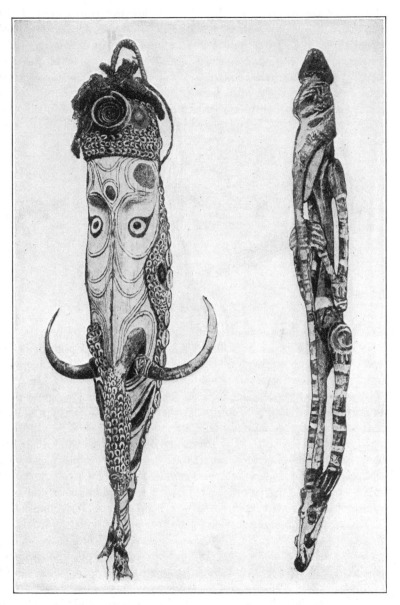

PL. X. MASKS, SEPIK RIVER, NEW GUINEA (after Chauvet).

tion may be the result of technical exigencies, the adjustment of the design to the form of the raw material or to the decorative field. But more often distortion is quite independent of formal requirements and is the result of a selection and emphasis of what are considered the significant parts of the body (Figs. 94, 95). The emphasis of sexual organs in African and some Melanesian sculpture and Paleolithic drawings is an example of mild distortion; the general outlines of the body resemble the living model and the relation of the parts is as

Fig. 94. Ancient Bushman drawings (after Boas).

in life; only the relative sizes are distorted. The sexual organs are exaggerated at the expense of other parts, which are correspondingly reduced in size and undeveloped in details. Distortion may even be carried still further, and the whole outline of the body and the relation of parts may be sacrificed to the formal treatment of the significant portions. We have seen in the art of the Kwakiutl to what lengths the distortion of the animal form may be carried. A very different type of distortion, with a symbolism based on wholly different premises, is shown in the representations in Navajo sand paintings. These paintings, made in colored sands on the floor of the ceremonial hut during ceremonies, represent anthropomorphic deities, cosmological principles, and incidents from myths. The figures of the masked gods are greatly elongated; male gods are symbolized by round masks, females by square masks. The identities of the gods are shown in their costumes, headdresses, and appendages. There is a fixed color symbolism associated with the four cardinal points: white for east, blue for south, yellow for west, black for north. The clothing of the gods and the corn plants which are conventionally represented are of the colors appropriate to the directions with which they are associated. In this way the universe, bounded by the sky (the rainbow) with a spring of water at its center, and covered with verdure and peopled with healing gods, can be represented on the floor of the medicine lodge. The same system of symbolism which appears in the sand paintings is even more fully developed in myth and song.[16]

Color symbolism similar to that of the Navajo is found among the neighboring Pueblos. These Indians recognize six cardinal directions,

Fig. 95. *Left.* Fetish Representing Antelope. Bambala, French Sudan
Right. Female Figurine, Baoulé, Ivory Coast (after Kjersmeier).

including up and down. The color symbolism, carried out consistently in all ceremonial objects and elaborated in songs and myths, is as follows: yellow for north, blue for west, red for south, white for east, speckled for above, black for below. There is a second symbolism of color, blue for male and yellow for female; blue and yellow paired, as they are in certain prayersticks, stand as a symbol of fecundity. The prayersticks of the god of love, music, and butterflies at Zuñi are paired blue and yellow. The butterflies attached to ceremonial objects or painted on masks or ceremonial garments are symbols of erotic

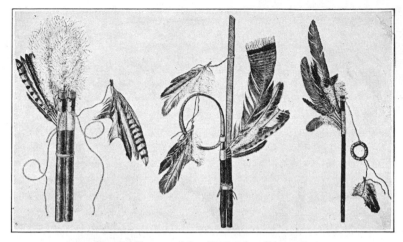

Fig. 96. Prayer sticks, Zuñi (after Parsons).

attraction. However, this use of the butterfly to attract is on the fringe of magic. It resembles the use on all classes of ceremonial objects of designs of frogs, tadpoles, dragonflies, and a mythical water serpent "to call the rain." In the Pueblos the chief offering to the gods is the prayerstick, a small painted wooden stick to one side of which feathers are attached with a cotton cord (Fig. 96). At Zuñi the prayerstick represents a person, the messenger to the gods. The stick is his body, the paint his flesh, the feathers his clothing, the cotton cord his belt, the hanging feathers his hair feather. Sex is indicated by color, or else a shield-shaped face on one side indicates a female. The color of the paint and the feathers all are symbolic of the individual for whom the offering is intended. Certain deities, such as the Rain Makers, are associated with special directions, and their sticks are appropriately colored. The tail feathers of the eagle are associated with warrior gods, the downy eagle feather with the sun, the red-dyed downy feather with the bear and other medicine gods; the tail feather of the male turkey with the Rain Makers and the breast feather with the dead and the masked gods; and the duck feather with the masked gods.

Similar symbolism is found in the sacred objects of the Pawnee.[17] One of the important ceremonies of this tribe, a ceremony directed toward fecundity and the increase of the tribe, is named from two feathered pipestems which figure prominently in all the rituals. The female stem, painted blue for heaven, with a red groove representing life, is decorated with a fan-shaped ornament of ten feathers from the brown eagle, a bird representing male power. "This stick represents the north, the moon, and the night. It is the mother and it always leads. To one end is fastened a woodpecker's head to avert danger from storms; to the other end a duck's head for protection on water. Owl feathers are fastened near one end to protect by night. The blue paint symbolizes the clear sky, the red and white streamers day and night. The male stem, the father, is painted green, the color of the Earth Mother, and has an ornament of feathering of the white eagle, a bird that is not sacred. This stick represents the day, the sun, the south. It is male and it can never lead but must always follow."

Fig. 97. Votive placque, Huichol Indians, Mexico (after Lumholtz).

A case of religious symbolism expressed in more obviously decorative form is found in the wicker shields which the Huichol Indians of Mexico hang in the temples of their gods as votive offerings (Fig. 95). They symbolize at one time the attributes of the god and the prayer of the donor. The geometric designs on these placques convey this complex message. Lumholtz [18] gives the following explanation of such a shield offered to the Sun: "The section within the blue ring is expressive of the sun with his various colors. The figures in white outside the ring, with the blue and yellow crosslike figures within them, are the shaman's plumes. The crosslike figures represent *hikuli* (a narcotic and vision-producing drug about the use of which many ceremonies center) or, what is considered the same thing, corn. The broad section of white, black, red, yellow outside them symbolizes the rays of the sun. . . . Between the shamanistic designs are seen figures of the double water-gourd. The prayer thus indicated is addressed to the great shaman, the Sun, whose powers are manifest in heat, that he may rise surrounded by clouds, bringing rain and hence corn." The explanation is complete and consistent. But when we examine the system of symbolism we see that in other shields each of the elements represents other ideas. The cross, for instance, is variously interpreted as *hikuli*, corn, the four cardinal points, fire. The parallel stripes in different contexts represent "back shield," another type of votive offering, candles, rain, serpents, and feathers.

Among all these highly ritualized tribes the symbolism in the decoration of sacred objects is only one phase of the symbolism of rituals as a whole. The whole ritual is symbolic; therefore every object connected with it, every word spoken, every gesture, carries its weight of meaning. The specific details of the symbolism, consistent within the ritual complex, are not carried over into secular arts. When we turn to the nonceremonial articles of any people and try to unravel the symbolism, we are on much less sure ground. It is not difficult to find among almost any people one or two fixed symbols or emblems, religious symbols like the cross, or symbols of political groups like the swastika or the hammer and sickle, or symbols of social status like heraldic devices. But the use of symbols of this type is less common among primitive than among sophisticated people. There are some analagous cases: a figure much used in Polynesian art, two figures turned back to back, represents one of their gods. It is common in western America pottery and basketry for the most important structural line of the design to be left incomplete. It is said that this line represents life and that is left unjoined lest the maker end her own life in completing the pattern. But for the most part the mystic symbols of primitive peoples are simple conventional representations, like the familiar cloud and sun symbols of the Pueblos. The one valid generalization about symbolism is that it must never be assumed or inferred. We find many peoples, for instance, using the cross in their decorative art. But it must not be assumed that for all of them it has the same significance. To the Zuñi it symbolizes the four quarters of the world; to the Arapaho, the morning star; to the Huichol it represents corn or peyote or a spark.

The art of the Arapaho Indians has often been taken as an example of highly developed abstract symbolism. But Kroeber, after his exhaustive analysis in which he recorded the symbolism of hundreds of objects and hundreds of decorative motives, found that the same pattern was interpreted in many different ways, and that the same idea was embodied in many different forms. A simple rectangle was variously named life, a brush hut, a camp circle, ocean, the earth, mountains, an eye, a buffalo. On the other hand, life is represented as a square, a diamond, a square inclosing three rectangles, a small rectangle, a large rectangle, a trapezoid, a figure resembling the butt of an arrow, a right angle, and five triangles inclosed within a rectangle. No one would venture to interpret the meaning of an article which was not his.[19] On the whole the meanings imputed to abstract designs are less likely to belong to a fixed system of symbolism than to a set of personal and temporary associations.

Discussions of symbolism have been greatly confused by failure to distinguish between true symbolism, the consistent and intelligible use of one form to represent another, and *post hoc* reading of meanings into designs. An observer's interpretations of designs embody both cultural preoccupations and personal symbolism, which may not necessarily be those of the maker. Even where maker and interpreter are one the symbolic content of the designs may not have been in the mind of the maker when the forms were first conceived and projected. Often the "meaning" does not emerge until the ethnologist asks for it, and then the answer will be colored like any free association by many factors, including what the informant thinks the ethnologist wants to hear. There is usually no difficulty in recognizing this type of personal symbolism. However, the fact that different interpretations of the same design may be offered is not in itself evidence of lack of fixed symbolism. The symbolic content may be esoteric, like the symbolism of early Christian art. Nevertheless, aside from picture writing, cryptic symbolism is less common in primitive art than many writers would have us believe, although it is exceedingly common in primitive literature, both myth and song. Multiple interpretations are, however, very common. Boas quotes an excellent example in the case of a Chilkat blanket made by the Tlingit Indians of the Northwest Coast of America. The specimen in question was interpreted by one informant as "a whale diving with two ravens," and by another as "a wolf with young." Since all art among these Indians serves to display the crests and totemic prerogatives of the owner, each individual refers any decorated object which comes into his possession to his own totemic myth. But in spite of these different interpretations it is evident that the designs of these people all have a conceptual content. But when the same individual explains the same design differently at different times, and when he applies the same name to designs having no formal resemblance, or assigns different meanings to formally related designs without being able to formulate any general principles, we may at once suspect that we are dealing with a *post hoc* interpretation. The names of Zuñi designs illustrate this tendency. A famous Zuñi potter drew a collection of designs and identified them on two separate occasions. Here maker and interpreter were the same individual. Out of a collection of 91 drawings for household pottery, 77 were identified on both occasions. In 34 cases the two interpretations agreed in substance; in 43 cases they were quite different. Sometimes a design which was given some symbolic interpretation on one occasion was described formally on the other, as a design of interlocking scrolls called (1) "Bow of the Masked Gods, with feathers hanging from it"; (2) "Jar stomach design." Sometimes very different symbolic interpretations were offered such as (1) "Spider web, a prayer for skill in weaving," later called (2) "Feathers and drumsticks, and the seeds which the Masked Gods carry in their hearts." Or (1) "Grandfather standing; a prayer for long life"; (2) "Circle with drumsticks (of medicine men)." Or (1) "Broken trail; the trail is blocked with a line of cornmeal to save us from our enemies; a prayer for safety in war"; (2) "Black cloud terraces rising, with red clouds also." Or (1) "Rainbow carrying clouds, with arrow points and drumsticks"; (2) "Wall in the cloud house, yucca suds and flowers; a prayer for luck in hunting." [20]

The explanations that do not refer directly to rain and clouds refer to ceremonial paraphernalia. All indicate the same preoccupations; the associations, while not inherent in the designs, are definitely patterned. Interpretations from other women, while somewhat less explicit, deal with the same preoccupations. Obviously we are here dealing with a tribal rather than individual symbolic tendency. In some cases it is possible to isolate personal patterns of symbolism. In San Ildefonso one man invariably sees clouds where another sees birds, just as individuals among ourselves react differently to the inkblot test. All these tribal and personal patterns of association, while of great importance to the ethnologist and the psychologist, have little to do with art and exert no influence in the creation or development of form. They are as irrelevant as the fantasies of program annotators with reference to music. Reading meanings into artistic creations is very different from primary symbolism, which is a conscious attempt on the part of the artist to use art to express nonesthetic concepts.

FOOTNOTES

1. Himmelheber, H., *Negerkünstler* (Stuttgart, 1935).
2. For Maya art see: Maudslay, A. P., *Biologia Centrali-Americana, Archaeology* (London, 1889–1902); Totten, G. O., *Maya Architecture* (1926).

3. Sweeney, J. J., *African Negro Art* (Museum of Modern Art, 1935); Torday, E., and Joyce, T. K., *Les Bushongo*, Annales du Musée du Congo Belge (Brussels, 1911); Einstein, Carl, "Afrikanische Plastik," *Orbis Pictus*, vol. 7 (Berlin, 1922).

4. Swanton, J., *Contributions to the Ethnology of the Haida*, Jesup Expedition, vol. 5, Part I (1905–09); Boas, F., *Primitive Art* (Oslo, 1927), pp. 183–298.

5. d'Harcourt, R. S. M., *La Céramique ancienne de Pérou* (Paris, 1924); Schmidt, M., *Kunst und Kultur von Peru* (Berlin, 1929); Lehmann, W., and Doering, H., *Kunstgeschichte des alten Peru* (Berlin, 1924); Reiss, W., and Stübel, A., *The Necropolis of Ancon in Peru* (Berlin, 1880–87); Gayton, A. H., and Kroeber, A. L., "The Uhle Pottery Collections from Nazca," *University of California Publications in American Archaeology and Ethnology*, vol. 24, no. 1 (1927), pp. 1–46.

6. Dixon, R. B., *Basketry Designs of California Indians*, Bulletin of the American Museum of Natural History, vol. 17 (1902), pp. 1 ff.; Kroeber, A. L. "Basket Designs of the Indians of Northwestern California," *University of California Publications in American Archaeology and Ethnology*, vol. 2, no. 4 (1905), pp. 105 ff.; Barrett, S. A., "Pomo Indian Basketry," *University of California Publications in American Archaeology and Ethnology*, vol. 7, no. 3 (1908), pp. 134 ff.

7. Emmons, G. T., *The Chilkat Blanket*, Memoirs of the American Museum of Natural History, vol. 3 (1907), pp. 329 ff.

8. Illustrations of Pueblo altars in Stevenson, M. C., *Zuñi Indians*, Annual Report of the Bureau of American Ethnology, vol. 23 (1904).

9. Reichard, G. A., "The Complexity of Rhythm in Decorative Art," *American Anthropologist*, vol. 24 (1922), pp. 198 ff.

10. Boas, F., *op. cit.*, pp. 46 ff.

11. Fewkes, J. W., *Archaeological Expedition to Arizona in 1895*, Annual Report of the Bureau of American Ethnology, vol. 17, Part II (1898), and *Designs on Prehistoric Hopi Pottery*, Annual Report of the Bureau of American Ethnology, vol. 33 (1919), pp. 207 ff.

12. Guthe, C. E., *Pueblo Pottery Making* (1925); Bunzel, R., *The Pueblo Potter*, Columbia University Contributions to Anthropology, vol. 8 (1929).

13. Boas, F., *op. cit.*, pp. 166 ff.

14. *Ibid.*, pp. 183 ff.

15. Bunzel, R., *op. cit.*

16. Matthews, W., *The Navajo Night Chant*, Memoir of the American Museum of Natural History, vol. 6 (1902); Newcomb, F. J., and Reichard, G. A., *Sandpaintings of the Navajo Shooting Chant* (1937).

17. Fletcher, A. C., *The Hako: A Pawnee Ceremony*, Annual Report of the Bureau of American Ethnology, vol. 22 (1904).

18. Lumholtz, C., *Symbolism of the Huichol Indians*, Memoir of the American Museum of Natural History, vol. 3 (1900).

19. Kroeber, A. L., *The Arapaho*, Bulletin of the American Museum of Natural History, vol. 18, Part II (1902).

20. Bunzel, R., *op. cit.*

GENERAL REFERENCES

Balfour, H., *The Evolution of Decorative Art* (London, 1893).

Boas, F., *Primitive Art* (Oslo, 1927).

Grosse, E., *The Beginnings of Art* (1897).

Hirn, Y., *The Origins of Art* (London, 1900).

Scheltema, F. A. van, *Die altnordische Kunst* (Berlin, 1923).

Semper, G., *Der Stil in den Technischen und Tektonischen Künsten* (Munich, 1878–79).

Wundt, W., *Völkerpsychologie*, vol. 3, "Die Kunst" (Leipzig, 1919).

For Bibliography see Eckert von Sydow, *Die Kunst der Naturvölker und der Vorzeit* (Berlin, 1923).

CHAPTER XII

LITERATURE, MUSIC, AND DANCE

Franz Boas

Among some of the most primitive tribes very few objects of artistic value are found. This is easily understood, for the roaming life of the hunter and the necessity of constant application for obtaining the bare necessities of life do not leave much time for manual work beyond that required for the pursuit of game and the collection of other kinds of food. Furthermore, the whole amount of property that can be carried along is small. The family cannot burden itself with many unnecessary or unfinished products, and the completion of artistic work requires time. The Eskimo who returns to his semipermanent house every day and whose hunting gear is in good condition may amuse himself with ivory-carving, which he may take up in long evenings or during snowstorms that make hunting impossible, but the total amount of such work and its size are necessarily restricted. Still more unfavorable are conditions for the Bushman who has to travel on foot and who has still less leisure to follow artistic inclinations. Leisure is indispensable for artistic handiwork, and a certain amount of stability or transportation by means of animals seems indispensable for its development. Stone work, stone architecture, and heavy wood work presuppose stability of residence.

Such restrictions are not present in the arts of literature, music, and dance, for the hunter watching for game or leisurely attending to his traps may give free rein to his imagination without interfering with his watchful waiting. Out of the daydreams of the hunter and of the woman attending to her housework, stories and songs may be spun.

The world-wide distribution of tales and songs shows that these considerations are valid. The Bushman and the eastern Eskimo, although poor in the production of art, are rich in tales and songs, of which they possess a well-nigh inexhaustible treasure. The poor hunters of the Malay peninsula and the Australians have their literature no less than economically more advanced people. Songs and tales are found all over the world. These are the fundamental forms of literature among primitive people.

The essential traits of song are rhythm and melody. Rhythm belongs not only to song but also to prose. Repetition, particularly rhythmic repetition, is a fundamental trait of both. All prose narrative consists in part of free elements the form of which is dependent upon the taste and ability of the narrator. Inserted among these passages we find others of fixed form which give to the narrative its formal attractiveness. Often these passages consist of conversation between the actors, in which deviations from the fixed formula are not permitted. In other cases they are of rhythmic form and must be considered poetry or chants rather than prose.

It is very difficult to gain a correct understanding of the form of primitive prose, because most of the available material has been recorded in European languages only, and it is impossible to determine the accuracy of the rendering. In most of the records there is an obvious attempt to adopt European literary styles. Even when the material is available in the original text we may assume that, at least in the majority of cases, it does not reach the standard of excellence of the native narrative. The difficulty of phonetic rendering of foreign languages requires such slowness of dictation that the artistic style necessarily suffers. The number of collectors who have complete mastery of the native language is altogether too small. The best approximation to the art of narrative of primitive people is probably found in those cases in which educated natives write down the texts, or in the records taken down by missionaries who, in long years of personal, intimate contact with the people, have acquired complete control of their language, and who are willing to give us just what they hear. In some cases natives have been trained to write with such ease that their writings may be considered as good representation of style. Early examples of this kind are tales published by Eskimos. Recently some attempts have been made to take down texts on the phonograph and to have them redictated sentence by sentence.

In almost all reliable collections the fixed formal parts are of considerable importance. It is not easy to form a correct opinion regarding the rhythmic character of the formal prose, partly because the rhythmic sense of primitive people is much more highly developed than our own. The simplification of the rhythm of modern folk song, and of poetry intended to appeal to popular taste, has dulled our feeling for rhythmic form. It requires careful study to understand the structure of primitive rhythm, more so in prose than in song, because in this case the help of the melodic pattern is lacking.

I believe the liking for the frequent repetition of single motives is in part due to the pleasure given by rhythmic repetition. For example, the tales of the Chinook Indians are always so constructed that five brothers, one after another, have the same adventure. The four eldest perish while the youngest one comes out successful. The tale is repeated verbatim for all the brothers, and its length, which to our ear and taste is intolerable, probably gives pleasure by the repeated form. Conditions are quite similar in European fairy tales relating the fates of three brothers, two of whom perish or fail in their tasks while the youngest one succeeds.

Repetitions leading to a climax are also found. Thus in Tsimshian tales [1] an eagle is said to screech every morning. The hero comes out of the house following the call and finds every day a larger animal on the beach in front of his house. A similar device occurs in the German tales of the fisherman whose wife sends him day after day to ask a wonderful fish to give him ever greater gifts. Every time he uses the same verse when calling the fish.

In the tales of the Pueblo Indians [2] the same incident is repeated four times, happening to four sisters: the yellow, red, blue, and white girl. In a Papua tale from New Guinea [3] the birds come one after another and try to peck open the stomach of a drowned person so as to let the water he has swallowed run out. In a New Ireland tale [4] the birds try to throw the cassowary off the branch of a tree on which it is perched. One after another alights next to him on the same branch but nearer the trunk. Thus he is compelled to move out farther and farther until finally he drops down. Similar repetitions are found in the German tale of Red Ridinghood, in the widely spread European story of the rooster who goes to bury his mate, and in the story of the Three Bears. In Oriental tales the incidents of the tale are sometimes repeated verbatim, being retold by one of the heroes.

Much more striking are rhythmic repetitions in the formal parts of tales or in those cases in which connecting discussion is omitted. An example is the following Eskimo tale [5] of a woman and the spirit of the singing-house:

"Where is its owner? Where is its master?
Has the singing-house an owner? Has the singing-house a master?
It has no owner." — "Here he is, there he is!"

"Where are his feet? Where are the calves of his legs? Where are his
knees? Where are his thighs?" — "Here they are, there they
are!"
"Where is his stomach?" — "Here it is, there it is!"
"Where is his chest? Where is his arm? Where is his neck? Where is
his head?" — "Here it is, there it is!"
He had no hair. *

Sometimes these parts of tales are in an archaic form or in a foreign
language, so that they may be quite unintelligible. Their impressiveness rests on their form and the general emotional trend of the passages in which they occur.[6]

In oratory, rhythmic repetitions are used for purposes of emphasis
and impressiveness. An Indian who welcomes his guests in his house
and who wishes to recall the greatness of his ancestors addresses his
hearers as follows:[7]

"This is the house of my great-great-grandfather Mahwa who invited
you here.
This is the house of my great-grandfather Mahwa who invited you
at Sandy Beach.
This is the house of my grandfather Mahwa who invited you at
Crooked Beach.
This is the feasting house of my father who invited you at Tide
Beach.
Now I have taken the place of my father. I invited you, tribes, that
you should come and see my house here."

Similar are the Polynesian chants in which the ancestors are
enumerated:

Hulihonua the husband,
Keakahulilani the wife;
Laka the husband, Kapapaiakele the wife;
Kamooalewa the husband,
Nanawahine the wife;

and so through twenty-seven pairs.[8]

In oratory rhythm is also applied to give fixed form to free dis-
course. This is sometimes obtained by a delivery in which the phrases
are given somewhat equal length with accent on the last, sometimes
an added, syllable. Thus the Kwakiutl will address his guests: "Wel-

* This means that the woman felt for the supernatural owner of the singing-
house. He is supposed to have bandy legs, no hair, and no occipital bone. To
touch his soft head is immediate death.

come-ai', brothers-ai', at my feast-ai'," always connecting the -ai firmly with the preceding word; or by introducing every phrase with ha. Similar devices are used in the recital of myths, as when the Fox Indians repeat after every phrase of their Culture Hero myth the syllables *nootchee nootchee*.[9] Sometimes the phrasing is made by a pause in which the listeners supply the rhythmic break. Thus, in Africa, the narrator may tell, "The Turtle killed the Leopard," and the audience will repeat, clapping their hands, "The Leopard, the Leopard."

More definite and clearer rhythmic structure appears in poetry. Primitive rhythmic poetry that is not sung is, as far as I am aware, unknown. It is therefore more correct to speak of song rather than of poetry. All song is accompanied by body movements that are often associated with noise, such as hand-clapping or stamping the ground; also by swaying of the body. Therefore poetry, music, and dance form an inextricable unit. Only gradually is poetry dissociated from music and dance, and music from dance, while dance seems to be almost indissolubly connected with music.

Since song is so often accompanied by movement, there is commonly a coördination of two kinds of rhythms: that of song and that of movement. On the whole the regularity of emphasis on every second, third, or fourth time-interval which is characteristic of modern folk music, forming our regular two, three, and four part measures, is not the rule in primitive music. Longer units are found, such as five or seven part rhythms as well as long units that cannot be divided into regular measures, but which are regularly repeated.

The coördination of song and movement is also often different from ours. We are accustomed to move in accord with the accented measures, but very commonly the coördination follows different patterns leading to various types of syncope, to the combination of one rhythm in song with another in movement. When the movement is accompanied by sound, as in hand-clapping or stamping, we have a new acoustic rhythm developing through the combination of the two. In Africa this multiplicity of interweaving rhythms is augmented by the independence of rhythmic movements of different parts of the body, particularly of the two hands and the two feet, which create new complexities.

The great variety of forms in which rhythm appears, as rhythm of time in music and dance, rhythm of space in decorative art, shows that the theory of Bücher,[10] who derives rhythm from the regularity of movements in communal work, or the parallel theory of Wundt,[11] who derives it from dance, cannot be maintained. The pleasure given by regular repetition of embroidery designs, painting, or the complex arrangement of strings in rhythmically repeated order cannot be explained by conditions imposed by the technique, and there is no indication that this rhythm is later than the one determined by motor habits.

In primitive music we find numerous songs in which the melody is carried solely by vocables, like our *la-la-la* in songs the words of which are not familiar to us, or in the frequent refrains. The musical elements of such songs are solely tune and rhythm. Sometimes the vocable itself may have a significance indicating a certain emotion or situation. Such are the vocables of wails or those suggesting the cries of animals or of definite spirits. In other cases the song may be interspersed with a single word here and there, like an outcry adjusted to the regular course of the tune, while the rest is carried on by vocables. In many cases the words, even when forming continuous sentences, are distorted by lengthening or abbreviation — an extended use of the method we employ in using the apostrophe, wrong accents, or extraordinary lengthening in order to fit words to a tune. This, however, is not always the case. In recitations and chants the words are often controlling, and musical phrases are added or omitted when the words require it. In the music of the Dakota Indian we find both tendencies, the words adapted to the tunes and the tunes adapted to the words.[12]

The contents of poetry are as varied as the cultural interests of the people. It is difficult for us to appreciate the poetic value they may have for the composer or singer, since the contents may have no emotional appeal to us. When the Eskimo women sing, "Our husbands are coming down there, I am going to eat!" it may sound utterly prosaic to us who do not know the privations of Eskimo life, and it may well be that the combined joy of seeing the safe return of the men from the dangers of the chase and the prospect of a jolly evening when all the people are assembled over the meal and are joking and conversing finds exuberant relief in these insignificant lines. The effect of poetry does not depend upon the power of description that releases clear and beautiful images, but upon its ability to arouse strong emotion.

As we may underestimate the poetic value of such trifling songs, we may easily overestimate the actual poetic value of stereotyped symbolic poetry that appeals to us on account of its strange imagery, but that may have to the native no other than the emotional appeal of the ritual.

When the occasions of singing are varied we find commonly distinctive types of song for every one of these. Thus the Kwakiutl Indians of Vancouver Island have children's songs which father or mother sings, letting the child dance on the arms; love songs, generally sung in chorus by the young men walking up and down the street; feast songs praising the greatness of the host; war songs; and various types of ritual songs sung in their religious ceremonials. The types are clearly distinct and easily recognizable. They are built on a common principle, but each has its own style.

While the style of songs may be defined by a study of their rhythm and melody, it is much more difficult to define the style of prose — even setting aside the paucity of reliable material. The style depends to a great extent upon linguistic form. What may be appealing in one language may be repellent in one of different form. Thus the structure of many American languages compels the narrator to express himself explicitly in regard to the location where an event happens while other languages remain vague in regard to this point. To one accustomed to strict localization the latter style is lacking in color.

The inclination to diffuse detail characterizes the style of some tales while others may strive for such pregnant conciseness that the most intimate knowledge of the culture is required to make the contents intelligible. Devices for securing emphasis are probably present everywhere. There are pathos and fun. A generalized treatment of prose style seems hardly possible.

Certain devices may be discussed. One of these is characterization of individuals by peculiar ways of behaving or talking. The mere introduction of a trickster in a tale arouses the expectation of some exhilarating exploit. Often he and other actors in the tale are characterized by peculiar mannerisms of speech that set them off from other personalities. The character of various animals or persons is liable to be stereotyped, and their mere introduction may call forth the expectation of events that conform to their supposed nature.

Similes are found more often in songs and oratory than in narrative prose. Still, they are not lacking in prose. The Polynesians seem to appreciate their poetic value. Thus we read in the Fornander collection of Hawaiian tales: "His skin was like a ripe banana. His eyeballs were like the young buds of a banana. His body was straight and without blemish and he was without an equal." In the Hawaiian story of Laieikawai [13] it is said: "I am not the mistress of this shore. I came from inland, from the top of the mountain which is clothed in a white garment."

In Indian oratory there is ample use of similes. I will confine my remarks to their use among the Kwakiutl,[14] with whose speech forms I am familiar. Similes are used particularly when describing the greatness of a chief or of a warrior. The chief is compared with a mountain; a precipice (from which rolls down wealth overwhelming the tribe); a rock that cannot be climbed; the post of heaven (that supports the world); the only great tree (that raises its crown over the lower trees of the woods or that rises in lonely height on an island); a loaded canoe at anchor; the one who makes the whole world smoky (from the smoke of the fire in the house in which he gives feasts); the thick tree; the thick root (of the tribe). Through his great acts he burns up the tribes (relating to warlike exploits). The people follow him as the young sawbill ducks follow the mother bird. He makes the people suffer with his short-life maker; he shoves away the tribes. The greatness of the chief is called the weight of his name. When he marries a princess he lifts her weight from the floor; his wealth of blankets (which are piled up before being distributed) is a mountain that rises through our heavens; in the feast, surrounded by his tribe, he stands on his fortress. Wealth is the salmon caught by him.

Examples of similar kind may be found in the oratory and poetry of many peoples. They occur also commonly in sayings. The Tsimshian of British Columbia say, "A deer, though toothless, may accomplish something."

Allusions are also a device used particularly in oratory. The Tsimshian, to whom I referred before, have a saying, "Is this war, father?" which refers to a story in which a boy who has been told by his father that there will be a great war, endures many hardships and asks every time this question. The Dakota Indians say, "Did you not see his palate?" referring to the striped palate of the trickster of their mythology and implying that the person referred to is unreliable and tricky. Such allusions are intelligible only to those who know the tribal lore. Therefore, they are not often found in published material. Allusions of this kind are common in African proverbs. A Lamba saying is, "The slave was redeemed through his castor-oil," referring to the story of a slave who paid for his freedom by presenting his master with oil from plants he had sowed.[15] Another is: "It is

an evil omen of the Nsenga. We shall question it on our return." [16]
This means that one will not be discouraged easily. It refers to the
tale of a trading expedition to the Nsenga country on which many
evil omens were encountered. The leader refused to be discouraged
and on his return journey received satisfactory explanation of every
one of them. A Djagga proverb says, "Do not cheat me like Kitiko
who cheated Ivere." [17] This refers to two men who bet that they
could fast for ten days. Kitiko was fed by his wife, although he was
being watched, and thus won the bet.

There are great differences in the manner of composition. Some
people have a preference for long, complex stories; among others,
brief anecdotic tales prevail. On the whole the incidents of which
complex stories are built up are brief, disconnected anecdotes which
are woven into a whole by various devices. Often this is accomplished
by concentrating all the anecdotes around one personage. When this
person is given a definite character a somewhat greater unity is
secured. Thus the Raven tale of Alaska consists entirely of unrelated
episodes.[18] The only connecting link, besides the identity of the hero,
is the voracity of the Raven. Similar in structure are the Spider tales
of Africa,[19] the Dwarf Antelope tales of Malaysia, [20] and the Fox
tales of Europe.[21]

Sometimes the incidents are strung on the slight thread of a tale
of adventure and travel. To this class belongs the Eskimo tale of a
hero who follows his escaped wife and meets on the way with dangers
which he overcomes — like the Argonauts in their search for the
Golden Fleece. Similar is the structure of the migration legends of
the Creek [22] and Pueblo.[23] An interesting case is that of a modern tale
of the Tlingit of· Alaska. In the early days of Russian colonization
of Alaska the Tlingit attacked the fort of Sitka. The governor,
Baranoff, had to flee. After a few years he returned and reëstablished
the fort. This interval is filled by the Tlingit with a marvelous story,
telling how he went in search of his son. He encounters fabulous
beings that are known from other tales, visits the entrance of the
lower world, and communicates with the souls of the deceased.

There are also tales in which the incidents are brought into closer
inner connection. The creation legends of the Polynesians are of
this character, as are their war histories, the incidents of which are
held together by a single plot or a single purpose. As an example
we may give the abstract of the origin story of the Baganda,[24] a simple
case of a connected story.

The first ancestor of the people, Kintu, arrived in Uganda and brought with him a cow. There was no other food in the country. A heavenly woman came down with her brother and wished to marry him. Her father, the Lord of Heaven, objected to the marriage on account of Kintu's poverty. In order to test Kintu's powers he stole his cow. The girl told him of the whereabouts of his cow and took him up to the sky, where he saw multitudes of houses, people, cattle, goats, sheep, and fowl. Kintu had to show his powers by being subjected to a number of tests. He had to eat large quantities of food, split a rock with a copper axe, and find his cow and her calves among a large herd. Finally he was accepted and sent back with the herds of the young woman. He was warned not to take her brother, Death, along. Owing to a mistake made by his wife, Death accompanied him, and thus death was introduced in the world. An attempt of another brother to have Death go back to Heaven failed.

Similar well-integrated stories are also found among other tribes, even those of simpler structure than the Baganda. Thus the Eskimo have a tale belonging to the Swan Maiden type.[25] A youth surprises some bird girls bathing, takes away the dress of one, and marries her. Eventually she recovers her dress and flies away with her son to the land of the birds beyond the hole of the sky. He follows her, and the obstacles and dangers of the way to the sky fill the larger part of the story, which ends with the finding of the wife.

The literary forms of the world are not uniform. We may observe that a number of extended areas have peculiar characteristics. Certain literary forms are found among all the races of the Old World while they are unknown in America. The important position held by the proverb in the literature of Africa, Asia, and also of Europe until quite recent times is well known. In Africa particularly the proverb is in constant use. It is even the basis of court decisions. The importance of the proverb in Europe is illustrated by the way in which Sancho Panza applies it. Equally rich is Asiatic literature in proverbial sayings. On the contrary, hardly any proverbial sayings are known from American Indians.

The same conditions are found in regard to the riddle, one of the favorite pastimes of the Old World, which is almost entirely absent in America. Riddles are known from the Yukon River, a region in which Asiatic influences may be discovered in several cultural traits, and from the Eskimo of Labrador.[26] In other parts of the continent careful questioning has failed to reveal their occurrence. It is striking that even in New Mexico and Arizona, where Indians and Spaniards have been living side by side for several centuries and where Indian literature is full of Spanish elements, the riddle, nevertheless, has not been adopted, although the Spaniards of this region are as fond of riddles as those of Europe.*

The distribution of epic poetry is also wide, but nevertheless limited to a fairly definitely circumscribed area — namely, Europe and a considerable part of central Asia. We know in America long, connected tribal traditions, but up to this time no trace of a composition that might be called a romance or a true epic poem has ever been discovered. Polynesian legends telling of the descent and deeds of their chiefs may perhaps be designated as epic poetry. The distribution of this form can be understood only on the basis of the existence of ancient cultural relations.

On the ground of the distribution of these types two conclusions may be established: the one that these forms are not necessary steps in the development of literary form, but that they occur only under certain conditions; the other that the forms are not determined by race, but depend upon historical happenings.

If at the time when Europeans first came to the New World the literature of the Americans did not possess the three types of literature we mentioned, it does not follow that they would have appeared at a later time. We have no reason to assume that American literature was less developed than that of Africa. On the contrary, the art of narrative and poetry is highly developed in many parts of America. We must rather assume that the historical conditions have led to a form different from that of the Old World.

The distribution of these forms among Europeans, Mongols, Malays, and Negroes proves the independence of literary development from racial descent. It shows that it is one of the characteristics of the enormously extended cultural area which embraces almost the whole of the Old World and which in other features also appears in distinct contrast to the New World. I mention here only the development of a formal judicial procedure, founded on the taking of evidence, the oath, and the ordeal, and the absence of this complex in America; and also the rarity in America of the belief in obsession and the evil eye, and of the use of artificial amulets, which are widely known in the Old World.

* Two Omaha riddles given by J. O. Dorsey in his work *Omaha Sociology*, 3d Annual Report Bureau of Ethnology (1884), p. 334 are presumably of European origin.

These conclusions are much strengthened by the study of the literature of more restricted areas. The investigation of European fairy tales has led to the conclusion that in contents and form they embrace many survivals of past times. Not only Grimm's [27] theories but also Gomme's [28] views are based on this opinion. It is quite evident that the modern European fairy tales do not reflect the political conditions of our times, nor the conditions of our daily life, but that they give us an imaginative picture of rural life in semifeudal times, and that, owing to the contradictions between modern intellectualism and the ancient rural tradition, conflicts of viewpoints occur that may be interpreted as survivals. In tales of primitive people it is otherwise. A detailed analysis of the traditional tales of a number of Indian tribes shows complete agreement of the conditions of life with those that may be abstracted from the tales. Beliefs and customs in life and in tales are in full agreement. This is true not only of old native material but also of imported stories that were borrowed some time ago. They are quickly adapted to the prevailing mode of life. The analysis of tales from the Northwest Coast [29] and from the Pueblos gives the same result. Only during the period of transition to new modes of life, such as are brought about by contact with Europeans, do contradictions develop. Thus it happens that in the tales of Laguna, one of the Pueblos of New Mexico, the visitor always enters through the roof of the house, although the modern houses have doors. The headman of the ceremonial organization plays an important rôle in many tales, although the organization itself has largely disappeared. The tales of the Plains Indians still tell of buffalo hunts, although the game has disappeared and the people have become tillers of the soil and laborers.

It would be erroneous to assume that the absence of survivals of an earlier time can be explained as due to the permanence of conditions, to a lack of historical change. Primitive culture is a product of historical development no less than modern civilization. Mode of life, customs, and beliefs of primitive tribes are not stable; but the rate of change, unless disturbances from the outside occur, is slower than among ourselves. What is lacking is the pronounced social stratification of our times that brings it about that the various groups represent, as it were, different periods of development. So far as my knowledge goes we find the cultural, formal background of the art of narrative of primitive people almost entirely determined by its present cultural state. The only exceptions are found in periods of an unusually rapid change or of disintegration. However, in this case also a readjustment occurs. Thus the stories of the modern Negroes of Angola reflect the mixed culture of the West African coast. In the cultural background of the narrative, survivals do not play an important rôle, at least not under normal conditions. The plot may be old, but it undergoes radical changes.

These remarks relating to literature do not mean, of course, that in other aspects of life ancient customs and beliefs may not persist over long periods.

The general cultural outlook is felt also in the fundamental plots of the stories. For example, in the tales of the North American Indians the conception of the relation of man to the supernatural powers [30] is entirely different from the conception that is characteristic of Siberian tribes.[31] The Indian seeks the spirits that are to help him, or at least encourages their coming. The Siberian is seized by the powers, no matter whether he wants them or not. Even among American tribes there are striking differences that color their tales. In one group the powers are supplicated, and they grant their gift in response to the prayer; in others they are coerced to bestow their gifts.

Instructive examples of the influence of culture upon the elaboration of themes are found in tales borrowed from Europe. In a nativity story of the Zuñi of New Mexico, recorded by Dr. Benedict and Dr. Parsons,[32] Jesus appears as a girl, the daughter of the sun. After the birth of the child the domestic animals pay homage by licking it; only the mule refuses, and it is punished by sterility. The whole story has been given a new aspect. It is made to account for fertility, a thought uppermost in the minds of the Pueblos. Changes in the mythological significance of tales will be treated in the chapter on mythology.

The differences of cultural life which are reflected in literature have a far-reaching effect not only upon the contents but also upon the form of the narrative. The motives of action are determined by the mode of life and the chief interests of the people, and the plots give us a picture of these.

In many typical tales of the Chukchee of Siberia the subject of the tale is the tyranny and overmastering arrogance of an athletic hunter or warrior and the attempts of the villagers to free themselves.[33] Among the Eskimo [34] a group of brothers often take the place of the village bully. Among both groups of people who live in small settlements, without any hard and fast political organization, the fear of the strongest person plays an important rôle, no matter whether his power is founded on bodily strength or on supposed supernatural qualities. The story uses generally a weak, despised boy as savior of the community. Although tales of overbearing chiefs do occur among the Indians, they are not by any means a predominant type.

The principal theme of the Indians of British Columbia,[35] whose thoughts are almost entirely taken up by the wish to obtain rank and high position in their community, is the tale of a poor man who attains high position, or that of the struggles between two chiefs who try to outdo each other in feats that will increase their social standing. Among the Blackfoot [36] the principal theme is the acquisition of ceremonies, possession and practice of which is a most important element in their lives.

The differences of cultural life also influence the form of the narrative, because the incidents are tied together in different ways. The same motive recurs repeatedly in the tales of primitive people, so that a large mass of material collected from the same tribe is liable to be very monotonous, and after a certain point has been reached we obtain only new variants of old themes.

Music. We have discussed the phenomena of rhythm in connection with song. It remains to describe the general characteristics of melody, polyphony, and musical instruments.

The all-important element of music is tonality, the use of fixed intervals that may be transposed from one point of the tone series to another and which are always recognized as equivalent. There is a certain similarity between the tonality of music and the tonality of language. Many languages, like Chinese, many African, and many American languages, give to their vowels or to syllabic consonants different values according to their pitch. This is not absolutely fixed, but the relative intervals between tones are maintained. Dr. George Herzog [37] has shown that parts of the songs of the Navajo and West Africans, whose languages have pitch, are musical renderings of the natural pitch of the spoken phrases. That means that the tones are held more constant and the changes of absolute pitch that occur in conversation are avoided. On this basis the Africans have developed a drum language in which the different tones produced by striking the middle or rim of the drum imitate the pitch-sequence and rhythm of words. These are understood. In these cases the melody is derived from the melody of speech. Herbert Spencer suggests that this is the origin of all melody, but it seems doubtful whether it explains the origin of the consistent tonality of a song which is not characteristic of fluent speech in which intervals and absolute pitch vary with emotional tone. This theory would also presuppose either that by origin all languages had fixed pitch, or that all music originated among a people that had pitch language. Since the origin of pitch is often secondary we can hardly assume that it was a trait common to all the earliest languages. Carl Stumpf [38] is of the opinion that the sustained cry has been the most important element in the development of music, because it used fixed intervals and stable tones. Whatever the origin of music may have been, we must recognize the existence of fixed intervals and transponibility as fundamental requirements of all music.

Many primitive tribes have no musical instruments except those used for expressing rhythm. The tonality is carried exclusively by the human voice. Sometimes the range of the melodies is a few tones, as among the Chukchee; sometimes it extends over more than an octave.

The selection of tones used presents difficult problems. Ordinarily, to the untrained ear, the octave appears as a single tone and the tones of the song stand in definite relation to the octave. The octave may be divided according to overtones in a harmonic series, or it may be subdivided in equidistant intervals. The fifth is found often as a harmonic interval, but a neutral third which divides the fifth in two equal parts may also be observed. On account of the uncertainty of intonation of the untrained singer and the lack of exactly constructed instruments among primitive people, it is difficult to decide what they want to sing, particularly since intervals vary with the degree of emotional excitement of the singers. Notwithstanding these uncertainties, the definite tonal character of each musical phrase stands out distinctly.

The musical systems of eastern Asia prove that our system is not by any means the only possible one. The Javanese, for instance, divide their octave into five, the Siamese into seven, equidistant steps,[39] while we have made an adjustment of the harmonic scale by dividing the octave into twelve equal intervals.

The universal use of instruments that accent rhythm has been mentioned. While rhythm may be indicated by hand-clapping or stamping, there are commonly instruments in use that give a fuller sound. These may be simply sticks with which resounding objects, like boards, are beaten. More complex are drums — wooden boxes, or much more commonly hoops or hollow cylinders, covered on one or both sides with a drumhead of skin; notched sticks which are pulled over the edges of hollow vessels, producing a rasping sound; rattles of varying form, either hollow receptacles containing pebbles or seeds which when shaken produce a rattling sound, or objects like loose deer hoofs which are shaken and produce sounds when striking one another. Drums give different tones according to the way they are struck and the tension of the skins. Where skins are used, the drums are no longer employed solely for marking rhythm, but support melody. This is still more the case in those drums that consist of a hollowed log one side of which has a long slit into which two tongues of different lengths are inserted. When struck they produce different tones. The gongs of southern Asia and the xylophone of Africa are also percussion instruments, but they are accurately tuned and are used not only for marking rhythm but also for melodic purposes. A curious intermediate position is occupied by an instrument used in New Ireland, consisting of a block of wood, one side of which is carefully leveled and divided by deep curved notches into a number of sections. By rubbing over these or striking them different tones are produced (see Fig. 46, p. 248).

Wind instruments are not as widely distributed as percussion instruments. Their simplest forms are probably calls used by the hunter and warrior. Others are employed for ceremonial purposes. Large shells, horns of animals, and hollowed tusks are used. These have only a single tone. When made of wood, lip pipes and reed pipes are found. More complicated are flutes and flageolets provided with stops which allow the playing of melodies. The ordinary forms are similar to our instruments, but others, blown with the nose, occur in the Pacific island area. In the Pandean pipe of Asia, Europe, the Pacific islands, and South America a number of pipes, each of one tone, are tied together in a line so that they can be blown in any desired order.

Before the advent of the Europeans in America, string instruments were entirely confined to the Old World. Since the tone of the vibrating string is weak, all these instruments are provided with a resonance chamber. This invention does not belong to string instruments exclusively, for it is also inherent in the construction of cylindrical and box drums and in the so-called water drums, in which the body of the drum is partly immersed in water. It is also used with the xylophone.

The simplest string instrument is the musical bow. In some forms a broadened part of the string is held in front of the mouth, which serves as a resonance chamber; * in others a hollow receptacle, such as a gourd, is attached to the middle of the bow stave. The string is pulled or struck with one hand, and its length is varied with the other. The harp and lyre are still widely distributed in Africa.† A hybrid between xylophone and string instruments is the African zanza, which consists of iron strips of varying length stretched over a resonance box provided with a bridge. These are pulled at their ends like strings. Instruments of the type of our violin do not seem to occur among primitive people.

With the use of instruments capable of producing melodies we find also instrumental music without song, or accompanying song. Thus, the American Indian plays tunes on his flageolet. Polyphony received a strong stimulus by the development of instrumental music. Polyphonous singing has already been referred to.

Dance. Almost all singing is accompanied by movements of the body. The clapping of hands and stamping of feet accentuate the rhythm, but other parts of the body are in motion too. Trunk and head sway, and arms are swung even without hand-clapping; in short, simple dance movements are a common accompaniment of song. In every region they have their own style. The Eskimo drummer holds his drum at about the height of his head and bends the body from side to side. Among some tribes the singer dances; often his singing accompanies the dance of others. On the Northwest Coast of America the singers sit still and beat time while one or a few individuals dance; in certain dances of the Pueblo Indians a chorus sings and the dance is often performed by large groups moving in formation. The style of body movement is also typical for each area. Polynesian singers are seated and swing their bodies; Northwest Coast Indians dance bending their knees with each step and holding their palms forward and trembling at about the height of the head. A characterization of styles of dancing and a description of their distribution cannot be given, because too little is known about this subject.[40] Joint dances of the two sexes are rare, and dancers do not often so move that their bodies are in close contact.

Symbolic or descriptive movements akin to gestures accompanying speech appear with dance movements. Thus the chorus of the Indians of the Pueblo of Laguna in New Mexico sing:

* See Figure 47, page 248.   † See Figure 48, page 249.

In the east rises the sun youth.
Here westward he moves with life and vegetation,
Carrying them in his basket while walking along.

When this song is sung the dancers are drawn up in formation and perform their steps and movements in rhythmic accord with the song. The singers stand in a close group around the drummer and accompany their song with gestures. First they face west and move a step forward. The word "vegetation" is expressed by pushing the hands alternately upward, symbolizing the growing corn. The word "basket" is designated by describing a wide circle with both hands and bringing them together in front of the body. "Walking" is indicated by stretching the hands out forward in front of the body and waving them up and down.

The Kwakiutl sing as follows:

I am going around the world eating everywhere with the Cannibal spirit.
I went to the center of the world; the Cannibal spirit is crying "food."

The singers beat time, but the dancer accompanies the song with descriptive movements. With the words "I am going," the arms are stretched out to one side; with "around the world," they swing around in a wide circle; with "I," the shoulders are brought alternately forward and backward; with "eating everywhere," the right hand is stretched far out as though taking food, and then brought to the mouth while the left describes a wide circle indicating "everywhere"; with "Cannibal spirit," both hands are bent inward and the finger tips are moved toward the mouth. In the second line, after making the sign indicating the Cannibal spirit, the arms are stretched far back, palms down, and the head is lowered. This is the position of the Cannibal when he utters his terrifying cry "ham" (that is, "food"). When the words "the center of the world" are sung, the dancer looks at the middle of the rear of the house in the attitude of the Cannibal, the rear of the house symbolizing the center of the world.

The last example shows the close association between dance and pantomime. As the cannibal dancer represents by movements the ideas that are expressed in the song, so the artistic aim of the performance is often the mimic representation of some impressive experience or event. To this class belong the numerous examples of animal dances. In New Guinea a dance has been observed imitating the wooing of a hen by a rooster, including the battle between two rival roosters. The Indians of the Southwest impersonate in their dances flying eagles. The Fijians are even said to have performed a group dance imitating the surf of the ocean. In still other cases the dance movements become subordinate to the pantomimic representation. Thus the Indians of British Columbia represent the contents of their myths and family histories. An artificial whale made of wood may be seen to rise from the water and to bring back the ancestor who has had a supernatural experience at the bottom of the sea. The impressiveness of mimic dances is increased by the use of imitative masks and dresses.

On account of the intense emotional value of music and dance they enter into all those social situations which imply heightened effects, and in their turn they call forth intense emotional reaction. Thus it is that war and religion offer numerous situations which are accompanied by music and dance, which are in part an expression of the excitement inherent in the situation, in part a means of exciting the passions. It would be an error to assume that the sources of music and dance must be looked for in these situations. It seems more likely that they share with other ethnic phenomena, particularly religion, the tendency to associate themselves with all those activities that give rise to emotional states similar to those of which they themselves are expressions.

FOOTNOTES

1. Boas, F., *Tsimshian Mythology*, Annual Report of the Bureau of American Ethnology, vol. 31 (1916), pp. 225 ff.
2. Boas, F., *Keresan Texts*, Publications of the American Ethnological Society, vol. 8, Part I (1928), pp. 82 ff.; Benedict, R., *Tales of the Cochiti Indians*, Bulletin of the Bureau of American Ethnology, vol. 98 (1931), pp. 49 ff.
3. Ker, A., *Papuan Fairy Tales* (London, 1910), p. 106.
4. Meier, P. J., *Mythen und Erzählungen der Küstenbewohner der Gazelle-Halbinsel* (Münster, 1909), p. 262.
5. Boas, F., "Eskimo Tales and Songs," *Journal of American Folk-Lore*, vol. 7 (1894), p. 45.
6. See for instance, Boas, F., *Keresan Texts, op. cit.*, Part II (1925), pp. 342, 343.
7. Boas, F., *The Social Organization and the Secret Societies of the Kwakiutl Indians*, Report of the United States National Museum for 1895 (1897).
8. *Fornander Collection of Hawaiian Antiquities and Folk-lore*, Memoirs of the Bernice P. Bishop Museum, vol. 4, Part II (Honolulu, 1917), p. 371.
9. Jones, W., *Fox Texts*, Publications of the American Ethnological Society, vol. 1 (Leyden, 1907), p. 337.
10. Bücher, K., *Arbeit und Rhythmus* (Leipzig, 1909).

11. Wundt, W., *Völkerpsychologie*, vol. 3 (Leipzig, 1919), p. 507.
12. Densmore, F., *Teton Sioux Music*, Bulletin of the Bureau of American Ethnology, vol. 61 (1918), p. 162.
13. Beckwith, M. W., *The Hawaiian Romance of Laieikawai*, Annual Report of the Bureau of American Ethnology, vol. 33 (1919), p. 403.
14. Boas, F., *The Social Organization and the Secret Societies of the Kwakiutl Indians*, p. 346.
15. Doke, C. M., *Lamba Folk-Lore*, Memoirs of the American Folk-Lore Society, vol. 20 (1927), p. 357.
16. *Ibid.*, p. 403.
17. Gutmann, B., *Volksbuch der Wadschagga* (Leipzig, 1914), p. 244.
18. Boas, F., *Tsimshian Mythology*, pp. 567 ff.
19. Cronise, F., and Ward, H., *Cunnie Rabbit, Mr. Spider and Other Beef* (1903); Tremearne, A. J. N., *Hausa Superstitions and Customs* (London, 1913).
20. Skeat, W., *Fables and Folk Tales from an Eastern Forest* (Cambridge, 1904).
21. Dähnhardt, O., *Natursagen*, vol. 4 (Leipzig, 1912), pp. 217 ff.
22. Gatschet, A. S., *A Migration Legend of the Creeks* (1884), pp. 214 ff.
23. Cushing, F. H., *Outlines of Zuñi Creation Myths*, Annual Report of the Bureau of Ethnology, vol. 13 (1896), pp. 321 ff.
24. Roscoe, J., *The Baganda* (London, 1911), pp. 460 ff.
25. Boas, F., *The Central Eskimo*, Annual Report of the Bureau of (American) Ethnology, vol. 6 (1888), p. 615.
26. Boas, F., "Notes and Queries," *Journal of American Folk-Lore*, vol. 39 (1926), p. 486.
27. Grimm, J., *Deutsche Mythologie* (Berlin, 1875–78).
28. Gomme, G. L., *Folklore as an Historical Science* (London, 1908).
29. Boas, F., *Tsimshian Mythology*, pp. 393 ff.; and *Kwakiutl Culture as Reflected in Mythology*, Memoirs of the American Folk-Lore Society, vol. 28 (1935).
30. Benedict, R., *Concept of the Guardian Spirit in North America*, Memoirs of the American Anthropological Association, no. 29 (1923).
31. Bogoras, W., *The Chukchee*, Jesup Expedition, vol. 7 (1904–09), p. 418.
32. Parsons, E. C., "Nativity Myth at Laguna and Zuñi," *Journal of American Folk-Lore*, vol. 31 (1918), pp. 258 ff.
33. Bogoras, W., *op. cit.*
34. Rink, H., *Tales and Traditions of the Eskimo* (London, 1875).
35. Boas, F., *Tsimshian Mythology;* and *Kwakiutl Texts*, Jesup Expedition, vol. 3 (1902–05).
36. Wissler, C., and Duvall, D. C., *Mythology of the Blackfoot Indians*, Anthropological Papers of the American Museum of Natural History, vol. 2 (1909), pp. 1 ff.
37. Herzog, G., "Speech-Melody and Primitive Music," *The Musical Quarterly*, vol. 20, no. 4 (1934).
38. Stumpf, C., *Die Anfänge der Musik* (Leipzig, 1911).
39. Stumpf, C., "Tonsystem und Musik der Siamesen," *Abhandlungen zur vergleichenden Musikwissenschaft*, vol. 1 (1922), pp. 127 ff.
40. An interesting attempt to analyze the dance steps of American Indians, principally Pueblo, has been made by Bessie Evans and May G. Evans, *American Indian Dance Steps* (1931).

CHAPTER XIII

MYTHOLOGY AND FOLKLORE

FRANZ BOAS

Myth and folk tale. It is impossible to draw a sharp line between myths and folk tales, because the same tales which occur as myths appear also in the form of folk tales. If we define myths as tales that give an interpretation of natural phenomena, we are confronted with the difficulty that a tale may conform with this definition in one case, while in another it may be a purely human tale, sometimes even void of wonderful elements. Thus the same tale would at one time be classed as a myth, and at another time as a folk tale.

If we take as the basis of our definition the personification of animals, plants, heavenly bodies, and natural phenomena, another difficulty arises, for such personifications appear also in folk tales that are purely imaginative or even considered as true events that have happened to contemporaries.

The reference to religious ideas and rituals does not constitute a useful criterion either, for these may enter into myths as well as into folk tales relating to recent occurrences.

Mythological concepts. Definition of mythological concepts is much easier than definition of mythological tales. Mythological concepts are the fundamental views of the constitution of the world and of its origin. These enter into tales relating to incidents in the lives of mythical beings, and into folk tales referring to the exploits and sufferings of our contemporaries, often of known individuals. Thus the African tells of encounters with ancestral ghosts and of the misdeeds of witches; the Koryak shaman recounts his fights with evil spirits; the European relates the incidents of the lives of the saints and dealings with the devil; the Oriental listens to stories of demons controlled by magic rings, and the American Indian to visits to the land of the ghosts. In all these legends the mythological concepts appear as part and parcel of the tales.[1]

It is fairly clear that stories are unhesitatingly classed as myths if they account for the origin of the world and if they may be said to have happened in a mythical period, different from the one in which we live now. The difference is clearly recognized by many tribes, like the North American Indians, the Andaman Islanders, and the Australians.

Origin of tales. In a treatment of tales the question whether they are myths or folk tales may be disregarded. The problem relates rather to the elucidation of the history and origin of tales, and to the question how and to what extent mythical concepts become the principal subject of tales. The significance of Hesiod's account of the history of the gods is obviously different from that of the deeds and sufferings of Odysseus.

We shall first of all consider the question of the origin of tales. In an inquiry for which no record of past times is available we must try to establish the processes that are active at the present time and see whether they may help us in an attempt to reconstruct the past. There is no reason for assuming that the same processes should not have been active in earlier times, at least as long as the types of culture conformed to the standards of modern primitive tribes. This has certainly been the case ever since the later part of the Paleolithic period, for the remains of modern primitives found after thousands of years would conform strictly to the level indicated by the remains of these early times.

An analysis of folk tales shows that they deal almost throughout with events that may occur in human society, with human passions, virtues, and vices. Sometimes the events are quite plausible, but more often they are fantastic and of such a character that they cannot have had their origin in human experience, but may be understood as the results of the play of imagination with everyday experience. The products of imagination are not simply reproductions of sense-experiences, although they are built of them. They are the result of daydreams that play with them, and of their emotional tone. We are filled with an ardent desire, and our imagination lets us see our wish fulfilled, no matter how impossible it may be. An event strikes us with wonder, and in our imagination the wonderful elements will be exaggerated. We are threatened with danger, and the cause of danger may appear to us endowed with extraordinary powers. In all these situations the actual experience may be exaggerated or turned into its opposite, and the impossible will be realized.

After the death of a dear friend neither we nor primitive people speculate as to what may have become of his soul; but we feel the ardent desire to undo what has happened, and in the free play of fancy we see the dead come back to life. The slain leader in battle whose dismembered body is found is restored to full vigor. The warrior surrounded by enemies, when all means of retreat are cut off, will wish to pass unseen through the ranks of the foe, and in a strong imagination the wish will become a reality.

Other mythic forms may be understood as exaggerations of experiences. Thus the beauty of form of the human body may transcend the realm of reality. The shining youths with resplendent hair may thus be understood. Deformations of the body also supply the imagination with material. Monstrosities that cannot survive are assumed to live and to become a source of danger. Wrinkles, moles, warts, supernumerary limbs, discolorations, are all elements from which the play of imagination may build its figures.

The very fact that these experiences and situations occur in every human society and that the psychological stimulus for imaginative transformations is present everywhere is sufficient to explain the general similarity of many fantastic figures and happenings in folk tales.

Mythology and folklore cannot be understood solely from the point of view of a primitive philosophy, as the result of speculative thought about the origin and structure of the world and of human life. It is no less an outflow of artistic, more specifically literary activity. The one-sided emphasis laid upon the intimate relation between religion and mythology obscures the imaginative play that is involved in the formation of myths.

Folk tales must be considered as analogous to modern novelistic literature. The attempt which has often been made to refer all of them to phenomena of nature, to the moon [2] or sun,[3] does not take into consideration the actual play of imagination that is common to mankind the world over. It is not necessary to identify a person who is covered with warts with the moon, on account of the suggestive shadows on her surface; or to assume that the cutting up or swallowing of a hero's body represents the waning of the moon. The elaborate theories of psychoanalysis seem also unnecessary for the purpose of explaining the wonderful elements of folk tales or of mythological figures. The free play of imagination operating with everyday experiences is sufficient to account for their origin. The vocabulary and grammar of languages of primitive tribes possess forms that express "if I could," "if I were," "if this had not happened," and others that can be understood only as the expression of imaginative happenings. Equally clear evidence of the importance of imaginative thought are the numerous similes and metaphorical expressions in the languages of primitive tribes. There is no need to search for the origin of metaphor [4] when actually the vocabulary of every language proves that the process of restriction, expansion, and transfer of meaning is constantly at work shaping and reshaping the significance of word symbols. Every transfer of meaning may become the stimulus for metaphoric use, if it is not itself a metaphor.

For these reasons it does not seem necessary to search in nature for prototypes of beings endowed with extraordinary qualities and of events that are exaggerations or distortions of what happens in everyday life. These are material from which tales and many mythological concepts are built.

Dissemination of tales. A study of tales as they are now found gives very slight evidence of the ability of man to invent new motives. It seems rather that his imagination is restricted by the current forms of tales.

The similarity of tales found in many parts of the world has given rise to prolonged discussion. While Tylor,[5] Brinton,[6] and other early investigators were inclined to see in these correspondences evidence of a psychic unity of mankind, and assumed that each one of the analogous stories had an independent origin wherever told, careful investigation of the distribution and recent spread of tales has proved that in most cases the occurrence of similar tales is due to dissemination. This has been shown most satisfactorily for European and Asiatic folk tales and for those of North America. The place of origin of each tale cannot be ascertained, but the lines along which it traveled may be traced. In Europe and Asia literature was a powerful means of spreading tales; in America the large continuous areas of distribution of certain tales are ample evidence of their common origin.[7] This evidence is corroborated by the spread of European tales imported into the continent after the arrival of the Spaniards and Portuguese.[8] French stories [9] are widely known among the Indian tribes of North America. Spanish tales are found even in the remote, unexplored forests of the Amazon basin.[10]

A few complex stories consisting of a sequence of unrelated elements have an exceedingly wide distribution. Perhaps the most convincing one of these is that of the Magic Flight, the outstanding elements of which are the flight from an ogre, and objects thrown back over the shoulder forming obstacles — a stone which becomes a mountain; a comb which becomes a thicket; oil which becomes a body of water The tale is known from the Atlantic border of Europe eastward over Asia and North America, reaching the Atlantic coast in Greenland.[11] It is hardly conceivable that such a group of unrelated incidents should arise independently in regions far apart. The continuous area over which the tale is distributed also indicates that it was carried from people to people, from tribe to tribe. Thus it is possible to trace with a high degree of probability the historically determined distribution of complex tales.

Origin of elements of tales. The same method cannot be pursued when irregularly distributed elements of tales are concerned. Their occurrence has been used to prove that they must arise not only from the similar working of the mind among all races, but from a deep-seated tendency to express the ever-recurring phenomena of nature in the same imaginative terms. It is true that the moon appears the same, that she waxes and wanes all over the world, but this does not prove that every tale of a disfigured face or of growth and decline, of being swallowed up or killed and being reborn, must refer to the moon, for there are endless other experiences in human life that suggest the same group of ideas. Nor is it necessary to claim that every ferocious snake must be the lightning, and that every shining youth must be the sun.

One of the widely distributed elements is that of the swallowed person or animal who regains freedom and, as a frequent incident, loses his hair by the heat in the body of the swallowing monster.[12] It is familiar to us from the stories of Jonah and the Leviathan and of our Tom Thumb. The actual swallowing of a whole animal may be observed in the feeding habits of snakes. The birth of young animals suggests the possibility of naked living beings coming out of the body of a larger animal. Added to this are the curious feelings of bodies moving in the stomach and intestines in cases of indigestion, and the noises produced by gases that lead to the idea of animals infesting the body, of which the patient ultimately rids himself. Such observations may well have stimulated the imagination and given rise to the theme of swallowed animals, without having resort to the far-fetched idea that in every case this animal must be the moon. It is not claimed that this must be the only origin of the tale. It is merely intended to show that there are human experiences that furnish all the elements. It is also interesting to note that notwithstanding the accurate knowledge of the anatomy of animals the most fanciful distortions appear. The swallowed animal reaches up to the heart and cuts it off. It slides straight through the alimentary canal of the monster — like the piece of bacon attached by Münchhausen to a fishline which was swallowed by one duck after another. The monster is so huge that whole tribes camp in its stomach, and its breath is so strong that it inhales whatever approaches it.

Another example of widely and irregularly distributed incidents is the ascent to heaven by means of a chain of arrows. Visits to the skyland are probably universal, but the methods of ascent differ. Of course, nobody has ever seen a chain of arrows that can be climbed, but it seems entirely within the reach of imagination to extend the the game of hitting the notch of an arrow with a second one to develop an idea of this kind. It cannot be denied that the rays of the sun shining through the clouds in a moist atmosphere may have helped to develop the idea.

It does not seem plausible that all incidents of the class here referred to are immediate reflexes of natural phenomena that suggested the tales, for those explainable as a play of imagination with the events of human life are far too numerous. It seems most likely that the imagination of the storytellers transferred these elements to the anthropomorphized natural phenomena which were thus drawn into the circle of human society.

After a mythology of this kind had developed and in course of time lost its vigor and meaning, it may well have disintegrated again and become the subject matter of folk tales. Thus Grimm derived the story of the Sleeping Beauty surrounded by an impenetrable hedge of thorns from the fire surrounding the rock of the sleeping Valkyrie.[13]

Character of mythological concepts. The most important characteristic of mythological concepts is personification. It is not difficult to understand why animals should be personified, for their behavior resembles in many ways that of man. Their actions are easily understood as motivated by hunger, fear, anger, and love. When their strength is superior to that of man and he succumbs to their attack, it is proof of their greater power that is pitted against him.

These personified animals appear everywhere in tales. In striking contrast to the human actors, they are sharply characterized according to their observed habits. The cunning fox and the greedy, stupid wolf of European folk tales, the monkey of India, the coyote, raven, and rabbit of North America, the jaguar of South America, the turtle and spider of Africa, are types whose mental characteristics reappear in every tale. The habits of the species are concentrated in one individual. Furthermore, what happened to the one representative individual has determined the fate of all the members of the species. When in the European tale the cat and dog quarrel, this brings about eternal enmity between the two species [14]; when the bear pulls off his tail trying to free it from the hold of the ice, it accounts for the shortness of the tails of all bears.[15] Stories of this kind are often told for entertainment and are not taken seriously, while at other times they are believed to account for the actual conditions of the world. Still more frequently the observed fact is given as proof of the truth of the tale.

Actually the relation between tale and explanatory element is very loose. Many examples show that the same tale appears with a great variety of explanatory elements and that the tale has its independent existence without any attached explanatory element. Waterman has given a list of these for North America.[16] The elements of mythological concepts are thoughts suggested by the contents of the preëxisting tale, and therefore depend upon its literary interest. It is not the story that has been added to the observation, but the observation that has been attached to the story on account of its appropriateness.

Explanatory tales of this kind do not refer to the characteristics of animals alone. Sometimes traits of the human body or phenomena of nature are explained in the same way. Thus the occurrence of limping or of defects in bodily proportions is explained by the tale that when a mass of skeletons were revived the bones of different individuals were confused [17]; or it is said that wood burns because an animal running away with fire hid it in wood.[18]

The extension of the belief that will power exists in natural phenomena that interfere in the life of man is also perfectly intelligible. Destructive floods, gales, thunder storms, rock slides, are not considered as due to natural causes, but are believed to be endowed with the will to destroy. All moving objects that have any influence upon human life are thus easily viewed as endowed with human passions and human will power. Sun, moon, stars, clouds, are included in this group. If the phenomena of nature are once endowed with human qualities, it is not hard to understand why imagination should not also endow them with human form. The substitution of mythical concepts for natural phenomena is illustrated by many examples.

Thunder is produced by the flapping of the wings, lightning by the opening of the eyes of the thunderbird; the sun is the resplendent nose ornament of the sun god; dangerous whirlpools are the home of sea monsters; spring is due to the victory of the south wind over the north wind; the earth is the mother of all vegetation or of all life, the sky the father; rivers are living persons; the rainbow carries water from the earth up to the sky. Wundt has discussed this process of personification of nature in his work on mythology.[19] Since the phenomena of nature were considered as anthropomorphic it came about easily that novelistic tales were transferred to the domain of mythological beings.

Myths. The mythological beings preëxisted the modern order of the world. They may still appear as actors in tales relating to the modern world, but their great feats belong to a mythological period.

It would not be fair to assume that the myths dealing with the origin of the world or of the gift of arts and ceremonials to mankind were the result of a light play of imagination, as we suppose the rather insignificant animal tales to have been. The importance of the subject matter and the seriousness with which they are treated suggest that they are the result of thought about the origin of the world and of wonder about cultural achievements and the meaning of sacred rites. The only causality known in an anthropomorphic world is the one prevailing in human society, and thus it comes about that the incidents of human life that result in achievements are transferred to the mythical beings. As man takes by force or fraud from his fellows a coveted possession, so the mythical beings overcome others and take away from them valued possessions which thus become their property and that of mankind conceived as their tribe. In other cases they may freely bestow their gifts upon their people. When offended they punish the offender. As the war leader overcomes enemies and as the fearless hunter destroys dangerous animals, so the mythical characters rid the country of giants and monsters. Like the craftsman who fashions his tools and works of art, they create man and animals or useful and beautiful objects. As the wise man plans for the future, so the mythical being plans and his thoughts become reality.

A detailed study of mythologies shows clearly that, viewed from this angle, they reflect in detail the cultures of which they form part. The mythical beings of the Eskimo are Eskimo; those of the Australians, Australians. The chiefs of the Polynesians have their counterpart in their deities; the gods of the Dahomeans are Dahomeans; and the gods on Olympus lead the life of Greek royalty.

One trait of the animal tale has been carried over almost consistently into mythology: the idea that what happened once has determined the fate of the world. Because a certain person died and it was decreed that he should not rise again, all men must die and remain dead, although before this death was unknown [20]; because the sun at one time was very hot, the high mountains are rocky and full of cracks.[21] We may recognize the same thought in idealized form in the story of Adam and Eve. Because they disobeyed the order not to eat of the tree of knowledge all mankind is punished with them. The individual remains the representative of the species or society to which he belongs and is identified with it.

Tales referring to events that result in permanent changes are more easily understood. The islands fished up from the deep by the Polynesian hero Maui are still there [22]; the rivers into which West Africans were transformed are still running [23]; the hunters who were wafted up to the sky and became stars may still be seen.[24]

The formation of myths must be so understood that the imagination applied human experiences to mythological times and then, by a reversion of order, made the mythical time the pattern on which the world and life were shaped. When in Semitic mythology God created the world, the whole world as it is now preëxisted in his thought, and the creation was a process of reobjectivation of the thoughts representing man's knowledge of the world.

The same attitude may be observed in many mythological tales which explain customs, particularly rituals. According to the tales, the customs or rituals were given to man by mythological beings who ordered the observance of a taboo or other custom, or who allowed the mortal visitor to see a ritual.[25] The uniformity of many such rituals over large areas and the diversity of mythological explanations show clearly that the ritual itself is the stimulus for the formation of the myth. As in the Semitic creation the known world was subjectivized as the thought of God and then reobjectivated, so the known ritual was transferred to a mythical world and explained as revealed to a visitor. The ritual existed, and the tale originated from the desire to account for it.

On account of the character of its origin the mythology of many primitive tribes consists of disconnected, often of contradictory, tales. Thus among the Eskimo the sun and moon are brother and sister [26];

but at the same time in another tale the moon is a house.[27] Among the Tsimshian of British Columbia the Sun was kept in a box and liberated by the Raven,[28] but he is also a man wearing a flaming mask.[29] These contradictions are not necessarily felt as incongruous. They may be held as true by different individuals in the tribe, or the contradiction may never rise into consciousness.

The forms of mythologies show quite consistently that systematization goes hand in hand with greater systematization of cultural life. Where political or religious organization is highly integrated, we are likely to find also integration of mythological concepts that correspond to the types of organization found in human society. The converse is even more true. When the order of social life is loose, when instead of a firm integration of social life a loose organization prevails, the mythological world corresponds to these conditions and the mythology is full of contradictions.

Many tribes have social divisions which are analogous in their functions but sharply set off from one another. Quite commonly these divisions have myths which though specifically distinct are expressions of the same fundamental concepts and of analogous type. Examples of this kind are the tales of the totemic ancestors of the Australian Arunta,[30] who were cut out of preëxisting mythological animals and who later disappeared underground; or the origin myths of the Kwakiutl Indians, who derive their family lines from beings that came down from the sky or up from the sea in the form of animals that took off their dresses and became men.[31] Identical mythological concepts appear also in the Kaliths of the Pelew Islands [32] and in the ritualistic origin tales of the Blackfoot,[33] although neither of these belongs to the mythical period. In these cases certain groups of mythological concepts are brought into order. The formal agreement of such classes of tales corresponds to a general principle, for if one social group is characterized by certain features, all others of the same kind have analogous features. If one is named, all are named; if one has certain insignia or taboos, others will be characterized also by insignia or taboos. If one has certain social duties, others are likely to have other duties.

Effect of individual thought upon mythology. There are, however, higher levels of mythology in which the mass of mythological concepts is worked into a more harmonious unit. It would seem that this happens particularly wherever a small group of people devote much thought to ritual and mythology and where for this reason a systematization of concepts, sometimes also of tales, develops. In many cases the results of such speculation take on the form of esoteric knowledge guarded by a few individuals, priests or chiefs, whichever the case may be. In this manner the systematic mythologies owned by the various families of the Bella Coola [34] developed out of the unorganized mass of myths and tales of British Columbia; in this way must have grown up the mythologies of Polynesia — perhaps under the influence of the highly developed mythologies of south-eastern Asia.

An example of this kind are the tales of the Andaman Islanders. Certain men are believed to have special knowledge as to the spirits and as to the magical efficacy of remedies for sickness. These are the authorities on the legendary lore of the Andamanese.[35] Although the tales are not in any way esoteric, only certain men are regarded as having authority to speak, and in telling and retelling the tales they modify them even in important traits. It is intelligible that, if some of these men are of philosophic mind, they may adapt the current tales to phenomena of nature and reinterpret them. This is analogous to the processes of reinterpretation which are common in the development of the symbolic significance of art designs and of rituals. If Radcliffe-Brown's interpretations may be accepted, many tales have been centered around two deities representing the southwest and northeast monsoons.

Mythologies of these types give us the impression of being the results of philosophic thought coupled with deep emotion. They are found particularly among tribes in which a mythology of sacred character is not the property of the whole group but is in the jealously guarded keeping of a small group of priests, chiefs, or other guardians; in other words, they occur where we find an esoteric and an exoteric mythology. There is abundant proof showing that esoteric mythologies have arisen on the basis of widespread concepts.

An excellent example is furnished by the family traditions of the Bella Coola of British Columbia, which are considered the exclusive sacred property of the family. The material of which these traditions consist is the same as that of neighboring tribes. Among the Kwakiutl, some distance to the south, the year is divided into a secular and a sacred season, but there is no myth connected with them. The Bella Coola say that the keepers of the sacred ceremonial live beyond the ocean and bring it at a certain time each year to this world. At the end of the season they depart with it. Among the

Kwakiutl, animals are said to live in separate villages inland and in the sea. Among the nearer neighbors of the Bella Coola, in Rivers Inlet, all animals and plants are said to reside in one house where they perform sacred ceremonies. Among the Bella Coola this house has been lifted to the sky, and the beings living in it have assumed the functions of gods that rule over the destinies and cultural activities of man.

Foreign elements appear also in the myths connected with sacred rituals. The myth accounting for the cannibal ceremony of the tribes just referred to is a good example.[36] It is not an esoteric myth, but is referred to as the origin of the ceremonials. The tale contains the well-known theme of the Magic Flight, which is circumpolar in its distribution and has been woven into the complex.

Among the Navajo the complete knowledge of an origin myth must be acquired by long training. There are only a few whom the keepers of the traditions consider competent to be taught. The material of which the whole tradition is composed is known, but the sequence and symbolic significance belong only to those who have been taught.

In general it may be said that the patterns of ritualistic behavior are old. Their mythological explanation is fitted to the ritual according to the patterns of tribal thought. There has been frequent borrowing of myths and also of sacred rites which have been assimilated according to local conditions. Examples are the North American Sun Dance,[37] which has fundamentally the same form everywhere, but varied explanations; the various forms of the Ghost Dance [38] and the Mescal ceremonials,[39] which are derived from old elements intermingled with Christian teachings; and the elaborate Melanesian rituals.

Esoteric and exoteric mythology. Esoteric teaching refers to rituals and is often largely based on mythological concepts. Wherever it became the exclusive charge of a small, select group of guardians, opportunity was given for a more or less conscious attempt at systematizing the heterogeneous mass of beliefs and practices current in the tribe. The thoughts of the men charged with the keeping of sacred rites are occupied with questions relating to their form and meaning. It is intelligible that in the course of generations the esoteric knowledge which its guardians had to teach to their successors increased in cohesion. It therefore seems likely that the esoteric doctrine must have been evolved on the foundation of the exoteric knowledge of the tribe and must be considered as a secondary development. It expresses the reaction of selected minds of the community to their general cultural environment. It is their attempt to systematize the ideas that underlie the culture of the community. The more or less strictly esoteric doctrine exerts its influence upon popular belief so that there is a mutual and inextricable interrelation between the two.

The historical investigation of popular antiquities in Europe leads to analogous conclusions. While a romantic love of the early life of a nation assumed naively a spontaneous and autonomous growth of its culture from earliest times, the historical inquiry has shown that "the knowledge of the great, historical intermixtures of cultures in Europe, of the dependence of the popular elements of culture upon the 'high culture,'* as revealed in popular art, costume or in popular poetry and music, superstitions, popular medicine, etc., has shaken our belief in a purely ethnic, 'national' origin of folk culture which was the beginning of the study of folk lore and folk antiquities in almost every European country." [40] As an example of the complex relations between esoteric and exoteric doctrine we may refer to the divination of antiquity, the middle ages, and modern times. The continuity of the ancient tradition and its gradual infiltration into popular belief can be proved.[41] On the other hand, the belief in witches and the elaboration of the ideas underlying the trials of witches require for their understanding not only the traditional transmission of belief but also the current beliefs in witchcraft. The strength of the effect of popular belief upon the cultivated classes may be judged from many examples. One of these is the famous order of Ernst August, Duke of Sachse-Weimar, 1742, who ordered that wooden plates inscribed with a magic formula should be thrown into burning buildings in order to extinguish fire; another, the various magical means by which the priests extinguished fire. The resurgence of palmistry, spiritualism, and astrology at times of particular social stress shows also how readily folk beliefs are taken up by the educated and how they may be organized into systems. There is a constant give and take between the beliefs of the select, leading classes of society and the folk beliefs; and the relation between the guardians of esoteric teachings to current beliefs must be conceived in the same way.

For this reason the esoteric teachings of the secret societies of all continents have contents which agree with the popular beliefs although they may differ in tone. In Africa we find systems of mythology

---

* That of the classes in close contact with the technical, scientific, philosophical, and artistic tendencies of the whole continent.

based on ancestor worship. Of this kind are the Yoruban Orisha, the ancestors of every member of the extended family; and the Dahomean Tovodun, the ancestor gods. The complex system of these tribes is in part the result of a conscious coördination of distinct cults for the political purpose of unification of the states, but built on the popular beliefs of the constituent elements.[42] The east Polynesian genealogies are no less built on the popular belief in the divinity of the chiefs. The modern American cults, like the Ghost Dance religion, the Shakers of the Pacific coast, and the Peyote cult are built on ancient tradition mixed with Christian teaching.

Relation of mythology to other aspects of culture. If it is true that myths are built on the experiences of everyday life, we may expect that the dominant cultural interests are reflected in them. The incidents mirror the life of the people and their occupations, and social life may in part be reconstructed from these tales.[43] Only when a rapid change of culture occurs may the tales refer to earlier conditions, as in the fairy tales of Europe, or in the tales of those primitive tribes that are in process of Europeanization.

The influence of cultural life is not restricted to this field but appears also in the manifold forms of cultural concepts. The emphasis upon the space relations among the Pueblo Indians is an example. The four points of the compass, the above and below, are to them of greatest importance, and the mythological world is divided up according to these ideas.[44] The importance of the southwest and northeast winds in the mythology of the Andaman Islanders has been referred to before. The Omaha [45] have a division of sky, the male, and earth, the female. The Winnebago [46] distinguish between the heavens, the sky, earth, the water, and the world under the waters. The Eskimo [47] have one or two worlds above, our world, and one or two worlds below. The Polynesians believe in an order of worlds, one over the other, which are at the same time considered as representing a genealogical sequence.[48] Local concepts of the Kwakiutl [49] are of different character. The ancestors and supernatural beings have their homes in the sky, or in the sea. West, beyond the ocean, is the home of the salmon; upstream along the coast (that is, northward) that of copper; inland the house of the land animals, who live in villages; underground the land of the ghosts.

A similar variety of ideas is found in regard to time concepts. The frequent occurrence of a mythical age preceding the modern age has been mentioned as one of the fundamental characteristics of mythologies. In some cases the line between these two ages is not sharply drawn. This is particularly true in Africa. The idea is clearly developed in the highly organized states of West Africa. Other tribes, like the Bafiote,[50] Pangwe,[51] Bushongo,[52] and Barotse tell of a deity Nsambi, Chembe, or Nyambe, as he is called among the various tribes, who lived on earth but retired from mankind on account of their importunities. The Bafiote follow this with a story of an ancestor who brought the fire and, migrating with his children, gave fertility to the earth wherever he went. Many of the innumerable African animal stories can hardly be considered as mythical, but are analogous to the European animal tales. Others, like the widespread African tale of the origin of death [53] due to the slowness of the chameleon or some other animal who was sent to announce that man should be immortal but was overtaken by the lizard who brought the opposite message, are of a more serious character, being based on actions of a deity and belonging more or less clearly to a mythological period. At the same time the high development of ancestor worship which transforms the immediate ancestors into mythical beings [54] disturbs the concept of a mythical period. In North America we find both the concepts of a mythical past and that of a future when the mythical beings will return and bring happiness to mankind. Thus it is said that the "Old Man" and Coyote of the Thompson Indians will come back from their retirement and bring back the shades of the Indians.[55]

Each particular mythology has its own character according to the cultural interests of the tribe. In some regions the problem of creation is foremost in the minds of the people, while others do not trouble themselves about this question but assume heaven, earth, sun, and moon as without beginning or end, while they may have thoughts about the creation of man and of animals. Instead of a creation we may hear about transformation of a preëxisting world into its present shape, a work generally achieved by a culture hero who makes the world habitable by killing monsters and by giving man his arts and rituals.

When we find complex tales that are interpreted by the native or may be interpreted by the student as explanations of natural phenomena, it is always necessary to ask whether we are dealing with a preëxisting human story which is symbolically applied to phenomena of nature. The numerous and varying interpretations of the same stories prove that the tendency exists of using stories for the purpose of explaining phenomena of nature.

FOOTNOTES

1. Wundt, W., *Völkerpsychologie* (Leipzig, 1909), vol. 2, Part III, p. 19.
2. Ehrenreich, P., *Die allgemeine Mythologie und ihre ethnologischen Grundlagen* (Leipzig, 1910); Siecke, E., *Mythologische Briefe* (Berlin, 1909).
3. Frobenius, Leo, *Das Zeitalter des Sonnengottes* (Berlin, 1904).
4. Werner, H., *Die Ursprünge der Metapher* (Leipzig, 1919).
5. Tylor, E. B., *Primitive Culture* (1874).
6. Brinton, D. G., *The Myths of the New World* (1896).
7. Boas, F., *Tsimshian Mythology*, Annual Report of the Bureau of American Ethnology, vol. 31 (1916).
8. Espinosa, A. M., "Comparative Notes on New-Mexican and Mexican Spanish Folk-Tales," *Journal of American Folk-Lore*, vol. 27 (1914), p. 211.
9. Teit, James, *Mythology of the Thompson Indians*, Jesup Expedition, vol. 8 (1913), pp. 385 ff.; Thompson, Stith, *Tales of the North American Indians* (1929), pp. 201 ff. See also "Index of the Journal of American Folk-Lore" in Memoirs of the American Folk-Lore Society, vol. 14 (1930), under European Folklore in America.
10. Koch-Grünberg, Th., *Vom Roroima zum Orinoco* (Stuttgart, 1924), vol. 2, pp. 140 ff.
11. Bolte, J., and Polivka, G., *Anmerkungen zu den Kinder- und Hausmärchen der Brüder Grimm*, vol. 2 (Leipzig, 1915), p. 140; Thompson, Stith, *op. cit.*, p. 333, note 205.
12. Tylor, E. B., *Researches into the Early History of Mankind* (3rd ed., 1878), pp. 344 ff.; Thompson, Stith, *op. cit.*, p. 321, notes 158, 159.
13. Bolte, J., and Polivka, G., *op. cit.*, vol. 1 (Leipzig, 1913), p. 441.
14. Dähnhardt, O., *Natursagen* (Leipzig, 1907–12), vol. 4, pp. 103 ff.
15. *Ibid.*, vol. 3, p. 49; vol. 2, p. 251.
16. Waterman, T. T., "The Explanatory Element in the Folk-Tales of the North American Indians," *Journal of American Folk-Lore*, vol. 27 (1914), pp. 41 ff.
17. Boas, F., *Kwakiutl Tales, New Series*, Columbia University Contributions to Anthropology, vol. 26, Part I (1935), p. 3.
18. Thompson, Stith, *op. cit.*, p. 289, note 63.
19. Wundt, W., *Völkerpsychologie* (1905), vol. 2, Part I, pp. 577 ff.
20. Thompson, Stith, *op. cit.*, p. 284, note 51.
21. Boas, F., *Bella Bella Tales*, Memoirs of the American Folk-Lore Society, vol. 25 (1932), p. 27.
22. Dixon, R. B., in *The Mythology of All Races* edited by L. H. Gray (1916), vol. 9, p. 43.
23. Talbot, P. A., *The Peoples of Southern Nigeria* (London, 1926), vol. 2, p. 93.
24. Koch-Grünberg, Th., *op. cit.*, vol. 2, p. 55; Boas, F., *Kwakiutl Tales*, p. 92.
25. Wissler, C., and Duvall, D. C., *Mythology of the Blackfoot Indians*, Anthropological Papers, American Museum of Natural History, vol. 2, Part I (1908), pp. 74 ff.
26. Thompson, Stith, *op. cit.*, p. 273, note 6.

27. Boas, F., *The Central Eskimo*, Annual Report of the Bureau of Ethnology, vol. 6 (1888), p. 598.
28. Boas, F., *Tsimshian Mythology*, p. 641.
29. *Ibid.*, p. 727.
30. Spencer, B., and Gillen, F. J., *The Native Tribes of Central Australia* (1899), pp. 123, 388.
31. Boas, F., *Kwakiutl Culture as Reflected in Mythology*, Memoirs of the American Folk-Lore Society, vol. 28 (1935).
32. Bastian, A., *Allerlei aus Volks- und Menschenkunde* (Berlin, 1888), vol. 1, pp. 1 ff.
33. Wissler, C., and Duvall, D. C., *op. cit.*, pp. 74 ff.
34. Boas, F., *The Mythology of the Bella Coola Indians*, Jesup Expedition, vol. 1 (1898), pp. 26 ff.
35. Radcliffe-Brown, A. R., *The Andaman Islanders* (Cambridge, 1922), p. 186.
36. Boas, F., *Bella Bella Tales*, pp. 46 ff.
37. Spier, Leslie, *The Sun Dance of the Plains Indians*, Anthropological Papers, American Museum of Natural History, vol. 16 (1921), p. 451.
38. Mooney, James, *The Ghost-Dance Religion*, Annual Report of the Bureau of Ethnology, vol. 14, Part 2 (1896).
39. Petrullo, V., *The Diabolic Root* (1934); Radin, P., *The Winnebago Tribe*, Annual Report of the Bureau of American Ethnology, vol. 37 (1923), pp. 388 ff.
40. Haberlandt, A., "Die Volkskunde und ihre Grenzgebiete," *Jahrbuch für historische Volkskunde* (Berlin, 1925), vol. 1, p. 5.
41. See for instance articles "Horoskopie" and "Hydromantik" in *Handwörterbuch des deutschen Aberglaubens*, vol. 4 (Leipzig, 1931–32).
42. Frobenius, Leo, *Atlantis*, vol. 10: "Die atlantische Götterlehre" (Jena, 1926), p. 86; Herskovits, Melville J. and Frances S., *An Outline of Dahomean Religious Beliefs*, Memoirs of the American Anthropological Association, vol. 41 (1933), p. 35.
43. Rink, H., *Tales and Traditions of the Eskimo* (Edinburgh, 1875); Boas, F., *Tsimshian Mythology* and *Kwakiutl Culture as Reflected in Mythology*.
44. Bunzel, R. L., *Introduction to Zuñi Ceremonialism*, Annual Report of the Bureau of American Ethnology, vol. 47 (1932), p. 514; Boas, F., *Keresan Texts*, Publications of the American Ethnological Society, vol. 8 (1928), Part I, p. 283; Dumarest, F. Noël, *Notes on Cochiti, New Mexico*, Memoirs of the American Anthropological Association, vol. 6 (1919), p. 182.
45. Fortune, R. F., *Omaha Secret Societies*, Columbia University Contributions to Anthropology, vol. 14 (1932), p. 13.
46. Radin, P., *op. cit.*, p. 186.
47. Boas, F., *The Central Eskimo*, p. 588.
48. Gill, W. W., *Myths and Songs from the South Pacific* (London, 1876), pp. 1 ff.
49. Boas, F., *Kwakiutl Culture as Reflected in Mythology*, p. 47.
50. Pechuël-Loesche, E., *Volkskunde von Loango* (Stuttgart, 1907), p. 267.
51. Tessman, G., *Die Pangwe* (Berlin, 1913), vol. 2, p. 24.
52. Torday, E., and Joyce, T. A., *Notes ethnographiques sur les peuples communement appelés Bakuba*, Annales du Musée du Congo Belge, Série III, vol. 2 (1910), p. 235.

53. Bleek, W. H. I., and Lloyd, L. C., *Specimens of Bushman Folklore* (London, 1911), p. 57.
54. Junod, H. A., *The Life of a South African Tribe* (2nd ed., London, 1927), vol. 2, p. 371.
55. Teit, James, *Traditions of the Thompson River Indians*, Memoirs of the American Folk-Lore Society, vol. 6 (1898), p. 49.

GENERAL REFERENCES

Boas, F., *Tsimshian Mythology*, Annual Report of the Bureau of American Ethnology, vol. 31 (1916).
Ehrenreich, P., *Allgemeine Mythologie* (Leipzig, 1910).
F.F. Communications (Helsingfors).
Gomme, G. L., *Folklore as an Historical Science* (London, 1908).
Handwörterbuch des deutschen Märchens (Berlin, 1930–   ).
Lang, A., *Myth, Ritual and Religion* (London, 1887).
Wundt, W., *Völkerpsychologie. Mythus und Religion*, vol. 2, Part I (Leipzig, 1905), pp. 527 ff.

CHAPTER XIV

RELIGION

RUTH BENEDICT

There is a fundamental difficulty in the problem of religion that
is not present in the study of other cultural traits. All other social
institutions rise from known bases in animal life, and our problem
is to relate them to their point of departure among the natural
endowments and note the very different forms they have assumed
among different peoples. The social organizations of the world, however diverse, are built on the physical facts of sex, infancy, and the
interdependence of individuals living in groups. Economic complexities are varying organizations of the quest for food and shelter and
of man's need for stability in material things. However small the
original starting points may bulk in the final traits, they are nevertheless of prime importance in their interpretation and integrate
our studies of the institutions that have been built around them.

With religion this is not true. We cannot see the basis of religion
in animal life, and it is by no means obvious upon which of the
specifically human endowments it is built up. All studies of religion
reflect the chaotic disagreement of its students on this point. The
most diverse origins [1] of religion have been proposed. Herbert
Spencer regarded the fundamental datum of religion as respect for
the elder generations of one's family, and derived all its manifestations from an original ancestor worship. Tylor believed that dreams
and visions furnished the experiences from which man organized
the concept of his own soul as separate from his body; this concept
man then extended to the whole material universe, arriving at animism or the belief in spirits. This belief, in Tylor's formulation, was
the inescapable minimum and least common denominator of all religions. Durkheim,[2] on the other hand, believed that religion was
the outcome of crowd excitement. Over against the unexciting daily
routine which he regarded as typically pursued by the individual in
solitude or in small groups, he saw in group ritual, especially that
connected with totemism, the original basis on which all religion has
been elaborated. Religion therefore, he says, is ultimately nothing

more than society. J. W. Hauer [3] has derived religion from mystic experience, which, he argues, is a permanent endowment of a certain proportion of the individuals of any community, and this experience communicates itself with such overwhelming authority that it outranks other experiences and seeks expression through dogma and through rite.

There are innumerable other theories of the origins of religion. One of the most familiar is that popular version which derives religion from fear, and to which Petronius gave the classic expression. It is somewhat the fashion now to derive it from the dissatisfactions of life, and a modified version of Durkheim's social theory of religion is gaining ground,[4] according to which the religious life is the social life at those points at which it is felt most intensely.

According to our emphasis upon one or other of these "origins" of religion we shall regard very different aspects as important or as negligible. The mere fact of their diversity and contradiction is proof of our bewilderment about the essential bases of religion. In no case are any of these origins related to the total complex in the way, for instance, that the physiologically determined food quest is related to economic arrangements.

Methodically it is evident that we need to keep closer to the concrete material of primitive religions, and until we are surer of our ground concern ourselves with their religious categories rather than our own. Fortunately for our purpose, once we turn from theoretical discussions of religion to the concrete data from all parts of the world, there is an amazing unanimity. No observer of even the most alien culture has ever failed to recognize certain aspects of its life as religious and to set them down as such. It is only the closet philosopher afterward who denies religion to the Australians because they have no belief in an all-powerful god [5]; the man in the field never confuses the nature of a nonreligious Crow Indian age-society ceremony with the religious character of their sun dance rites.

The concept of the supernatural. The striking fact about this plain distinction between the religious and the nonreligious in actual ethnographic recording is that it needs so little recasting in its transfer from one society to another. No matter into how exotic a society the traveler has wandered, he still finds the distinction made and in comparatively familiar terms. And it is universal. There is no monograph in existence that does not group a certain class of facts as religion, and there are no records of travelers, provided they are full enough to warrant such a judgment, that do not indicate this category.

• This category, moreover, is commonly made explicit in language. There are several terms that have been widely used in discussions of religion. Three of these, in three different American Indian languages, are *manitou, orenda,* and *wakan,* and they have all the same general range. They are all terms for supernatural power. They do not mean specifically a supernatural person — that is, a god — though *manitou* may be used in this sense without further composition, and *wakan* when it is used with the adjective "great." The Great Wakan is now the Siouan term for the Christian God, just as Great Manitou is the Algonquian term. But these are only specific applications of the terms. *Manitou* by itself has no implication as to whether it is personal or impersonal, but it becomes one or the other according as it is given the personal or impersonal gender of the Algonquian languages. In the sense of a virtue, a property, it is used with inanimate gender; in the sense of spirits, with animate gender. It means either supernatural power in the abstract, or a Supernatural Power. It has other extensions of meaning. A *manitou* means not only a supernatural being but a holy man, a religious practitioner. In ordinary speech the term is constantly recurring, too, in the sense of "wonderful," "surprising." A traveler comes upon fine high-bush cranberries on the prairie and they are *manitou;* Coyote, in the tales, sees a piece of dung he does not recognize, and it is *manitou.* This simple meaning of "wonderful" underlies all its extensions however it is used.

This fundamental meaning of *manitou* is kept even more explicitly in the case of the Siouan term *wakan.* It is used in essentially the same range of meanings as the Algonquian *manitou,* but there are a large number of words in Dakota that have been made with the term *wakan* and that have become fossilized, and the essential meaning of *wakan* in these uses is clearly not "sacred" or "holy," but "wonderful." Thus one of the commonest adverbs is *wakanya,* "wonderfully," used just as we use "very," and *wakan washteya* is their common way of expressing the superlative. The most important things the White man brought were all compounded by the use of this adjective: *Miwakan,* a sword; literally, "wonderful knife." *Shunkakan,* horse; literally, "wonderful dog." *Mazawakan,* a gun; literally "wonderful iron." *Mniwakan,* whisky; literally, "wonderful water."

Not all people have the same range of meanings in their analogous terms. Distinctions are made along various lines. Especially can a distinction be made dividing personal from impersonal, a distinction that is not made in terms like *wakanda* and *manitou*. The Melanesian term *mana* is definitely a term for impersonal power. Objects are regarded as having *mana* in varying degrees, and this *mana* makes them religiously important. But *mana* is not a term that designates supernatural beings.

The fundamental concept that is represented by these native terms is the existence of wonderful power, a voltage with which the universe is believed to be charged. This voltage is present in the whole world in so far as it is considered supernatural, whether it is regarded as animate or inanimate. A stick or a stone is *wakan* and is used as an amulet; a place, and is used as a sacred grove; a formula, and by faithful repetition it will accomplish what is inaccessible to the techniques of everyday routine. Or it may be persons of particular attainments or in particular circumstances that are *wakan:* a seer who can foretell events or bring about wonderful cures, a warrior who has killed an enemy, a menstruating woman, the dead. Different civilizations regard as *wakan* different objects or aspects of life, sometimes in narrowly limited designated objects, sometimes very unsystematically, almost pantheistically. They are at one only in the universal recognition of the existence of this wonderful power. Always, moreover, the manipulation of this wonderful power, and the beliefs that grow out of it, are religion. They are elaborated by specifically religious techniques.

We have tended in our civilization to keep the phraseology of religion and to discard the ideas that, throughout the history of religion, have been associated with it, and this makes it particularly difficult for us to be explicit about the basic attitude on which religion has been built. We have definitely discarded the picture of the universe as operating on two parallel and contrasted sets of causations, but this has been the fundamental premise of religions. Primitive peoples recognized a matter-of-fact universe that obeyed definite causal relations, where work could be checked against achievement, and trial and error were possible. They built good boats and knew the rules for building them; they cooked wholesome food, or knew the rules for making it wholesome. On the other hand, they recognized also more wonderful causations, the techniques of which were not checked against natural laws and the inalienable properties of the objects they dealt with, but which were solely concerned with manipulating a special potency that had its own rules quite distinct from these matter-of-fact ones of craft and industry. This is often quite clearly phrased by primitive people. An Omaha, pressed to put into words some aspect of his religion, drew his hand contemptuously over the typewriter and camera that were on the table and said witheringly, "But we are not talking of *these things.*" And quite rightly. The distinction they make between the workaday techniques and supernatural ones is a fundamental one. *Wakan* and *manitou* are in the baldest translation simply "the wonderful," and the human imagination has elaborated in religion a really "wonderful" world, freeing itself from the limitations of natural law and material causation. In this new world, results instead of being painfully achieved by tracking game or fitting planed board to board were achieved by believing them to be achieved; they were achieved by virtue of the will to have them achieved. Techniques, of course, developed in this realm, and were as definite as those of industry or craft. The point is that the two types of technique followed different kinds of causation, and that they present a fundamental contrast in the worlds that are manipulated.

For this world of *mana* and *manitou* we have only the term "the supernatural." We cannot get along without it in an English discussion; yet it is a term open to grave misunderstanding. Every culture defines *natural* in its own way, and hence also *supernatural.* With our increasing knowledge of the natural world, the supernatural has by definition become increasingly constricted, and that fact schematicizes the whole history of religion in a way that would not have been true if our word for the concept had been something like *mana* or *manitou* instead of *supernatural.* In this discussion I use the term without reference to this etymological implication, to mean the "wonderful" causations, the extra dimension, which in religion have everywhere been imputed to the external universe.

This supernaturalism among primitive peoples has two different formulations, and they both are extensions of the knowledge man had gained in dealing realistically with the universe. On the one hand, in so far as he extended his concepts and experience of inanimate objects and made these a basis of supernaturalism, he saw this supernatural quality as an attribute of objects just as color and weight are attributes of objects. There was just the same reason that a stone should have supernatural power as one of its qualities as there was that it should have hardness. It did not imply the personification of the stone in one case or the other. On the other hand, in so far as man extended his knowledge of himself and his fellows as the basis of his religious notions, the supernatural was a function of the fact that the external world was person just as he was himself. The tree or the storm felt love or resentment toward the seeker just as he himself did toward other men or other men toward him, and it had the power to act upon its feeling just as men had.

These two religious formulations have had different consequences in the development of religion. The whole train of ideas that is set up is different according as the imputed power is patterned after analogies with color and weight and other properties of objects, or after analogies with will and intention in the human world. These two beliefs have been distinguished as animatism,[6] or the belief in *mana;* and animism, or the belief in spirits. There have been efforts to relate them chronologically and by logical sequences.[7] There is no need to argue the one or the other; methodologically such attempts at single origins are unnecessary and grow out of our human desire to make the argument as trim and neat as possible. Logically it is quite conceivable that supernaturalism should have followed two analogies instead of one, and that neither should have priority over the other. In both the analogies, man seized upon a major aspect of the external world and projected it; these gave him two patterns well-known in his experience, both of which his imagination seized upon and elaborated in its creation of the supernatural world. In the process of this elaboration the two patterns intersected each other in innumerable ways, and there is a middle ground in which distinction between the two concepts is unnecessary. Nevertheless at the extremes of the gamut the two poles are always apparent, and without a recognition of them much of religious practice is unintelligible.

Before we discuss the techniques of religion that are associated with these concepts that form the core of religion, it will help to define our problem if we point out what religion is *not*. There are certain aspects of the religions of our own cultural background that we tend to make fundamental also in the history of religions, whereas they are local developments of our particular culture area or fortunate by-products of a complex civilization.

In the first place religion is not to be identified with the pursuit of ideal ends. It is so natural to us to associate with religion the desire to live more virtuously and to interpret the transitory in terms of the eternal that we introduce unnecessary complications even when we are concerning ourselves with religion in our own civilization. But to select this particular development of the higher ethical religions as the thread which holds together the history of religions and explains that of primitive people is to misconceive that history. Spirituality and the virtues are two social values which were discovered in the process of social life. They may well constitute the value of religion in man's history just as the pearl constitutes the value of the oyster. Nevertheless the making of the pearl is a byproduct in the life of the oyster, and it does not give a clue to the evolution of the oyster.

Religion was used. Its function was to accomplish something, and it was first and foremost a technique for success. It was as material, in that sense, as the agriculture or the hunting which it furthered. Anything that came within the range of an individual's wishes, without regard to its ideality, was sought in religion. The prayers are for definite desired objects:

Let me kill a Pawnee. See, I have cut off strips of my skin; have pity upon me. Give me a scalp.

Or the Indian lifts up a buffalo chip from his medicine bundle and says:

Hello, Old Man. I am poor. Look at me and give me good things. Let me live to be old, let me capture horses, let me take a gun, let me count coup. Like a chief, asking help of no one, may I make a good living, may I always have plenty.

He cuts off a joint of his finger and says:

Old Woman Grandson, I give you this. Give me good pay for it.

Some petitions are capable of more socialized interpretation than others. Some individuals easily pursue altruistic ends and this finds expression in their religious practices. Nevertheless the fundamental fact remains that religion is not historically a citizenship in an ideal world, but had to do with success in this world. What ends were sought was a matter of the conventions of the particular culture, but anything that was desired might be sought by way of religion.

It follows that there is no segment of human life — for instance, interest in the welfare of others, need for personal security, desire for health or offspring — that can be universally identified with religion. These may be overlooked in any particular religion in favor, for instance, of providing for the fate of the soul in the hereafter or inducing rainfall. The objects of religion are not constants that can be isolated and defined. There is probably nothing that at some time and place has not been of fundamental religious importance. Thus there are tribes of California who come together to try out who has the greatest proficiency in sleight of hand, for these persons by definition are those destined to religion. Other tribes, as the Greeks did, have valued fools and neurotics as the primarily religious. We shall see later how diverse the aspects of human life are that have been regarded as belonging fundamentally to the religious realm.

The orientation of the house may be of prime religious significance while marriage and sex relations in general may be locally regarded as nonreligious and primarily economic. Nor does this selection of certain segments of life for religious elaboration necessarily show the functional relation to culture that Malinowski describes.[8] Among an agricultural people the religion may be centered around fertility, but it need not be and often is not. Among a hunting people this center may be success in the hunt, but other objectives may dwarf it. Often the curing of disease is regarded as especially the function of the religious man, but there are some people among whom it is as nonreligious as it usually is in our own civilization.

Mana — supernatural power as an attribute of objects. The theory that a wonderful power is present in the external world as simply as hardness is present in the stone or greenness in the grass is found to some degree among every people of the world. It may in any society be dwarfed in comparison with a great development of the alternative theory of animism, the personalizing of the universe. But even in such a society there may be amulets of specially shaped or colored stone, for example, that have no connection with the predominantly animistic reading of the universe. They are *per se* powerful, not, as spirits are, contingently so. If they have the rough shape of an animal, they are carried in the belt on the hunt and their magic power will give success in the killing of that animal. If they have instead the shape of a fruit, they are laid at the root of the tree and it bears 'a rich harvest in its season. No spirit is entreated, no rapport needs to be achieved with the power used; the power that is imputed to these amulets is as axiomatic as any other attribute of the same object.

Logically enough, the kind of magic power that is imputed to objects in this way is most often suggested by some analogy with its other material attributes. Not only does its shape suggest the use to which it shall be put as an amulet for the hunt or for fertility, but its outstanding qualities as an object may be transferred bodily to the magic realm. In order to secure long life for themselves, the Eskimo sew to their clothing bits of the hearth stone, which has proved its enduring qualities by resisting the fire. Similarly, to make a boy a great hunter, they sew on the talons of the hawk, the greatest hunter of the Arctic. To give him the fox's cunning they attach a bit of the fox's dung. In parts of Melanesia where every magic procedure must have its potency given it by the magic "specific" that is the esoteric secret of every magician, these specifics are chosen because of similar analogies. A twin berry is the specific of the curse that will cause a woman to have twins, and the leaves of a lush-growing water plant are a well-known garden specific.

Acts as well as objects have magic power of the same sort, as a quality of the acts. Planting sugar cane, the gardener sucks noisily as if half-choking himself with the luscious juice of the ripened cane. He makes his yams root deeply by touching them with a bone of an animal that has been killed in the deepest recess of a cave. The lover binds closely together a hair from his own head and from that of the girl he desires, and his desires will be realized. These are acts of magic automatically effective, and supernatural power is regarded as an axiomatic quality of the act.

Formulaic spells are one of the frequently recurring expressions of this attribute theory of supernatural power. If the proper words are said, the spell has power *per se*, just as an herb has curing virtues. In the everyday world, if a dam is built the water will rise; in the supernatural world, formulas in this case act in a matter-of-fact fashion as dams do in the matter-of-fact world. It is only necessary to know the formula. Techniques develop luxuriantly in the soil of this idea, and have had great consequences in the history of religious practices (see page 637).

Animism — supernatural power as will and intention. The alternative theory of the supernatural is based not on man's experience with things and their attributes, but on his recognition of power in himself and in his fellows; power is attributed to the external world after the analogy with human will power.

Animism is a confusion between two of our most carefully separated categories, the animate and the inanimate. Tylor and Spencer, who first examined animistic beliefs in their relation to religion, found animism bewildering and well-nigh incredible. They were exponents of nineteenth century rationalism, and were accustomed to rely upon the rationality of the human processes. This ascription of being to the external world, and the behavior that this occasioned in religious practice, were from their point of view gratuitous and irrational.

Tylor derived animism from those experiences which give man the notion of the separable human soul. These are primarily dreams, but also shadow, reflection on the water, etc. Once primitive man had arrived at the hypothesis of his own soul, he transferred the notion first to other humans and then to the inanimate world. It was a belief, according to Tylor, based on a logical chain of reasoning. Modern psychology is less given to tracing the origins of fundamental human attitudes to logical chains of reasoning. We are more inclined to see the concept as secondary and the total reaction to the situation as primary.

It is important to realize that this division of the world into animate and inanimate, with accompanying appropriate behaviors for each, is a sophisticated one that is alien to folk custom even among ourselves and has to be learned by each generation of our children. Modern child psychology is full of examples of the personalization of the inanimate world. The child endows a moving object with the will and intention a human being has. He strikes the door that has slammed upon him to pay it back for the injury. These are expressions of an attitude that has not yet made our fixed distinction into animate and inanimate, but brings the whole of experience under one rubric, treating the entire external world according to the pattern that has been acquired in dealings with human individuals.

Throughout man's history it has been the mechanistic theory of the universe that he has found fantastic, not the animistic one. He is equipped with a consciousness of his own purposes and motivations, but no stretch of the imagination is sufficient to give him a conception of the workings of inanimate life. His experience of his own inner life he uses to picture to himself those other sequences of which he has no such knowledge. Instead of admitting his ignorance of the reasons for the succession of rain and drought, he sees in it rain gods blessing their chosen people — or, at the least, rain falling on the fields of the just. He uses the motivations he is familiar with in himself to explain the world that would otherwise remain a puzzle to him. He domesticates the world and makes it intelligible. He sees in the external world the playing out of a human drama actuated by moral significance; that is, he sees it humanly directed toward rewarding those who have performed their required obligations and denying those who have failed in them. He is no longer in a blind and mechanistic universe. This wishful thinking, which is embodied in the religions of the world, and is worked out conceptually in mythology and theology (see pages 609 ff., 660 ff.) and behavioristically in the religious techniques of petition and rapport (see pages 639 ff.), ranks with the great creations of the human mind.

Techniques of religion. Just as the theory of the supernatural swings between two poles, one of which is magic power as an impersonal attribute of objects and acts and the other the will power of a personalized universe, so also religious techniques cover a gamut one extreme of which is mechanistic manipulation of impersonal magic power, and the other personal relations with the supernatural.

Magic is mechanical procedure, the compulsion of the supernatural according to traditional rules of thumb. It is, in the realm of the supernatural, the technique of science in the realm of the natural. As Frazer has pointed out,[9] magic is primitive man's science. As opposed to other techniques of the magico-religious realm, it operates with cause and effect sequences. It does not involve submission, petition, conciliation, consecration. If a man knows the rules and follows them in detail, the effect is secured. The danger lies all in faulty knowledge, involuntary missteps, oversights on the part of the practitioner. From his point of view, and according to his view of the universe, which does not separate natural from supernatural, he is following inexorable law. He is, in Frazer's word, the primitive scientist.

The distinction between magic and science, nevertheless, is as obvious as the procedure they have in common. Science has no place for supernaturalism, whereas it is the sole concern of magic. The distinction in any given procedure is always clear. If the object is to secure a good harvest, in so far as primitive man is scientific he prepares the ground, buries the seed at the proper depth, keeps it weeded, and frightens away insect, bird, and animal pests. But he employs also stones shaped like the desired fruit, and these are considered to have *mana* to increase the harvest. This is making use of supernatural power by sympathetic magic. Or, when the taro has come up, the magicians go through the field breaking off its lower leaves, because full-grown taro sheds such leaves, and this magical procedure therefore ensures its arrival at that stage. These acts are as mechanistic as the scientific procedure, but they employ a completely different cause and effect sequence.

Science and magic therefore depend upon mechanistic procedures. Science deals with cause and effect sequences in the natural world, and what these are can be experimentally determined and the results gauged. Magic deals with cause and effect sequences in the supernatural world, and these are fabrications of the human mind. Since supernatural cause and effect does not exist in nature, man creates out of analogies the sequences he employs. Most of the techniques of magic are based on these analogies and propinquities — in Frazer's terms, sympathetic and contagious magic. If the enemy's image is melted before the fire, he will waste away and die; if the arrow taken from the wound is kept clean and cool in a wrapping of damp leaves, the wound will heal; a girl at adolescence digs long trenches that she may always work hard, and a boy goes without food that he may be magically inured to hunger; an enemy's nail paring is put in an opened grave box that the propinquity with the corpse may cause his death.

All such practices are built on the fundamental idea that a course of action can be laid down for the universe by these analogous acts, and the universe will be compelled to follow the pattern set. The simplest form, and the one which gives us some of the most explicit and highly dramatized expressions of primitive emotion that we possess, is that of simple preënactment or prestatement of the desired end. Religion and magic are commonly acts and rites of wish fulfillment, but the emotional satisfaction is, other things being equal, the more direct the simpler and less symbolic the technique, and magic formulas and preënactments of this type give the maximum possibilities of release. The medicine man [10] hollows out a shallow grave before him and lays in it a rotting log to represent his enemy. He chants over it the torments of the dying. He applies red-hot tongs to the points that are symbolically his enemy's eyes, heart, and groins. He seizes a spear and runs the "body" through from side to side with violent thrusts. No actual killing of the enemy could be so satisfactory in details of vindictiveness as this preënactment that is staged in the interests of magic.

The same kind of emotional satisfaction may be obtained in

words as well as in acts. Since magic is the stronger the more one concentrates upon one's desires and the greater the detail with which one invests them, it is the perfect occasion for full and satisfying expression of emotions. The magic spells of the Chukchee of Siberia are explicit expressions of major desires.[11] The incantation of the woman whose husband has shown pleasure in another woman is typical: "You are this woman! You have so much of my husband's love that he begins to lose all liking for me. I make you into carrion lying on the pebbly shore — old carrion puffed up with its rot. I make my husband into a big bear. The bear comes from a distant land. He is very hungry; he has been starving for a long time. He sees the carrion. Seeing it, he eats it. After a while he vomits it out. I make you into the stuff vomited. My husband sees you and says, 'I do not want it!' My husband despises you. Then I make this body of mine into a young beaver that has just shed his hair; I make smooth every hair of mine. My husband will leave his former liking, and turn again to look upon me."

Such simple and emotionally satisfying prestatements of the end desired are less common than one would *a priori* suppose. The techniques of magical procedure that are found everywhere in the world are more devious. They employ analogies of every sort, and the emotional satisfaction is lost in the meticulous observance of small rules. It is difficult to regard magic as man's technique of compensation in emotionally charged situations. Magic is for the most part cold and technical and nonemotional, a rule-of-thumb procedure. The emotional satisfaction of planting lush leaves in a garden to secure a rich harvest, or burying banana-shaped stones at the roots of a banana tree, is only that of following routine courses of action that are believed to be efficacious. They have none of the direct emotional release of the Algonquian medicine man or the jealous woman among the Chukchee.

Frazer grouped these analogies of which magic makes use as sympathetic (or homeopathic or imitative) magic and as contagious magic. One can be satisfied with these groupings or can classify endlessly. The available analogies are countless. As our collections of primitive magic are increased, it becomes clear that practically all the similitudes in nature have been employed somewhere in the magic of some people.[12]

Behavior toward the personalized universe. The alternative religious technique is that which grows out of animistic beliefs. If the universe

is person in its motivations and purposes, behavior toward it must be
the familiar behavior men have found useful in their relations to their
fellows. Love, punishment, reverence, command, are all tried and
tested means of attaining ends in dealing with persons, and they are
indicated therefore in dealings with the personalized universe.

One of the types of behavior that are used toward the supernatural
by virtue of its known availability toward persons is reverence, or
awe as it is usually called in religious connections. Awe has been
singled out by some writers as the comprehensive religious attitude,
that attitude which sets off religion from other human traits.[13] Awe,
however, is only one among many attitudes characteristic of religious
behavior. Cajolery and bribery and false pretense are common means
of influencing the supernatural, and are especially characteristic of
regions of Melanesia. The Kai of New Guinea "swindle ghosts as they
do men," and the near-by Tami deceive the spirit in the grossest
fashion, "outwitting it like an arrant blockhead," and giving as
offerings the shabbiest things they can find. Reprisals and vehement
expressions of anger also are relied upon in dealing with the supernatural. The Tsimshian of the Canadian Pacific coast, when they
suffer great misfortune, vent their anger against heaven without inhi-
bition. Scolding is one of the recognized means of dealing with the
recalcitrant supernatural. "They raise their eyes and hands in savage
anger to heaven, and stamp their feet on the ground. They reiterate,
'You are a great slave.' It is their greatest term of reproach." The
Manus of the Bismarck Archipelago keeps in his house as a tutelary a
skull of a recent ancestor, and expects from its aid good fortune in all
his undertakings. If he is not satisfied, he consults an oracle or a
diviner to find out for what the tutelary has punished him, and will
immediately make restitution. If his business does not prosper thereafter or if the illness is not alleviated, he is justly angry at his
tutelary and threatens that he will throw him out of the house, "to
be washed by all rains, scorched by all suns," to be homeless and
forgotten. "You will then be made to understand! You will have no
house to rest in; you will be cast out and you will be miserable a
long time before you become a crab or a jellyfish." [14]

On the other hand the accepted attitude toward the supernatural
may be that of courteous hospitality. If human beings are the more
likely to be gracious after they have been happily entertained, how
much more might this not be true in the case of the gods. Among the
Langalanga of Northern Mala, of the Solomon Islands of Melanesia,

the dead are the recognized supernaturals and are represented by
their skulls, which are kept in a house prepared for them. When the
Langalanga play the panpipes for dancing in the village, they bring
the skulls out of their house and range them in an honored audience,
saying, "Now you may watch the dance." They gather the leaves
of fragrant herbs with which the women are accustomed to perfume
themselves, and stuff these up the noses of skulls. They desire that
they shall enjoy the most hospitable entertainment that they know
how to provide.[15] The same attitude is found also in the Southwest
pueblo of Zuñi. There too the dead are the supernaturals. They dance
continuously in the sacred lake, but they prefer to return to dance in
Zuñi. Therefore impersonation in the masked dances provides them
with the opportunity to indulge themselves. They come and are
entertained by participation in a dance, the favorite pastime of the
people. It is the most pleasing hospitality that the Pueblos know how
to give either to humans or to the supernaturals.

There is probably no customary behavior toward one's fellows that
is not to be found somewhere as a religious technique, even acts that
belong to specific situations in human life such as birth and courtship.
In the Malay peninsula the rice at planting is given all the ceremonies
of childbirth and cradled by the wife of the planter; the tree whose sap
is sought is appealed to as a mother: "O mother, often before you
have given me the breast, yet still I thirst. I ask four potfuls more."
Or before the tree is cut it is wedded with all the appropriate human
ceremony and taken as bride by the woodsman. In these cases it is
the appropriate behavior of the mother and the child and the bridegroom that has set the pattern for behavior toward the supernatural.

The power that is ascribed to the gods takes its form, just as behavior toward them does, from man's experiences in the human world.
We are accustomed by our knowledge of the higher ethical religions
to connect omnipotence with the gods. But this is a late and meta-
physical tenet. Primitive man had no idea of imputing omnipotence
to his gods. He saw in them the same kind of powers he felt in himself,
often less in quality than his own. The gods are often represented as
fools and as foiled by doddering old women. Their power is strictly
limited. The Indian of the Plains collects power from personal encounters with a rabbit, an eagle, and a rock. He flees from his enemy
by the power of his rabbit skin till that is exhausted, by the power of
his eagle feather till that is exhausted, and he stands to face his enemy
with the boulder's power of invulnerability when he is reduced to his

last resource. He does not regard any one of them as inexhaustible any more than he regards his own powers as inexhaustible.

In animistic belief and practice, therefore, man created the universe in his own image. He extended his human attitudes toward his fellows to an anthropomorphic universe. But this did not mean that his animistic techniques were his only techniques; he hoed the ground and cut his harvest as well as cradled the rice seed and betrothed the fertility goddess. The emphasis upon man's animistic behavior has often obscured the facts concerning the bulk and the exactness of man's knowledge of natural processes. He knew how to build a seagoing canoe, how to select the tree out of which to make it, and how to convey it to the shore and fashion it. This took, to be sure, only a fraction of the time that was lavished upon the total undertaking, because the canoe could not be built without elaborate religious observance. There is, however, no mystery about the fact that man elaborated anthropomorphic behavior toward the canoe at the same time that he continued to employ matter-of-fact techniques in its building. The tree, along with the rest of the external universe, was person, and he knew the attitudes that were effective toward persons. Therefore his relations with it were incomplete without giftgiving, prostrations, reverence, any of the behaviors he used toward men. It is an attitude that is familiar in our behavior even today. We know the physical things that must be done for our children. We must feed and clothe them and provide them with the necessary wherewithal. But it is repulsive to us to stop there, and parents who do so, we think, are running a great risk of failure. For children are people, and we must not treat them only as things. As persons, for successful handling, they call for love and consideration and praise. It is just the attitude of primitive man toward the external world. The tree, the sea, the pot, the corn, are all persons, and after he has employed all the matter-of-fact skills in relation to them, his greater obligation to them as living beings still remains, and it is a major function of religion to discharge this obligation.

Forms of religious behavior. Every form of religious behavior runs the gamut between the two techniques we have discussed: a technique patterned on behavior toward things, and a technique patterned on behavior toward persons.

Prayer. Speech that is intended to achieve supernatural ends is at the one extreme the prayer of the saint whose only object is to place himself in the most intimate communion with the god, and at the other the recital of magical formulas. The prayer of intimate personal dependence upon the god is found even among primitive people, and a great many offerings to the supernatural are accompanied by prayers which detail the efforts of petitioners to please and gratify the supernatural. The Winnebago of the region of the Great Lakes pray to the Thunderbird: "Oh grandfather, Thunderbird, here I stand with tobacco in my hand. Grant us what you granted our grandfathers! Accept our humble offering of tobacco. We are sending you buckskins from which you can make moccasins, feathers from which you can make a headdress; we are preparing a meal for you from the meat of an animal who is like ourselves. And not I alone, but all the members of my clan and all the members of the other clans present here, beseech you to accept our gifts. We have prepared ourselves fitly, and I and all my kinsmen sit here humble in heart, a sight to awaken pity, so that we can receive your blessing and live a good life."

Speech to the supernatural may also be magical forms of words which achieve their end automatically, and this may be in a given society the accepted way of dealing with the supernatural. In parts of Melanesia it is strictly denied that gardens can grow without the use of the magic fertility formulas, and this even in the face of missionaries' gardens which have flourished in certain islands for many years. In northern California [16] there is a strong development of compulsive formulas of this sort which detail incidents in the travels of the animals who figure in the myths of this area. They are used as magic. If recited word-perfect, an incident in Coyote's successful encounter with Wolf and the healing of his wounds will cure bullet wounds after a battle. Every dangerous occasion of life is provided with these incidents from mythology which are used in this magical fashion.

Divination. Divination, or control by foreknowledge, is similarly of two contrasted types. Divination among many primitive peoples is accomplished by persons who are possessed by the supernatural spirit. The god himself speaks through them as through the Greek oracle at Delphi. This is a common practice in Africa, in Polynesia, and in Siberia. The priest divines only by himself uttering the words of the supernatural person.

At the opposite pole is divination from the entrails and the scapulae of animals. In order to ascertain the future in this way one requires a technical training in the significance of spots on the liver or the configuration of lines on a scapula.[17] The result is entirely without reference to having placated a god or having achieved any other form of communication with him.

Sacrifice. Sacrifice, or control by gift, is at the one extreme a bought-and-paid-for trafficking with a supernatural that cannot choose but accept the arrangement offered it; if the payment is given, the aid must be forthcoming. Sacrifice on the other hand may be one of the means of pleasing the god, and all possible human attitudes toward a gift are found in various religions. The Plains Indians regarded self-inflicted torture as the most important sacrifice to the supernaturals, and they offered it in order to gain their pity. Such sacrifice on the Plains was one of the most important ways of establishing a personal relation with the supernatural. In Melanesia, on the other hand, it is more common to regard objects given to the supernatural as in themselves compulsive, and as having no bearing upon establishing personal relations. The objects are given as an integral part of magical procedure — so many betel nuts or so many skulls, along with a magic formula, to make the canoe seaworthy or the wind propitious.

Taboo, or the control by abstention, is a constantly recurring aspect of man's dealings with supernatural power. Because the supernatural is power, it is dangerous. A whole religion may be devoted to the ritual punctiliousness by means of which this danger is surmounted. The dangerousness of the supernatural to which taboo is the response may be conceived as automatic and an attribute, or as a human quality, and taboo will have a different character in the two cases.

At their most mechanical, taboos are exemplified by the *tapu* charms of Samoa and parts of Melanesia or the *tie-tie* of West Africa, which capitalize the dangerousness of the supernatural. These charms are taboos placed on private property and evidenced by a mark or a dangle placed on the object. Property sanctions in these regions are thus given over to the supernatural. The Fan in West Africa trust all their property to the operation of the supernatural taboo of the *tie-tie,* even a wealth of ebony or ivory tusks left far out in the bush. If anyone desired the ebony he would hold it policy to kill the human owner before breaking the ban. Only after he had thus nullified the supernatural power the owner had affixed to his property would he make off with the ebony. The West Africans have a proverb, "One charm does the work of twenty slaves."

But taboo can be on the other hand a punctilio patterned after that observed toward powerful persons. It may be a removing of one's hat or one's shoes or one's blanket when one enters the presence of the supernatural just as one shows these marks of respect to any person of power and prestige. In Polynesia, in the treatment of chiefs, punctilio is carried to the point where by virtue of their great sacredness and dangerousness chiefs may not feed themselves or be touched by anyone, but are fed on long prongs which are manipulated carefully so that they will not touch the sacred teeth. The chiefs can do no work, nor go out of the confinement of the chieftain's house. The supernatural power which fills them makes them too sacred, too dangerous for participation in ordinary life, and sets them apart by elaborate taboos. Sacred places, sacred objects, the defiling, and the dead have usually been surrounded by taboo. A medicine bundle or fetish has always its rules of punctilio consequent upon its not being an object to handle lightly.

Taboo may be, in its most extreme use as an element in a relationship with a personal supernatural, the asceticism of the saint. The higher ethical religions have elaborated formal restrictions and proscribed indulgences not for their magic efficiency but for the sake of ruling out "the world." Primitive peoples also have retreats and sacred personages, and the taboos associated with them are sometimes thought of as setting them off in a peculiar dedication to the supernatural. Such taboos are characteristic of the American Indian vision quest and of the Siberian shaman, and are very differently conceived from the *tapu* of Polynesia.

Taboo is one of those subjects under which a great deal of miscellaneous material can be grouped; it has in consequence been given great prominence in discussions of religion. This is due very largely to the fact that taboo is by definition all that is forbidden; that is, it is the negative aspect of everything. It is a category of prohibitions. Taboos and prohibitions are fundamental in religions, but the category loses its significance when it is separated from the positive aspects of which it is the negative. For this reason taboo is best regarded not as a primary aspect of the religious complex but as a ubiquitous form of religious behavior, that form which takes into account the dangerous aspect of supernatural power and surrounds it with punctilious observance.

Fetishes and amulets. Material objects when they are treated as supernatural are either amulets if they are the seat of supernatural power in its guise as an attribute of things, or fetishes in its animistic guise. Amulets by definition possess supernatural power in the same fashion and by the same token that they possess color or any other attribute. They work automatically, as fire does, or pressure, and are not prayed to or personified.

The term "fetish" is that used in Africa where the material object is handled on the opposite theory. The fetish is given gifts and talked to, and reviled if necessary. It is regarded as being strongest in its youth, and after use it is laid aside to recuperate its powers as a man rests after a campaign. It may or may not be conceptually regarded as person, but the behavior toward it is behavior between persons, not that of a person toward an inanimate object as in the case of amulets. Most West Africans treat not only medicine bundles but all material objects in this fashion. The native about to set out for a hunt sits about for days talking to his spear, rubbing it, and telling it how much he has given it and how great his reliance is upon it. He addresses it in terms of friendship as he does all objects he wishes to use.

The weather or the river he treats in the same way. Miss Kingsley [18] says, "You will see him bending over the face of a river talking to its spirit with proper incantations, asking it when it meets a man who is an enemy of his to upset his canoe, or drown him, or asking it to carry down with it some curse to the village below that has angered him."

The contrast between West African religion and that of such Melanesian tribes as the Orokaiva or the Dobuans is largely a consequence of this contrast between the attitude toward the fetish and toward the amulet.

Tutelary spirits. The guardian spirit of the North American Indian was a personal tutelary with which he alone had dealings. This relationship was strictly according to the pattern of human relationships between a benefactor and his protégé. In order to obtain the tutelary in the first place, the youth had to go out alone fasting, concentrate on the blessing he desired, and often torture himself in order to make himself more pitiable to the spirits. At last he entered into complete rapport with the supernatural and his tutelary appeared to him. All his life thereafter he could ask for help from his spirit, but in return he had to give a place of honor in the tipi to the bundle which he kept as a sacred memento, feed it at every meal, observe punctilio in regard to it, and open and incense it at due seasons. If his tutelary was displeased with him at any time, the power was no longer available. All his prayers to it were a statement of the human relationships between them. At the same time the tutelary spirit might assume obligations and become the "servant" of the person who had acquired him.

The attitude toward the individual supernatural in witchcraft often contrasts strongly with this. The supernatural slave was obtained by a legalistic contract, and compulsion was the technique that was relied upon. This slave technique is, of course, one that has been notoriously used toward human beings, but it is that of dealing with persons as things and it is for that reason that it is repulsive to present-day ethics. Witchcraft, like many primitive magic practices, carried it into the supernatural realm. You had only to rub the lamp and the djinn came. You had only to obtain the name of the demon and he was at your service.

Summary. These two techniques for handling the supernatural — at the one extreme compulsion and at the other rapport — occur in all types of religious behavior. It is clear that they are always alternative methods for dealing with the supernatural, and that neither gives any indication of being derivative from the other. They are two poles between which religious behavior ranges, each pole representing one of the two major human experiences outside of the religious realm: on the one hand man's experience with things, and on the other his experience with persons.

Varieties of primitive religions. We have been discussing those things which are universal in the religious complex: its core of supernaturalism, and its two contrasted and omnipresent techniques for dealing with this supernatural. In the study of primitive religions, however, it is not this core which they all have in common which is most immediately obvious. It is rather the great diversity they exhibit, and this is the more striking the better the accounts of religion that are available. The sacred dairy ritual of the Todas of India and the vision quests of the American Indians of the plateau of British Columbia have almost no objective facts in common. It is this unlikeness that has made so many discussions of primitive religions appear fruitless because they seem a mere heaping up of unrelated facts.

This unlikeness of historically unrelated religions is a consequence of the fact that, as we saw above, religion is quite impartial as to what arc of cultural life it shall supernaturalize. Historical causes, most of them now beyond our unraveling, have determined that in one region it shall be the means of livelihood, like the Toda pastoral techniques, that is the concern of religion, and in another part of the globe the life crises of the individual such as birth, puberty, marriage, and death. Religion is a spotlight that swings quite indiscriminately, in one region bringing it about that property and all the concepts that center around it are religiously guaranteed, and in another leaving property entirely secular; in one region centering upon weather control, in another upon curing.

Peoples differ, of course, as well in the amount of cultural life that is handled by supernatural techniques as in the particular traits they handle in this way. In some cultures, like Samoa,[19] supernaturalism is at a minimum, while in others, as for instance in New Zealand, which belongs to the same culture area, the concern with the supernatural is almost omnipresent and is deeply felt. One of the generalizations about the contrast between our civilization and primitive peoples that are most nearly true is that there has been a continuous secularizing of life. A much greater area of life is commonly handled by religious means among primitives than among any civilized peoples. Nevertheless the contrast exists as well on the primitive level, and it is only one aspect of the larger fact that religion is always developed among any people in relation to culturally selected traits. Religions therefore have totally different aspects of life as their content in different parts of the world, and their whole character develops differently according as they are built, for instance, upon relationship with the dead or upon control of the hunt.

There are very few ethnographic accounts of religion that are adequate for clear description of this interrelation of religion with other elements of culture. The religions described below have been selected as showing different developments, and have been summarized as briefly as possible.

Varieties of primitive religion: Siberia.[20] Religion in Siberia, as so often in the Old World, is characteristically concerned with divination. Religious occasions are those upon which the spirits are consulted concerning their pleasure or displeasure, and the religious persons are not those who will successfully put into effect the power received from the spirits, but those who report it.

These oracles from the supernatural are obtained among the Siberian tribes by those procedures which in western civilization are known as spiritualism. The shaman is in a trance, he speaks with strange voices, ventriloquism is used, the tent is lifted bodily, objects fly about, and spirit controls speak through the mouths of the mediums. These controls are not thought to be the dead, but the supernatural beings with which the Siberian tribes people the world.

Religious persons in Siberia are recognized in their youth. They are persons of definite instability which may take the form of trance or epileptic seizures, of abnormal periods of sleep, of irresponsible wandering, and of illness and emaciation. Usually most of these symptoms are present, though some tribes emphasize one and others another. This period is known as the "call," and no one can disregard it on pain of serious illness and calamity. It is usually dreaded, and they speak of being "doomed to inspiration." In its less severe forms it is very common among these people. Every adult male occasionally "takes the drum" — that is, engages in the self-hypnotic swaying and monotonous rhythm which is always a prelude to any shamanistic demonstration; and everyone, in so far as he is susceptible to such stimuli, has some power from the supernatural. Every family has a family seer who can consult the spirits for them on lesser family occasions, and the recognized shamans of the tribe are only those who are more richly gifted in this direction.

The call is a period of illness or extreme instability which is ended or cured by assuming the shamanistic rôle. The individual then becomes a vehicle for the spirits. The Chukchee consider each religious performance a dramatization and reënactment of this painful period of the call. Again the spirits seize their victim, he foams at the mouth, sweats bloody sweat, falls in a trance, and finally delivers the word of the spirit and is again calm and refreshed and in his right mind.

Especially powerful shamans change their sex. There are many degrees. Some men only assume women's dress and continue to live with their wives and children. Some add women's occupations to the assumption of women's dress; they are thought to learn these quickly and well because of their instruction by the spirits. The final stage is that of the assumption of femininity. The body outlines change, and the shaman is supposed to marry another man. He has now a spirit husband in the supernatural world, a control who is more powerful than the spirit wife he could have had as a man. He outranks, therefore, the shamans who have not undergone the change of sex, and also the women shamans, who are never thought of as equaling men in power.

There are, of course, other aspects of Siberian religion besides this great development of shamanism. Incantations are known by every-

one, and no occasion is too trifling or too momentous for the use of
these spells. Amulets are also universally used. Siberian religion,
nevertheless, is distinctive because of the degree to which it ignores
fertility or sex situations, crisis ceremonialism, or the dead, and pre-
occupies itself with mediumship, specializing in making use of various
unstable types of individuals. These individuals report, as returned
visitors from another realm, the pleasure of the spirits; they find lost
objects; they divine in answer to the questions of the crowd. They can
summon the spirits to the lodge. So far as the activities of the shamans
go, Siberian religion is thoroughly animistic, a religion of rapport
with personalized spirits. This does not rule out magical practices,
which are employed by everyone, shamans and non-shamans, but
religion develops in this region primarily as a phenomenon of mediumship, and religious persons are individuals who can develop this trait.

The Pueblo Indians of the Southwest.[21] The Pueblo Indians of New
Mexico and Arizona have a religion which has little in common with
that of the Siberian peoples. No use is made, not only of capacity
for mediumship, but of any psychic instability; religion is little used
for divining; and in place of the highly specialized individualistic
approach to the supernatural by the shaman, there is here no shaman
at all. It is rather by the group that the supernatural may be approached. Religious organization and practices differ of course in the
different Pueblos, and the description given here applies specifically
to Zuñi.

Religion in Zuñi is highly formalized. It follows the calendar
throughout the year with elaborate ceremonies performed by permanent societies and priesthoods which stand to each other in intricate
interrelations. Until it was introduced by White contact, there was
no secular authority in the Pueblos except such as was exercised
incidentally by these religious groups. The nearest parallel, in our
own cultural background, to the Pueblo religion, in scope and in
formalism, is that of Catholicism in its great period.

The religion of the Pueblos is directed most importantly toward
securing fertility. They ask for both human and agricultural fertility,
and in the desert region they occupy it is the prayer for rain which
overshadows all else. There are specific ceremonies for the cure of
bodily ailments, for deliverance from danger, and for success in the
hunt, but even in these the prayer for rain is also present.

Religion in Zuñi is always a prescribed group affair. There is no
room in it for individual initiative. All the times and seasons are set

by custom, and any man, even the highest priest, performing his most individual act, the planting of prayersticks, at an hour or season not designated by tradition is suspected of witchcraft. The only way to approach the supernatural is as a member of a duly constituted group. There is no avenue by which a man may obtain power by any experience of his own; power comes solely by membership in a cult or priesthood. There are therefore no shamans, in the sense of a religious leader who has personally received supernatural power, but only priests. There are no medicine men who cure by virtue of their gift or of personally acquired supernatural power; curing is done only by those who have bought their way into the highest order of curing societies, and all that is required is this membership and the teaching that has gone along with it. Individuals receive power either by inheritance of membership in a cult, or by purchase into a society. In any case they qualify for the exercise of such power by meticulous memorizing of ritual both of word and of act. They never seek the spirits by forms of communication outside of normal sensory experience. Rather, they are provided with endless detailed rules which, if they are complied with, will guarantee success.

These rules are largely magical. Their purpose is to constrain the gods so that success will follow of itself and not necessarily as the result of some emotion, such as pity or the desire to grant a reward, on the part of the supernaturals. On their altars they set a full bowl of water that the springs may always be full; they beat up suds from a native plant that the clouds may pile in the heavens; they blow out tobacco smoke that mist may visit the earth. The gods which they impersonate in their dances are the rain, and they constrain their blessing by dancing with their bodily substance; that is, with their paint and their masks. In the same way they constrain the blessing of the bear, which is a cure of disease, by wearing the skin of his forepaws upon their arms when they conduct a cure. These are all magically compulsive acts, and they must be carried out in scrupulous detail.

The ritual prayers are likewise compulsive by virtue of being word-perfect. These poetic rituals of Zuñi are very extensive.[22] Every ritual post, every act of participation in Zuñi religion, has its word-perfect ritual that is part of the procedure that will insure success.

The religion of the Pueblos is one of great formalism, which distrusts any individual approach to the supernatural and even in group rites makes use of no ecstatic experiences. It has a great pantheon of gods who are impersonated in dances and identified with the rain and with the dead — though with no individual dead — a series of beast gods who give power in curing, and most holy fetishes which are entrusted to hereditary priesthoods. Magical techniques of great punctilio are associated with the worship of all these supernaturals, and religious men are those who have learned and either inherited or bought the power to use these procedures. It is a religion that stresses neither sin nor conflict with the gods. Joy and dancing and freedom from care are, as Dr. Bunzel says, pleasing alike to man and gods, and by their impersonations they share with the gods the pleasure of dancing, and by their magical formulas they constrain the course of nature to their own ends.

The Plains Indians. The Indians of the Plains based religion upon a personal experience. Religion was an individual handling of supernatural power, and every man received power from a personal contact with the supernatural. He went out to solitary places to seek this before many undertakings, but especially in one great experience of his young manhood when he obtained a lifelong guardian spirit. This experience is usually called a vision, and some of them were complicated experiences of automatic vision and automatic audition. They might, however, according to native ideas, be much less marked experiences. A man recognized the power he had received by the thrill it communicated to him, and it rested with him to try out the power and to practice it.

Many visions were sought with self-torture. Either strips of skin were cut from the arm, or a finger was sacrificed, or the skin was cut and the strong muscles of the back or chest were pulled out sufficiently so that the suppliant could be suspended from them. If a man was particularly fortunate, however, he might be granted a vision without torture. In any case, he fasted usually for four or eight days, and went without water. He concentrated his mind upon what he desired, and he prayed to the spirits to pity him. When he received the vision, whatever he saw, an animal or a plant or a bird, adopted him as its protégé and gave him a song and a particular power, either to heal a bullet wound, or to be invincible, or to run fast, or to live long, or to gamble successfully. He gave pinches of food and tobacco to his supernatural patron all his life. He made up a medicine bundle which was a memento of the experience and which he cared for religiously. His song he used whenever he used the power.

Religious observances were essentially the rites of opening, incensing, and singing the songs of the medicine bundle that commemorated the vision. Many of these fetishes passed down the generations and grew by accretions till they were bundles of tribal importance and great monetary value. Their handling, however, remained fundamentally that of the simplest feather granted to a young faster and worn in his hair in a war raid. It was a sign of an individual responsibility to a personal guardian spirit. In some tribes men who had the same type of bundle — that is, the same visionary tutelary — recognized some sort of bond which almost constituted them a society. Such a bond, however, never changed the fundamental basis of their religion, which had regard strictly to the individual in a personal relationship to an individual guardian spirit.

Theoretically whatever the faster saw and heard in his vision he and his tribe carried out in faithful detail. If he was given power to lead a war party he went back and collected young men to go under his leadership. If he was given a variant version of a society ritual, he went back and founded an order of the society which conformed to the new instructions. Actually, of course, even on the Plains where this dogma of the vision is acted on more whole-heartedly than it is in many regions of North America which profess the same doctrine, such rampant individualism developed institutional checks. Visions became vested interests, and they were bought and sold and inherited. On the Plains, however, it was required that everyone who in any of these ways obtained a vision at second hand must qualify by seeking also his own vision of the tutelary. It is probable that such visions were in many cases mechanical, and complied with as a part of the routine requirements in the transfer of sacred objects, and the same observation undoubtedly applies also to other "visions." The point to be emphasized in this connection is the tribal doctrine which demanded always that power be acquired in a supernatural vision.

The ends for which power was sought in the Plains visions were those which brought the greatest reward in their culture, particularly war exploits. They sought visions to give them power to take an enemy's picketed horse, to count coup on a living enemy, to take a scalp. There was no religious sponsoring of more idealistic social ends.

The vision monopolized their mythology and theology. Tribes like the Blackfoot and the Crow have a minimum of cosmology, and no pantheon. Their religious myths are all accounts of the great visions of great men in the olden times, and of the exploits they were thereby enabled to perform.

The Dobuans of Melanesia.[23] Dobu is a small island off the east coast of New Guinea. It belongs to a large region where magical techniques are supreme. There are gods, but none of the characteristic human relations are entered into with them; they are not besought for pity like the Plains supernaturals, nor entertained with dancing like the Pueblo masked gods. They are constrained by magic formulas.

The most striking difference between the religions of North America and that of Dobu lies in the fact that the Dobuans believe that nothing can be accomplished in any field of activity without supernatural manipulation. Magic is indispensable. Whether it is a matter of the fish in the sea, of the growth of their gardens, of sex relations, of economic exchange, of illness, or of death, there are magical formulas to which success in each undertaking is attributed. They categorically deny that gardens can be grown without magic, and that in the face of gardens, in one district, of White settlers which have flourished for two generations.

These magic formulas are owned as individually as the Plains vision, but they are wholly traditional, learned lore. They can only be acquired by gift from a relative, and the most bitter enmities are pointed by dissatisfactions as to a relative's disposal of his magic. This right of inheritance can pass traditionally only to the sons and to the sisters' sons, and the sisters' sons must receive the lion's share. A man's rôle in life is determined beforehand by the amount of this magic ritual which he obtains.

Food is scarce in Dobu, and the gardens are given the greatest care. This is not, of course, attention to the needs of the plant in our sense. It is magical routine of planting, and later of keeping the yams at home in the garden of the owner, and luring as many more of his neighbors' yams as his magic can accomplish. The yams are persons. They are thought to be footloose, and it is necessary to keep them at home. Magic for this purpose should not be pronounced over them too early in the season, for they resent unnecessary curtailment of their visiting. But it cannot be long postponed. The top shoot of the yam vine is bent over and bound to the main stem, and the ritual pronounced. In the spells the yams are identified with the hardest wood in the bush, the kasiera palm.

> Where stands the kasiera palm?
> In the belly of my garden,
> At the foot of my house platform
> He stands.

He will stand inflexible, unbending,
  He stands unmoved.
The smashers of wood smash,
The hurlers of stone hurl,
  He remains unmoved.

The yam *kulia*
He (also) remains inflexible, unbending,
He remains, he remains unmoved,
  In the belly of my garden.

The spell is repeated for each of the yam varieties in the garden. If such magic prevails, the gardéner will possess his due crop at harvesting. If his magic to entice others' yams is successful, he will have an unusual harvest. Every man's harvest is therefore an evidence of his magical thievery, and as such is suspect. Harvest, indeed, is the occasion of the most carefully guarded privacy. No one outside the immediate family is allowed to see a family's magically gotten foodstores.

It is not only in agriculture that one man's gains are regarded as another man's losses. In every effort to succeed at the cost of another man's failure, magic is the chief reliance. Magic is not, as in Zuñi, the constraint of the supernatural for ends in which the whole community is concerned. The ends are definite and exclusive to one individual. Magic is used to bring success in the next trading undertaking of the individual who owns the charm. It is used to gain access to a particular woman, or to protect the fruit trees that are the owner's particular property.

The asocial nature of Dobuan magic is strikingly illustrated in their use of it in this last instance. In order to protect their betel nut or coconut trees they use the spells which every family possesses for causing and curing disease. These spells are placed on the trees by the individual owning the magic, and the thief is then visited with meningitis, cerebral malaria, elephantiasis, gangosa, or tertiary yaws. The only reason the owner can pick his own fruit is that the knowledge of the exorcism inevitably accompanies the knowledge of the curse, and he removes the spell before he approaches the tree.

Dobuan spells to cause sickness are thought to be infallible, and the sorcerer, in laying them upon the person he wishes to harm, imitates to the last degree the agonies of the death from the imposed disease. Religion in Dobu is used in the great majority of instances to harm and to steal. It is a civilization where jealousy and fear are highly developed, and the supernatural techniques serve, as is usual, the ends that are sought in that society.

Recurring aspects of the religious complex. It is clear that there are several constantly recurring elements in these diverse religions. This would be the more striking the more religions we were able to pass in review and the more in detail we were able to describe them. The most important are ceremonialism, the use of border-line psychological states, the development of dogma, and the ethical sanction. None of these are elements that are peculiar to religion. They are all found often in secular connections. The fact that they have special religious importance springs in each case from certain aspects of the nature of religion.

Ceremonialism. Ceremonialism is used so often with religious connotations that its secular forms are often overlooked. This secular aspect is usually called pageantry; that is, the formal patterning of occasions when many individuals are publicly participating. In our own culture, secular pageantry — even though the spectacle includes incidental prayer — is characteristic of ceremonies of presidential inauguration, of the rites of many men's societies, of school graduations, and similar occasions. In primitive communities, though many more occasions are likely to be supernaturalized than with us, the rites of the men's societies of the Crow or of the *fono* of Samoa are equally secular. Formal traditional rules of procedure are obviously overdetermined in public spectacles of any sort, secular or religious, and symbolic acts — analogies, for instance, from sex behavior or from eating — readily serve as patterns for group behavior in which all the participating persons may unite.

Durkheim has derived all religion from ceremonialism.[24] Lowie,[25] on the other hand, has defined it as a free show on the basis of the nonreligious pleasure the majority derive from their tribal rites. Durkheim, however forced the steps of his argument, is right in pointing out the way in which group participation has contributed to religion, and Lowie is right in emphasizing the nonreligious satisfaction in religious ceremonialism. It is not necessary to define ceremonialism in the one way or in the other. Ceremonialism is the consequence of a process that is evident in the study of any culture trait, and should be accepted in the same way that we accept the fact of grammar in language, without deriving speech from grammar, or without misunderstanding the fact that grammar is distinct from vocabulary.

Any of the themes of religion which we have seen developed in various parts of the world can be ceremonially developed and made the basis of great ritual. The medium's demonstration of his powers in Siberia, the impersonation of the masked gods or the tribal healing by the beast gods in Zuñi, the handling of the medicine bundles that are the visible symbols of the vision of the Plains, divinations, first fruit observances, sacrifices — all these and many more are occasions for the elaboration of ceremonial.

Besides these clearly marked themes of ceremonial there are other cases where the ceremony is as valued but the purpose of it is vague in the extreme. It is carried out because it must be for the life of the tribe, but reasons that are read into it are clearly rationalizations. As Marett has pointed out, the rite has usually surprisingly little conscious idea or purpose behind it. "It is danced out, not thought out," and becomes, as soon as it has received traditional form, a standard of reference — "from it proceed the random whys, and to it return the indeterminate therefores."

A further consequence of this secondary rôle of the theme or purpose in ceremonialism is the fact that ceremonials are often distributed over wide areas with a surprising similarity of detail, while the reason for which the ceremony is performed is hardly twice the same. The best studied of these cases is that of the Sun Dance of the Plains Indians.[26] It is the major tribal ceremony of the Plains and adjacent tribes. Everywhere, for the erection of its sacred lodge, a center pole is scouted for, counted coup on, and brought into camp as if it were an enemy killed by scouts. Except on the edges of sun dance distribution a peculiar and bloody torture is associated with it. It is a ceremony which has been spread by diffusion over a wide area. But it is its outward observances that have similarity in the tribes that hold it; the purposes for which it is performed are different in each tribe. Among the Dakota it is given as the last step in the qualification of high-degree shamans. Among the Crow it is given by an uncle to obtain supernatural power to avenge the death of his nephew by a war expedition. Among the Ponca it is the annual ceremony of the Thunder society. Among the Hidatsa it is given as part of the ceremonial of the son's purchase of the family medicine bundle from his father. Among the Cheyenne it is votive; a warrior in danger or a father with a sick child vows to give it the following year if his prayers are granted. The purpose for which the ceremony is performed is the least stable and most local element in the sun dance complex.

Vision and ecstasy. The use of border-line psychological states in religion is found in all the great areas of the primitive world. It is not universal, as we saw in Pueblo religion, and even in those regions where religion is unintelligible without this type of behavior it is often only the shamans, a very small proportion of the tribe, who indulge in it. It has been called the religious experience, and from this or from "the religious thrill" [27] religion has been derived. Hauer's statement of the case [28] for this origin of religion shows how much there is to be said for this point of view.

In the first place it is essential to understand that the experiences of this type of which religion has made use in various parts of the world are not by any means the same. Each religion lays down one or more types of experience as having religious value, and all the religious experiences of that area conform to that type. We have seen that in Siberia it is the gifts of mediumship that are religiously valued, and the words of the control are for them the words of deity and their way of learning the will of the supernaturals. Among the American Indians, on the other hand, the experience that was valued as the source of religious power varied with different tribes and different individuals from a major hallucination to a dream to which meaning was felt to be attached. It was in general an experience of automatic sight and of automatic audition. The Plains Indians were never mediums. Many of their visions are stereotyped in the extreme, but so were those of the medieval monks or of the Eastern mystics. In all countries where this kind of experience has been valued, men have seen in their sought visions those things which their culture has taught them to expect. And they have received their power in an experience which their culture has taught them to regard as powerful.

Trance has probably been the most often valued of such experiences. In our own cultural background the epileptic and the person liable to trance were valued in Greece as oracles and spokesmen of the gods. The Protestant church today has swung to the opposite extreme, so that even a person with minor mystical tendencies is aberrant, and cataleptic phenomena are thought to have religious power only by scattered cults. Trance has often been, however, the only gate of entrance into the religious profession. In some California tribes [29] a woman signalized her call to shamanism — shamans are women in this region — by falling rigid and remaining in this condition for several hours, hardly breathing. When she recovered she was carefully watched, for she had been taught the spirit's song in her trance, and her moans as she emerged from trance were interpreted as repeating this song and calling upon the spirit's name. When she had spoken the name, blood oozed from her mouth. Her initiation dances were a further demonstration of her intimacy with the spirit, proven by further cataleptic seizures. The most dangerous of these occasions was that on which she received the spirit's power into her body; if those about her did not catch her before she fell in the trance, the power would kill her, but if she survived she had in her body from that time a small, white, iciclelike object, the "power" so well known among tribes of California.

Trances of this sort merge easily into experiences known as possession. In West Africa, especially, trances are sought in order to receive messages from the dead king. The seer is seated on the king's stool in the shrine of the dead ruler. He trembles violently, foams at the mouth, has convulsions, dances in frenzied fashion, and repeats the message of the dead.[30] In the Marquesan Islands of Polynesia the inspired priest who sought such messages from the supernatural in trance ranked with the highest chiefs, and the practice was common in this part of Polynesia. The mouthpiece of the god told Williams in the early years of exploration, "I do not know what I say. My own mind leaves me, and while it is gone, my god speaks through me."[31]

Just as varied as the forms of mental abnormality that are made use of in different regions are the means of inducing the state. It is sometimes regarded as sacrilegious to induce it at all; it must come unsought or not at all. This is the attitude among California Indians. Usually, however, as among the Oriental mystics and the medieval saints, certain methods of inducing the state are recognized. These vary from drugs to concentration. In Uganda, in East Africa, it is said to be produced by the use of tobacco, in some parts of Polynesia by kava, in southern California by the datura, in Siberia by monotonous drumming, in India by breath control. It is clear that there is widely distributed in the human race a potentiality for these types of experience, and if the culture bestows rewards upon those who have them, a certain number of the population will achieve such experience. If, however, the culture does not reward the experience, very few and aberrant individuals will give evidence of it.

The nonreligious aspects of border-line psychological states are obvious to anyone in our civilization. Like the other traits we have been considering, they have nonreligious provenience. The problem that arises constantly is therefore: What is there in experiences of this type that has so often allied them with different religions? Why is it that they have tended to be so characteristic of religion?

The answer lies in the fact that the supernatural world is by its nature an "other" world. Those who have experiences which, by breaking through the routine world of the senses in any way, give them experience of an "other" world are often held to be its messengers and interpreters and to have the power of that world. The use by religion of such experiences seems therefore almost overdetermined, and it is easy to see why there is no uniformity in the particular type of experience regarded as religious. Any breaking through the routine sense experience will serve, but no culture can develop them all, and each region specializes in one or two which it approves as religious.

Cosmology and belief. The question of belief is of such importance in the churches today that it is necessary to justify its omission up to this point in a discussion of religion. With us a person is religious or nonreligious according to whether or not he holds certain beliefs. If he loses these he loses his religion. Our studies of comparative religions therefore tend to discuss the history of religion as if it were a history of certain dogmas.

The situation in our own civilization that has brought about the great emphasis upon belief and disbelief is a very special one. Scepticism is a habit in modern thought, and its extension in the field of religion has made the issue of belief acute. But in primitive societies beliefs about the gods are rarely the subject of scepticism. What any people knows about the supernatural is handed down in the same way as their conventions about forbidden degrees of marriage or about propitious behavior on the part of a hunting party. It is traditional knowledge and is accepted as such. The question of belief or disbelief in the gods arises only in that slight fashion in which scepticism about agricultural techniques or exogamous restrictions may also arise.

Nevertheless there is belief; that is, there is a superstructure of dogma and of cosmology that is built upon the fundamental behavior that is religious in that locality. This superstructure of belief, like the other traits of the religious complex we have just discussed, is strictly analogous to the superstructures that are built up around other cultural traits. Chieftainship may be secularly conceived and be elaborated as in Samoa with traditional genealogies and tales of folklore, quite after the fashion of religious cosmology. The great potlatching system of the Northwest Coast of North America is similarly buttressed by traditional history and songs. Culture traits of any kind may acquire this kind of elaboration if they are strongly emphasized in any culture; it is by no means a peculiarity of religion.

Nevertheless the fact that the strongest single characteristic of religion is that it handles the world as animate gives special impetus to this myth-making faculty in religion. Myths grow up around kings and potlatching, but these institutions do not give the kind of freedom to the human imagination that is provided by the religious idea that the whole world is animate and that man can entreat it and make it propitious. The supernatural is an "other" world that he can picture as he pleases.

Cosmology and supernatural lore therefore have developed richly upon religious soil. They have expressed themselves quite differently in different parts of the world, sometimes finding rich expression in myth and sometimes in temple practices, sometimes becoming an absorbing interest in the culture, sometimes pared down to a minimum. Sometimes this myth-making centers itself around pantheons, sometimes around the dead or the unborn. With our increasing knowledge we no longer raise questions as to whether we can call peoples religious who have no idea of gods or of reward in the afterworld. Myth-making may take very diverse forms and still be analogous. No peoples need to expend their cosmological energies in the same way, and they have by no means done so.

Cosmology should be studied always in relation to the life of the tribe in question, the behavior of its members, and the institutions it exalts. Cosmology is often a commentary upon this life that is not to be excelled, and sets forth the virtues and vices of the culture from the point of view of the native himself. It gives free play to the wishes that are uppermost under the forms of society that prevail in that culture. It is for its help in understanding an individual culture that the study of a cosmology is primarily important. Generalizations as to the nature of primitive religious beliefs are singularly unrewarding.

Nevertheless there are a few misconceptions that may be pointed out. There is no evidence of an evolutionary development of belief which ends in monotheism. Various situations, in many different parts of the world and in tribes of very different degrees of cultural complexity, have brought about the idea of one highest and supreme god, and there seems to be no reason for giving this dogma any particular prominence in discussions of religion.

The question of the nature of the supernatural, whether the dead, or spirits of places, or freely fabricated deities, is of greater interest. The supernaturals are locally animals or ghosts or gods, and characteristic practices develop on the basis of each of these beliefs. In North America religion makes only the most tenuous use of the dead. The association of the masked gods of the Pueblos with the impersonal dead is unusual in America, and even that is slightly developed. In much of Africa, on the other hand, religion is directed primarily toward the family dead. All the circumstances under which an individual would give help to another in this life are thought to hold also for the other life, and the ghost is thought to have the greater power. Therefore a strong and influential man is considered still a strong and influential ghost, and a person of the immediate family group is considered still the ghost to whom a petition and gifts supporting it should be presented. The good spirits are those who are still kept in human remembrance by their families. When memory of them lapses, they are no longer helpful to man, but join the class of bad spirits. This family cult of the dead is basic in the greater part of Africa even when there are also gods and fetishes that play important rôles.

In our own cultural background supernaturals are personifications of good and of evil. This follows out in cosmology our prevailing picture of the cosmic conflict of these two forces. But this is not a usual theme of cosmologies. Just as supernatural power is in most religions either good or bad according to the use made of it, so a god is either good or bad according to circumstances. This has made for much misunderstanding in missionary work. It has led to much misinterpretation of primitive mythology and religion also. Many cosmologies cannot be understood at all unless we can lay aside our categories of good and evil. This is most true in cosmologies of the trickster type. The trickster is a fairly common character in primitive mythology, in many cases the person foremost in the religious thought of the tribe. He brought the world to its present shape; he instituted the customs; he especially blessed the tribe to which he belongs. But he is a figure without honor and without dignity even from the point of view of the ethical standards of the tribe in question. He is lascivious, or a gormandizer, or foolish, or a boaster. He is often a dupe in the most trivial circumstances. He made this world what it is in the course of pursuing his own pleasures. According to the ideas of the natives no veneration is due him, and of course no thanks. But he is their favorite figure of mythology, and he is the crux of their religious conceptions.

Ethical sanctions. The higher ethical religions are often distinguished from the primitive religions. All the former are elaborations of the theme of the conflict of good and evil, and it gives a particular cast to their moral sanctions. As we have just seen, primitive cosmologies are often elaborated in direct contradiction of this theme. Supernatural power, likewise, is usually not thought of as a power for good alone. Religion has not in such cases, therefore, the thoroughgoing identification with morality to which we are accustomed. The aspiration to lead a better life is not in such religions the reason for seeking relationship with the supernatural.

This should not blind us to the fact that religious sanctions are often massed behind many points of conduct. Behavior that is regarded as wrong is often supernaturally punished. The charms placed upon fruit trees in Dobu act to inflict disease upon the thief. Any unjustified claim to power on the Plains is punished by the outraged spirit which a man has presumed to use. But there is the greatest diversity in different cultures as to what behavior is supernaturally guaranteed and what is not. Often neighboring tribes will differ, one of them punishing the breaking of an incest ruling, for instance, by supernatural agencies, and the other punishing the same crime by action of an assembly of old men.

Nor are all the cultures that use religion as a sanction for ethical conduct found upon the plane of complex civilization. The Manus people of the Bismarck Archipelago have an ethical religion, and it would be hard to imagine a culture that more consistently used all their supernatural concepts to back a puritanical code of morals.[32] The recently dead, the fathers and elder brothers of the household, become the guardian spirits of the heads of the households. They watch their mortal charges in every word and deed. When any illness occurs in the village, mediums consult these guardian spirits as to the reason why they have withheld their protection from their protégés. The answers give multitudes of reasons why friction has occurred, for the mediums are women who know intimately the persons involved, and who are in complete command of their wits. Of these causes of friction the chief are instances of wrongdoing that have offended the guardian spirits, and the wrongdoers must make restitution. Minute sex offenses are held up years afterward as the cause of deaths in related families. Feeling runs very high, and the strict moral code of Manus is rigidly upheld by the supernatural sanctions.

It is far commoner, however, for any local form of morality to be upheld without recourse to religion. In our own civilization marriage has at times been a sacrament with religious sanction, and at other times a secular affair. We are quite familiar with the fact that strong affect which has no religious connection may accompany errors in behavior. On the other hand, when some item of behavior is backed by religious sanctions, like the Jewish food taboos, though the physical repulsion is not necessarily stronger than in our taboo against dog flesh, there is a tendency for the taboo to be maintained as long as the religion is intact, and to collapse with it when it disappears.

FOOTNOTES

1. The study of "origins" in religion has never been anything but a convenient way of designating efforts to isolate the core of religion. The "origin" given by each student is only what he conceives to have been the fundamental basis of religion in human life. For a discussion of certain anthropological origins that have been proposed, see Lowie, R. H., *Primitive Religion* (1924), pp. 106–163.
2. Durkheim, E., *The Elementary Forms of the Religious Life* (English translation, London, 1915).
3. Hauer, J. W., *Die Religionen*, Bd. I: "Das religiöse Erlebnis auf den unteren Stufen" (Berlin, 1923).
4. King, I., *The Development of Religion* (1910); Ames, E. S., *Religion* (1929).
5. Frazer, J. G., *Totemism and Exogamy* (London, 1910), vol. 3, p. 142.
6. Marett, R. R., *The Threshold of Religion* (1914), p. 17.
7. *Ibid.*, pp. 1–72.
8. Malinowski, B., "Magic, Science, and Religion," in *Science, Religion, and Reality*, edited by Joseph Needham (1925), pp. 73–83; also "Anthropology," in *Encyclopaedia Britannica*, Supplement to 13th Edition.
9. Frazer, J. G., *The Golden Bough* (3rd ed., London, 1907–15), vol. I, p. 221.
10. *The Jesuit Relations*. See Kenton, Edna, *Indians of North America*, vol. 1 (1927), pp. 117–118.
11. Bogoras, W., *The Chukchee*, Jesup Expedition, vol. 7 (1904–09), pp. 499–507.
12. The standard collection of magic practices is Frazer, J. G., *The Golden Bough;* see also Skeat, W. W., and Blagden, C. O., *Malay Magic* (1900); Williams, F. E., *Orokaiva Magic* (London, 1928).
13. Lowie, R. H., *Primitive Religion* (1924), p. 322.
14. Fortune, R. F., "Manus Religion," *Memoirs of the American Philosphical Society*, vol. 3 (1935), pp. 215, 216.
15. Ivens, W., *Island Builders of the Pacific* (London, 1930), p. 217.

16. Goddard, P. E., *Hupa Texts*, University of California Publications in American Archaeology and Ethnology, vol. 1 (1904), pp. 252–368.
17. Speck, F. G., *Naskapi* (1935), pp. 127 ff.
18. Kingsley, M., *West African Studies* (1901), p. 110.
19. Mead, M., "A Lapse of Animism among a Primitive People," *Psyche*, vol. 9 (1928), pp. 72–77.
20. Bogoras, W., *op. cit.*; Czaplicka, M. A., *Aboriginal Siberia* (Oxford, 1914).
21. Stevenson, M. C., *Zuñi Indians*, Annual Report of the Bureau of American Ethnology, vol. 23 (1904); Bunzel, R., *Introduction to Zuñi Ceremonialism*, Annual Report of the Bureau of American Ethnology, vol. 47 (1932), pp. 467–1086.
22. Bunzel, R., *Zuñi Ritual Poetry*, Annual Report of the Bureau of American Ethnology, vol. 47 (1932).
23. Fortune, R. F., *Sorcerers of Dobu* (1932).
24. Durkheim, E., *op. cit.*
25. Lowie, R. H., "Ceremonialism in North America," *American Anthropologist*, vol. 16 (1914), pp. 602 ff.
26. Spier, L., *The Sun Dance of the Plains Indians*, Anthropological Papers, American Museum of Natural History, vol. 16 (1921), pp. 451–527.
27. Goldenweiser, A. A., *History, Psychology and Culture* (1933), pp. 377–388.
28. Hauer, J. W., *op. cit.*
29. Dixon, R. B., *The Shasta*, American Museum of Natural History, Bulletin 17, Part V (1907).
30. Ellis, A. B., *Ewe Speaking Tribes of the Slave Coast of West Africa* (London, 1890), p. 148.
31. Williams, T., *Fiji and the Fijians* (London, 1860), vol. 1, p. 228.
32. Fortune, R. F., *Manus Religion*.

GENERAL REFERENCES

Durkheim, E., *The Elementary Forms of the Religious Life* (English translation, London, 1915).

Hauer, J. W., *Die Religionen*, Bd. I: "Das religiöse Erlebnis auf den unteren Stufen" (Berlin, 1923).

Lowie, R. H., *Primitive Religion* (1924).

Radin, P., *Primitive Religion* (1937).

Santayana, G., *The Life of Reason*, vol. 3, "Reason in Religion" (1926).

CHAPTER XV

METHODS OF RESEARCH

Franz Boas

The attempts to explain ethnic phenomena by analogy with those of other sciences appear to be an expression of the helplessness of the investigator, of whom the development of a rigid method of handling his problems is demanded. Herbert Spencer based his system on the analogy between society and an organism.[1] This analogy was still more rigidly worked out by A. Schäffle.[2] Later on, stimulated by biological observations and hypotheses, the analogy between ethnic phenomena and organic recapitulation of phylogeny in ontogeny became a favorite theme of theorists who sought in the development of the child a repetition of the development of the race, and tried to explain child psychology on the basis of a constructed history of human culture and *vice versa*. This is largely the basis of certain investigations of developmental psychology.[3] At present the peculiar customs of many primitive people which remind us of actions of the mentally deranged are being made use of to explain ethnic phenomena of perfectly healthy groups of primitive man. The doubtful — in my opinion fanciful — interpretations of psychoanalysis are transferred to the domain of primitive life although conflicts in alien cultures may be based on social conditions entirely distinct from our own. Such analogies seem to me entirely misleading. We must rather attempt to investigate primitive life purely objectively.

It must be asked what are the data that may be secured and what are our objectives.

For a long time conditions were such that we had to find first of all a standard by which the activities of members of alien cultures could be described. In other words, the handicrafts, economic conditions, beliefs, and practices of primitive people had to be described according to general observations and information received by the observer. The individual was unimportant compared with the general standards of culture. Even in books describing the characteristics of European or Asiatic peoples there is a clear tendency to isolate from out of the mass of varying individual behavior that which is characteristic of a people as a whole. The fatalism of the Turk, the logical mind of the French, the sentimentality of the German, are such traits that are mere abstractions derived from general impressions.

The essential difficulty in obtaining a clear understanding of the problem is that we do not know how primitive cultures came to be what they are. The standardized picture appears as a stable fabric. We do not know whence it came nor whither, if left alone, it would drift.

In the development of scientific inquiry a number of questions develop; first of all, the problem whether a cause can be found for the particular static behavior that has been observed. The answer may be sought in various directions: it may be asked whether it is determined by the physical character of the people or by geographical and social environment; or whether it is due to historical causes. Speculative answers have been attempted along all these lines. On pages 117–121 we have discussed and criticized the theory that ascribes the character and customs of a people to their bodily build. We repeat that the proof of an important influence of racial descent has not been given. Individually the hereditary determination of behavior under given conditions is presumably important; but since each race includes a large number of biologically distinct strains which in regard to their functional activities overlap, race alone cannot have an essential influence upon cultural behavior. The distinction between the behavior of pure-bred strains of domesticated animals that do show decidedly distinct racial personalities and the human races which include many varieties of personalities must again be emphasized.

Not even the most opinionated biologist would dare to claim that the cultural pattern of a group of people of the same descent has always remained the same. The pure-blood pygmy living in the woods and his congeners forming regiments under orders of the Mangbattu are hardly culturally identical; nor are the Turks who swept over Europe the same as the Kemalites of our day. The Indian of the Plains in the days when distinction was obtained by warlike deeds and his poverty-stricken descendant of our days are culturally worlds apart. The Zulu of Chaka's time and the one who is assiduously studying arts and sciences are of the same blood, but their minds run in different channels.

It cannot be shown by the widest stretch of the imagination that descent makes it impossible to partake of any given type of culture, provided the individual is completely socially one of the people among whom he lives and, what is more important, is considered also by society as one of its members.

The biological approach is not promising when we wish to understand the history of cultures. We have also shown the limitations of the attempts to explain culture as due to environmental and economic factors. These have their influence upon existing cultures, limiting certain activities and facilitating others, but they do not create culture. In an analysis of culture these influences have to be considered, but they do not explain the foundations of the fabric.

The indispensable means for clearing up the history of culture are data that exhibit, not the static picture of our time, but the actual changes of earlier times. Unfortunately these data are not amenable to observation. Under unusually favorable conditions archaeological data give us information on the gradual changes of material culture and allow also inferences regarding a few aspects of the inner life of the people. Arid countries like Egypt, large parts of Asia, southwestern United States, parts of Mexico, Peru, and Bolivia are of this character. Every one of these countries has yielded data that allow us to see changing cultures, local types developing here and there, inner developments and foreign elements giving rise to new forms. The prehistory of Europe, notwithstanding all its doubtful problems, presents the same picture.

By far the larger part of the world does not permit the application of this method, either on account of lack of prehistoric material, or because of breaks in the record due to a sudden displacement of one people by another. Under these circumstances there is no truly historical material available, and whatever results can be obtained must be based on conditions as they existed at the time when each culture was studied. Historical data can only be inferred from these.

The tradition of primitive people is an unsafe guide for the reconstruction of cultural history. Generally the knowledge of the past treasured by primitive people is underestimated. In many cases the names of seven or more generations of ancestors are remembered, but the details regarding their lives are scanty and often tell no more than their marriages and warlike deeds, which from the point of view of cultural history give little light. In North America one may hear of the time when horses were first introduced among a certain tribe. The Eskimo of Frobisher Bay recall many details of the visit of Frobisher in 1577. More often remote tradition becomes fantastic and intermingled with mythical tales. Tales of migrations are particularly liable to be purely mythological. Therefore traditions of early times that contain elements apparently important from an historical point of view can be utilized only if there is ample corroborative evidence.

If every culture were absolutely isolated the only possible method would consist in a comparison of similar features and of inferences that could be based on these. The compilations of Frazer,[4] Spencer, Bastian, and many others are founded on this assumption. The method is vitiated by two facts: one, that cultures are not isolated but interdependent; the other, that analogies of cultural traits are often fallacious and lead to faulty identifications of diverse phenomena.

The very fact that cultures are interdependent permits us to reconstruct historical happenings with a fair degree of certainty. It is Ratzel's great merit to have emphasized this possibility. In some cases concrete results may be obtained. As an example we may recall the distribution of maize in America. When it became known that Mexico was the home of the wild plant from which Indian corn is descended, it followed that the cultivation must have spread from there north and south. Similarly with all other features the home of which can be determined. If by good fortune archaeological evidence gives us a clue as to the time when they first appeared in parts of the area, it may even be possible to reconstruct some sort of approximate chronology. Similar conditions prevail when the importation of foreign materials indicates the direction of trade, particularly when the handling of the material imitates the methods in use in the place of its origin.

The observation that many cultural features are spread over limited geographical areas and do not occur outside of these gives us a means of studying cultural relations. The Sun Dance, for example, is confined to the Mississippi basin and part of the immediate neighborhood. It has many distinctive local features, but the complex as a whole, with many details, is common to the whole area. It is therefore safe to assume that it originated here and was adopted by many tribes that differ in many other respects.

Here, however, the question arises whether we can determine the place of origin. Many ethnologists hold to the opinion that wherever a certain cultural feature shows its strongest development, decreasing in complexity and importance as distance from its center increases, there must be its origin.

It does not require much thought to recognize that, while this may be the case, it is not by any means a necessary conclusion to be derived from the facts. It would be just as possible to assume a wide distribution of the basic feature which gained its highest development locally. It might even be that a foreign importation took root and developed vigorously in a new soil. The argument is as little conclusive as if we were to assume that a plant, like the Ginko, that is confined nowadays to one locality must have originated there, while paleontology proves that its distribution in earlier times was very wide.

In other words, while we can prove in many cases the fact of dissemination, it is often impossible to determine its direction. In some instances there is a strong plausibility for the direction in which cultural traits may have traveled, particularly when stray lines of diffusion emanate from a center or when a few stray elements are interspersed in a foreign culture. An example of such an occurrence is the American story of the deluge, which is ended by animals diving for earth. This occurs in a solid area in the region of the Great Lakes and farther west. On the Pacific coast it is found in a few isolated spots along trade routes, in British Columbia and California, but in very fragmentary and highly modified forms. It does not seem likely that we should search for its origin on the Pacific coast. If it were of wide distribution in that region the question would be open to doubt. An example of the stray occurrence of foreign elements is that of a few Indian stories among the Eskimo, few in number and rather distinctive in character. Another case is that of agriculture in North Australia, a cultural feature foreign to the rest of the continent. On the whole the direction of diffusion and the location of origin cannot often be ascertained, while historical relations can be demonstrated.

Distributional areas are most impressive in the domain of material culture, because under similar methods of obtaining sustenance, which are controlled by geographic conditions, whole complexes of objects and activities are common to fairly large areas. On this basis the concept of "culture areas" has developed — first of all as a convenience in museum administration, because it made it possible to group material from many different tribal units in one comprehensive scheme.

Unfortunately the primary object of this grouping was soon forgotten and the culture areas were assumed to be natural groups that divided mankind into so many cultural groups. Actually the student interested in religion, social organization, or some other aspect of culture would soon discover that the culture areas based on material culture do not coincide with those that would naturally result from his studies. This is most easily seen in the complete disagreement between linguistic groups and culture areas. Attempts to map the distribution of definite cultural traits that occur over continuous areas prove that various forms overlap irregularly. Culture areas have a meaning only from the particular point of view from which they have been obtained. To give only one example. The form of material culture of the tribes of northern Vancouver Island is so similar to that of the northern coast of British Columbia that it would be difficult to differentiate between the two. On the other hand the social organization and the concept of the origin of families are totally different.

The establishment of culture areas as units of general validity has also led to the concept of marginal cultures which are liable to be considered as inferior to the centers in which the traits of the culture area are most fully developed. Here also serious misunderstandings arise if we generalize this concept. It may well be that a culture is not so thoroughly institutionalized as another neighboring one and that, at the same time, the material possessions may be less complex. It does not follow that the cultural life of the people is poorer, because it is not so easy for the observer to formalize a culture permitting greater freedom to the individual. The concept of culture area should therefore always be used with a clear understanding of its limitations.

We have spoken so far of the possibility of analyzing a culture in regard to the provenience of the elements composing the whole. There are other indications that permit us now and then to infer that new developments have occurred. This is the case particularly when a cultural trait appears in a strong contrast to the needs of everyday life. An example is the tent of the Reindeer Chukchee, an exceedingly clumsy affair, difficult to transport on account of the weight of the cover and the many tent poles required for its erection. Its plan may be derived from the semi-subterranean house of the

Maritime Chukchee, which has low walls and a flat roof. The arrangement of the low walls is imitated by a series of low tripods placed in a circle over which the roof is erected. The contrast between this tent and the light tent of the Eskimo, which may be transported on a single sledge, is striking. A similar case is probably the semi-subterranean house of Northwest America, which extends through part of California and has its analogue in the ceremonial kiva of the Pueblos, in whose home climatic conditions do not require the protection offered by this structure in more inhospitable climates.

The whole group of "survivals" which has been so thoroughly exploited by Tylor belongs to this group. There is no doubt that a thorough analysis of cultures will indicate the persistence of earlier stages. I am inclined to believe that the custom of the Northwest Coast Indians of having certain initiates come in through the roof, and their tales of supernatural beings who approach through the roof, indicate that in early times subterranean lodges with entrance through the roof were used or at least known to the people.

In these attempts we are naturally led to the problem as to whether it can be decided which are the oldest traits of a culture. If it were possible to point out chronologically those traits that are late introductions, this problem would be solved, but it seems more than doubtful whether a generally valid method can be discovered except in the cases of the occurrence of discordant survivals. Examples are: the custom of using stone implements in rituals long after the use of bronze or iron had been invented; the production of fire by drilling when more effective methods were known; and the many cases of conservative resistance in our own culture to changes the usefulness of which is readily recognized — for example, resistance to changes in the forms of our alphabet, the keyboard of the piano, our calendar, our system of measures.

If it were possible to determine certain groups of ethnic phenomena that are exceptionally constant and that are always stable our problem might be solved. Physical type, language, social organization, invention, religious ideas, may all be stable or unstable, according to local and historical conditions. As long as, on account of their diverse degrees of stability or instability, no grave inner conflicts develop, the most heterogeneous congeries of cultural traits may exist, in which it is impossible to determine what is old and what is new. Some kind of formalization always develops that makes apparently contradictory ideas compatible.

The study of the distribution of cultural traits which we have so far discussed will give us a limited amount of information in regard to historical facts, illustrating the former relations between tribes.

The problem of the development of culture is not by any means exhausted by even the fullest information that may be obtained by the study of archaeology and of distribution. Notwithstanding incongruities that are never entirely absent, each culture is a whole, and its form has a dynamic force which determines the behavior of the mass of individuals. It is only from their thoughts and acts, from the products of their actions, that we derive the concept of their culture. How far an individual is able to free himself from the fetters that culture lays upon him depends not only upon his individuality but equally, if not more, upon the culture imposed upon him. History gives us no direct clue to an understanding of the expression of culture in individual life.

To give an example. For the illiterate speaker the history of his language is irrelevant. What is important for an understanding of the function of language in cultural life is the question how the Procrustean bed of language shapes ideas; how the emotional tone of words and phrases influences action; and how the activities of man modify language. The same is no less true in other fields. The cultural conditions of a people have had a long history. We want to know that history; but even an intimate knowledge of the past does not explain the reactions of an individual living at a given moment to the cultural and individual stresses that determine his actions. While historical data may permit us every now and then to infer from observed changes the forces that are released by the interplay of all the different elements of culture acting upon each person according to his individuality and resulting in stability or change, we can never obtain a clear insight into these except by the study of a multitude of individuals reacting to a culture, and by study of the cumulative effect of these reactions.

A detailed study of the behavior of many individuals at a given moment may disclose tendencies of change, because some of them will lag behind and represent an earlier stage of culture while others forge ahead of their time. In some cases it will be possible to evaluate the relative strength of lag and of forward push that permits a fairly safe prognosis of the direction in which cultural phenomena may be moving. An excellent example of such analysis has been given by Alexander Lesser in his monograph on the hand game of the Pawnee [5] in which, through a study of the changes that occurred during the past sixty or seventy years, adjustments of new tendencies and old customs have been traced. In a similar way adjustments may be observed in the household arrangements of the Kwakiutl Indians. In olden times the people used to sit at meal time leaning against a backboard, their knees drawn up, the food being spread on a mat. In feasts they continue this habit, but when eating in the family circle they use nowadays a low table, about fifteen centimeters high, and a very low stool. It may be predicted that the height of table and stool will increase. The modern houses are also an adjustment of the American frame house to their social requirements. The front room is large and unfurnished, with a stove in the center, corresponding to the old square house with a fire in the middle; the living quarters, which in olden times consisted of small sheds surrounding the central room, have now been relegated to the rear of the house. In our own culture the increasing tendency to socialization, to the better adjustment between the needs of the individual and those of society as a whole, presents a similar spectacle.

We may perhaps compare the problem of the predictability of cultural changes with that of the predictability of the movements of a number of bodies distributed in space, the velocity of each being known. On the basis of our knowledge of the laws of gravitation the future movements and positions of these bodies may be predicted. In the case of social phenomena the "laws" are not so well known, and on account of the multiplicity of contradictory elements prediction is not certain. Nevertheless the general dynamic tendencies of cultural change may be understood by such an analysis.

The historical study needs as its supplement knowledge of the dynamic processes that may be observed in living cultures. These in their turn will throw light upon historical happenings, for conditions of the past may be better understood by knowledge of the processes that may be observed at the present time. Based on these considerations, the hope has arisen anew that laws of general validity may be found that control all historical happenings, that allow us to state not only the dynamic conditions controlling the interplay between the different manifestations of cultural life, but also the necessary sequences of cultural forms.

A number of social tendencies that are apparently generally valid may be isolated. Their psychological basis and the forms in which they find expression may be studied. Thus the solidarity of social groups and their antagonism toward the outsider; the forms and motives for coördination and subordination; imitation of, and resistance to, outside influences; competition between individuals and between groups; division of labor; amalgamation and segregation; attitudes toward the supernatural — to mention only a few — may be investigated. These expressions of social life are generally valid. The same is true of individual mental states and processes. Fear and hope, love and hate, the valuation of good and bad, of beautiful and ugly, are general human characteristics that find expression in social conduct. From these studies a cultural morphology may be constructed and a social psychology developed, based on the variety of manifestations of these categories.

A cultural morphology is necessarily founded on comparative studies of similar forms in different parts of the world. If its data are to be significant for the development of social laws, similarities due to cultural dissemination must be eliminated. Thus the similarities between administrative organization and judicial procedure found in Africa cannot be considered as expressions of a law of development of human culture, because they must be considered as part of the general cultural development of Europe, and of a large part of Asia. This is proved by the contrast between Old World and aboriginal American institutions. The development of African iron industry and cattle-breeding is also historically related to those of other parts of the Old World. If these are excluded, there remain morphological similarities that require study.

To this group belong similarities in the forms of relationship systems based on distinct principles of classification, many of which are so irregularly distributed that historical unity of origin is practically excluded. Their similarities may be compared to those expressed in language in which similar principles of classification of concepts are found in disconnected areas; such as masculine and feminine, animate and inanimate.

The morphological classification leads to two problems: the one, how far the various types represent a progressive series; the other, whether they can be reduced to general socio-psychological laws.

The system of forms established on the basis of morphological likeness and unlikeness has no historical value unless it can be proved that the forms actually follow one another in historical sequence. Errors, based on the assumption that these classes represent a historical sequence, are found mainly in the writings of the evolutionary school. They appear in a variety of forms. Thus the classification of certain art forms beginning with naturalistic representation and leading to conventionalized forms is valid; but this does not prove that this classification coincides with an historical sequence, unless actual historical proof can be given. In its absence validity can be claimed only for the constant interplay between realism and conventionalism.

Art is also quite often associated with religious ideas; but this does not prove that the origin of art must be looked for in religious motives. A classification of the forms of art from this viewpoint has no necessary relation to their historical development. In some cases the religious significance of the work of art will stimulate the development of a higher style; in other cases it will induce slovenly execution, perhaps due to the short-lived usefulness of the object.

To this group also belongs the much discussed problem of the development of family organization, whether maternal institutions must precede paternal succession. The various chapters of the present volume show that the proof of a uniform historical sequence cannot be given.

The question of development in a definite direction is closely connected with our concept of progress. The very concept of progress presupposes a standard toward which culture advances, and a decision cannot be avoided as to what this standard is to be. It seems almost unavoidable that this standard will be based on our own experience, on our own civilization. It is clear that this is an arbitrary standard and it is perhaps the greatest value of anthropology that it makes us acquainted with a great variety of such standards. Before the question can be decided as to what progress is, we must know whether general human values exist by which we may measure progress.

In one respect we may well speak of progress. Since earliest times knowledge and control of nature have received constant additions without any serious losses. New powers have been acquired and new insight has been opened. The ability of man to cope with his environment has improved, and new resources have been made available. At the same time the progress of knowledge has led to the elimination of error. The conflict between rational thought, on the one hand, and emotional reactions and rigid tradition, on the other, has tended to lead to the supremacy of reason, although the

METHODS OF RESEARCH 677

emotional elements have continued and still continue to shape the form of culture.

The step from knowledge acquired for the most part accidentally, through daily experience, to systematic inquiry has not often been made. The astrologers of Babylonia and Mexico, the mathematicians of India and Yucatan, the Chinese, and the Greeks succeeded in taking this step. Even when this advance was made, imagination and tradition were not at once eliminated, but entered into the structure of early science.

If we should value progress entirely by the development of invention and knowledge, it would be easy to arrange the divisions of mankind in order of progress, beginning with the simplest cultures of early Paleolithic man and leading up to modern civilizations in Europe and its colonies and in many parts of Asia.

It is not so easy to define progress in other aspects of culture, except in so far as increasing knowledge weakens the hold of older concepts. This may be illustrated by the advance in ethical behavior. Westermarck,[6] Hobhouse,[7] and Sutherland[8] have given us full data on the evolution of ethical behavior, but it is not by any means clear that this is identical with an advance in ethical ideas. Ethical behavior may well be understood as reflecting the same moral ideas in different types of society and modified by existing institutions and by the extent of knowledge. The languages of people all over the world prove that the vices that we know, such as murder, theft, lying, rape, are recognized and in most cases discountenanced within the social group in which mutual duties are recognized. The difference consists largely in the increasing recognition of rights of those outside of one's own group, and these are based on an appreciation of similarities that were previously not recognized. While in early times the outsider was an enemy just as much as a wild beast, his human rights were slowly understood, a process that is not yet completed, since to us the rights of the alien are still considered on a level different from the rights of the citizen.[9]

It is perhaps still more difficult to define progress in social organization since in this field our own ideals are not uniform. "The extreme individualist might consider anarchy as his ideal. Others may believe in extreme voluntary regimentation; still others in a powerful control of the individual by society or in subjection to intelligent — or emotional and unintelligent — leadership. Developments in all these directions have occurred and may still be observed in the history of modern States. We may speak of progress in certain directions, hardly of absolute progress, except in so far as it is dependent upon knowledge which contributes to the safety of human life, health, and comfort." [10]

The widening of the concept of humanity has had a very slow influence upon the breaking up of the concept of the status of an individual. The French Revolution tried to abolish it and the young American Republic rejected it, although it continued to maintain the status of slavery. In modern western civilization the extent to which the status of a person is determined by birth or by social segregation has been losing in force. In the United States the racial status of the Negro and East Asiatic still prevails, and Germany has relapsed into the crudity of determining the status of an individual by his racial descent. In primitive societies of complex structure the status of a person as member of a clan, an age group, a ranking group, is often absolutely determined. In the group of relatives it depends upon his position in the family, as parent, uncle or aunt, parent-in-law, and so on. In most societies the status determined by sex is rigid because it depends upon the unescapable economic duties of man and woman and upon the limitations put upon woman by her sexual life. With the change of these conditions in modern life the status of woman has lost most of its fixity, and it may be predicted that its artificial reëstablishment which is being attempted in Germany will prove futile.

These considerations show that a historical interpretation of classifications of social forms as expressing progress can be achieved to a very limited extent only.

Another problem of the morphology of culture refers to the interrelation between various manifestations of cultural life.

There is an obvious interrelation between economic conditions and other aspects of life. Hunting tribes compelled to wander about, following the game, and having no domesticated animals to help in the transportation of goods, cannot amass bulky property. Their industrial products will be confined to the necessities of life. Their handiwork may be technically perfect and even show an appreciation of adornment, but the necessity to avoid encumbering the wanderer will act as a hindrance to the development of industries. If the conditions happen to be more propitious, so that food may be accumulated and stored for a longer period, perhaps to such an extent that larger gatherings of members of the tribe and of friendly tribes become possible, new stimuli may arise, connected with the periodic stability of the groups and their stronger social contacts. On the other hand, a stable population with a plentiful food supply that does not necessitate constant exertion on the part of every member of the tribe to procure the necessary food supply will give opportunity for more varied industrial activities and the accumulation of property. A dense population, which can arise only when the food supply is ample, leads, if the group forms a political unit, to division of labor and necessitates a more rigid social organization. When the political units remain small, the influence of the density of population may be very slight.

It is advantageous to investigate those types of social conduct that are mutually contradictory and therefore cannot exist side by side. Sparsity of population and complex political organization; isolation of small groups of individuals that are economically self-sustaining and elaborate division of labor; inability to preserve food supply and capitalism; nomadic life and high development of architecture; elaborate music and absence of wind, string, or other tuned instruments; formal law without any kind of legal sanctions, are such contradictions. Others not so evident may be discovered. In their study it will be found that sometimes the most devious ways are used to make it possible for contradictory types of behavior to exist side by side. Thus the Toda insist on strict endogamy in formal marriage, but permit exogamic relations. Some North American tribes insist on valor as a proof of manhood, but honor at the same time a person who refuses to go to war.

The existence of certain fundamental relations between social phenomena of distinct types may be illustrated by many examples. In an attempt to apply them to specific cultures many important variations are found, so that the fundamental points are often obscured. The poor hunters and food-gatherers of Tierra del Fuego are, so far as their food supply is concerned, no worse off than the fishing and hunting people of both coasts of the North Pacific Ocean. Though they lack abundance of vegetable products and of wood easily worked, this alone does not sufficiently explain the difference, both in quality and quantity, of their industrial products. In their case other causes have interfered with the clear expression of the relation between food supply, possibility of stable location, and cultural development.

The attempts to correlate forms of relationship systems with different cultural levels have also failed. It is quite true that in a small, inbreeding population the system of social relationship may include all the members of the community, while in widely scattered groups the social bond uniting members of common descent or those bound by ties of affinity may be highly modified. Nevertheless there is no evidence that density of population, stability of location, or economic status is necessarily connected with a particular system of relationship and of behavior connected with it. The scattered community may preserve part of its unity in a sib organization, or it may break apart in small families held together by cultural interests of a different order.

The dynamic conditions controlling the permanence of large groups of relatives and their breaking up may be described. Their manifestation in any particular society cannot be determined on the basis of these dynamic laws alone, but is dependent upon each particular social constellation.

The lack of specific coherence between various aspects of culture has been effectively illustrated by Andrew Lang in his introduction to K. Langloh Parker's book, *The Euahlayi Tribe*,[11] where he shows that social organization and types of religious ideas cannot be considered as mutual determinants.

The very existence of society must depend upon the preponderance of unity over disruptive forces. Native cultures are subject to such disruptive forces during periods of transition to modern standards. Thus the Pueblos of the North American Southwest have split into separate groups of conservatives and progressives with the result that the progressives in some cases have established villages of their own. The struggle between the uniting and disrupting forces does not mean that every culture strives for a maximum of harmony. On the contrary, there are many in which the individual cannot lead a happy life without conflicts within the tribe. Societies torn by vendetta or by fear of witchcraft are examples of this condition. The extent to which disrupting forces are tolerated depends entirely upon the type of culture and the emotional strength of the contradictory tendencies.

It seems most desirable and worth while to understand each culture as a whole and to define its character. In our modern civilization the social groups are so highly differentiated that it would be difficult to indicate more than general tendencies resulting from many conflicting or even contradictory attitudes. The political fanatic, the scientist, the unskilled laborer, the industrial magnate, cannot be welded into the picture of one personality, although all of them are part and parcel of our civilization. The impression prevails that in simple cultures in which there is no cultural differentiation the individual is much more strictly a representative of the whole culture, and that in these cases it is possible to give a picture of the culture which is at the same time a picture of a personality. It is not quite easy to determine the value of such a picture. Is it that of a "typical" representative personality? In how far is such a picture schematic? Can the investigator grasp this picture without coloring it by his own subjective attitudes?

The difficulties of this problem are obvious and are analogous to those confronting us in the attempt to understand a personality as a whole. Many psychologists try in vain to determine the traits of a personality by means of experimental observations of its attitude in a number of simple, controlled situations. The answers they receive cannot give any information containing more than the observed reactions to these situations. The personality as a whole is not the sum of these single reactions, which are determined in part organically, in part culturally. The multiplicity of experiences brings about variable reactions determined by conflicts of wishes and desires, and only by grasping the whole of these can we gain a picture of the personality. In interpreting these results many psychologists are concerned in the question how far the varying reactions are organically determined. The personality of the observer and its influence upon his interpretations play an important rôle in the result of these studies. Otherwise we should not have so many contradictory interpretations of historic figures. When the psychologist or psychiatrist attempts to enter more deeply into the manifestations of mental life, he may perhaps give us new data for an understanding of personalities. Nevertheless the contradictions between the interpretations that are given to us prove that the picture is deeply influenced by the mind of the observer. When the attempt is made to establish types on this basis additional difficulties of interpretation are added.

New obstacles arise when we try to apply these methods to the study of types of culture. No matter how strongly a community may be controlled by dominating thoughts, they do not influence the behavior of the same individual at all times in the same ways, and different individuals also react to them each in his own way. A tolerably clear picture results only when the dominating form has such vigor that individualities are suppressed by it. The range of variations in the behavior of members of the tribe, the frequency or rarity of conflicts with the common behavior, determine the strength of custom in the life of the people. The mightier their influence, the more difficult it is for the individual to withstand it.

Marriage regulations may serve as an example. When endogamous marriages are strictly forbidden, there exists apparently, on the whole, sexual indifference between members of the opposite sexes who are not permitted to marry. Nevertheless passionate love between man and woman of tabooed relationship does occur, strong enough to run counter to custom. How far real sexual indifference exists can be determined only by means of a most detailed and thorough knowledge of the individuals. Observations of the customary behavior may be quite misleading. Our own experience of the sexual relations between brothers and sisters allows us to conclude that, owing to the presence of custom, sexual indifference is the rule. This inference is strengthened by the observation that in cultures that are disintegrating under the influence of European contact, restrictions of permitted marriage rules are liable to resist for a long time. It is more difficult to understand sexual indifference in those cases in which the choice of mates is restricted to few individuals, as it is in Australia, or in group exclusions in which the marriage of a man with a woman of another group prevents all reciprocal marriages of a man of the second group with a woman of the first group, as among the Gilyak.[12]

The customs regulating the hunt on which depends the well-being of the whole community are another example. Such dependence is found among the Eskimo. The individual is hardly in a position to free himself from their compelling force, for the danger of starvation is ever present; for this reason every member of the tribe is subject to the supervision of his acts by his tribe fellows.

In some cases the orientation of the tribe in relation to certain aspects of its culture finds expression even in its language. Thus the Dakota distinguish rigidly between the possession of objects that are the exclusive property of one person and can never belong to anyone else, such as the parts of his body; possessions that may be transferred to others; and another group that can never be the property of a single person, such as food, including meals prepared by a single individual, and objects of nature — in short, anything that the tribe needs for its sustenance. The categories of different types of possession are clearly and definitely expressed by linguistic forms.

These examples prove that behavior in relation to certain aspects of life may be governed by fundamental concepts and that these are amenable to objective observation.

In most cases their influence does not extend over the whole range of social forms, but is restricted in its scope. For the characterization of a culture we need a knowledge of those fundamental concepts that find expression in the widest range of social forms and activities.

Most attempts to characterize the social life of peoples are hampered by the lack of uniform behavior of all individuals, by the diversity of social activities, and by the subjective interest of the student, which is challenged by the contrast between the observed behavior and his own accustomed attitudes. The Eskimo are often described as good-natured, of sunny temperament. This seems to form a striking contrast to the difficulties of life in an Arctic climate. It is true that they are indifferent to the hardships of daily life and possess a tenacity of purpose that makes them feel as slight discomfort what might appear to us as unsupportable hardship, and the poor comforts of their homes give to them rest and social pleasures which they enjoy thoroughly. By contrast we observe among them subservience to the brutality of "strong men." The maltreated community endures their dominion until finally it rises and kills the tyrant. We note cases of treacherous murder among friends of long standing, fear of sickness, and a belief in the inclination of some to live the life of hermits. There is no fundamental trait from which the varied manifestations of social life can be viewed. Perhaps it might be said that in a community lacking stratification and characterized by general mutual friendliness a man of unusual physical and mental qualities and filled with an abnormal desire for power may become a tyrant; more so than in a tribe in which the privileges of every individual are subject to fixed norms and in which each has recognized rights and duties — provided these are not centered in one individual or in a small group. Perhaps even the tendency to isolation of individuals might be considered as due to the general conditions of life that force everyone to the utmost degree of self-reliance. Making allowance for all this, a clear-cut picture does not result. The love of the men for a playful practice of the art of carving which leads to the manufacture of well-executed figures of animals — a feature that is even more pronounced among the Chukchee and Koryak; the care which the women use in developing beautiful designs of clothing by means of contrasting effects of color of fur; the striking poverty of stories relating to animals as contrasted with folk tales dealing with human life, cannot be considered as closely correlated with other traits of their life. Notwithstanding the importance of economic conditions, there does not seem any reason why these features of social life should be designated as superstructure, for it cannot be shown that they are determined by economic conditions, although they bear a relation to them, as to all other phases of culture.

Much clearer and of unified character is the picture in those cultures in which a dominant idea rather than the predominant occupation controls life. This seems to be the case, for instance, among the Indians of the Plains. Not only was war a principal occupation, but the worth of a man depended to such an extent upon the glory of warlike deeds that the whole life seemed to be filled by the desire for what were considered heroic deeds. The imagination of the Eskimo dwells on the dangers and successes of the hunt of sea animals. The leading motive in the life of the Plains Indian was the desire for fame as a warrior. The difference in the situation among these two groups may perhaps be seen in a difference of affective emphasis. The Indian finds relief in an affective situation by going on the warpath either alone or with some friends. Mourning, shame, annoyance, are conquered by warlike deeds. Conventional ornament is interpreted as referring to war. Thus a design of two triangles with apices touching is viewed as two groups of warriors meeting in combat. To the observer this attitude seems the most prominent trait of their culture, a feature entirely foreign to the Eskimo.

Another trait is their love of elaborate ceremonialism, which is present on all occasions and plays an important rôle in their conduct of war. Every important affair calls for complicated and ostentatious ceremonies.

Nevertheless, this does not give an exhaustive picture, for the domestic life of these people opens other vistas. Within the tribe liberality, integrity, chastity, and mercifulness are subjects of praise. Neither is it permissible to generalize from the valor of the warrior and to assume that the Indian is free of fear. Not only the supernatural fills him with awe and frightens him; disease also breaks his courage and finds him full of fear of sorcery and of death.

Evidently, the wider the scope of a leading motive of culture the more it will appear as characteristic of the whole culture, but we must not be deceived into believing that it will give us an exhaustive picture of all the sides of culture.

As an example I may refer again to the Indians of the Northwest

Coast of America. The leading motive of their lives is the limitless pursuit of gaining social prestige and of holding on to what has been gained, and the intense feeling of inferiority and shame if even the slightest part of prestige has been lost. This is manifest not only in the attempts to attain a coveted high position, but equally in the endeavor to be considered the most atrocious member of the tribe. Rank and wealth are valued most highly, but there are also cases of criminals (in the sense of the culture we are discussing) who vie with each other in committing atrocities. A loss of prestige in either sense is a source of shame which must be made good by some action reëstablishing the lost respect. If this is not possible it leads to suicide. Art consists in the glorification of the family crest or of family histories. A pretense of excessive conservatism, often contradicted by obvious changes of behavior, is closely allied with the jealous watch over all privileges.

These tendencies are so striking that the amiable qualities that appear in intimate family life are easily overlooked. These are not by any means absent. In contrast to the jealousy with which prerogatives are guarded, everyone within the family circle belittles his position. Husband and wife address each other as "You whose slave I am," or "You whose dog I am." Parents and grandparents designate themselves in the same way when talking to their children, who in turn use nicknames when addressing their parents and grandparents.

The less pronounced the leading ideas of a simple culture, or the more varying the ideas of a tribe divided into social strata, the more difficult it is to draw a valid picture that does not contain contradictions. We cannot hope to do more than to elucidate the leading ideas, remembering clearly the limitations of their validity.

The socio-psychological study, more than any other aspect of anthropological investigation, requires that freedom from cultural prejudice which in itself can be attained only by the intensive study of foreign cultures of fundamentally distinctive types that make clear to us which among our own concepts are determined by our modern culture and which may be generally valid, because based on human nature.

FOOTNOTES

1. Spencer, H., *The Principles of Sociology* (3rd ed., 1888), vol. 1, pp. 435 ff.
2. Schäffle, A., *Bau und Leben des socialen Körpers* (Tübingen, 1875).
3. Briefly discussed in Kafka, G., *Handbuch der vergleichenden Psychologie* (München, 1922), vol. 1, pp. 412 ff.

4. Frazer, J. G., *Totemism and Exogamy* (London, 1910) and *The Golden Bough* (3rd ed., London, 1907–15).
5. Lesser, A., *The Pawnee Ghost Dance Hand Game*, Columbia University Contributions to Anthropology, vol. 16 (1933).
6. Westermarck, E., *The Origin and Development of Moral Ideas* (London, 1906).
7. Hobhouse, L. J., *Morals in Evolution* (London, 1906).
8. Sutherland, A., *The Origin and Growth of the Moral Instinct* (London, 1898).
9. Boas, F., *Anthropology and Modern Life* (1932), pp. 220 ff.
10. *Ibid.*, p. 228.
11. See page xvi.
12. Sternberg, L., *The Gilyak* (Ms.).

INDEX

INDEX

Abel, O., bipedal habit of man, 40; effect of desiccation of Central Asia, 116

Abortion, 384

Abstract concepts in language, 142

Acculturation, Zuñi, 356

Acheulian, epoch, 150; industries, 154, 178, 196

Acoma, pottery, 568, 569, 575

Acquisitiveness, 338

Adamaua, conquest by Fulbe, 520; society, 520–522; throwing knife, 242

Adjectival ideas expressed by nouns, 142

Adjustment of conflicting tendencies in social order, 426

Administrative organization in Old World, 675

Admiralty Islands, affinal exchange in, 389; trade, 399

Adultery, among harvesters, 509; cause of divorce, 449; punishment of, 496

Adze, 252

Aëta, climbing trees, 267

Affinal exchange, 364, 387, 388, 389, 441, 442

Affinity. *See Kinship terms*

Afghanistan, cultivation of rye, 291

Africa, adoption, 416; adultery, 449; alloys, 199; art, 538, 546, 547, 548, 550, 557, 580, 581; avoidance, 448; bark cloth, 256; bellows, 246; bride price, 329; cattle breeding, 675; cheese, absence of, 307; cöopera- tion, 516; copper, 199; courts, 348, 469; cult of the dead, 662; diffusion of maize and manioc culture, 296; economic value of women, 336; etiquette, 482; ex- cision of clitoris, 271; fetish, 646; filing of teeth, 538; folk tales, 477, 593, 597, 615; gorilla, 28; intro- duction of banana, 298; iron in- dustry, 210, 675; kingdoms in, 469; legal procedure, 518; lin- guistic and musical pitch, 602; markets, 397; maternal uncle, 420; menstrual blood, fear of, 371; metals in, 199; migrations, 106; monopolies, 349; musical instru- ments, 248, 605; mythologies, 621, 623; oracle, 643; origin of hominids, 39; pictographs, 272; prehistory, 154, 155, 196–198; proverbs, 478, 482, 596, 598; races, 102, 104; rhythm, 593; secret so- cieties, 429, 516; slavery, 402; status of women, 384, 470, 516; taxes, 392; throwing knives, 243; twins, 482; wild rice, 294, 502

— Central, caste, 403; lack of fixed territory, 491; pygmies, 491

— East, education, 480; feudalism, 349

— Northeast, throwing sticks, 243

— South, age groups, 410; colonization, 106; military groups, 412, 428; prestige, 462

— West, cowrie shells, 350; farming societies, 515; land ownership, 516; murder, 481; mythology, 623; prestige, 462; secret societies, 428, 518; slave raiding, 402; ta- boos, 644

See also Adamaua, Angola, An- kole, Ashanti, Badari, Bafiote, Baganda, Ba-Ila, Bakitara, Ba- kwiri, Bambala, Bantu Banya- nkole, Baoulé, Barotsi, Batanga, Bathonga, Bavenda, Benin, Bongo, Bornu, Bushmen, Bushongo, Cam- eroon, Congo, Cross River, Da- homeans, Duala, Egypt, Fan, Fulbe, Guanchos, Hamitic tribes, Haussa, Herero, Hottentot, Ibo, Ivory coast, Jagga, Kabyles, Kaf- ficho, Kafir, Lake Chad, Lango, Loango, Madagascar, Mangbattu, Masai, Negro, Nuba, Nyassa, Pangwe, Ruanda, Sudan, Togo, Tutsi, Twa, Unyoro, Urundi, Wa- huma, Yoruba, Zulu

Aggression, economic, 335

Agriculture, 286, 290–302; American, 216; geographical distribution, 221–222; government among agricultural societies, 515–519; of nomadic tribes, 313; origin, 201, 299; participation of sexes in, 299, 369, 370; Polynesian, 205; Polynesian and American compared, 209, 210, 294; use of hoe and plow, 282, 283, 298, 299; use of terraces, 202. See *Gardens, Plants*

Ainu, racial type, 102, 112

Alaska, languages, 136, 139; racial types, 102. See *America, Eskimo, Northwest Coast*

Alcoholic drinks, 255

Aleutians, slavery, 500

Algonquian, hunting territories, 289, 378; languages, 138, 139; medicine man, 639; terms for God, 629

— Northeast, hunting territories, 498

Allen, G. M., American dogs, 308

Alloys, in Africa, 199

Alpaca, 309, 310

Alpine type, 114

Altruism, 479

Amazon basin, folk tales, 612

Ameghino, F., prehistory of Argentina, 213

America, agriculture, 216, 302; art forms, 539; avoidance, 448; canoes, 269; contact with Whites, 120; democratic organization of tribes, 511; dog, 308; earliest man, 90, 91, 212, 215, 216; economics and totemism, 507; education, 478; flageolet, 605; Ghost Dance, 620, 622; gifts, 392; gorgets, 549; guardian spirit, 429, 646; harvesters, 503; historical traditions, 668; intertribal alliances, 518; legal procedure, 518; maize, history of, 669; marriage, 329; migrations, 107; myths, history of, 670; oratory, 592; racial types, 102; raiding, 403; religion, 662; steam bath, 270; stone-working processes, 161, 162; Sun Dance, 620; tales, 478, 601, 609, 612, 614, 615; trade, 397; twined blankets, 258; use of fertilizers, 302; vision, 647; war, 679

— and Pacific Islands, relations between, 212

— Northwest Coast, adaptation of tales, 600; adoption, 416; analysis of cultures, 671; art, 540, 543, 546, 548, 571–574; berry patches, 290; canoes, 269; chiefs, 461; clans, 410; climbing, 267; clothing, 265; crests, 426; dances, 605, 607; destruction of property, 459; endogamy, 438; exogamy, 423; houses, 264; leisure, 377; marriage ceremony, 444; massage, 270; names, 451; pattern of culture, 684; potlatch, 444, 661; prestige, 459, 460, 463; racial types, 102, 112; sailing, 247, 269; social organization, 330; solstice observed, 274; standards of measurement, 277; tales, 597, 602; trade, 465; villages, 285. See also *Bella Bella, Bella Coola, British Columbia, Haida, Kwakiutl, Tlingit, Tsimshian*

— Plains Indians, 512–515; dog, 305; guardian spirit, 652, 653; horse, 312; hunting grounds, 285; hunting regulations, 375, 378; kin groups, 514; medicine societies, 428; officials, 513; pattern of culture, 684; police duties, 418; polyandry, 433; private ownership, 514; religion, 652, 653, 663; sacred bundles, 657; self-torture, 644; Sun Dance, 657; tales, 600; vision, 641, 658; warfare, 462

— Central, markets, 397; money, 400; trade, 396, 397, 399; use of gold and copper, 552

See also *Acoma, Aleutians, Algonquian, Apache, Arapaho, Arizona, Athapascan, Aztecs, Bella Bella, Bella Coola, Blackfoot, British Columbia, Cahuilla, California, Carib, Cherokee, Cheyenne, Chichicastenango, Chilcat, Chinook, Coeur d'Alêne, Colorado River, Comanche, Coronation Gulf, Costa Rica, Creek, Crow, Dakota, Eskimo, Fox, Guatemala, Gulf of Mexico, Hidatsa, Hopi, Huichol, Hupa, Indians of the Southwest, Iroquois, Kiowa, Kutenai, Kwakiutl, La-*

guna, Mackenzie, Mandan, Maya, Menominee, Mexico, Mississippi, Miwok, Mohave, Montagnais-Naskapi, Nahua, Naskapi, Navajo, New Mexico, Nez Percé, Nootka, Ojibwa, Omaha, Paviotso, Pawnee, Ponca, Pueblo Indians, Puget Sound, Quiché, Rio Grande, Sahaptin, Salish, San Ildefonso, Santa Clara, Santee, Santo Domingo, Sauk and Fox, Shoshone, Sioux, Teton, Thompson Indians, Tillamook, Tlingit, Tsimshian, Washo, West Indies, Winnebago, Wiyot, Yucatan, Yukon River, Yurok, Zuñi

America, South, blowgun, 245, 251; bark cloth, 256; calendar, 274; canoes, 269; cassava, 295; chiefs, 515; climbing, 267; coöperation, 516; extinct mammals, 213, 214; farming societies, 515; fishermen, 491; harvesters, 503; rollers, 242; slit drum, 248; status of women, 516; tales, 614. See also Arawak, Aymara, Bakairi, Botocudo, Brazil, Chaco, Chile, Choroti, Fuegians, Guiana, Kaingang, Matto Grosso, Patagonia, Peruvians, Taulipang

Amphletts, trade, 397

Amputations, 270

Amulets, 599, 635, 645, 646, 650

Amur River tribes, permanent settlements, 285; status of women, 319

Anatolia, cultivation of rye, 291

Andamanese, division of labor, 369; mythology, 619, 622; preservation of meat, 377; racial type, 113; respect shown to age, 336

Andes, distribution of languages, 139

Angkor-Vat, 200

Angola, tales, 601

Angora cats, hair of, 109

Animals, communication between, 124; domestication, 201, 221, 283, 290, 302–312; kept for divination, 304; kept for sport, 305; representation in Northwest Coast art, 572; social life, 409, 410; use of technical devices, 238

Animatism, 632

Animism, 632, 635, 639–642

Ankole, conquest by herders, 317

Antevs, E., advent of man in America, 91; chronology of Ice age, 15, 74

Anthropoidea, 26

Anthropometry, 95–99

Antiquities, arts implied by, 147–148

Antler implements, prehistoric, 165–166

Antonius, O., descent of dog, 308

Anxiety, influence of, on economic institutions, 350

Apache, avoidance, 445; baskets, 585; bride price, 383

Ape and man, ancestry, 39, 41; apeman of Java, 44, 49; bipedal gait of apes, 40; bipedal habit of man, origin of, 39, 40; brachiation, 34; brain, 36, 46; blood tests, 35; central bone, 33, 35; cerebral localization, 37; cheek pouches, 33; chimpanzee, 33, 34, 35, 37, 38, 40; clothing, beginning of, 265; comparison of anatomy, physiology, and psychology, 31 42; diseases, 36; Dryopithecus pattern of teeth, 33; female sexual rhythm, 35; femur, 48; foot, 40; frontal sinus, 33, 34; gestation, 35; gibbon, 28, 33, 46; gorilla, 28, 33–40; ischial callosities, 33; jaw, 48, 57; language, 37; laryngeal air sacs, 32; life span, 35; menstruation, 35; mentality of apes, 37; orangutan, 33; orthograde, 34; placenta, 35; posture, 41; pronograde, 34; speech, 37; sphenoidal sinus, 34; teeth, 47; uterus, 35; vermiform appendix, 33; vocal signals, 38; whooping cough of gorilla, 36

Arabia, coffee, 296

Arabic, words in English, 136

Arabs, conquests by, 317; dromedary, 311; herding, 313, 315; milking, 315

Arapaho Indians, art of, 584

Arapesh, coöperation, 375; economic security, 331; lack of permanent settlements, 329

Arawak, languages, distribution of, 139

Archaeology, Africa, 196–198; America, 212–216; Asia, 199–202; Australia and Tasmania, 202–203; definition, 146; Europe, 170–196; function of, in cultural history, 668;

Indonesia, 201–202; Melanesia, 203–204; methods, 149; Micronesia, 204; Polynesia, 204–208; problems, 148; summary of results, 230

Arctic hunters, government, 498–502; preservation of meat, 377; settlements, 285; fermentation of food, 502

Argentina, surface finds, 214

Argonauts, tale of, 597

Arizona, lack of riddles, 599

Arkansas, pottery, 550

Arkell, W. J., geological age of Nile terraces, 196

Armenian, diaspora, 106; nose, 116

Arrogance, as a privilege, 460

Arrow, 245, 246; straightener, prehistoric, 165

Art, abstract, 576; African, 546, 547, 548, 550, 581; Aztec, 543; conventionalization, 578; decorative, 539 ff.; distortion of representative forms, 578 ff.; factors influencing, 540; formal principles, 558 ff.; Hopi, 538; influence of technology, 540; Maori, 549; materials, 542, 545, 549; Maya, 543–545; New Guinea, 549; Northwest Coast of America, 546, 571–574; objects among hunters, 589; photography as, 577; prehistoric, 535, 543; realism, 577; representative, 577; Sauk and Fox, 536; specialization in industries, 539; stability, 576; symbolism, 576; textile, 552, 554, 556, 557, 558; Thompson Indians, 536, 561; trade in art objects, 540; utility and art, 538

Arunta, division of labor, 369; land tenure, 342; rituals and songs, 509; tales, 618

Aryan, languages, distribution of, 139

Ashanti, inheritance, 423; position of women, 467; rights of queen, 469

Asia, bellows, 246; migrations, 106, 139; music, 603; origin of hominids, 39; Paleolithic bone culture, 172; poetry, 599; proverbs, 598; stone flaking, 157; tales, 612
— Central, prehistory, 200
— Northern, prehistory, 200

— Pacific Coast, languages, 139
— Southern, bark cloth, 256; megaliths, 199; pile dwellings, 265; prehistory, 154, 199; relation of race to Australians, 112; use of rice, 294
   See also Afghanistan, Anatolia, Armenia, Assyria, Babylonia, Bedouins, Bokhara, Ceylon, China, Chukchee, Dayak, Formosa, Gilyak, Hebrew, Huns, Hyksos, Ifugao, India, Indo-China, Indonesia, Iran, Japan, Java, Kababish, Kafiristan, Kamchadal, Karen, Khasi, Kirghiz, Koryak, Lakka, Malay, Manchu, Mongols, Ostyak, Persia, Philippines, Rwala, Semang, Semites, Siam, Siberia, Tashkent, Tibet, Toda, Tungus, Turkestan, Turks, Yakut, Yukaghir

Associations, 428, 429

Assyria, pollination of date palm, 291; use of horse, 311

Astronomical observations, 274

Asturian implements, 186–187

Asylum, right of, 510, 526; in Polynesia, 525

Athapascan, distribution of languages, 136; hunting, 288

Aurignacian, art, 535; epoch, 150; industries, 180–181; of Africa, 197; of Northern Asia, 200

Australia, absence of bow and arrow, 245; agriculture, 670; arrival of man, 86, 106; canoes, 269; distribution of game, 507; economic function of sib, 418; education, 476; elders, 496, 497, 505, 509, 510; environment, 412; exogamy, 682; group marriage, 432; harvesting, 502, 503, 506; intertribal ceremonies, 505; intertribal trade, 505, 507, 508; land cession, 497; literature, 589; message sticks, 272; mythical beings, 616; permanence of habitat, 329; prehistory, 202, 203; property in quarries, 493; punishment for adultery, 496; race, 46, 102, 104, 111, 112, 117; sexual license at ceremonials, 436; shields, 263; size of camp, 504; social organiza-

Benin, bronze-casting, 552; ivory-carving, 549
Berckhemer, F., Neanderthal man, 66
Bering Sea area, connecting Old and New Worlds, 111
Berry, E. W., Pithecanthropus, 45
Berry patches, burning of, 290
Berry picking, control of, 289
Betel nut, 255, 293
Betrothal, of children, 442; Melanesia, 440; Trobriands, 436
Bibliographies, art, 588; economics, 408; government, 534; human origins, 94; inventions, 281; language, 145; mythology and folklore, 626; prehistoric archaeology, 237; race, 123; religion, 665; social life, 486; subsistence, 326
Black, D., Sinanthropus, 51–55
Blackfoot, cosmology, 653; origin tales, 618; subject matter of tales, 602
Blankets, twined, 258
Blondness of domesticated mammals, 109
Blowgun, 245; manufacture of, 251; poisoned darts, 255
Blue eyes of domesticated mammals, 109
Blumenbach, J. Fr., classification of races, 113
Boas, F., art, 569, 573, 578; definition of institutions, 489; Eskimo chiefs, 500; property concepts among Dakota, 495; symbolism, 585; totemism, 430
Boastfulness, 464
Boats, double, 269; Micronesia, 275
Bodily form and mental characteristics, correlation between, 120
Bogoras, W., on Chukchee, 369, 498, 500
Boiling, 241
Bokhara, cultivation of rye, 291
Bola, 243
Bonarrelli, G., Heidelberg man, 61
Bone, age, in Norway, 165; culture of northern Asia, 172; implements, prehistoric, 163–167; Polynesia, 207; Tasmania, 203
Bongo, use of poultry, 304
Bontoc, trial marriage, 437
Boomerang, 243
Boreopithecus dawsoni, 59

Bornu, division of agricultural labor, 298
Borrowing, 346
Boskop man, 89, 90; skull, 78
Botocudos, duels among, 492; punishment for adultery, 496; territorial group, 491
Boulders, erratic, 9
Boule, M., Neanderthal man, 64, 69
Boundaries, among Arctic hunters, 498; violation of, 491, 492, 497, 504
Bow and arrow, 244; absence in Australia, 245; antiquity of, 245; prehistoric use, 165
Braiding, 257
Brain, size of, Australians and Veddas, 46
Bravery, prestige gained by, 462
Brazil, absence of dog in parts of, 308
Breasted, J. H., chronology of Neolithic age, 227; early pottery in Egypt, 198
Bride price, 329, 383–387; return of, in case of barrenness, 441, and divorce, 449
Bridge, 267; suspension, 268
Brinton, D. G., folk tales, 612; invention of compound implements, 250
British Columbia, mnemonic devices, 271. See America, Northwest Coast
Bronze, 261; range of use in prehistoric times, 199, 201, 223, 225
Bronze age, 149, 150, 168, 169, 192, 193, 221, 552; pictographs, 192
Broom, R., Australopithecus, 30, 31; Homo capensis, 89
Brückner, E., on glacial moraines, 11
Brünn race, 53, 77, 81
Bryn, H., classification of races, 116
Bücher, K., on food supply, 493; origin of rhythm, 593
Buffalo hunt, Plains Indians, 289, 513
Buffalo of India, milking of, 309; of Indonesia, 310
Bühl phase of glaciation, 11
Buin, distribution of wealth, 336; feudalism, 349; money, 399
Bull-roarer, 247
Bunya-bunya, 502, 504
Bunzel, R., rank, 459; Zuñi religion, 652; Zuñi women, 468
Burma, chicken-raising, 303

tion, 343, 412, 413; steam bath, 270; subsistence, 282; taboos, 427; territorial limits, 284; throwing board, 244; throwing club, 242; totem groups, 428; tribal territory, 491; words in English, 136
— Queensland, harvesting grounds, 289
    See also, *Arunta, Carpentaria Gulf, Gregory River, Kurnai, New South Wales, Tasmania, Walaroi*
Australopithecus, 28, 29, 30, 40
Austrian Alps, variation of type in isolated villages, 107
Avoidance, 413, 444–449, 467; expression of reserve, 448; in Manus, 444; mother-in-law, 413, 436; name, 445; Navajo, 445; of parents-in-law, 445, 448; Teton, 457
Avunculate, 419, 420
Axe, 252
Aymara, cultivation of potato, 296
Azilian epoch, 150; implements, 184–185; pictographs, 184
Azilian-Tardenoisian flake industry, 159
Aztecs, art, 543; king, 404; sculpture, 538, 546; warfare, 403; writing of numbers, 276

Babylonia, antiquity of domesticated horse, 310; astrology, 677; cultivation of rice, 294; early agriculture, 290, 300
Bacsonian culture, prehistoric, southern Asia, 199
Badari, early agriculture, 290
Bafiote, deity, 623
Baganda, Cesarian operation, 271; division of labor, 319, 321; origin story, 597; political organization, 374; rights of king, 321; taboos, 304, 307; trance, 659; use of banana and maize, 296, 297; women as gardeners, 298; women excluded from milking, 319
Ba-Ila, beliefs regarding names, 450; divorce, 449; matriliny, 330; sexual license at ceremonials, 436
Bakairi, pets kept by, 304
Bakitara, class system, 374; hereditary occupations, 373; monopolies, 349

Bakwiri, social organization, 516
Ballast, 247
Bambala, pigeons raised by, 304; sculpture, 581; wood-carving, 558
Banana, history, 295; origin, 291, 298, use in Uganda, 297
Bánaro, division of labor, 298
Banteng, relation to zebu, 309
Bantu, division of labor, 319; garden culture and herding, 312; languages, 132, 134, 135, 139; migrations, 139; use of beef, 307
Banyankole, hereditary occupations, 373; monopolies, 349
Baoulé, sculpture, 581
Bark cloth, 256
Barley, 291; place of origin, 297
Barlow, F. O., on Rhodesian skull, 88
Barotsi, basket, 555; deity, 623
Barrenness, cause of divorce, 450; desired in Melanesia, 384
Basketry, 256; California, 555; coiled, 258; designs, 555
Bastian, A., theory of culture, 669
Batanga, social organization, 516
Bathonga, attitude toward food, 378; causes for divorce, 450; circumcision school, 476; division of food, 346; division of labor, 369; litigation regarding bride price, 385; marital rights, 439; maternal and paternal lines, 420; social organization, 413
Batons-de-commandement, prehistoric, 165
Battering of stone, 252
Bavenda, sham marriages, 383
Beach lines, 13
Beam scales, 277
Beans, cultivated by women, 298
Bedouins, branding of animals, 316; camels, 315; horses, 308; relations to fellahin, 314; subsistence, 313
Bee, use of honey, 286, 287
Bella Bella sibs, 417
Bella Coola, cosmology, 620; family traditions, 619; rank in pantheon, 460
Bellows, 246, 260
Bending of wood, 253
Benedict, R., European tales in Zuñi, 601; inheritance of property, 383; Mohave grandmothers, 422

Bushmen, art, 589; attachment to home territory, 285; digging stick, 262; gora, 248; hunting, 287; nutrition, 118; paintings, 580; property rights, 288; punishment of criminals, 497; racial type, 117; stature, 109; storing of food, 288; sucking tubes, 246; territorial groups, 491; use of honey, 287
Bushongo, deity, 623
Busk, G., Gibraltar skull, 63
Butter, use in Africa, 307

Cahuilla, subsistence, 285
Calendar, 274, 275
California, basketry, 538, 555; languages, 139; magic formulas, 643; marriage, 444; religious practices, 634; shamanism, 468; sibs, 417; standards of measurement, 277; trance, 659; variations of type, 107; villages, 285
Calmette, A., life span of apes, 35
Camels, antiquity of domestication, 311; milk as exclusive diet, 313; origin of domestication, 309; raising of, 284; use of, 306
Cameroon, family organization, 516; secret societies, 517
Campignian implements, 186–187; forms from Solomon Islands, 204
Campignian-Asturian epoch, 173
Cannibalism, 481
Canoes, 246, 269; bark, 268, 269; double, 247, 269; outrigger, absent in America, 209
Capitalism, 336, 338
Capsian industry, Africa, 197
Carib languages, distribution of, 139
Carpentaria, Gulf of, fermentation of food, 502
Carving in wood, 546
Caste, herders as ruling, 318; in Polynesia, 524
Castration of domesticated animals, 271
Cat, domestication of, 310
Catarrhines, 26
Catlin, G., on Indian harvesting tribes, 506
Cat's cradles, 257, 258
Cattle, 303, 311; antiquity of domestication, 311; descent of, 309; raising of, 284; use of, 307

Cauterization, 270
Cave dwellings, 263
Celebes, stone industry, 202
Cement, 251
Cenozoic period, 8; divisions, 9
Central Africa. See Africa, Central
Central America. See America
Ceramics. See Pottery
Cercopithecidae, 26
Cereals, 290
Ceremonialism, 656–657
Ceremonials, diffusion, 657; purchase, 509
Ceremonies, underwriting of, at Zuñi, 356
Cesarian operation, in East Africa, 270
Ceylon, racial type, 112
Chaco, use of algaroba, 503
Chamberlin, T. C., on Ice age, 11, 15
Chancelade man, 79, 81, 82
Chapelle-aux-Saints man, 53, 63–64, 75
Chardin, Teilhard de, Sinanthropus, 51
Chariot, early use, 268
Cheese, 307, 312
Chellean epoch, 150, 154; implements, 154, 176, 177; industries in Africa, 196
Chemical processes, 248
Cherokee, political organization, 518
Cheyenne, bride price, 385; marital exchange, 387; Sun Dance, 657
Chichicastenango, markets, 400
Chicken-raising in Burma, 303
Chiefs, behavior of, 463; Chukchee, 500; Eskimo, 500; in farming societies, 515; among harvesters, 509; among herdsmen, 520; among hunters, 497; Kwakiutl, 511, 512; Naskapi, 500; Omaha, 513; Plains Indians, 513, 515; Polynesia, 524; powers of, 482; privileges of, 321; Trobriand, 363
Chilcat blanket, 558, 559, 585
Childe, V. G., chronology of Neolithic age, 227; food-gatherers, 285
Children, adoption, 416; economic value, 384; ownership by, 412
Chile, dog hair used for weaving, 305
Chimpanzee. See Ape and Man
Chin, Simian shelf, 58
Chinese, conflicts with nomads, 317; deformation of feet, 538; extension of region where spoken, 139,

140; milk not used, 303; racial type, 55, 111, 113; science, 677; subsistence, 284; status of women, 319; traps, 242; use of pork, 307; viticulture, 301; walnut, 301

Chinook, loan words, 136, 137; sound symbolism in, 132; syntactic cases, 138; tales, 591

Chipping process, 157

Chiseling of stone, 162

Choroti, raising pets, 305

Choukoutien, Sinanthropus, 51, 52, 56

Chronological classification of prehistory, 150

Chronology of prehistoric times, absolute, 15, 226–230; of African prehistory, 196; of Argentine prehistory, 214; correlation of geological, racial and cultural changes, 174; determined by tree rings, 16; of development of culture, 227; geological, 8

Chukchee, art, 683; chiefs, 500; environment, 351; exploitation among, 350; feasts, 395; filial piety, 481; hunting units, 499; individualistic traits, 498; influence of domesticated reindeer upon social life, 320; insecurity of, 334; language, 130, 132, 138; leisure, 377; magic, 639; oath, 502; procedure in criminal cases, 501; reindeer as dowry, 382; reindeer-breeding, 328; serving for wife, 386; shamanism, 649; slavery, 500; songs, 603; standards of comfort, 332; tales, 601; temperament, 335; tent, 671; villages, 498, 499; women participating in herding, 319

Chwalnyak skull, 77

Cinquefoil roots, tended in gardens, 290

Circumcision, 271, 477; school, Bathonga, 476

Civilizations, higher, in New World, 526

Clactonian epoch and industry, 150

Clan, definition of, 414

Class organization, due to conquest, 374; in primitive society, 373

Clay, art in, 549; work in clay, 259. *See Pottery*

Cleanliness, 480

Climbing, 267

Clothing, 265, 266

Clubhouses, Trobriand Islands, 436, 441

Coca, 255

Coconuts as receptacles, 250

Coeur d'Alêne, kinship terms, 456; prestige among, 464

Cohuna skull, 86, 87

Collective ownership, Polynesia, 525

Collectivism, 374, 376

Color symbolism, 581, 582

Colorado River, marriage, 444

Comanche, adjustment of crimes, 514; raiding, 401

Combativeness of animals, 411

Combe-Capelle man, 77

Comfort, standards of, 332

Common property of fields of wild rice, 506

Communication between animals, 124

Communistic traits among Eskimo, 498

Competition and coöperation, 376

Congo, carved bowls, 557; masks, 546, 548; musical instruments, 249; pictographs, 272; pile cloth, 557; wood-carving, 546

Consanguineous group. *See Kin group, Kinship*

Conservatism, in use of domesticated animals, 312

Cook archipelago, axes, 538

Cooking, 239

Coöperation, 376, 499, 500; and competition, 376; in farming, 516; in hunting, 375; in modern industry, 376; in payment of bride price, 440; subsistence obtained and distributed by, 380; Zuñi, 352, 355

Copper, age, 150; implements, prehistoric, 168, 169; industries, prehistoric in southern Asia, 199; malleable, 168; range of prehistoric use, 225; use in Africa, 199; use of, 260

Copyright law, 505, 526; among harvesters, 509, 511; Kwakiutl, 512; Plains Indians, 514

Coracle, 269

Core industry, 154–155

Coronation Gulf, racial type, 102

Correlation between bodily form and mental characteristics, 120

Cosmology and belief, 660
Costa Rica pottery, 551
Council of elders, Australia, 496, 497
Counting, 276
Counting coup, 462
Coup-de-poing, culture, 172; in Africa, 196; distribution of, 154, 155
Cousins, cross, 421, 422, 438, 439, 446, 448, 456; parallel, 422, 438; second, 439; selective effect of cousin marriages, 103
Cow. *See Cattle*
Cowrie, 350
Creek, migration legend, 597
Crest, 426; methods of acquisition, 427
Cretans, deformation of body, 527
Crickets, kept by Chinese, 305
Crime, definition of, 478, 480
Crimea, Neanderthal man, 68
Criminal law, Adamaua, 522; Bushmen, 497
Criminals, habitual among Arctic hunters, 501
Cro-Magnon man, 53, 75, 77, 78, 80–83; trade, 252
Cross-cousins. *See Cousins*
Cross River, family organization, 516
Crow Indians, avoidance, 448; bride price, 383, 385; ceremonialism, 656; cosmology, 653; massage, 270; matrilineal descent, 320; raiding, 401; subsistence, 314; Sun Dance, 657; tobacco, 293
Crusades, influence on mixture of populations, 106
Cultivation of plants. *See Agriculture*
Culture, areas, 670; comparative studies, 669, 675; conceived as personality, 681; development, 673; dissemination, 211, 232, 670; dynamics, 673; history of, inferred indirectly, 668; integration, 671, 678; laws of development, 674; marginal, 671; morphology, 675; places of origin, 670; predictability of change, 674; prehistoric cultures, distribution, 216 ff.; progress, 675, 676; rate of growth, 232; relation to individual, 666; relation to speech, 141; stability and instability, 667, 672; standardized descriptions, 666; types, 667, 681–685

Cupping, 270
Curr, E., on Australian tribes, 504, 505, 507, 510

Dagger, 252
Dahomean Tovodun cult, 622; myths, 617
Dakota, attitude towards food as property, 346, 378; concept of property, 495; economics, 393; kinship terms, 456; language, 129, 130, 132, 135; music, 594; necessities of tribal life not possessed individually, 495; pictographs, 272; prestige gained by liberality, 462; similes, 596; Sun Dance, 657; use of dog, 305; wakan, 629; wealth, symbolic importance of, 338
Dance, 605
Dart, R. A., on Australopithecus, 29
Darwin, C., descent of man, 31; selection, 116
Date palm, pollination in Assyria, 291, 292
Daun phase of glaciation, 11
Dawson, C., Piltdown man, 57
Dawson, J., Australians, 497, 504
Dayak, inverted symmetry, 563
Dead, as supernaturals, 641
Death, economic implications, 393
De Candolle, A., home of sweet potato, 295
Deformation of body, 267
De Geer, G., chronology of Ice age, 15
DeLamothe, L., on Ice age, 13
Deluge myth in America, 670
De Morgan, H., chronology of Neolithic age, 227
Deniker, J., classification of races, 114
Denmark, shell heaps, 187
Densmore, F., on harvesting grounds, 506
Deperet, C., on Ice age, 13
Descent, among tribes of various levels of subsistence, 320; bilateral, 414; unilateral, 414
Design, in pottery, 550; in weaving, 554
Determinism, economic, 318, 410; geographic, 320
Diffusion, 211, 232, 670; conditions of, 297; of cultivated plants, 297
Digging stick, 262, 300

Diminutive, formation of, 138
Dingo, use of, 305
Discovery, of useful devices, 238
Disruptive forces in native culture, 680
Divination, 304, 643, 658
Divine right, 461
Division of labor, 298–300, 319, 321, 369, 370
Divorce, 449, 450
Dixon, R. B., classification of races, 113
Djagga. *See Jagga*
Dobu, charms, 663; concept of property, 341; economic conditions, 334, 345; fear of hunger, 379; magic formulas, 348; monopolies, 349; religion, 654–656
Dog, ancestry of, 308; antiquity of domestication, 311; distribution of, 308; draft animal, 267, 268, 305, 312; eaten, 305; hair for weaving, 305; Pekinese, hair of, 109; in Polynesia, 310; sledge, 312
Domesticated forms, variability of, 22
Domestication, in man, 108; of animals, 283, 302–312; nonrationalistic motives in, 305
Donkeys, antiquity of domestication, 311
Dorsey, J. O., on Omaha riddles, 599
Douglass, A. E., chronology determined by tree rings, 16
Dowry, 382–383, 442
Drilling, of stone and bone, 251, 252
Dromedary, introduced by Arabs, 311
Drum, 248
Drum language, 602
Dryopithecus, 28, 39, 51; pattern of teeth, 28, 71
Duala, social organization, 516
Dubois, E., Homo wadjakensis, 84; Pithecanthropus, 44 ff.; Sinanthropus, 52; Solo man, 86
Duckworth, W. L. H., classification of races, 113
Dugout. *See Canoes*
Durkheim, E., religion, 627, 628, 656; totemism, 430
Dyeing, 248

Earth mother, symbol of environment, 342
Earthquake, fear of, 380
East Africa. *See Africa, East*

Easter Island, banana, 298; language, 139; massage, 270; monumental figures, 543; pottery, 207
Economic, determinism, 318; interrelation of economic institutions, 328; life not controlled by efficiency alone, 331; significance of marriage, 440; types of economic structure, 351; units, Australia, Menomini, Winnebago, 507
Economic mechanisms, 367
Economics, definition, 327; intertribal, 396–400
Economy, acquisitive, 515
Ecstasy, 658–660
Education, 470–478; by criticism, 472, 473; symbolic acts, 477; punishment, tests, trials, 476
Eggs, 303
Egypt, antiquity of horse, 311; antiquity of plow, 300; ceremonial knives, 158; division of labor, 299; domestication of cat, 310; domestication of pig, 304; early agriculture, 290; endogamy, 423, 438; lily root, 502; pigs and sheep, 307; representation of human form, 577; traps, 242; wigs, 538
Eickstedt, E. von, classification of races, 114
Elasticity, of wood, 245
Elders, function of, 496, 497, 500, 505, 509, 516, 517, 520
Elephants, do not breed in captivity, 303
Ellis, A. G., fields of wild rice, 506
Elopement, 443
Emetics, 270
Emmer wheat, 290
Endogamy, 417, 423, 427, 431, 438, 682; in Egypt, 423, 438; preferential, 431; tribal, 431
Enemata, 270
Engagement. *See Betrothal*
English, sound symbolism in, 132
Environment, influence upon human forms, 20, 103; relation of culture to, 340
Envoys, 504
Eoanthropus dawsoni, 45, 53, 56–60
Eocene, 9; Primates in, 27
Eolithic, forms, Tasmania, 202; **period,** 150, 170–172

Eoliths, 58, 170, 176
Epic poetry, distribution, 599
Epipaleolithic, dogs in, 308
Esbaikian industry, 155
Eskimo, absence of reindeer-breeding, 328; amulets, 635; art, 589; attachment to home territory, 340; belief regarding names, 450; borrowing, 346, 498; carvings, 538, 546; cement, 251; character, 683; chiefs, 500; clothing, 265; contradictory myths, 617; coöperation in hunting, 375; cosmology, 622; division of labor, 369; dog, 305, 308; dog sledges, 305; double-bladed paddle, 247; drum, 605; economics, 328, 344; historical traditions, 669; hospitality, 481; hunting, 288; hunting regulations, 682; hunting territories, 498; hunting units, 499; icing of sledge runners, 246; individualism, 374; ivory carving, 589; jaws, compared with Sinanthropus, 55; knots, 257; lack of boastfulness, 464; lack of individual specialization, 371; language, 130, 134, 135, 138; lever, 241; looseness of local units, 343; maritime hunters, 343; murder, 481; mythical beings, 616; needle cases, 578; oars, 246; obsidian flaking, 543; pattern of culture, 684; polyandry, 433; preservation of meat, 378; prestige, 464; pulleys, 242; punishment, 501; racial type, 82, 102, 117; relation to land, 343; relation to sea, 342; respect due to physical strength, 335; rhythmic repetition in tales, 591; riddles, 598; rollers, 242; sailing, 247, 269; sawing, 253; Smith Sound, 107; snow house, 265; songs, 501, 594; standards of comfort, 332; stone kettles, 255; subsistence, 285; swan maiden tale, 598; tales, 590, 597; temperament, 335; tent, 263; throwing board, 244; trade, 396; traps, 242; vegetable food, 285; wifelending, 436; women, duties of, 466
Esoteric teachings, 621
Esthetic emotion, 536

Ethical conduct, relating to members of family, sib, society, 478, 479; sanctions, 663
Ethics, 478-483; instruction in, 477; and religion, 632-633
Etiquette, 478-483
Eugenics, 121, 122
Europe, coup-de-poing in, 154, 155; dog as draft animal, 268; end of hunting era, 159; epic poetry, 599; fox tales, 597; popular antiquities, 621; proverb, 598; racial types, 101, 104, 111, 112; repetition in tales, 591; selective mating in, 103; stone flaking, 157; tales, 600, 609, 612, 614. See also Cretans, Crimea, Denmark, English, German, Greece, Irish, Italians, Jews, Lapps, Poles, Portugal, Scandinavians, Scotch, Spain, Switzerland
Evidence, legal, distribution, 599
Evil eye, 599
Evolution, technological, 150-170
Exchange, between affinal relatives, 364, 387, 388, 441, 442; between kin, 381
Executive agencies, Australia, 496; Arctic hunters, 501
Exogamy, 417, 423, 427, 431
Exploitation, among Chukchee, 350; in Micronesia, 350
Extinct mammals, South America, 213-214
Extramarital relations, 435
Eye, Mongoloid, 113

Face, cross section of, 98
Falconry, 313
Family, definition, 414; lines, 19, 104; organization, 411-414; organization in animals, 409; theories, 411, 412, 424; types, 414, 417
Fan, taboo, 644
Farming. See Agriculture
Father, duties among Bathonga, 420; function in matrilineal sib, 419; relation to child, 419, 425, 481
Feast, general give-away, 394; multiple uses, 332; Zuñi, 354, 356
Feige, E., descent of cattle, 309
Fermentation, 248, 502
Fertilization of gardens, 302

Fetishes, 645, 646
Feudalism, essential features of, 348; in Uganda, 321; Wahuma, 316
Fidelity in marriage relations, 433
Fiji, conquest in, 403; land ownership, 302; pantomimic dances, 607; political organization, 302
Fingerprints, 99
Fire, antiquity of use of, 239; methods of fire-making, 239, 240; preservation, 239; use, 240; used for hollowing out wood, 253
Firth, R., Maori feasts, 395
Fischer, E., classification of races, 114; Cro-Magnon man, 83; effects of domestication, 110; survival of Neanderthal man, 77
Fish basket, 262
Fish hook pendant, New Zealand and California, 212
Fish weirs and nets, 286
Fishing, 212, 262, 286, 287
Fison, L., on rights of individual, 494
Flageolet, 605
Flake industry, time extent of, 159
Flaking process, 152–157, 252
Fletcher, Alice C., on Omaha police, 515
Fleure, H. J., chronology of Neolithic age, 227; Copper-Bronze stage, 229
Flint-mining, 160, 162, 543
Floats, 246
Florida, submerged shell mounds, 14
Flutes, 248
Fly agaric, 255
Folk song, rhythm of modern, 590
Folk tales. See Tales
Folsom industry, 215
Food, attitudes toward, 378; baking, 255; boiling, 254; devices for obtaining, 261; distribution, 346; fermented, 502; in Paleolithic times, 253; poisonous plants prepared for food, 254; preparation of, 254; preservation, 254; rights to, 494; storage, 286
Food-gatherers, 491–497
Food-gathering patches inherited, 289
Food-pounders, Hawaiian and American compared, 212
Food supply, effect of seasonal, 379; protection of, 378

Formosa, shell heaps, 202
Fornander, A., Hawaiian poetic diction, 595
Fortune, R., on gifts in Melanesia, 392
Fowl, 303; domesticated in Polynesia, 310; not eaten in Unyoro, 304
Fox Indians, education, 474; rhythmic syllables, 593
Fractures, treatment of, 270
Fraser, J., tribal territories, 492
Fratricide, Kwakiutl, 360
Frazer, J. G., avoidance, 446, 447; magic, 637, 638, 639; theory of culture, 669; totemism, 430
Freud, S., on avoidance, 447, 449
Friction, musical friction instruments, 247, 248; used in mechanical devices, 246
Friederichs, H. F., Eoanthropus, 59
Fritsch, G., classification of races, 117
Fuegians, clothing, 265; dog, 305; food supply, 679; subsistence, 282; territorial group, 491
Fulbe, conquests by, 317, 520
Functionalism, in art, 575

Galapagos Islands, variation in island fauna, 107
Galilee skull, Neanderthal type, 66
Galton, F., on domesticated animals, 303
Game, distribution of, among hunting tribes, 494
Games, 269
Gardens, cinquefoil roots tended in, 290; fertilizing 302; protection, 301. See Agriculture
Garrod, D., Gibraltar skull, 63
Gason, S., Australian trade expeditions, 507
Gathering stage, 284
Gazelle Peninsula, secret societies, 517
Geikie, J., Ice age, 11
Genetic lines, 19
Genotype, 19, 100, 104
Gens, definition of, 414
Geographic, determinism, 320; distribution of cultural stages, 216 ff.; range of culture stages, 220
Geologic periods, absolute chronology of, 8; premises, 7
Geometric principles, knowledge of, 278
Gestures, 125, 606

Ghost Dance, North America, 620, 622
Gibbon. See Ape and Man
Gibraltar, Neanderthal man of, 63
Gieseler, W., Oldoway skull, 90
Gifts, 346, 390; for obtaining wife, 441;
    Kwakiutl, 361; meaning of, 338;
    psychological implications, 392;
    Trobriand, 366; Zuñi, 355
Gillen, F. J., right of asylum, 510
Gilyak, exogamy, 682; hunting terri-
    tory, 498
Glacial moraines, 11
Glaciation, phases of, 11; in North
    America, 12
Goats, raising of, 284
God, supreme, 661, 662
Gold, casting in lost forms, 260; pre-
    historic use of, 168, 170
Goldenweiser, A., avoidance, 448;
    totemism, 430
Gomme, G. L., origin of fairy tales,
    600
Gorilla. See Ape and Man
Gorjanović-Kramberger, K., Neander-
    thal man, 66
Gourds, as receptacles, 250
Government, 487–534
Graebner, F., definition of State, 490
Grammar, 132–134
Grandparents, function of, 422
Gratitude, expression of, 495
Greece, deities, 617; divination, 643,
    658; religious practices, 634;
    systematic science, 677; temples
    as asylum, 526
Greek, influence upon Latin, 143
Gregory, W. K., Dryopithecus, 28, 71;
    on jaw of ape and man, 57; man's
    posture, 41; Notharctus, 26
Gregory River, neutral territory, 505
Grimaldi race, 78, 79, 80; trade, 252
Grimm, J., theory of folk tales, 600, 614
Grinding of stone, 160–162
Gritstones, 252
Groom, payments to groom's family,
    385
Grosse, E., legal forms, 497
Group hostility, as explanation of
    avoidance, 447
Group marriage, 432
Gschnitz phase of glaciation, 11
Guanaco, 309
Guanchos, 82, 83

Guardian spirit, 429; of Plains Indians,
    652, 653
Guatemala, decorative clothing, 539;
    industrial specialization, 372;
    stone carvings, 543
Guiana Indians, cultivation of cassava,
    295
Gulf of Mexico, distribution of lan-
    guages, 139
Günz phase of glaciation, 11

Habitat, correlated to mode of life,
    329
Haddon, A. C., art, 578; classification
    of races, 114
Haeckel, E., descent of man, 32; origin
    of man, 44
Hahn, E., domestication of animals,
    302, 303, 311; effects of domesti-
    cation, 109; hoe and plow, 300;
    nomadism, 313; types of agricul-
    ture, 282, 283, 298, 299; women
    as gardeners, 299
Haida, art, 574; cultivation of tobacco,
    293; language, 129; matrilineal
    descent, 320; racial type, 102;
    sibs, 426
Hair, forms, 102
Haircut as crest, 427
Hairiness of domesticated forms, 109
Hamitic herders in East Africa, sub-
    sistence of, 314
Hamy, E. T., on Guanchos, 82
Handles, 251, 253
Harp, 249, 605
Harpoon, 165, 286; Neolithic, Tierra
    del Fuego, New Zealand, 166
Hartmann, R., on apes and man, 32
Harvesters, 502–512; legal norms of,
    510, 511; size of camps, 503, 504
Harvesting, America, Australia, New
    Guinea, 503; restrictions, 504
Harvesting grounds, South America,
    North America, 506
Hatt, G., domestication of animals,
    283; Lapp reindeer, 307
Hauer, J. W., on ecstasy, 658; on re-
    ligion, 628
Haussa embroideries, 569
Hawaii, endogamy, 438; Hawaiian and
    American food pounders com-
    pared, 212; language, 139; poetic
    diction, 596; relation between ma-

ternal uncle and nephew, 446; romantic love in, 443

Head, hunting, 402; measurements, 96

Hearne, S., woman's work, 466

Hebrew patriarchs, 416; right of gleaning, 347

Heidelberg man, 45, 60–61

Heine-Geldern, R., on Polynesia, 524

Hellman, M., Dryopithecus, 28

Hemp, 293

Hennepin, L., on buffalo police among Dakota, 289

Herding, influence of plagues, 286; by men, by women, 369; at Zuñi, 354

Herds, as wealth, 307

Herdsmen, as conquerors, 520 ff.; as ruling caste, 316–318; government among, 519–523; individual property among, 499

Hereditary occupations, 373

Heredity, law of, 16

Herero, status of women, 320; matriliny, 330

Herzog, G., relation of language to music, 602

Hesiod, mythology, 610

Hidatsa, agricultural labor, 298; castration practised by, 271; cultivation of maize, 295; cultivation of tobacco, 293, 298; matriliny, 320; sibs, 418; storage of seed, 301; Sun Dance, 657; women as gardeners, 298

Hilzheimer, M., descent of dog, 308

History of languages, 134

Hobbes, T., law, 488

Hobhouse, L. J., ethics, 677

Hodgson, C. P., harvesting in Australia, 503

Hoe, 262, 298, 300

Hogben, L., on heredity and environmental determinants of behavior, 119

Hogbin, H. J., Samoa, 524

Holmes, W. H., antiquity of man in Argentina, 214, 215

Holocene epoch, 8, 12

Hominidae, 32

Hominids, origin of, 38, 39

Homo, capensis, 89; heidelbergensis, 60–61; modjokertensis, 50–51; neanderthalensis, 53, 61–74; primigenius (see neanderthalensis);

rhodesiensis, 53, 87; soloensis, 85; wadjakensis, 84

Homo sapiens, 74–84; antiquity of, 74; origin of, 76, 78

Honey, Bushmen, 287; Vedda, 286

Hooton, E. A., Canary Island type, 83

Hopi, art, 538, 563, 571, 578; basketry, 562; dowry, 382; exchange of property, 381; pottery, 538, 564, 567, 569, 570, 576; subsistence, 283, 314

Horse, 268; antiquity of domesticated, 311; origin, 309, 311; raising, 284; used with chariot, 311; use with travois, 268

Horticulture. See Agriculture

Hospitality, 390, 417, 463, 481

Hottentot, calendar, 274; castration of animals, 271; women participating in herding, 319

Household, generations represented in, 415; group, Zuñi, 353; Kwakiutl, 357; sibs represented in, 416

Houses, clay, 265; rectangular, 265; snow, 265; underground, 264; wooden, 264

Howitt, A. W., Australia, 493, 494, 507

Hrdlička, A., antiquity of man in Argentina, 214, 215; evolution of modern man, 78; Pithecanthropus, 54; Rhodesian skull, 89; Sinanthropus, 52, 55

Huichol Indians, symbolism in art, 583, 584

Humboldt, A. von, types of agriculture, 283

Hunger, fear of, 379

Huns, conquests of, 317

Hunt, communal, among Eskimo, 498; among Plains Indians, 513

Hunters, 490, 491; division of labor, 299

Hunting, 284; coöperative, 375; among nomadic tribes, 313; Paleolithic, 253; restrictions, 287; rules for preservation of game, 378; rights to hunting grounds, 492; stage, 282, 285–290; territories of Arctic tribes, 498; territories, inheritance of, 289

Hunting tribes, differences among, 329; inheritance of privileges, 289; social organization, 288; units, 499

Hupa, basket, 555; kinship terms, 457; measurements, 277
Huts, 263; round, 264
Huxley, T. H., classification of races, 113; man's place in nature, 24, 41; Neanderthal man, 62; South Asiatic racial types, 112
Hyksos, migrations, 491
Hylobatidae, 28

Ibo, pictographic writing, 273
Ice age, 9; climate, 12; evidences of, 9; extent of ice cap, 10; ocean level during, 10
Ifugao, capitalistic tendencies, 336; dowry, 382; economic conditions, 344; lack of arable land, 351; seasonal food supply, 379
Ila. See Ba-Ila
Immorality, concept of sexual, 436
Implements, Asturian, 186–187; Azilian, 184, 185; Bronze age, 192, 193; Campignian, 186, 187; compound, 250; Danish shell heaps, 186, 187; Iron age, 194, 195; Magdalenian, 183; Maglemosian, 184, 185; Neolithic, 188–191; Robenhausian, 190, 191; Solutrean, 182; Tardenoisian, 184, 185
Incest, 437, 438, 443, 448, 480, 481
Independent development, 296, 308
India, cultivation of rice, 294; folk tales, 614; mathematics, 677; Paleolithic culture, 172; polyandry, 433
India, southern, throwing sticks, 243
Indian, American. See America
Indian corn. See Maize
Indians of the Plains. See America, Plains Indians
Indians of the Southwest, pantomimic dances, 607
Individualism in production, 374
Indo-China, use of buffalo, 309
Indo-European, languages, 134, 135, 139
Indonesia, prehistory, 201, 202; use of buffalo, 309, 310
Infanticide, 384, 482; female, 432, 433
Inheritance, 423; among herdsmen, 520
Initiation, 428; ceremonies, 505; educational function, 476, 477; tests, 476

Insecurity, economic, 334
Instinct of animals, 409, 410
Intertribal leagues, Plains Indians, 515
Intoxicants, 255
Invention of useful devices, 238
Iran, cultivation of walnut, 300
Irish, selective mating of, 103
Iron, 210; meteoric, 210; smelting, 249; use of, 260
Iron age, 149, 150, 168–170, 221; implements, 194, 195; northern Asia, 201; range of prehistoric iron industries, 170, 225; southern Asia, 199
Iroquois, land ownership, 516; language, 138; political organization, 518; status of women, 467, 469
Irrational aspects of domestication of animals, 302 ff.
Irrigation, 203, 263, 294
Iselin, I., types of agriculture, 283
Isolation, 107
Italian immigrants, intelligence of, 120; selective mating of, 103
Ivory, art in, 548; prehistoric use, 165
Ivory Coast, mask, 547

Jade, sawing of, 163
Jagga, land laws, 519; proverbs, 597; ruler as sole landowner, 302
Japan, art, 542
Java, musical system, 603
Jealousy, 411, 433, 436, 440
Jews, American, changes in type, 115; diaspora, 106
Jochelson, W., Yukaghir marriage, 442
Joking relationship, 420, 422, 444–449, 457
Judges, Adamaua, 522
Judicial procedure, distribution of, 599; in Africa, 518, 675
Junod, H. A., maternal uncle, 420
Jurisdiction among herdsmen, 520

Kababish camel herders, 315
Kabyles, relation to Cro-Magnon man, 82
Kafficho, law in, 522
Kafir, clubs, 242
Kafiristan, use of plow by women, 299
Kaingang, attitude towards food, 378; division of food, 346, 380; lack of permanent settlements, 329, 379;

lex talionis, 496; standard of comfort, 332
Kamchadal, dog sledges, 305
Karen, divination, 304
Keith, Sir Arthur, brachiation, 33; internal secretion, 116; isolation, 111; man's posture, 41; Paleolithic man, 30, 58, 67, 68, 71, 80, 82, 86, 87, 90
Kent's Cavern, Paleolithic finds in, 43
Kenya caves, prehistoric remains, 198
Keysser, C., Kai chiefs, 515
Khasi, divination, 304
Kin group, solidarity, 514; supernatural relationship, 427
King, W., Neanderthal man, 62
Kings, Polynesia, 524; Sudan, 522
Kingsley, M., African religion, 646
Kinship, economic obligations imposed by, 364, 381; systems, 131, 416, 450–458, 679
Kiowa warfare, 401
Kirghiz, cattle, 307; cultivation of cereals, 294; herding, 284, 314–316; horse, 312; milk, 312; milking, 315; oxen, 307; subsistence, 312, 313
Kitchen middens, cattle and sheep bones in, 311
Klaatsch, H., classification of races, 117
Klatt, B., effects of domestication, 110
Klineberg, O., intelligence of Negro children, 120
Knabenhaus, A., on legal forms, 497
Knots, 257
Knotted strings as mnemonic device, 271
Knowledge, practical, 471
Koenigswald, G. H. R. von, Paleolithic man, 47, 49, 50, 51, 85
Köhler, W., mentality of apes, 37
Koppers, W. P., definition of State, 490; domestication of animals, 283, 309, 310
Koryak, art, 538, 683; calendar, 274; reindeer, 320; tales, 609
Krämer, A., Samoa, 524, 525
Krapina, Neanderthal man of, 66
Kula, 350, 365, 366, 460; potlatch and kula compared, 460, 461
Kumiss, 307
Kurnai, elopement among, 443

Kutenai, cultivation of tobacco, 293
Kwakiutl Indians, art, 571, 574; burning of berry patches, 301; chiefs, 512; clover gardens, 301; coöperation, 376; cosmology, 620; counting, 276; deformation of head, 538; destruction of property, 331; economics, 357–361; fishing grounds, 343, 344; geometrical devices, 277; gestures, 606; gifts, 391, 392; houses, 674; hunting grounds, 511; individual property, 512; language, 136, 138; marriage, 390; nobility, 512; observation of time, 274; origin myths, 618; pawning of names, 348; potlatch, 394; prestige, 465; sacred season, 619; similes, 596; social structure, 425; songs, 595; symbolic values, 350

Labor, division of, 369–374; between sexes, 466; in animals, 409
Ladders, 267
La Ferrassie skeletons, Neanderthal type of, 64
La Flesche, F., Omaha police, 514
Lagoa Santa man, 213
Laguna, gestures, 605; tales, 600
Lake Chad tribes, men as gardeners, 299
Lakka, division of agricultural labor, 299
Lance, 243
Landes, Ruth, fields of wild rice, 506
Landownership, 302, 341–344, 353, 357, 358, 511, 513, 516, 519, 526
Landsteiner, K., blood of apes, 36
Lang, A., coherences of cultural traits, 680
Lango, banana, 297; bride price, 384, 385; burning over of fields, 301; butter, 307; coöperation, 375, 376; division of labor, 298, 319; gardeners, 301; land tenure, 302; litigation, 331; milk, 307; millet, 297; partnerships, 376; sweet potato, 297
Language, categories of classification, 126; classification of experience, 451; distribution of, 139; general characteristics, 124; gesture, 125; relation of speaker to language spoken by him, 673

Lapps, cheese, 312; individual property, 499; reduced to fishing, 286; reindeer, 307, 312
La Quina, Neanderthal type of, 64
Latin, influence upon modern European languages, 143
Laufer, B., domestication, 303, 310; home of sweet potato, 295; olive tree, 301; types of agriculture, 300; use of milk, 307
Law, primitive, 487 ff. *See Legal norms*
Leaching, 248, 286
Leakey, L. S. B., Kenya archaeology, 90, 197
Learned, B. W., signals used by animals, 38
Learning, of animals, 409, 410
Legal norms, among hunters and food-gatherers, 497; complexity in early cultures, 526
Legal procedure, 518
Lehmann-Nitsche, R., antiquity of man in Argentina, 214
Leisure, 377
Le Moustier skeleton, 64
Lemuroidea, 26
Lemurs, 25
Leopard society, West Africa, 428
Lesnoyer, M., eoliths, 171
Lesser, A., Pawnee hand game, 673
Levalloisian epoch, 150; flaked implements, 155, 156
Levirate, 440
Lewis, G. E., Ramapithecus, 39
Lex talionis, among hunters and food-gatherers, 496
Liden, R., chronology of Ice age, 15
Lily root, use in Egypt, 502
Lime, preparation of, 249
Lineage constituting sibs, 417
Linguistic families, 135
Linné, classification of races, 25, 113
Literary forms, distribution, 599
Literature, 589 ff.; archaic forms, 592
Littorina terraces, 14
Llama, 268, 309, 310
Loango, exogamy in, 423
Love, romantic, 430, 437, 443
Lowie, R. H., avoidance, 448; definition of State, 490; economic determinism, 410; explanation of social phenomena, 449; public opinion, 513; religion, 656; Samoan and New Zealand political organization, 524; totemism, 430
Lund, P. W., archaeology of Brazil, 213
Lying, 479
Lyre, 249, 605

MacCurdy, G. G., survival of Neanderthal man, 77
MacEnery, J., Paleolithic man, 43
MacKenzie, Sir Colin, proto-Australoid race, 86
Mackenzie Indians, lack of boastfulness, 464
Madagascar, Malay language, 107, 136, 139; polyandry, 433
Mafulu, pig feasts, 331, 394
Magdalenian, decline of bone work in post-Magdalenian, 165; epoch, 150; flaking, 159; implements, 165, 183; industries, Celebes, 202; industries, northern Asia, 200; ornaments, 183; pictographs, 183
Magic, 635, 637–639; Dobu, 654; economic aspects, 362; formulas, 635, 643; Siberian magic formulas, 650; Zuñi, 651
Maglemosian, epoch, 150, 184, 185
Maize, 290, 296; American crop, 294; cultivated by women, 298; diffusion, 297; Europe, 297; method of cultivating, 295; origin, 295, 297; Uganda, 296; varieties, 296
Malay, betel chewing in, 293; blowgun, 245; bridges, 267; climbing trees, 267; firesaw, 240; houses, 265; languages, 136, 139; literature, 589; migrations, 107; prayers and ceremonies, 641; tales, 597
Malay-Polynesian, migration, 140
Malinowski, B., 412; primitive law, 489; religion, 634; theories of procreation, 425
Man, area inhabited in prehistoric times, 217; early types of, 43 ff.; place in nature, 24
Mana, 341, 630, 631, 634, 635
Manchu, conquer China, 317
Mandan Indians, bull boat, 269; maize, 295
Mandible, Piltdown skull, 57
Mangbattu, pygmies in Mangbattu army, 667

Manioc, an American crop, 294; technique of planting, 295
Manitou, 629, 630, 631
Mansuy, H., Tonkin archaeology, 199
Manus, affinal exchange, 389, 390; avoidance, 444; education, 474; ethical religion, 663; exchange of property, 381, 394; marital exchange, 389; marriage, 390; moral code, 664; religious behavior, 640; wedding ceremony, 444
Maori, art, 546, 549; attitude towards food, 378; calendar, 274; collectivism, 375, 376; cultivation of kumara, 295; division of labor, 298; dog, 305; exchange of gifts, 393, 394; fasts, 395; gifts, 391; political organization, 524; prestige, 337; property rights, 341; supernaturalism, 648; taboo, 345, 378, 525; territorial law, 525
Marett, R. R., ritual, 657
Marginal areas, 223
Marimba, 248
Marind-Anim, mixed descent of, 402
Marine terraces, 15
Marital rights, Miwok, 439; Thonga, 439
Market, 397, 399, 400
Marquesans, calendar, 274
Marriage, 430–440; by capture, 443; ceremonies, 444; cousin, 437, 438, 448; development of, 447; division of labor in, 370; economic aspects, 329, 390, 440, 441, 443; free choice in, 443; inheritance of widows, 440; instability, 434; Kwakiutl, 360; legitimacy, 442; Natchez, 523; preferences, 437–440; restrictions, 437–440; service of groom, 440; sister-brother, 438; theories of origin, 412; Zuñi, 352
Martin, H., Neanderthal man, 64
Masai, conquests by, 317; herding, 313, 317
Massage, 270
Mat weaving, 256
Material culture, spread of, in prehistoric times, 218 ff.
Materials for manufacture, 251
Mating, selective, 103
Matriarchate, 320, 416
Matriliny, 320, 424, 425, 516
Matrilocal residence, 421

Matting, designs in, 554
Matto Grosso, harvesting grounds, 506
Mauer jaw, 60
Maya, art, 543–546; calendar, 275; mathematics, 677; writing, 276
McCown, T. D., Neanderthal man, 67, 68
McGregor, J. H., Neanderthal and Cro-Magnon types, 75
Mead, M., coöperation and competition, 376; Melanesia, 392; Samoa, 524, 525
Measurements, standards of, 277
Mechanical principles, 241, 243
Medicine, 255, 270
Medicine bundle of Plains Indians, 652, 653
Medicine societies, Pawnee, 428
Mediterranean type, 114
Megalithic monuments, Indonesia, 202; Melanesia, 203, 204; Micronesia, 204; southern Asia, 199, 200
Melanesia, adoption, 416; age societies, 428; amulets, 635; art, 580; attitude towards children, 384; avoidance, 445, 447–449; bark cloth, 256; betrothal, 440; blowgun, 245; cannibalism, 481; coöperation, 516; death, 393; exchange, 392; farming, 515; harvesting, 502; houses, 265; landownership, 516; magic formulas, 643; mana, 629; megalithic structures, 203; monopolies, 397; prehistory, 203; premarital relations, 436; prestige, 337; racial types, 102; rituals, 620; sacrifice, 644; secret societies, 429, 516, 518; status of women, 516; taboo, 644; trade, 396, 397–399, 465; women raising pigs, 369
Melody, 590, 603
Mendel, G., heredity, 17
Mendelian heredity, 105, 121
Menghin, O., definition of State, 490; Paleolithic culture, 172, 173
Menominee tent, 264
Menstruation, beliefs regarding, 371, 469
Mental traits, variability of, 118, 119
Merrill, E. D., home of sweet potato, 295
Mescal. See Peyote
Message sticks, 272

Messengers, diplomatic, Polynesia, 524
Mesvinian phase, 150, 171
Metal, industries, 207, 216, 221, 260; prehistoric, 167–170, 199; use in art, 552
Metal ores, reduction of, 260
Metallurgical processes, range of, 225
Meteoric iron, use of, 260
Meteorological observations, 274
Mexico, art, 538, 539, 555; astrology, 677; calendar, 275; diviners, 248; dogs, 109; industrial specialization, 372; kings, 461; language, 134; stone flaking, 157; temples as asylum, 526; throwing board, 244; writing, 273
Micoquian stage, 172, 175
Micronesia, absence of bow and arrow, 245; canoes, 275; control of land, 350; prehistory, 204; sailing, 247; sailing charts, 275; stone money, 204
Migrations, 106, 107, 139, 216–218
Milazzian beach lines, 13
Milk, 284, 303, 307, 312, 315
Miller, G. S., Eoanthropus, 57
Millet, 291, 297
Mimbres Valley, pottery, 563
Mindel, phase of glaciation, 11
Mining for flint, 160, 251; prehistoric in Indonesia, 202
Minusinsk, bronze, 201
Miocene, 9, 27; apes in, 39
Miolithic stage, 173
Mississippi pottery, 550
Mississippi Valley, Indian types of, 112
Miwok, marital rights, 439
Mixed languages, 136
Mixture of populations, 105, 106
Modesty, 480
Mohammedan influence in Sudan, 520, 522
Mohave, function of grandmothers, 422
Moiety, 431, 447
Moir, R., eoliths, 171
Mollison, Th., Oldoway skull, 90
Monasterian beach lines, 13
Money, 399, 400
Mongols, division of labor, 319; milking, 315; pastoral nomadism, 313; racial types, 102, 104, 111; subsistence, 306, 307, 313; trade, 314
Monogamy, animals, 411

Monopolies, 349
Montagnais-Naskapi, hunting privileges, 499; punishment, 501
Montelius, O., chronology of Neolithic age, 227
Months, 274
Monumental remains, Polynesia, 205–206
Morant, G. M., Paleolithic races, 80, 83, 88
Morgan, L., definition of State, 490
Morphological traits as racial characteristics, 99
Mortillet, G. de, eoliths, 171
Morton, D. J., man's posture, 41
Mother-love, 421
Mother's brother's function in matrilineal sib, 419
Mother's sister, function of in sib, 421
Motu, trade expeditions, 398
Mount Carmel, Neanderthal man, 66, 67, 68, 78
Mousterian, 150; in Africa, 196; in northern Asia, 200; bone implements, 164; forms in Australia, 202; implements, 154–159, 179
Murder, 414, 479, 481, 482
Music, 602 ff.
Musical instruments, 247, 248, 603, 605
Mutilations, esthetic value of, 537
Mystics, oriental, 659
Mythological concepts, 609, 614
Mythology, 609 ff.; development of, 661; esoteric and exoteric, 620

Nahua language, 134, 136, 137
Nahuala, trade, 397
Name, beliefs regarding, 450, 451; change of, 476; of kin group, 427; method of obtaining, 451; as property, 451; rank of, 460
Narcotics, 255, 508
Naskapi, chiefs, 500; individual responsibility, 514
Natchez, organization of, 523
Nativity story of the Zuñi, 601
Navajo, art, 540; avoidance, 445; boastfulness, absence of, 464; bride price, 385; color symbolism, 581; counting coup, 468; cross cousins, 448, 449; divorce, 450; economic provision for children, 467; education, 473, 475; herding, 467;

joking relationship, 446, 448; kinship terms, choice of, 456, 457; marriage, instability, 434; marriage, preferences, 439; matriliny, 330; music, relation to language, 602; names, 450; origin myth, 620; peace chiefs, 468; polygynous families, 433; sibs, 417; sib rights to widow, 440; status of chanter, 463; status of women, 320, 369, 467; symbolism, 580; trade, 396; warfare, 401, 468

Neanderthal race, 54, 61-74; antiquity, 63, 65, 67; disappearance of, 74; foot, 72, 73; neck, 74; size of cranium, 70; structural features, 69-74

Needle, prehistoric, 165, 251

Negro, intelligence, 120; in Portugal, 106; racial types, 101, 102, 104, 105, 111; selective mating in United States, 103; status in United States, 678

Negroid traits among Europeans, 113

Neoanthropic man, 76

Neolithic, age, 43; agriculture, 224, 227, 229; art, 543; definition, 217, 218; dog, 308; implements, 161-163, 188-189; in Africa, 198; in Alpine area, 190, 191; in North America, 223; in northern Asia, 200; in Polynesia, 206; in South America, 215; period, 149, 150, 173; pig in China, 311; pottery, 551; range of, 219; stone chipping, 158

Nephew, privileges of sister's son in matrilineal sibs, 420

Nephrite, 163, 212

Nets, 262

Neutral territories, 505

New Caledonian digging stick, 262

New Guinea, art, 549, 580; feasts, 332; harvesters, 503; head hunting, 402; masks, 579; menstruation, 371; modesty, 480; musical instruments, 604; pantomimic dance, 606; racial type, 112; religious behavior, 640; size of settlements, 503; trade, 396, 398, 460

New Ireland, friction instrument, 248

New Jersey, submerged shell mounds, 14

New Mexico, lack of riddles, 599

New South Wales, division of labor, 299

New World, absence of iron industries, 170; crops of, 294

New York, selective mating in, 103

New Zealand. See Maori

Nez Percé, division of labor, 299; sound symbolism, 132

Ngandong, skull, 84, 85

Nile, shields on upper, 263

Nobility, Kwakiutl, 512

Nomadic herdsmen, 222

Nomadism, pastoral, 283

Nomenclature, systems of prehistoric periods and stages, 172-173

Non-Aryan languages in Europe, 139

Nootka language, phonetic changes, 135; words in Kwakiutl, 136

Nordenskiöld, Erland, on Oceania and America, 209

Nordic type, 114; analogous to domesticated forms, 109

North America. See America

North Australian agriculture, introduction from New Guinea, 670

Northwest Coast of America. See America, Northwest Coast

North Pacific Coast of America. See America, Northwest Coast

Nose, form of, 102

Nose flute, 604

Notched bones as friction instruments, 247

Notharctus, 26

Nuba, division of agricultural labor, 299

Numerals, 130

Nuttall, G. H., blood of chimpanzee, 35

Nyassaland, women as gardeners, 298

Oars, 246

Oath, 502, 599

Oats, 293

Obercassel type of man, 81

Obermaier, H., length of Holocene epoch, 15

Occupations, hereditary, 373

Oceania, affinal exchange, 338; maternal uncle, 420; methods of fire making, 240; nutrition, 118; outrigger canoe, 247; relations to America, 212

Oceania including Malaysia. See Ad-

miralty Islands, Aëta, Amphletts, Arapesh, Bánaro, Bontoc, Buin, Celebes, Dayak, Easter Island, Fiji, Gazelle Peninsula, Hawaii, Ifugao, Mafulu, Manus, Maori, Marquesas, Melanesia, Micronesia, Motu, New Caledonia, New Guinea, New Ireland, Orokaiva, Pelew Islands, Pentecost Island, Rossel Island, Samoa, Santa Cruz, Solomon Islands, Tahiti, Tami, Tonga, Trobriand Islands

Oceanian-American connections, 208–212
Ochre, preparation of, 249
Officials, Plains Indians, 513
Ojibwa, division of labor among northern, 369; hunting grounds, 342, 343, 378, 379; pictographs, 272; subsistence, 379
Old age, treatment of, 422
Old World, crops of, 294
Oldoway skull, 90
Oligocene, 9, 27; anthropoids, 39
Olive, cultivation of, 301
Omaha, chiefs, 513; cosmology, 622; officers, 513, 514; songs, 514; taboos, 427
Oppenheimer, F., theory of State, 490, 497, 511, 526, 527
Oppenoorth, W. F. F., Ngandong skull, 84, 85
Oracle. *See Divination*
Orangutang. *See Ape and Man*
Oratory, 464, 592, 596
Ordeal, 255, 599
Orenda, 629
Oriental tales, 609
Origin tales, 617
Ornamentation, 266; and technique, 558; Magdalenian, 165; prehistoric metal work, 169; Solutrean, 182
Orokaiva, death feasts, 393; exchange, 392
Os Incae, 108
Osborn, H. F., Eoanthropus, 59; origin of man, 51
Ostracism, punishment for breaking of taboo, 438
Ostrich hunting, 287, 288
Ostyak, reindeer nomads, status of women, 319

Outes, F., antiquity of man in Argentina, 214, 215
Outrigger canoe, 247, 269
Ownership, harvesters, 508, 509; private, Plains Indians, 514; Polynesia, 525
Oxen used for riding and hauling, 307

Pacific coast, linguistic differentiation, 140
Pacific Islands. *See Oceania*
Packstrap, 267
Paddles, 246; double-bladed, 247
Pageantry, 656
Paleanthropus, 61
Paleolithic, absolute chronology, 227; range of, 224; age, 43, 149, 150; art, 535, 543, 580; bow and arrow, 245; definition, 217, 218; forms in Solomon Islands, 204; industries, 172–185; in America, 223; in northern Asia, 200; in Indonesia, 201; in Old World, 223 ff.; in South America, 215; needles, 251; range of industries, 219; subsistence, 282
Palestine, Neanderthal man in, 63, 66
Pampean formations, 213–214
Pan vetus, 57
Pandean pipe, 604
Pangwe deity, 623; subsistence, 307
Pantomime, 606
Papago, woman's relation to religious activities, 468
Papua, attitude towards children, 384; tales, repetition in, 591; type, 112; warfare, 402
Parallel cousins. *See Cousins*
Parallelism, 22, 102
Parapithecus, 28, 39
Parental love not biologically determined, 421
Parsons, E. C., avoidance, 448; European tales in Zuñi, 601; explanation of social phenomena, 449
Pastoral nomads, 284, 307, 310, 312, 313, 315, 316, 317; economy, 330
Pastures, ownership of, 519; selection of, 315
Patagonians, stature of, 109
Patriarchate, 416
Patriliny, 424
Patrilocal residence, 420

Paviotso, rabbit hunting, 289
Pawnee, history of handgame, 674; medicine societies, 428; polyandry among, 433; symbolism in art, 582
Payment, obligatory and voluntary at time of marriage, 441
Peake, H., chronology of Neolithic age, 227; Copper-bronze age, 229
Pearson, K., relation between bodily form and mental characteristics, 120
Pecking of stone, 160, 161
Pei, W. C., Sinanthropus, 52
Peking man, 51, 54, 55; culture of, 56
Pelew Islands, ancestor tales, 618
Penck, A., glacial moraines, 11
Pentecost Islanders, betrothal, 440
Percussion instruments, 603
Perforation of cheek, ear, lips, nose, 266
Perry, W. J., American agriculture, 295; food gathering, 285
Persia, rye, 291; wheat, 294
Personification in mythology and religion, 614, 636, 637
Perspective drawing, 577
Peruvian, art, 552, 554, 556, 561, 564; beam scales, 277; copper, 169, 552; divine rights, 461; endogamy, 423, 438; gold, 552; llama, 310, 519; pottery, 538, 552 ff.; quipu, 277
Pestles of Hawaii and America, 212
Petri, B. E., Siberian archaeology, 200
Petroglyphs, Polynesia, 205
Pets, animal, 304
Peyote, 255, 620, 622
Phenotype, 19, 100
Philippine baskets, 555
Phonetics, 127
Phratry, definition of, 438
Physiological traits, variability of, 118, 119
Physiology and psychology, racial, 117–121
Picks for flint mining, 160
Pictographs, 272, 273; Africa, 198; Aurignacian, 180; Azilian, 184; Bronze age, 192; Magdalenian, 183; Polynesian, 206; prehistoric, 165
Pig, 284; absence in prehistoric America, 209; antiquity of domestication, 311; descent, 309; Egypt,

304, 307; Polynesia, 310; use for divination, 304; not used by pastoral nomads, 310
Pig feast, Mafulu, 394
Pigeons, raised by Bambala, 304
Pigmentation, 102
Pile cloth, Africa, 557
Pile dwellings, 191, 209, 264
Piltdown man. See Eoanthropus
Pinkley, G., Homo wadjakensis, 84
Pitch in language, relation to music, 602
Pitcheri, 255, 492
Pitfalls, 288
Pithecanthropus, 50, 84, 201; alalus, 44; brain, 46; erectus, 44–49, 53; femur, 48; jaw, 48; second adult cranium, 49; teeth, 47
Plains Indians. See America, Plains Indians
Planting patterns, 293
Plants, care of, without planting, 290; gregarious, cultivated, 290
Plaster casts of human types, 98
Platyrrhines, 26
Pleiades, observation of, 274
Pleistocene, 9, 27; Central Asia, 200; climatic changes, 116, 197; South America, 213, 214
Pliocene, 9, 27; apes, 39
Plow, distribution of, 294, 300; in Egypt, 263; origin, 262, 300; used by men, 299
Podkoumok skull, 77
Poetry, relation to music and dance, 593
Poisoned arrows, 246
Poisons, 248, 255, 270
Polack, F. S., Maori taboos, 525
Poles, selective mating of, 103
Police, control in hunting parties, 289, 513; function of sibs, 418
Polishing of flaked stone, 252, 253
Political organizations, New World, 527; Old World, 518; relation to war, 403
Pollination of date palm in Assyria, 291
Polyandry, 432, 433
Polygamous family, personal relations in, 433
Polygamy, definition of, 432
Polygyny, 432, 433; in animals, 411;

economic aspects, 363; relation to sororate, 439

Polynesia, absence of bow and arrow, 245; absence of influence on American agriculture, 295; asylum, 526; bark cloth, 256; boats, 269; chants, 592; chiefs, 321, 461; commoners, 321; cosmology, 597, 622; divination, 643; divine rights, 461; domesticated animals, 310; fermentation of food, 502; genealogies, 622; gifts, 392; government and law, 523-525; harvesters, 502; industrial specialization, 371; Maui, 617; mythology, 616, 619; poetry, 599; prehistory, 204-208; primogeniture, 336; sailing, 247; similes, 595; singing, 605; taboos, 525, 645; trance, 659

Polynesian Islands, variation of fauna in isolated spots, 107

Polynesian words in English, 136

Ponca, Sun Dance, 657

Pongidae, 28

Poodle dog, hair of, 109

Populations, composition of, 104

Portugal, Negro workers on plantations, 106

Possession, in African religion, 659; in Marquesan religion, 659

Post, A. H., law, 488

Postglacial epoch, 12

Potato, 294-296

Potlatch, 358-360, 394, 459-462

Pottery, 259, 541; art in, 549; Africa, 197, 198; Asia, 200; Costa Rica, 551; Danish shellheaps, 186, 187; Easter Island, 207; Indonesia, 202; Mississippi, 550; Neolithic, 186-191; Peruvian, 552, 553; Polynesia, 207; prehistoric, 152, 551, 563; Pueblo, 551, 565, 566

Poultry, taboo in Uganda, 304

Pound, R., definition of law, 489

Power and wealth, 335

Prayer, 633, 642-644

Pre-Chellean epoch, 150, 154, 176, 177

Předmost, Paleolithic man of, 53, 77

Prehistory, 146 ff.

Premarital intercourse, 436, 441

Pre-mousterian, fire used in Pre-mousterian time, 237; flake industry in northern Asia, 201

Preservation of meat in tropics, 377

Pressure, stone flaking by, 159

Prestige, 337, 458-465

Priesthood, religious, 650

Primariae, 32

Primates, 25, 27

Primogeniture, 373, 461

Privilege, in relation to property, 348

Procreation, primitive theories of, 424, 425

Prognathism, 98

Promiscuity, 424

Property, 340; among animals, 409; beehives as, 288; collective, 526; destruction of, 420, 423; among hunters and food-gatherers, 494, 495; incorporeal, 345, 348; individual, 512, 516; interpretation of, 344; among Kwakiutl, 358; marks on domesticated animals, 316; of dead person, 514; private, 526; use for obtaining prestige, 459

Property rights, disregard of property rights of maternal uncle, 446; restrictions, 347

Propliopithecus, 28, 39

Prose, 590

Prostitution, 435

Proto-Australoid types, 86

Protolithic stage, 173

Proto-Negroid stock, 90

Proverbs, 478, 596, 597, 598

Prudery between married mates, 437

Public law, Kafficho, 522

Public opinion, 494, 496, 500, 509, 513

Pueblo Indians, absence of visions, 658; architecture, 543; art, 540, 541, 560, 581; coöperation, 375; cosmology, 597; disruptive forces in culture, 680; division of labor, 299, 369; matriliny, 320; observation of solstice, 274; Os Incae, 108; pottery, 541, 551, 565; prayer-sticks, 582; religion, 650-652, 662; singing, 605; social organization, 413; symbolism, 581; tales, 591, 600; throwing sticks, 243; war, 401

Puget Sound, dog hair used for weaving, 305; houses, 264

Pulleys, used by Eskimo, 242

Pumpelly, R., age of Copper-Bronze stage, 229

Punishment, 501; used in education, 474

Purchase of wife, 441

Pygmies, 107, 112, 282, 667

Quaternary period, 8, 27

Quatrefages, A. de, Cro-Magnon race, 82; Guanchos, 82

Queensland. *See Australia*

Quiché, bride price, 383; division of labor, 370; economic conditions, 344; feasts, 332; individualism, 375; industrial specialization, 372; inheritance of land, 348; land as dowry, 382; serving for wife, 386; use of wealth, 337

Quipu, 271, 277

Race, 95–123; local, 104, 105; origin of modern races, 116; physiology and psychology, 117–121

Radcliffe-Brown, A. R., Andaman Islands, 619; definition of law, 489

Radloff, W., horse raising, 316; Kirghiz agriculture, 294; prehistoric bronze and iron in Siberia, 201

Rafts, 246, 269

Raiding, 401

Rainfall, distribution of, in geologic epochs, 12

Ramapithecus, 39

Rank, Kwakiutl, 359

Ranke, J., effects of domestication, 109

Ratio of sexes, influence upon marriage relations, 432

Ratzel, F., interdependence of cultures, 669

Raw materials, used by prehistoric man, 150–151

Reciprocity, Trobriand, 363; Zuñi, 354

Reck, H., Oldoway skeleton, 89

Reindeer, 303, 306; breeders, 502; domestication, 283, 309; earliest mention, 311; sledge, 312; stables, 314

Reindeer period, 74

Reinterpretation of customs, 449

Relationship systems. *See Affinity, Kinship, Sib*

Religion, 627–665; origin of, 627, 628; participation of women, 468; Siberian, 648–650; techniques of, 637; varieties, 647–656

Religion and ethics, 632, 633

Religious behavior, 642–645

Residence, matrilocal, 415, 421, 445, 447; patrilocal, 415, 420, 447

Resonance, 248

Respect, 479

Rhodesian man, 53, 78, 87–89

Rhythm, 560–562, 590, 591, 602

Rice, 294; wild, 502, 511

Rice fields, ownership of wild, 506

Rickard, T. A., beginning of use of iron, 229

Riddle, distribution of, 598

Ridicule, as punishment for breaking of taboo, 438

Riding, 268

Ridley, W., harvesting grounds in Australia, 504

Ripley, W. Z., classification of European types, 114

Riss phase of glaciation, 11

Ritual, symbolism in, 584

Rivalry, Kwakiutl, 360

Rivers, W. H. R., avoidance, 447, 448, 449; female infanticide, 434; Toda marriage, 432

Rivet, P., home of sweet potato, 295

Robenhausian epoch, 150; implements, 190–191

Rock systems, 8

Rollers for heavy loads, 242

Rome, Neanderthal man of, 66

Rossel Island, bride price, 388; interest on loans, 390; marriage, 390; money, 399

Rostro-carinate forms, 155

Ruanda, conquest by herders, 317; rights of king, 321; social organization, 318

Rubruk, use of mare's milk, 307, 319

Rutot, A., eoliths, 171

Rwala Bedouins, subsistence of, 313; use of camel, 306

Rye, 291, 293

Sacrifice, 644, 652

Sahaptin cases borrowed by Chinook, 138

Sailing, 247; charts of Micronesians, 275

Salisbury, R. D., Ice age, 11, 15

Salish languages, 134, 135
Saller, K., Chancelade skeleton, 82
Samoa, ceremonialism, 656; chieftaincy, 660; economic security, 351; marital exchange, 388, 389; massage, 270; squeezing out juice, 241; supernaturalism, 648; taboos, 644; territorial units, 524; use of wealth, 333
Sanford, K. S., geological age of Nile terraces, 196
San Francisco Bay, submerged shell mounds, 14
San Ildefonso, pottery, 538, 566, 567, 569, 576; symbolism, 586
Santa Clara, pottery, 551, 566, 569
Santa Cruz, taboos, 427
Santee, buffalo hunting, 289
Santo Domingo, pottery of, 567, 569, 575
Sarasin, P. and F., on bees in Ceylon, 494; on Celebes archaeology, 202
Sauk and Fox art, 536
Savenkov, I. T., Siberian archaeology, 200
Savigny, F. K. von, theory of law, 488
Sawing, 163, 252, 253
Scandinavians, selective mating of, 103
Scarcity of resources, 344, 380
Scarification, as medical treatment, 270
Schäffle, A., theory of society, 666
Schmidt, W., Australian trade, 507; definition of State, 490; domestication of animals, 283, 309, 310
Schoetensack, O., Heidelberg man, 60
Schoolcraft, H. R., Indian harvesting tribes, 506
Schrenk, L. von, hunting territories of Tungus, 498
Schultz, A. H., hairiness of apes, 32; man's posture, 41
Schultz-Ewerth, E., Samoa, 524
Science, of primitive man, 274; and magic, 637, 638
Scotchman, stature of, 109
Sea level, changes of, 14, 15
Secret societies, 429, 518, 621; in Africa, 429, 516, 517
Secretions, internal, 110
Security, economic, 334, 351
Selection, 19, 103, 116
Selective diffusion, of cultivated plants, 296

Semantic changes, 135
Semi-subterranean house, distribution in America, 672
Semitic mythology, 617
Sergi, S., Neanderthal man, 66
Service, as payment for wife, 386, 441, 442
Semang, division of labor, 299
Sewing, 251, 258
Sex ratio, influence upon marriages, 433, 434; symbolism in art, 582
Sexes, social position of. See Status
Sexual, immorality, concept of, among Toda, 436; license at ceremonials, 436; period of sexual activity, 434
Shakes, a Tlingit chief, racial type of, 102
Shamanism, in Siberia, 648
Shamans, women as, 468
Sheep, antiquity of domestication, 311; in Egypt, 307; raising, 284; wild, 303
Shell, implements and utensils, 207, 250; money, 350; pendants in California and Polynesia compared, 207
Shell heaps, Africa, 198; Australia, 203; California, 207; Denmark, 187; Formosa, 202; New Zealand, 205; submerged, 14, 74; Tierra del Fuego, 215
Shelter, 263
Shetland pony, size of, 109
Shield, 263
Shoshone, use of dog, 305
Siam, musical system, 603
Sib, affiliations, 417; avoidance in, 445; conflict between sibs, 417, 418; definition, 414; economic functions, 418; endogamy and exogamy, 417, 423; function of maternal and paternal uncle, 419; kinship terms, 416; lineages constituting, 417; maternal and paternal, 415, 416; police functions, 418; property, 418; religious functions, 418; residence of members, 415; trusteeship of ceremonials, 418
Siberia, avoidance, 445; canoes, 269; divination, 643; lack of boastfulness, 464; mediums, 658; migrations, 139; milking, 319; religion,

648–650; service for obtaining wife, 386; shamanism, 645, 657; taboos, 645; tales, 601; trance, 659; women prevented from inheriting herds, 319

Siblings, definition of, 422; economic relations, 382

Sicilian, beach lines, 13

Siebert, O., on Australian trade expeditions, 507

Signals, 271

Silver, use in prehistoric America, 169

Simferopol, Neanderthal man, 68

Simiidae, 28, 32

Similarity of Old and New World implements, 211

Similes, in literature, 595

Sin, definition of, 478

Sinanthropus pekinensis, 51–56, 84

Sioux, language, 129, 134; terms for God, 629

Sivapithecus, 39

Skin, preparation of, 256

Skis, 267

Skull, horizontal position, 98; measurements, 97

Slave-raiding, 401, 402

Slave trade, 402

Slavery, 402, 500

Sledge, 268, 312

Sling, 243

Slit drums, 248

Slow matches, 239

Smelting, 249

Smith, G. Elliot, agriculture in America, 295; Paleolithic man, 40, 47, 59, 80, 88

Smith Sound, isolation of, 107

Smoke signals, 271

Snake-bite, treatment of, 270

Snowshoes, 267

Social life of animals, contrasted with human culture, 410

Social organization, Adamaua, 521; Australia, 412–413; changes in hunting tribes, 412; pastoral nomads, 316; Pueblo, 413; relation to economic stage, 413; relation to environment, 412; Ruanda, 318; Thonga, 413

Social psychology, 675

Societies, military, 429; religious, 650; secret, 429, 518, 621; secret societies in Africa, 516, 517; women's, 429

Solidarity of sib and family, 440

Sollas, W. J., beach lines, 14; Chancelade skeleton, 82; Neanderthal man, 63; Tasmanian flint industry, 202

Solo man, 78, 84, 85, 89

Solomon Islands, Paleolithic forms in, 204; religious behavior, 640

Solstices, summer and winter, observation of, 274

Solutrean, epoch, 150; flake industry, 158, 159; implements, 165, 182; ornaments, 182

Song, 589, 595

Sororate, 439

Sosnovski, G. P., Siberian archaeology, 200

Soul, 636

Sound, number of sounds restricted in each language, 128; symbolism, 132; systems, mutual influences, 137

South Africa. See Africa, South

South America. See America, South

South Seas. See Oceania

Spade, 262

Spain, prehistoric pictographs, 165

Spanish, dialectic changes, 134; influence upon Nahua language, 136

Specialization of industries in relation to division of labor, 371–372

Species, description of, 16; origin of, 20

Speck, F. G., on hunting territories, 498

Speech, articulate, 126; relation to culture, 141

Spells. See Magic

Spencer, G., on right of asylum in Australia, 510

Spencer, H., theory of culture, 669; of religion, 627, 636; of society, 666; on origin of music, 602

Spinning, 258

Sport, animals kept for, 305

Spring traps, 244

Springbok skull, 90

Spy skeletons, Neanderthal type, 63

Squashes, cultivated by women, 298

Stair, J. B., Samoa, 524

Stalking game, 287

Standards, ethical, 479; of measurement, 277; of value, 358, 399, 400

State, development of, 526
Statistical method of anthropometry, 95
Stature, 96
Status, 678; determined by birth, 430; association, marriage, residence, wealth, 458; means of establishing, 463; of men, Zuñi, 353; of women, 299, 319, 320, 369, 370, 384, 440, 441, 465–470, 516
Steam bath, 270
Steaming of food, 240, 255
Steatopygous figures, Paleolithic, 79
Steering paddle, 247
Steinen, K. von den, chieftaincy among Xingu tribes, 516
Steinheim, Neanderthal man of, 54, 65, 66, 70
Stepmother, 421
Sterkfontein, Australopithecus of, 30
Stone, 149; chipping, 157–159, 541; chiseling, 162, 163; drilling, 163, 164; flaking, 152–157, 252, 542; grinding, 160, 161; pecking, 160, 161; sawing, 162, 163
Stone age, 149; kettles, 255; modern stone tools in Africa, 199; money, 204; tools, 252, 253; work, decline during Azilian stage, 165
Stone architecture, 265
Storage of food, by Bushmen, 286 ff.; of seed, 301
Stow, G. W., government, 490
Stratigraphy, applied to prehistory, 148
Stratz, C. H., classification of races, 117
Strehlow, C., game, distribution of, in Australia, 507; law among Arunta, 509
Strike-a-light, 240
String games, 258
String instruments, 248, 604
Stumpf, C., on origin of music, 603
Style, in decorative art, 564–576; of narrative, 595. See Textile arts
Sub-incision, 271
Sucking tubes, 246
Sudan, distribution of languages, 139, 140; wild rice, 502
Sun Dance, history of, 669
Supernatural, 628–634; relationship of kin group, 427
Surgery, 270
Surplus of supplies, importance of, 330

Survivals, 449, 672
Sutherland, A., ethics, 677
Sweet potato, 295, 297
Swimming, 267
Swiss pile dwellings, implements from, 191, 192
Switzerland, handles of stone tools, 251
Symbolism, in art, 572, 576, 580, 581, 585; in ritual, 584
Symbols, individual, 429; as privilege, 462
Symmetry, 562–564
Syntax, 138

Taboo, 427–429, 510, 644, 645; punishment for breaking, 438; as privilege, 461
Tahiti, cultivation of banana, 298
Tales, adaptation of, 600; climax in, 591; distribution, 560, 589, 612; educational function, 478; explanatory, 615; formal elements, 560, 591; motivation, 601; origin, 610, 613; structure, 597
Talgai skull, 78, 86
Tami, education of wood-carvers, 473
Taplin, G., Australian chiefs, 509
Tardenoisean epoch, 150; industries, 184, 185; microliths, 197, 198, 199; in southern Asia, 199
Tarsioidea, 26
Tarsius, 26
Tashkent rice, 294
Tasmanians, lack of dog, 308; prehistory, 202; racial type, 117; subsistence, 282; territorial groups, 491.
Tattooing, 266
Taubach, teeth of Neanderthal man from, 65
Taulipang, pets kept by, 305
Taungs ape, 28, 30
Taurodonty, 67, 71
Taylor, T. G., classification of races, 117
Teaching of crafts, 471
Technique, playful handling of, 245
Technology, 150–170, 215, 233; and art, 540
Teknonymy, 447
Tents, 263
Terra, H. de, Sinanthropus, 51
Terraces, 12

Territorial principle of government, 491, 497
Territorial rights, Botocudo, 493; Australia, 493–494
Tertiary period, 8, 27
Teton, joking relationship and avoidance, 457
Textile arts, 552, 554, 556–558
Thalbitzer, W., on Eskimo phonetics, 135
Theft, 479
Thompson Indians, art, 536, 561; calendar, 274; signals, 271; tales, 623
Thonga. *See Bathonga*
Throwing board, 244
Throwing clubs, 243
Throwing knives, 242, 243
Throwing loop, 244
Tibet, polyandry in, 433
Tides, observations of, 274
Tierra del Fuego. *See Fuegians*
Tillamook loan words, 137
Tilney, F., brain of apes, 37; Pithecanthropus, 47
Title, as symbol of prestige, 465
Tlingit Indians, art, 572–574; baskets, 555; blanket, 558, 559, 585; loan words, 137; matriliny, 320; racial type, 102; tales, 597
Tobacco, cultivation of, 293, 298
Toboggan, 268
Todas, 435, 481; dairy ritual, 647; divorce, 450; exogamy and endogamy, 431, 679; marriage, 432, 433; milking, 309; polyandry, 433; religious function of sib, 418; sex relations, 481
Togo pictographs, 272
Tomahawk, 243
Tonality, 602
Tonga, men as gardeners, 298; pottery, 207
Torsion, mechanical principle, 241
Totem group, collective responsibility, 508; economic function, 507, 508
Totem myths, 618
Totemism, 426–430
Toys as art forms, 538
Trade, 365, 396–398, 441, 505, 507, 540; prehistoric, 224, 252
Tradition, in art, 569; historical value of, 669

Trails, 267
Trance, use in religion, 658–660
Transportation, 267
Traps, torsion used as release in, 242, 261, 287, 288
Travois, 268, 306
Tree calabashes as receptacles, 250
Tree shrews, 25
Trenk, O., procedure in criminal process among Bushmen, 497
Trephining, 271
Trial marriage, 437, 440
Tribe, definition of, 413, 414
Tricks, 269
Trickster tales, 662
Trinil, Pithecanthropus, 45, 51
Trobriand Islands, betrothal, 437; cannibalism, 481; capitalism, 350; chief, 461; clubhouses, 436; cooperation, 376; distribution of property, 382; division of labor, 370; economics, 334, 344, 345, 347, 349, 361, 363, 364; exchange, 364; feasts, 332; industrial specialization, 371; insecurity, 334; marriage and sexual relations, 436, 437, 440, 443; monopolies, 349; prestige, 465; property rights, 347; sorcery, 345; theory of procreation, 425; transition from patriliny to matriliny, 424
Trumpets, 248
Trusteeship of ceremonies in sib, 418
Tsimshian, cosmology, 618; religious behavior, 640; sibs, 417; similes, 596; sound symbolism, 132; surgery, 270; tales, 591
Tungus, hunting territory, 498; reindeer, 312
Turkestan, pastoral nomadism, 313; subsistence, 307
Turkish tribes, languages, 139; migrations, 139; status of women, 319; subsistence, 313
Turks, Altaian, branding of animals, 316
Turks, behavior under varying conditions, 667
Tutelary spirits, 646, 647
Tutsi, conquests, 318; herding, 318; milking, 315
Twa, social status, 320
Twilling, 257

Twins, identical, 118; treatment of mother of, 482
Tylor, E. B., avoidance, 447; folk tales, 612; origin of pottery, 259; religion, 627, 636; survivals, 672
Types, racial, 99–101, 105, 115; variability of local, 95
Tyrrhenian beach lines, 13

Uganda. *See Baganda*
Uhle, W., archaeology of Peru, 215
Uncle, maternal, duties of among Thonga, 420
Units of value, Kwakiutl, 358
Unyoro, division of agricultural labor, 298; fowls, 304
Urundi, conquest by herders, 317

Valley terraces, Africa, 196
Valuables, as objects of trade, 399
Value, 331
Vancouver Island. *See America, Northwest Coast*
Variability of types, 95, 99
Veblen, T., wealth and prestige, 337
Vedda, beehives, 289; boundaries, 491; brain, 46; division of food, 346; division of labor, 299; honey, 286; preservation of meat, 377; racial types, 112
Vegetable food of hunters, 284, 285; of nomads, 313, 314
Verneau, R., prehistoric races, 79–82
Vicuna, use of, 310
Virchow, R., Neanderthal man, 62
Vision, 429, 658–660
Viticulture in China, 301
Vocables, in songs, 594

Wadjak man, 84; skull, 78
Wahle, E., hunting stage, 284
Wahuma, cattle feudalism, 316
Wakan, 629, 631
Wakanda, 630
Walarai, territory, 492
Walnut, wild in China, 301
War, economic aspects of, 400–404; means of gaining prestige, 462; Plains Indians, 513, 514; woman participation in, 468
Washo, inheritance of pine-nut trees, 289; rabbit hunting, 289
Waterman, I., explanatory tales, 615
Wealth, attitude towards, 361, 362;

compulsive pursuits of, 339; destruction of, 361; distribution, 377; symbolic use, 337; uses of, 333
Weaving, 256–258
Wedding, 440, 441, 444
Weidenreich, F., Sinanthropus, 54, 55; Solo skull, 85
Weimar-Ehringsdorf, Neanderthal man, 65
Weinert, H., Eoanthropus, 59; Paleolithic skulls, 54, 66, 73, 77, 90; Sinanthropus, 52
Werth, E., banana, 291
West Africa. *See Africa, West*
West Indies, drums, 248
Westermarck, E., ethics, 677; theory of survivals, 449
Wheat, 291, 297
Wheel, 268
Wheeler, W. M., convergence, 22
White, L. A., signals used by animals, 38
White race, 105
Wied, M. Prinz zu, Botocudos, 492
Wife-lending, 436, 481
Wigman, J., comparative law, 488
Wilbert, R., life span of apes, 35
Wilder, H. H., apes and man, 32
Will power imputed to nature, 615
Willey, A., convergence, 22
Williams, F. E., economics of Orokaiva, 393
Willis, B., antiquity of man in Argentina, 214
Wilser, L., Neanderthal man, 69
Wind instruments, distribution of, 604
Winnebago, camps, 504; cosmology, 622; prayer, 643
Winnowing, 263
Wisconsin, prehistoric copper in, 169
Witchcraft, 621, 647; cause for divorce, 450
Wiyot, prestige among, 464
Wolf trap, 261, 287
Wölfel, D. J., Guanchos, 83
Women, as chiefs, 516; disabilities of, 319; economic value of, 383, 384, 402; as gardeners, 298; as herders, 319; occupations of, 369; political status of, 469; as shamans, 468; societies, 429; status of, *see Status*

Wood, art in, 546; use of, 253
Wood-carving, distribution of, 546; teaching of, 473
Wooden implements, Polynesia, 207; prehistoric, 164, 167
Woodward, A. S., Eoanthropus, 56; Homo rhodesiensis, 87
Wool, lack of use of, in Egypt, 307
Words, number of, restricted in each language, 128; symbolic value, 142
Work-party, Zuñi, 368
Wounds, treatment of, 270
Writing, 271, 273
Wundt, W., origin of rhythm, 594; theory of folk tales, 616
Würm phase of glaciation, 11

Xylophone, 604

Yakut, use of horse, cattle, reindeer, 312
Yerkes, R. M., mentality of apes, 37; signals used by animals, 38
Yerkes, R. M. and A. W., life span of apes, 35
Yoldia terraces, 14
Yoruba, Orisha cult, 622; terra cotta head, 550; twins, 482
Yucatan. See Maya
Yukaghir, dog sledges, 305; service of groom, 442; subsistence, 285; trapping, 343
Yukon River, riddles, 598

Yurok, bride price, 441; divorce, 450; premarital relations, 441; social status of married woman, 441; tobacco, 293

Zanza, 248
Zebu, descent of, 309
Zither, of bamboo, 249
Zulu, behavior at varying conditions, 667; bride price, 383, 384
Zuñi, absence of groom price, 385; altars, 559; art, 582; attitude towards food, 378; attitude towards power and wealth, 336; concept of property, 341, 345; coöperation, 376; division of labor, 370; divorce, 450; economics, 351-357; economic security, 351; feasts, 332; gifts, 391, 392; impersonation of gods, 657; lack of industrial specialization, 372; marital exchange, 388; ownership of fields, 344; partnership in herding, 376; pottery, 568-570, 574, 575; prayers, 537; prayersticks, 582; prestige, 337; religion, 650; religious activities of women, 468; religious behavior, 641, 650; respect shown to knowledge, 336; ritual, 651; seasonal food supply, 379; status of women, 467; symbolism, 584, 585; taboos, 378; tales, 560; trade, 396; war, 401; water jars, 569; wealth, 334; work-party, 368